	IB	IIB	IIIA	IVA	VA	VIA	VIIA	0
								2 (4.00) **He** $1s^2$ Helium
			5 (10.8) 3 **B** $1s^22s^22p^1$ Boron	6 (12.0) ±4,2 **C** $1s^22s^22p^2$ Carbon	7 (14.0) ±3,5,4,2 **N** $1s^22s^22p^3$ Nitrogen	8 (16.0) −2 **O** $1s^22s^22p^4$ Oxygen	9 (19.0) −1 **F** $1s^22s^22p^5$ Fluorine	10 (20.2) **Ne** $1s^22s^22p^6$ Neon
			13 (27.0) 3 **Al** $[Ne]3s^23p^1$ Aluminum	14 (28.1) 4 **Si** $[Ne]3s^23p^2$ Silicon	15 (31.0) ±3,5,4 **P** $[Ne]3s^23p^3$ Phosphorus	16 (32.1) ±2,4,6 **S** $[Ne]3s^23p^4$ Sulfur	17 (35.5) ±1,3,5,7 **Cl** $[Ne]3s^23p^5$ Chlorine	18 (40.0) **Ar** $[Ne]3s^23p^6$ Argon
28 (58.7) 2,3 **Ni** $[Ar]3d^84s^2$ Nickel	29 (63.5) 2,1 **Cu** $[Ar]3d^{10}4s^1$ Copper	30 (65.4) 2 **Zn** $[Ar]3d^{10}4s^2$ Zinc	31 (69.7) 3 **Ga** $[Ar]3d^{10}4s^24p^1$ Gallium	32 (72.6) 4 **Ge** $[Ar]3d^{10}4s^24p^2$ Germanium	33 (74.9) ±3,5 **As** $[Ar]3d^{10}4s^24p^3$ Arsenic	34 (79.0) −2,4,6 **Se** $[Ar]3d^{10}4s^24p^4$ Selenium	35 (79.9) ±1,5 **Br** $[Ar]3d^{10}4s^24p^5$ Bromine	36 (83.8) **Kr** $[Ar]3d^{10}4s^24p^6$ Krypton
46 (106) 2,4 **Pd** $[Kr]4d^{10}5s^0$ Palladium	47 (108) 1 **Ag** $[Kr]4d^{10}5s^1$ Silver	48 (112) 2 **Cd** $[Kr]4d^{10}5s^2$ Cadmium	49 (115) 3 **In** $[Kr]4d^{10}5s^25p^1$ Indium	50 (119) 4,2 **Sn** $[Kr]4d^{10}5s^25p^2$ Tin	51 (122) ±3,5 **Sb** $[Kr]4d^{10}5s^25p^3$ Antimony	52 (128) −2,4,6 **Te** $[Kr]4d^{10}5s^25p^4$ Tellurium	53 (127) ±1,5,7 **I** $[Kr]4d^{10}5s^25p^5$ Iodine	54 (131) **Xe** $[Kr]4d^{10}5s^25p^6$ Xenon
78 (195) 2,4 **Pt** $[Xe]4f^{14}5d^96s^1$ Platinum	79 (197) 3,1 **Au** $[Xe]4f^{14}5d^{10}6s^1$ Gold	80 (201) 2,1 **Hg** $[Xe]4f^{14}5d^{10}6s^2$ Mercury	81 (204) 3,1 **Tl** $[Xe]4f^{14}5d^{10}6s^26p^1$ Thallium	82 (207) 4,2 **Pb** $[Xe]4f^{14}5d^{10}6s^26p^2$ Lead	83 (209) 3,5 **Bi** $[Xe]4f^{14}5d^{10}6s^26p^3$ Bismuth	84 (210) 2,4 **Po** $[Xe]4f^{14}5d^{10}6s^26p^4$ Polonium	85 (210) ±1,3,5,7 **At** $[Xe]4f^{14}5d^{10}6s^26p^5$ Astatine	86 (222) **Rn** $[Xe]4f^{14}5d^{10}6s^26p^6$ Radon

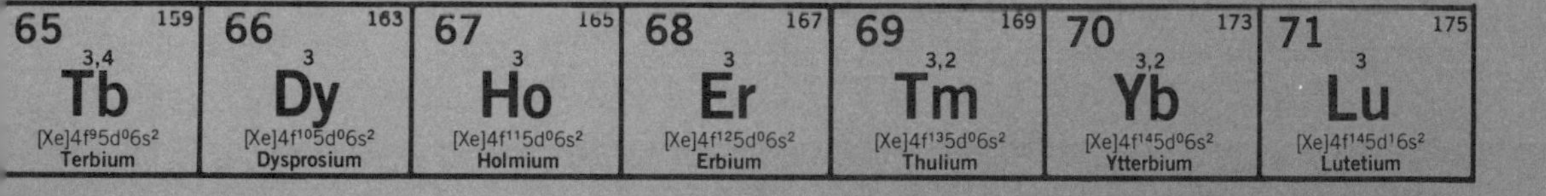

65 (159) 3,4 **Tb** $[Xe]4f^95d^06s^2$ Terbium	66 (163) 3 **Dy** $[Xe]4f^{10}5d^06s^2$ Dysprosium	67 (165) 3 **Ho** $[Xe]4f^{11}5d^06s^2$ Holmium	68 (167) 3 **Er** $[Xe]4f^{12}5d^06s^2$ Erbium	69 (169) 3,2 **Tm** $[Xe]4f^{13}5d^06s^2$ Thulium	70 (173) 3,2 **Yb** $[Xe]4f^{14}5d^06s^2$ Ytterbium	71 (175) 3 **Lu** $[Xe]4f^{14}5d^16s^2$ Lutetium
97 (249) 4,3 **Bk** $[Rn]5f^86d^17s^2$ Berkelium	98 (251) 3 **Cf** $[Rn]5f^96d^17s^2$ Californium	99 (254) — **Es** $[Rn]5f^{10}6d^17s^2$ Einsteinium	100 (253) — **Fm** $[Rn]5f^{11}6d^17s^2$ Fermium	101 (256) — **Md** $[Rn]5f^{12}6d^17s^2$ Mendelevium	102 (254) — **No** $[Rn]5f^{13}6d^17s^2$ Nobelium	103 (257) — **Lw** $[Rn]5f^{14}6d^17s^2$ Lawrencium

AN ADVANCED INTRODUCTION TO CHEMISTRY

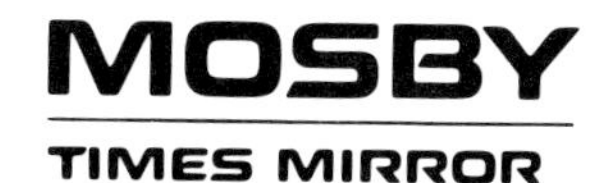

THE C. V. MOSBY COMPANY
11830 WESTLINE INDUSTRIAL DRIVE
ST. LOUIS, MISSOURI 63141

For prompt service, call (314) 872-8370

Instructor's Copy

SUGGESTED LIST PRICE $ 12.95

This text is sent to you with the compliments of The C. V. Mosby Company. Examine it at your leisure and see how effectively it can fulfill your course requirements. We would greatly appreciate any comments you may have.

AN ADVANCED INTRODUCTION TO CHEMISTRY by Gill and Norman

COMMENTS:

Name ____________________

Course ____________________ Enrollment ____________

School ____________________

City ____________________ State ____________

FF-371R

AN ADVANCED INTRODUCTION TO CHEMISTRY

STANLEY J. GILL
ARLAN D. NORMAN
University of Colorado

with 421 *illustrations by* **Michael Carpenter**

THE C. V. MOSBY COMPANY
Saint Louis 1975

Printed in the United States of America

Distributed in Great Britain by Henry Kimpton, London

Library of Congress Cataloging in Publication Data

Gill, Stanley Jensen, 1929-
An advanced introduction to chemistry.

1. Chemistry. I. Norman, Arlan D., joint author.
II. Title.
QD31.2.G5 540 74-12193
ISBN 0-8016-1813-4

TS/VH/VH 9 8 7 6 5 4 3 2 1

PREFACE

This text is written for a one-semester course in general chemistry at an advanced level. It is expected that students who use this book will have had high school chemistry and one year of college mathematics and physics (or its equivalent in high school). This background affords the opportunity to deal with general chemistry in a more efficient and rigorous way than is normally possible in a typical first-year course.

From our experience, we have found it highly advantageous to present first the macroscopic concepts of chemistry and then follow these with the more theoretical, microscopic ideas. The basic format of the book is based on this principle. We have also emphasized the structural and physical aspects of chemistry, since this approach most captivates students with good backgrounds in mathematics and physics.

We begin by reviewing the basic language and concepts of chemistry, because very often the students have not studied chemistry for several years. Next, the topic of solids is discussed in order to introduce ideas of structure and macroscopic properties. We continue with the discussion of thermal properties and energy relations involved in chemical thermodynamics. This approach provides a framework in which to consider equilibrium, free energy, and electrochemical processes. The student can then begin to appreciate the detailed structural features of molecules, ranging from small molecules to polymers. With this exposure to thermodynamics and structure, it becomes easy to rationalize the need for theories of atomic structure, chemical bonding, reaction mechanism, and the interaction of electromagnetic radiation with matter. These topics therefore occupy the latter portion of the book. Periodically throughout the text, material is presented that demonstrates the application of abstract principles to practical situations. These sections provide a brief break from the core material without undue distraction.

We have used this material successfully for a one-semester course offered to physical science students (engineering and physics students). We also feel that this approach could find more general application to other types of chemistry courses. Since the text is an advanced introduction to general chemistry, the book can be used in honors chemistry courses. A laboratory program based on material such as *Freeman Laboratory Separates* fits well with the level of this text. A following, second-semester course, based on Butler's *Introduction to Chemical Equilibrium*, can be used for programs where a strong emphasis is placed on the fundamentals of qualitative and quantitative analysis.

We wish to express appreciation to former students whose constructive criticism and suggestions have helped immeasurably in the development of this text. We also wish to thank Mrs. Sandra Easter for her patience in typing the manuscript through countless revisions.

Stanley J. Gill
Arlan D. Norman

CONTENTS

AN ADVANCED INTRODUCTION TO CHEMISTRY

1 CHEMICAL MATTER: BASIC CONCEPTS

Chemistry is a branch of science that deals with many aspects of matter. It is concerned with the physical properties of matter and the transformations matter undergoes in chemical reactions. Since it deals with basic properties, chemistry has a general application to many scientific areas. To both the theoretical and the applied scientist, a knowledge of chemistry is essential.

With a firm grounding in introductory college physics and mathematics, the physical science or engineering student can approach the study of modern chemistry in an efficient, sophisticated, and quantitative way. In this text, we present the general principles of chemistry at a level that assumes such a background. Particular emphasis is given to how the fundamental principles apply to an understanding of many practical problems in chemistry.

1.1 MATTER

Matter is that which occupies space and has mass. It occurs in three physical states: *gaseous*, *liquid*, and *solid*. All matter is comprised of some type of combination of the chemical elements. One method of subclassifying matter is outlined in Fig. 1-1.

Mixtures are combinations of pure substances (elements and or compounds or both) in which each substance retains its identity and properties. The constituent substances are in the same chemical form as when separated. Mixtures are of two types: homogeneous and heterogeneous. *Homogeneous* mixtures have a uniform composition at the microscopic (molecular) level; *heterogeneous* mixtures do not. Sodium chloride dissolved in water and sand mixed with sugar are examples of homogeneous and heterogeneous mixtures, respectively.

Pure substances are homogeneous forms of matter; all specimens of a pure substance have identical properties and composition. Pure substances that cannot be subdivided by chemical means into smaller units are called *elements*. Presently 104 chemical elements are known.

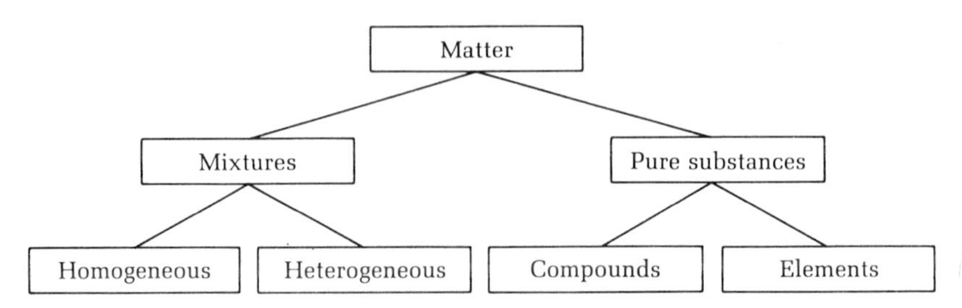

Fig. 1-1. Classes of matter.

A *compound* is a chemical combination of two or more elements into a pure substance that has its own unique properties. The properties of the constituent elements are lost. One definition states that a compound is a substance in which the elements are combined in a definite and constant ratio. This definition is somewhat restrictive, since it implies that the atom ratio in a compound is invariant; that, for example, the Ag:Cl ratio in AgCl must be 1:1. As shown below, this is not always the case.

Compounds can be stoichiometric or nonstoichiometric. *Stoichiometric* compounds always have a constant and definite ratio of constituent elements. Methane, CH_4, is such a compound. The C:H ratio is invariant and equal to 1:4. Solid compounds are sometimes *nonstoichiometric*. Their composition can vary slightly from a fixed ratio, although their properties remain essentially constant. For example, AgCl with a composition of $Ag_{0.99}\,Cl_{1.00}$ can be obtained, a variation of 1% from the stoichiometric ideal.

The smallest particle of an element that retains the identity of the element is the *atom*. The smallest independent particle of a compound is called a *molecule*. An atom or molecule that has an electrical charge is called an *ion*. If the ion is positively charged, it is a *cation*, such as Na^+; if it is negatively charged, it is an *anion*, such as Cl^-.

1.2 ATOMS

Atomic structure

An atom consists of a *nucleus* and the surrounding *electrons*. The nucleus contains several particles called *nucleons*, but the chemist's main interest is in only two of these, the *neutrons* and the *protons*. These and the electrons are principally responsible for the charge and the mass properties of the atom. The masses and charges of these three fundamental particles are shown in Table 1-1. Each proton contributes one unit of positive charge (+) to the nucleus. Neutrons carry no charge. Each electron carries one unit of negative charge (−). In a neutral atom the positive nuclear charge is exactly balanced by the overall charge of the outer electrons. In an atom the *atomic number (Z)* is the number of protons in the

Table 1-1. ELECTRON, PROTON, AND NEUTRON PROPERTIES

Particle	*Charge**	*Mass†*
Electron	−1	0.00055
Proton	+1	1.00728
Neutron	0	1.00866

*Charges are relative to that of a single electron (1.6021×10^{-19} coulomb) set equal to −1.
†Mass in atomic mass units (amu). One amu is 1.6604×10^{-24} grams (g).

nucleus; it also equals the number of electrons in the neutral atom. The *mass number (A)* of an atom is the number of protons and neutrons in the nucleus. Clearly, the mass of an atom is primarily in the nucleus.

Atomic volumes vary from atom to atom, but the bulk of the volume of any atom is due to the electrons. Experimental measurements indicate that for a typical atom the nuclear volume is about 10^{-15} of the total volume.

A list of the elements, along with their atomic numbers, is shown on the inside back cover. The elements are differentiated from one another by different values of Z. For example, H(Z = 1) has one proton in the nucleus, and Fe(Z = 26) has 26 protons. It is important to realize that although the atomic number is unique for a given atom, the *neutron number* (A − Z) is not. Since neutrons carry no electrical charge, their number can vary for a given element without greatly affecting the electronic or the chemical properties of the element.

Isotopes

Atoms of the same element that have different neutron numbers, that is, atoms with the same Z value but with different A values, are called isotopes. For example, oxygen (Z = 8) has stable isotopes of A = 16, 17, and 18 and unstable (radioactive) isotopes of A = 14, 15, and 19. Most elements occur naturally as a mixture of two or more stable isotopes, and as a result the atomic weights given for the elements in the periodic table (see inside front cover) can assume nonintegral values. However, some elements, such as Be, F, and P, have only one stable isotope.

Isotopes are designated in the following way: the chemical symbol for the element is given, the Z value is given as a lower left subscript, and the A value, as an upper left superscript. For oxygen-16 the symbol is ${}^{16}_{8}O$. Notice that exact masses are not given, only the numbers of nucleons involved. Usually, in chemical reactions the symbol for the element is sufficient, because all isotopes of the element react in essentially the same way. However, if the isotopes behave differently, and a specific isotope needs to be designated, the complete notation is used. In Table 1-2 the isotopes of the first eight elements and their percent abundances are shown. The

Table 1-2. ISOTOPES OF ELEMENTS Z = 1, 2, 3, . . . , 8

Element	*Stable isotopes (percent abundance)*	*Radioactive isotopes (half-life*)*
H	$^{1}_{1}H$ (99.985)	$^{3}_{1}H$ (12.3 y)
	$^{2}_{1}H$ (0.015)	
He	$^{3}_{2}He$ (0.00013)	$^{5}_{2}He$ †
	$^{4}_{2}He$ (100)	$^{6}_{2}He$ (0.85 s)
		$^{8}_{2}He$ (0.123 s)
Li	$^{6}_{3}Li$ (7.42)	$^{5}_{3}Li$ †
	$^{7}_{3}Li$ (92.58)	$^{8}_{3}Li$ (0.86 s)
		$^{9}_{3}Li$ (0.17 s)
Be	$^{9}_{4}Be$ (100.000)	$^{6}_{4}Be$ †
		$^{7}_{4}Be$ (53.4 d)
		$^{8}_{4}Be$ (2×10^{-16} s)
		$^{10}_{4}Be$ (2.5×10^{6} y)
		$^{11}_{4}Be$ (13.6 s)
B	$^{10}_{5}B$ (19.78)	$^{8}_{5}B$ (0.77 s)
	$^{11}_{5}B$ (80.22)	$^{9}_{5}B$ (8×10^{-19} s)
		$^{12}_{5}B$ (0.02 s)
		$^{13}_{5}B$ (0.019 s)
C	$^{12}_{6}C$ (98.892)	$^{10}_{6}C$ (19.1 s)
	$^{13}_{6}C$ (1.108)	$^{11}_{6}C$ (20.3 m)
		$^{14}_{6}C$ (5730 y)
		$^{15}_{6}C$ (2.4 s)
		$^{16}_{6}C$ (0.74 s)
N	$^{14}_{7}N$ (99.63)	$^{12}_{7}N$ (0.01 s)
	$^{15}_{7}N$ (0.37)	$^{13}_{7}N$ (10.0 m)
		$^{16}_{7}N$ (7.2 s)
		$^{17}_{7}N$ (4.2 s)
		$^{18}_{7}N$ (0.63 s)
O	$^{16}_{8}O$ (99.759)	$^{13}_{8}O$ (0.009 s)
	$^{17}_{8}O$ (0.037)	$^{14}_{8}O$ (71.0 s)
	$^{18}_{8}O$ (0.204)	$^{15}_{8}O$ (124 s)
		$^{19}_{8}O$ (29 s)
		$^{20}_{8}O$ (14 s)

*Half-life abbreviations are s, seconds; m, minutes; h, hours; d, days; and y, years.
†Value not available.

Table 1-3. COMPARISON OF ATOMIC WEIGHT SCALES

Element	*Old chemical scale*	*New chemical scale*
O	16 (exactly)	15.9994
^{12}C	12.00052	12 (exactly)
C	12.011	12.0111

natural abundances of radioactive isotopes generally are negligible. The half-life of each radioactive isotope is given. The *half-life* is the time it takes for one half of a sample of that isotope to disintegrate.

Atomic weights

The atomic weights of the elements are a set of numbers that define the relative weights of atoms. Originally, chemists defined atomic weights relative to the average atomic weight of naturally occurring oxygen. Naturally occurring oxygen, a mixture of ^{16}O, ^{17}O, and ^{18}O, was set equal to exactly 16. A recent (1961) redefinition of the atomic weight scale is set relative to the most abundant isotope of carbon, ^{12}C. The ^{12}C isotope is defined to be equal to exactly 12. The small difference between the old and new scales is shown in Table 1-3. The differences in atomic weights between old and new periodic tables arise from this change of the atomic weight base. For most measurements the difference is not significant.

Three methods of obtaining precise atomic weights are used: combining weights, gas-density measurements, and mass spectrometric measurements. The mass spectrometric method is best.

The mass spectrometric method yields the most precise atomic weight values even though the method is relatively simple. A schematic diagram of a mass spectrograph is shown in Fig. 1-2. The apparatus consists of four main parts: the ion source, the ion accelerator, the magnetic field, and the ion analysis chamber (here, a photographic plate). To obtain a mass spectrum we introduce the element, or material of interest in gaseous form into the source region, where it is bombarded with electrons from an electron beam. Electrons from the beam displace electrons from the element (M) to yield cations (M^+):

$$M + e^- \rightarrow M^+ + 2e^- \tag{1.1}$$

Because these cations are charged, they can be accelerated by an electric field of potential V volts. The accelerated cations move into the magnetic field region of strength B gauss. In the magnetic field a deflecting force perpendicular to the ion's trajectory causes the particle to follow a circular orbit. The radius, r, of the orbit followed by each cation is given by a combination of factors:

$$r^2 = \frac{2mV}{eB^2} \tag{1.2}$$

where e is the charge on the ion of mass m. The important quantity sought is the ratio m/e given by

$$\frac{m}{e} = \frac{r^2B^2}{2V} \tag{1.3}$$

In the legend of Fig. 1-2 the derivation of these equations is shown.

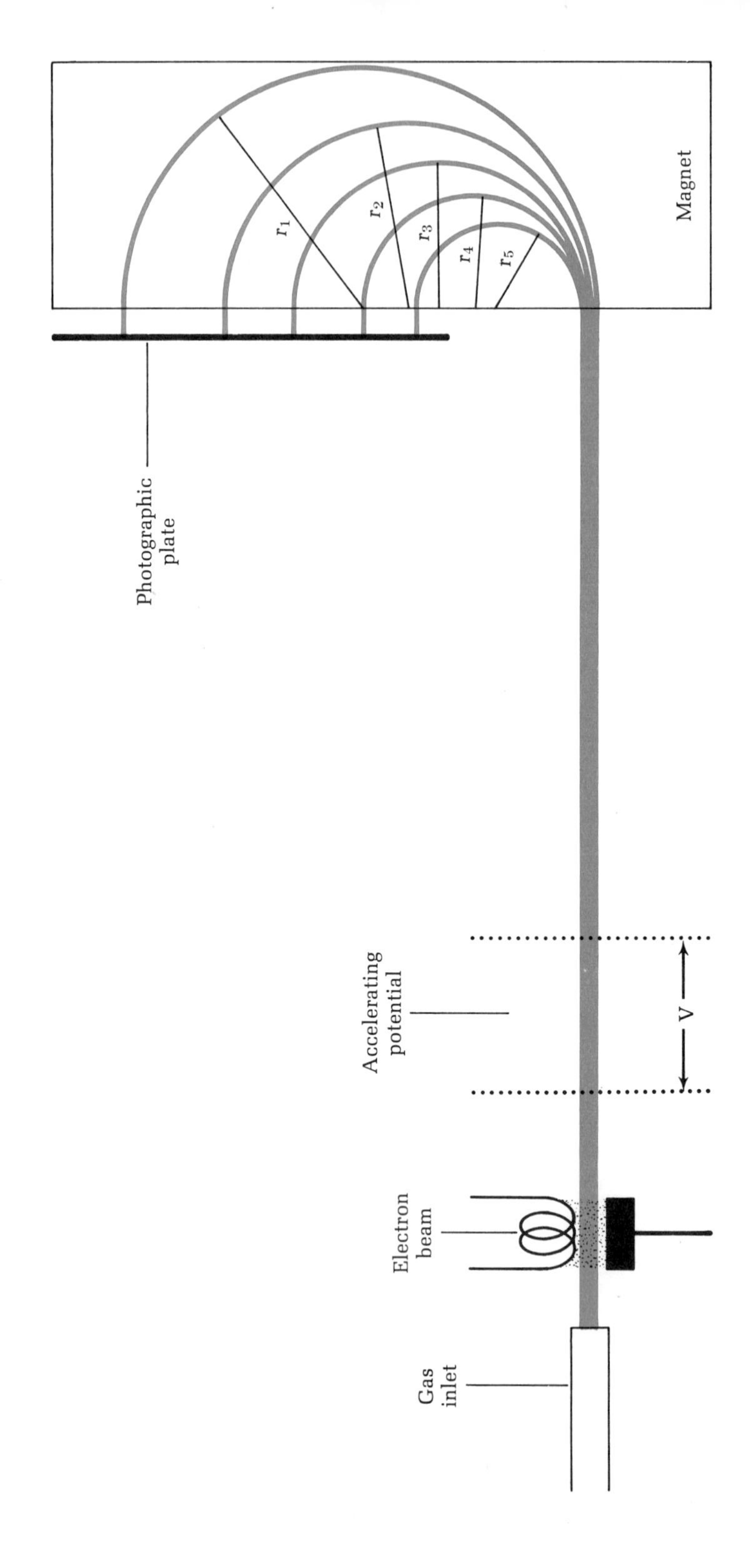
Magnet
r_1
r_2
r_3
r_4
r_5
Photographic plate
Accelerating potential
V
Electron beam
Gas inlet

At the end of the magnetic field region the ions, separated into beams according to their *m/e* ratio, impinge on a photographic plate. From the positions of the images on the plate, *r* can be determined for each ion. At constant *B* and *V* the instrument can be calibrated using the position of $^{12}C^+$ ions on the photographic plate as a standard, so that atomic weights of each isotope can be determined. The relative number of each ion type is directly proportional to the intensity of the image on the photographic plate. For naturally occurring elemental carbon we would find images corresponding to isotopes $^{12}_{6}C$ (12.00000 amu) and $^{13}_{6}C$ (13.00335 amu) in an intensity ratio of 98.892:1.108. Calculating the average weight of carbon:

$$\text{average weight} = 12.00000 \times 0.98892 + 13.00335 \times 0.01108$$
$$= 12.0111$$

we obtain a value of 12.0111 amu, the value given in the periodic table as the atomic weight of carbon.

Fig. 1-2. Schematic drawing of mass spectrometer. Electrons from electron beam bombard gaseous species to form positive ions. Ions are accelerated by voltage, *V*, into magnetic field region of *B* gauss. Energy of an accelerated ion entering field region is equal to *eV*, where e is charge on ion (in esu). Kinetic energy of ion of mass *m* moving at velocity *v* is given by $\frac{1}{2}mv^2$. Equating energy expressions:

$$eV = \tfrac{1}{2}mv^2$$

and

$$v^2 = \frac{2eV}{m}$$

Magnetic field imposes perpendicular force on ion, which is given by *Bev*. Since ion in circular orbit experiences force equal to mv^2/r, where r is radius of orbit, we see that

$$Bev = \frac{mv^2}{r}$$

and

$$v^2 = \frac{B^2e^2r^2}{m^2}$$

We can equate two expressions for v^2:

$$v^2 = \frac{2eV}{m} = \frac{B^2e^2r^2}{m^2}$$

and rearrange to obtain equation in terms of radius r, or mass to charge ratio *m/e*:

$$r^2 = \frac{2mV}{eB^2}$$

or

$$\frac{m}{e} = \frac{r^2B^2}{2V}$$

Periodicity of elements: periodic law

The properties of the elements are periodic functions of their atomic numbers. When the elements are listed in order of increasing atomic number, elements with similar properties occur at definite intervals along the list. A tabular arrangement of the atoms can be set up so that elements with similar properties occur in vertical columns in the table. Elements in these columns are similar because they have similar arrangements of their electrons. This relationship, the periodic law, was recognized independently by Mendeleev and Meyer in 1869. The periodic table currently in use, called the long form of the periodic table, is shown on the front inside cover of the book.

Electronic structure: quantum numbers

Each electron of an atom has a specific energy value. These values are quantized; that is, they assume distinct energy values. The total arrangement of electrons around an atom is called the *electronic configuration* of the atom.

The electronic configuration of an atom is given by a system of numbers called quantum numbers. Their origin lies in the quantum mechanical treatment of the electronic structure of the simple H atom and goes beyond our needs at this time. Quantum numbers are examined in detail in Chapter 11. The four quantum numbers, their symbols, and the values they can assume are given in Table 1-4.

A designation of the electronic state of the electrons of a given atom (or ion) follows from the idea that each electron of the atom has a different set of quantum numbers. The permissible quantum number combinations up to $n = 3$ are shown in Table 1-5. These combinations are derived using the numerical rules given in Table 1-4. From Table 1-5 we see that two electrons can have different sets of quantum numbers when $n = 1$; $n = 1$, $\ell = 0$, $\mathrm{m}_\ell = 0$, $\mathrm{m}_s = +½$; and $n = 1$, $\ell = 0$, $\mathrm{m}_\ell = 0$, $\mathrm{m}_s = -½$. Eight different combinations are possible at $n = 2$, and eighteen are possible at $n = 3$.

For many purposes an electronic configuration is adequately described by only the first two quantum numbers, n and ℓ. The ℓ quantum numbers of 0, 1, 2, and 3 are designated using alphabetic symbols s, p, d, and f, respectively. Thus, $1s$ stands for an electron in quantum state of $n = 1$, $\ell = 0$, $m_\ell = 0$, $m_s = +½$ or $-½$. Two electrons can have $1s$ designations. When this happens, the electronic configuration is written as $1s^2$. We see in Table 1-5 that whenever $\ell = 0$, designated by s, there can be only two electrons in such a state. When $\ell = 1$, which is a p state, there are six different combinations possible. Therefore, a maximum of six electrons can exist in a p state. If there are five electrons in p states for $n = 2$, we would write the electronic configuration as $2p^5$.

The quantum number combinations are used to designate the electronic configuration of an atom (or monatomic ion) and to examine the systematics of the periodic

Table 1-4. QUANTUM NUMBERS

Quantum number	*Symbol*	*Possible values*
Principal	n	1, 2, 3, . . .
Angular momentum	ℓ	0, 1, 2, . . . , n − 1
Magnetic	m_ℓ	0, ±1, ±2, . . . , $\pm\ell$
Spin	m_s	+½ or −½

Table 1-5. QUANTUM NUMBER COMBINATIONS

n	ℓ	m_ℓ	m_s	*Total state configuration*	*Total combinations (energy states)*
1	0	0	+½, −½	$1s^2$	2
2	0	0	+½, −½	$2s^2$	8
	1	+1	+½, −½	$2p^6$	
		0	+½, −½		
		−1	+½, −½		
3	0	0	+½, −½	$3s^2$	18
	1	+1	+½, −½	$3p^6$	
		0	+½, −½		
		−1	+½, −½		
	2	+2	+½, −½	$3d^{10}$	
		+1	+½, −½		
		0	+½, −½		
		−1	+½, −½		
		−2	+½, −½		

table of elements. For the time being we are interested only in ground-state electronic configurations. The *ground state* is the state that is lowest in energy.

Electronic configuration and the periodic table

The periodic table is a way of ordering the elements so that elements with similar chemical properties are placed together in groups. The basis for these chemical similarities lies in the similarity of the electronic configurations of the elements in each group.

An examination of the systematic buildup of electrons for the first 12 elements (H to Mg) should suffice to demonstrate the principles behind the observed periodic arrangement of the elements.

Hydrogen ($Z = 1$), with one electron, assumes the electronic configuration $1s^1$. The electron is in the $n = 1$, $\ell = 0$ (s) state.

Helium ($Z = 2$) has two electrons. They both can be accommodated in the $n = 1$, $\ell = 0$ level to give a $1s^2$ configuration.

Lithium (Z = 3) has three electrons. Two go into the $n = 1$, $\ell = 0$ level (i.e., $1s^2$). This level is now full, since the maximum occupancy at $n = 1$ is two (see Table 1-5). The third must go into $n = 2$, $\ell = 0$, to give an overall configuration $1s^22s^1$.

Beryllium (Z = 4), with four electrons, assumes a $1s^22s^2$ configuration. Since the $n = 2$, $\ell = 0$ level is now full, the next electrons will go into the $\ell = 1$ level.

Boron (Z = 5) has five electrons. The first four give a $1s^22s^2$ configuration. The fifth electron goes into the $\ell = 1$ (p) level to yield an overall configuration $1s^22s^22p^1$.

Carbon (Z = 6), nitrogen (Z = 7), oxygen (Z = 8), fluorine (Z = 9), and neon (Z = 10) have six, seven, eight, nine, and ten electrons, respectively. These electrons can go into the $\ell = 1$ level since it has room for a total of six electrons, five beyond boron. The configurations are C, $1s^22s^22p^2$; N, $1s^22s^22p^3$; O, $1s^22s^22p^4$; F, $1s^22s^22p^5$; Ne, $1s^22s^22p^6$. Since the $n = 1$ and $n = 2$ levels, which have maximum occupancies of two and eight, respectively, are now full, any additional electrons must go into the $n = 3$ level.

Sodium (Z = 11), with 11 electrons, assumes a $1s^22s^22p^63s^1$ configuration.

Magnesium (Z = 12), with 12 electrons, has a $1s^22s^22p^63s^2$ configuration.

Analysis of the above configurations reveals systematic relationships upon which chemical similarities and family groupings can be explained. First, we have elements whose electronic configurations reveal filling of the same n level: H to He($n = 1$); Li to Ne($n = 2$); Na to Ar($n = 3$); and so on. Within each group there is a similarity in the electronic configuration of outer electrons. For example, H, Li, and Na all have outer configurations of the s^1 type. Beryllium and magnesium have outer shells of the s^2 type. We can organize the elements we have examined into horizontal rows based on the n level of the outer electrons and into vertical groups based on similarities in the sublevel electrons. This is shown for the first 18 elements in Table 1-6. Only the outer electrons (electrons of highest n value) are shown. The overall order is in terms of increasing atomic number, or number of electrons.

Table 1-6. OUTER ELECTRON CONFIGURATION OF ELEMENTS H TO Ar

n level	*Configurations*							
1	H s^1							He s^2
2	Li s^1	Be s^2	B s^2p^1	C s^2p^2	N s^2p^3	O s^2p^4	F s^2p^5	Ne s^2p^6
3	Na s^1	Mg s^2	Al s^2p^1	Si s^2p^2	P s^2p^3	S s^2p^4	Cl s^2p^5	Ar s^2p^6

The position of He requires special mention since it might seem more reasonable to place it over Be and Mg. When a configuration reaches a completed shell (for $n = 1$, s^2; for $n = 2$, s^2p^6; etc.), the configuration becomes very stable. Because of the common features of high stabilities and completed outer shells, the elements on the far right (He to Ar, etc.) are placed in the same group.

The chemical properties of an atom are primarily determined by its outermost electrons (highest n level). The element's position in the periodic table describes its outer electron types. Frequent reference to the information in Table 1-6 is made when properties of elements are being discussed.

The outer-shell electrons are called *valence* electrons. The block diagram in Fig. 1-3 shows some generalizations about them. The elements in each block have the following outer electron types, which characterize them and largely determine their chemical properties: block I, ns electrons; block II, ns and np electrons; block III, $(n-1)d$ electrons; block IV, $(n-2)f$ electrons. In subsequent chapters the theoretical basis for the electronic configurations and the properties of elements in the four blocks are developed.

Further general observations about the grouping of elements in the periodic table can be made. Each horizontal row of elements is called a *period*. The first period contains two elements, the second and third periods, eight elements each, and the fourth and fifth periods, 18 elements each. The sixth and seventh periods each should contain 32 elements; the sixth period does, but the seventh period is still incomplete. Undoubtedly, as new elements are prepared in high-energy nuclear accelerators, these empty positions will be filled.

The elements fall into 18 vertical *groups* that define the chemical groups. The elements in groups IA to VIIA and in group 0 are called *main group* elements. Elements in groups IB to VIIB are called *transition* elements. The lanthanide and actinide elements, which are in reality 28 members of group IIIB, are sometimes called *inner transition metal* elements. In addition to these general classes, certain groups commonly are named even more specifically. Following are the most important of these:

Group IA	alkali metals (Li, Na, K, Rb, Cs, Fr)
Group IIA	alkaline earth metals (Be, Mg, Ca, Sr, Ba, Ra)
Group VIIA	halogens (F, Cl, Br, I, At)
Group 0	rare gases (He, Ne, Ar, Kr, Xe, Rn)
Group IB	coinage metals (Cu, Ag, Au)

1.3 COMPOUNDS

Compounds have been defined as pure substances composed of two or more elements. The subject of weight relationships of the elements in compounds is known as *stoichiometry* of compounds.

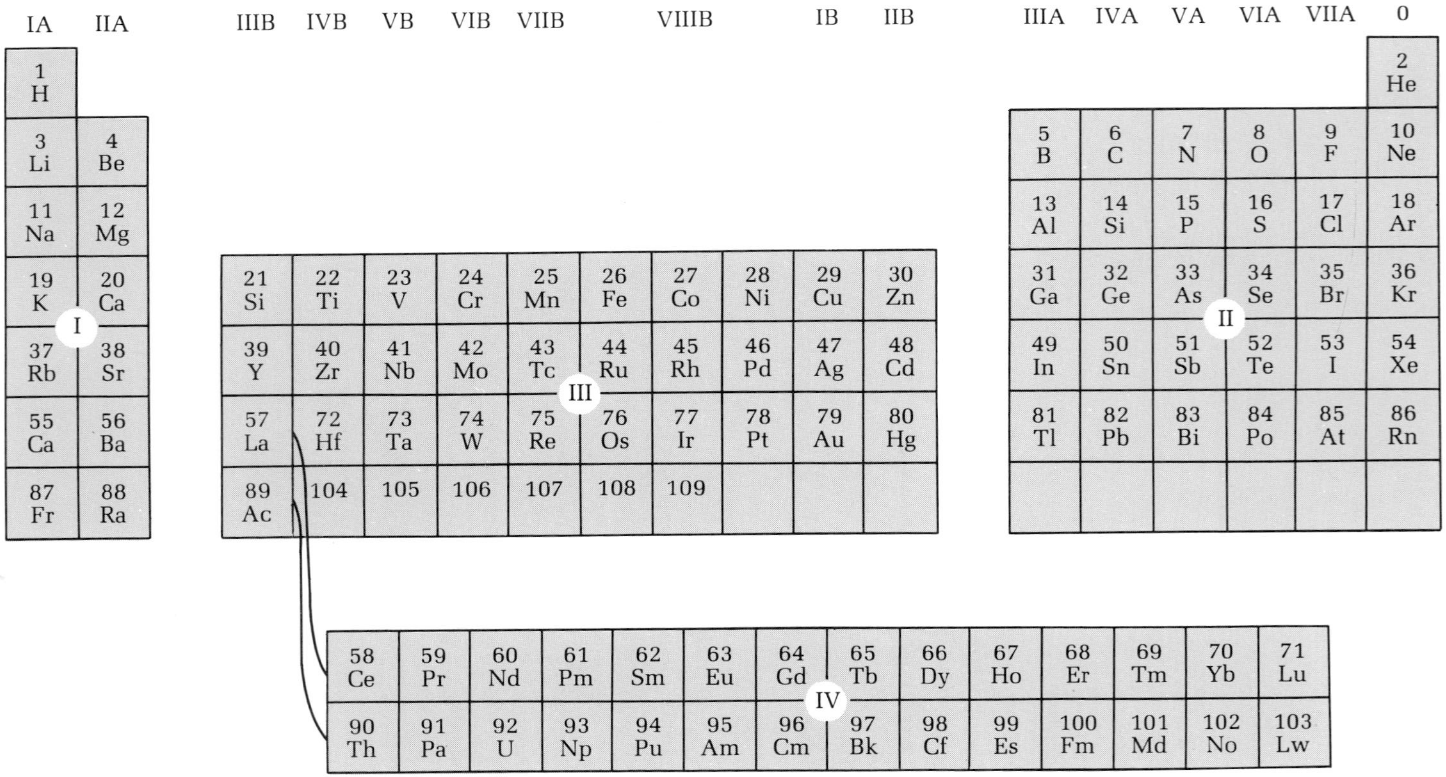

IA	IIA	IIIB	IVB	VB	VIB	VIIB	VIIIB			IB	IIB	IIIA	IVA	VA	VIA	VIIA	0
1 H																	2 He
3 Li	4 Be											5 B	6 C	7 N	8 O	9 F	10 Ne
11 Na	12 Mg											13 Al	14 Si	15 P	16 S	17 Cl	18 Ar
19 K	20 Ca	21 Si	22 Ti	23 V	24 Cr	25 Mn	26 Fe	27 Co	28 Ni	29 Cu	30 Zn	31 Ga	32 Ge	33 As	34 Se	35 Br	36 Kr
37 Rb	38 Sr	39 Y	40 Zr	41 Nb	42 Mo	43 Tc	44 Ru	45 Rh	46 Pd	47 Ag	48 Cd	49 In	50 Sn	51 Sb	52 Te	53 I	54 Xe
55 Ca	56 Ba	57 La	72 Hf	73 Ta	74 W	75 Re	76 Os	77 Ir	78 Pt	79 Au	80 Hg	81 Tl	82 Pb	83 Bi	84 Po	85 At	86 Rn
87 Fr	88 Ra	89 Ac	104	105	106	107	108	109									

58 Ce	59 Pr	60 Nd	61 Pm	62 Sm	63 Eu	64 Gd	65 Tb	66 Dy	67 Ho	68 Er	69 Tm	70 Yb	71 Lu
90 Th	91 Pa	92 U	93 Np	94 Pu	95 Am	96 Cm	97 Bk	98 Cf	99 Es	100 Fm	101 Md	102 No	103 Lw

Fig. 1-3. Separation of periodic table into blocks based on similarities in outer-electron configurations of elements.

The mole: molecular weight

The molecular weight (*MW*), or formula weight, of a compound is the sum of the atomic weights of the constituent elements. For example, the molecular weight of H_2SO_4, sulfuric acid, is

$$\begin{aligned}\text{molecular weight of } H_2SO_4 &= 2 \times 1.008 + 32.064 + 4 \times 15.999 \\ &= 98.076\end{aligned}$$

Whatever units of mass we choose, carbon will have a weight of 12 units, and H_2SO_4, a molecular weight of 98 units. The atomic weight in grams is called the *gram atomic weight*. The molecular weight of a substance in grams is called the *gram molecular weight*.

It has been determined experimentally that one gram atomic weight or one gram molecular weight of any substance contains 6.023×10^{23} atoms or molecules, respectively. This number, also called one mole, is known as *Avogadro's number*. Equal mole amounts of two substances have equal numbers of molecules. The number of moles of a compound equals the mass of the substance in grams divided by its gram molecular weight:

$$\text{moles of substance} = \frac{\text{mass of substance (in grams)}}{\text{gram molecular weight of substance}}$$

Molecular weights, like atomic weights, are most precisely determined with a mass spectrometer of the type shown in Fig. 1-2. For the compound CH_4 the unipositive ion (+1) of highest m/e ratio would be at $m/e = 16$, corresponding to the CH_4^+ ion. This simply corresponds to the parent molecule minus one electron.

Empirical and molecular formulas

Chemical formulas are abbreviations for compounds. The empirical formula of a compound is the formula expressed in the simplest whole-number ratio of the elements. It is established by determining the composition by weight of the elements in the compound. The weight of a given element in grams divided by its gram atomic weight gives the number of moles of that element in the sample. The ratio of the numbers of moles of the elements in the sample is converted to smallest whole numbers.

EXAMPLE **1.1**

What is the empirical formula of a compound that contains 56.5% P and 43.5% O?

Each 1.000 g of compound contains 0.565 g of P and 0.435 g of O. We obtain a gram-atom ratio of the elements by dividing each quantity by the gram atomic weight of the element:

$$\text{gram-atom ratio (P : O)} = \frac{\text{grams P}}{\text{gram atomic weight of P}} : \frac{\text{grams O}}{\text{gram atomic weight of O}}$$
$$= \frac{0.565 \text{ g}}{30.97 \text{ g}} : \frac{0.435 \text{ g}}{16.00 \text{ g}}$$
$$= 0.0182 : 0.0272$$

Dividing each of these numbers by 0.0182 yields a P:O ratio of 1:1.5. Since the empirical formula is given in terms of the smallest whole-number ratio of the elements, we multiply the ratio by 2 and obtain the formula P_2O_3.

EXAMPLE 1.2

Determine the empirical formula of glucose, a compound that contains C, H, and O in weight percentages of 40.0, 6.72, and 53.3, respectively.

Using the reasoning in example 1.1, we determine the gram-atom ratio of the elements:

$$\text{gram-atom ratio} = \frac{0.400 \text{ g}}{12.01 \text{ g}} : \frac{0.0672 \text{ g}}{1.008 \text{ g}} : \frac{0.533 \text{ g}}{16.00 \text{ g}}$$
$$= 0.0333 : 0.0667 : 0.0333$$

In smallest whole numbers the ratio is 1:2:1; the empirical formula of glucose is CH_2O.

The molecular formula of a compound gives the atom ratios expressed in numbers that denote the correct molecular weight of the compound as determined by mass spectrometry or other methods. For the compounds in examples 1.1 and 1.2 the molecular weights are found to be 220 and 180.2, respectively. Since the molecular weight of the phosphorus-oxygen compound in example 1.1 is twice that shown by the empirical formula, the molecular formula is P_4O_6. For glucose (example 1.2) the molecular weight is six times that given by the empirical formula; the molecular formula is $C_6H_{12}O_6$.

The percent composition of the elements in a compound can be computed from either the empirical or the molecular formula.

EXAMPLE 1.3

Calculate the percent composition of the elements in H_3PO_4.

The molecular weight is calculated as

$$MW = 3\ (1.008) + 30.974 + 4\ (15.999)$$
$$= 97.994$$

In 97.994 g of H_3PO_4 there are 3.024 g of H, 30.974 g of P, and 63.996 g of O. Thus the percentage of each element is:

$$\% \text{ H} = \frac{3.024}{97.994} \times 100 = 3.09\%$$

$$\% \text{ P} = \frac{30.974}{97.994} \times 100 = 31.60\%$$

$$\% \text{ O} = \frac{63.996}{97.994} \times 100 = 65.31\%$$

Structural formulas

The specification of how the atoms in a molecule are arranged and how they are bonded is represented by a structural formula. In this section we will consider only the simplest representation of structural formulas in two dimensions. These structures show the valence electrons of each atom and how they are arranged. Several examples are shown in Fig. 1-4. The valence electrons in a molecule are indicated individually by electron dots or in pairs by two dots or a single line.

Three rules are used in writing the formulas: the total number of electron dots must equal the sum of the numbers of valence electrons of all the atoms; when possible, electrons in molecules are grouped in pairs; elements in the first period can be surrounded by only two electrons, elements in the second period are surrounded by eight electrons if possible, and elements in third and successive periods can be surrounded by eight or more electrons.

Several features of the electron arrangements in Fig. 1-4 should be noted.

1. For the anions there are extra electrons equal to the charge on the anions.
2. In each example, eight electrons are placed around each atom except the N atom in NO_2. Nitrogen has an odd number of valence electrons, and, as a result, only seven electrons are put around N in NO_2.
3. In order to get eight electrons around each atom, it is necessary to put more than two electron pairs between some of the atoms. For example, in CO_2 there are two groups of four electrons, or two pairs, between carbon and each oxygen. These are called *double bonds*. Ethylene (CH_2CH_2), BF_3, NO_2, and the CO_3^{2-} ion have one double bond each.
4. In locating the electrons in BF_3, NO_2, and CO_3^{2-}, the double bonds can be placed in the system in more than one way. For BF_3, NO_2, and CO_3^{2-}, there are three, two, and three ways, respectively, to arrange the double bonds. This phenomenon is called *resonance*. Each resonance structure is equally good; in fact, the actual distribution of electrons in the molecule or ion is an average of the resonance structures.

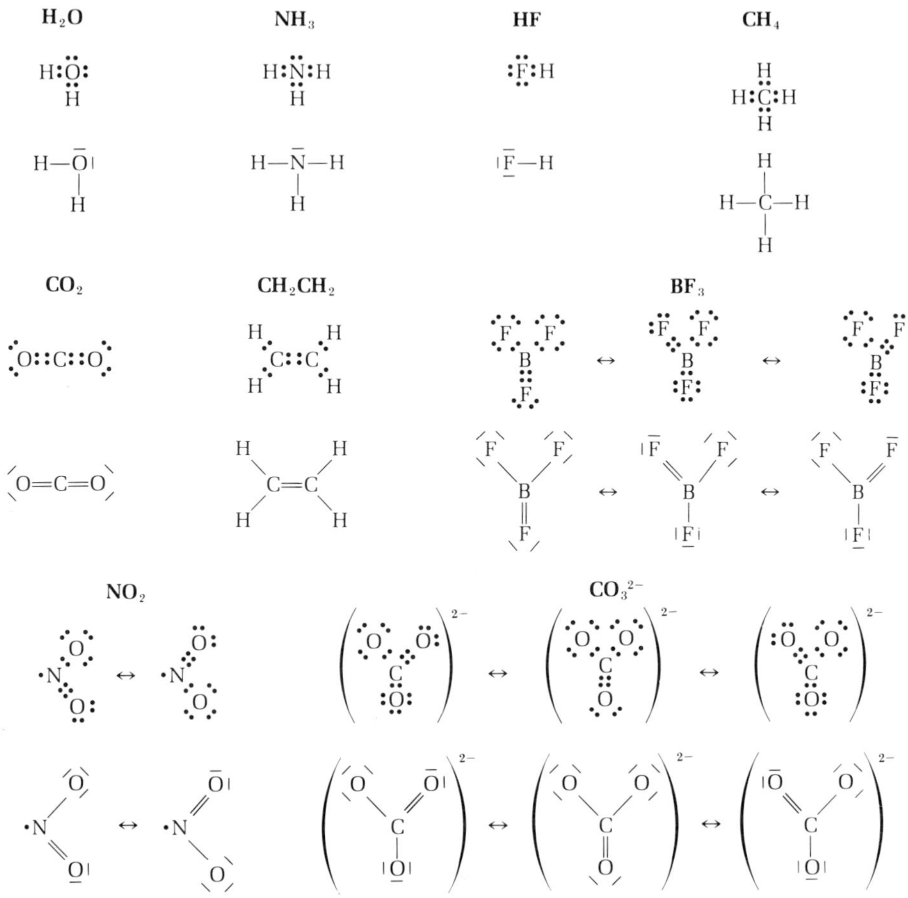

H_2O	NH_3	HF	CH_4
H:Ö: H	H:N̈:H H	:F̤̈:H	H H:C̤̈:H H
H—Ō| | H	H—N̄—H | H	|F̄—H	H | H—C—H | H

CO_2	CH_2CH_2	BF_3
:O::C::O:	H H C::C H H	:F: :F: B :F: ↔ :F: :F: B :F: ↔ :F: :F: B :F:
O=C=O	H H C=C H H	F F B F ↔ |F F B |F| ↔ F F B |F|

NO_2	CO_3^{2-}
·N:O: :O: ↔ ·N :O: :O:	(O O C :O:)$^{2-}$ ↔ (O O C O)$^{2-}$ ↔ (:O O C :O:)$^{2-}$
·N—O=O ↔ ·N=O—O	(O O C |O|)$^{2-}$ ↔ (O O C O)$^{2-}$ ↔ (|O O C |O|)$^{2-}$

Fig. 1-4. Electron dot formulas of molecules and ions.

5. Electron pairs that are not used in forming bonds are often present. These *nonbonding* or *lone-pair* electrons must be counted.

Electronegativity

When elements occur in chemical combination, they show markedly different tendencies to draw electrons toward themselves. The extent to which they attract electrons is called electronegativity, symbolized by χ. Electronegativity effects can be illustrated by comparing the distribution of electrons between the atoms in LiBr, BrF, and Br_2:

A	B	C
+ − Li :B̤̈r :	δ+ δ− :B̤̈r:F̤̈: →	:B̤̈r :B̤̈r :

Table 1-7. ELECTRONEGATIVITIES OF SOME ELEMENTS

H 2.1						
Li 0.97	Be 1.5	B 2.0	C 2.5	N 3.1	O 3.5	F 4.1
Na 1.0	Mg 1.2	Al 1.5	Si 1.7	P 2.1	S 2.4	Cl 2.8
K 0.90	Ca 1.0	Ga 1.8	Ge 2.0	As 2.2	Se 2.5	Br 2.7
Rb 0.86	Sr 1.0	In 1.5	Sn 1.7	Sb 1.8	Te 2.0	I 2.2

In *A* an electron has been lost by the Li atom to the Br atom to form Li^+ and Br^- ions. Lithium bromide is said to contain *ionic bonds*. This transfer of the electron arises because the electronegativity of Br is much greater than that of Li.

In *B* the electrons are shared between the Br and F atoms but are shifted toward the F atom. A bond of this type is called a *polar-covalent bond*. The polar nature of the bond is shown by the direction of the arrow and the δ^+ (partial positive charge) and δ^- (partial negative charge) notation. Although χ_F is enough greater than χ_{Br} to yield a polar bond, complete electron transfer to form ions does not occur.

In *C*, since the atoms are equivalent, the electrons in the Br-Br bond are shared equally to give a *covalent bond*.

Some important generalizations about relative electronegativities can be made. Elements on the far left of the periodic table (groups IA and IIA) show a low tendency to attract electrons. They have low electronegativities. Elements on the far right (except rare gases) strongly attract electrons and thus have high electronegativities. Elements in the middle region of the table possess intermediate electronegativities.

A scale of electronegativities has been devised that is based on a defined value of $\chi = 4.1$ for F. All other elements are defined relative to F and have lower χ values. Some elements for which χ values are frequently needed are shown in Table 1-7. In the horizontal rows (periods) the electronegativities generaly increase from left to right. Trends in groups are less clear-cut, but there seems to be a general decrease in moving down a group.

Oxidation state and number

Oxidation state is a concept used to describe the distribution of electrons in a compound. It is a numerical measure of the degree to which an atom in an ion or a molecule has formal charge. A given oxidation state is denoted by a number, either negative, zero, or positive, called its oxidation number.

By definition, the oxidation number of an element is 0. Simple ions (monatomic species) are assigned oxidation numbers equal to their actual charges. For example, the ions Ca^{2+}, Cl^-, and O^{2-} have oxidation numbers of 2+, 1−, and 2−, respectively.

In molecules and complex ions the determination of oxidation number is more difficult. Consideration of the relative electronegativities of atoms provides a guide for assigning oxidation numbers. In HCl chlorine is more electronegative than hydrogen ($\chi_{Cl} > \chi_H$), and as a result the electrons are displaced in the direction of the chlorine atom. We say that chlorine possesses an extra electron. Consequently, the oxidation number of hydrogen is 1+, and that of chlorine is 1−.

Several elements consistently assume the same oxidation numbers when chemically combined. The alkali metals (Li, Na, K, Rb, and Cs) occur in the 1+ state. The alkaline earth metals (Be, Mg, Ca, Sr, and Ba) occur in the 2+ state. Hydrogen, when bonded to a more electronegative element, is in the 1+ state. When bonded to elements less electronegative than themselves, halogens (F, Cl, Br, and I) assume 1− oxidation states, and oxygen and sulfur, 2− oxidation states. When these elements are present in a compound, they provide a starting point for calculating other oxidation numbers.

Table 1-8. CALCULATION OF OXIDATION NUMBERS

Example species	*Oxidation number of element in question*	*How arrived at*
MnO_2	4+	1. Sum of oxidation numbers must equal 0 2. Two oxygens equal 4− 3. ∴ oxidation number of Mn must equal 4+
ClO_4^-	7+	1. Sum of oxidation numbers must equal 1− 2. Four oxygens equal 8− 3. ∴ oxidation number of Cl must equal 7+
CCl_4	4+	1. Sum of oxidation numbers must equal 0 2. Four chlorines equal 4− 3. ∴ oxidation number of C must equal 4+
$NaBrO_3$	5+	1. Sum of oxidation numbers must equal 0 2. The sodium (1+) and three oxygens (6−) sum to 5− 3. ∴ oxidation number of Br must equal 5+

Examples of the calculation of oxidation numbers for a variety of species is shown in Table 1-8. The element in boldface in each example is the one of particular interest. In calculating oxidation numbers, we should remember two basic rules:

1. The sum of the oxidation numbers of the constituents of a neutral species must be zero.
2. In an ionic species, the sum of the oxidation numbers must equal the charge of the ion in sign and magnitude.

Notice that in ClO_4^-, chlorine assumes an oxidation number different from 1− because it is less electronegative than the element to which it is bonded.

Inorganic compounds

Inorganic compounds are compounds formed from elements other than carbon. Numerous inorganic compounds occur in nature. Most of the compounds in the earth are inorganic. In addition, many inorganic compounds, such as commercial bleaches, hydrazine rocket fuel, and silicone lubricants, are man made.

There are three main classes of inorganic compounds: binary, oxyanion-containing, and coordination. The first two will be reviewed in this section in order to familiarize the reader with the fundamental species and their names. A detailed review of the methods used for naming compounds in each class appears in Appendix C. Inorganic compounds and their nomenclature occur frequently throughout the text.

Substances composed of only two elements are called *binary compounds*. Examples are sodium chloride (NaCl), hydrogen chloride (HCl), and ammonia (NH_3).

Oxyanion compounds contain anions of the general formula XO_n^{y-}. In such anions, n oxygen atoms are bonded covalently to the central atom X, such as in sulfate (SO_4^{2-}) and carbonate (CO_3^{2-}) ions. Several of the most important oxyanion-containing compounds are given below.

COMMON OXYANION COMPOUNDS

Acids		*Salts*	
H_2SO_4	sulfuric acid	Na_2SO_4	sodium sulfate
H_3PO_4	phosphoric acid	Na_3PO_4	sodium phosphate
$HClO_3$	chloric acid	Na_2HPO_4	sodium hydrogen phosphate
$HClO_4$	perchloric acid	NaH_2PO_4	sodium dihydrogen phosphate
H_2CO_3	carbonic acid	$KClO_3$	potassium chlorate

Compounds that yield ions in solution are called *electrolytes*. Some of the most common cations and anions with their formal charges are given in Table 1-9.

Table 1-9. SOME COMMON IONS

Cations			*Anions*		
1+	*2+*	*3+*	*1−*	*2−*	*3−*
Ammonium, NH_4^+	Barium, Ba^{2+}	Aluminum, Al^{3+}	Bromide, Br^-	Carbonate, CO_3^{2-}	Arsenate, AsO_4^{3-}
Hydrogen, H^+	Calcium, Ca^{2+}	Chromium(III), Cr^{3+}	Chlorate, ClO_3^-	Chromate, CrO_4^{2-}	Nitride, N^{3-}
Potassium, K^+	Chromium(II), Cr^{2+}	Cobalt(III), Co^{3+}	Chloride, Cl^-	Dichromate, $Cr_2O_7^{2-}$	Phosphate, PO_4^{3-}
Silver, Ag^+	Copper(II), Cu^{2+}	Iron(III), Fe^{3+}	Cyanide, CN^-	Oxide, O^{2-}	
Sodium, Na^+	Iron(II), Fe^{2+}		Fluoride, F^-	Sulfide, S^{2-}	
	Magnesium, Mg^{2+}		Hydrogen carbonate, HCO_3^-	Sulfate, SO_4^{2-}	
	Mercury, Hg^{2+}		Hydride, H^-		
	Tin, Sn^{2+}		Hydroxide, OH^-		
	Strontium, Sr^{2+}		Hydrogen sulfate, HSO_4^-		
	Zinc, Zn^{2+}		Nitrate, NO_3^-		
			Perchlorate, ClO_4^-		
			Permanganate, MnO_4^-		

All electrolytic substances are electrically neutral, even though their constituent ions are charged. It is necessary when writing a formula to balance the total cation charge with the total anion charge. For example, consider the formulas of the four compounds that arise when Na^+ and Ca^{2+} are in combination with Cl^- and PO_4^{3-}. Total cation and anion charges are shown in parenthesis:

(+1) (−1)	(+2) (−2)	(+3) (−2)	(+6) (−6)
$NaCl$	$CaCl_2$	Na_3PO_4	$Ca_3(PO_4)_2$

The relative number of each ion in a formula is determined by the ion charges.

Organic compounds

Organic compounds are compounds that contain carbon atoms. They are called organic because many of them are found in living organisms. They can be obtained from laboratory or industrial syntheses, as well as from natural sources.

Organic compounds can be named by a variety of methods ranging from trivial (no system) to highly systematic. This section is intended to provide only a basis upon which additional and more complex compound types can be discussed as they occur. A more complete treatment of organic nomenclature is given in Appendix D.

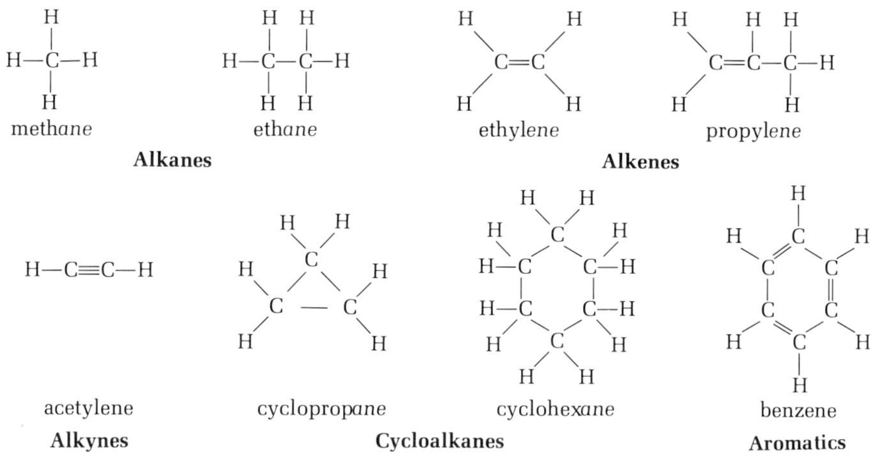

methane, ethane — **Alkanes**

ethylene, propylene — **Alkenes**

H—C≡C—H
acetylene — **Alkynes**

cyclopropane, cyclohexane — **Cycloalkanes**

benzene — **Aromatics**

Fig. 1-5. Hydrocarbons.

The simplest organic compounds are *hydrocarbons*, which contain only the elements C and H. Five types of hydrocarbons are alkanes, alkenes, alkynes, cycloalkanes, and aromatics. Examples are shown in Fig. 1-5 along with their commonly used names. The name endings are italicized when they are characteristic of the compound types.

Alkanes (formula C_nH_{2n+2}; ending *-ane*) contain only C—C single bonds. Since they have the maximum H/C ratio, they are said to be *saturated*. *Alkenes* (ending *-ene*) and *alkynes* are typified by C═C double and C≡C triple bonds, respectively. *Cycloalkanes* are alkanes in which end (terminal) carbons are joined to form a ring. They are characterized by the prefix *cyclo-*. *Aromatic* hydrocarbons have unusual bonding properties as a result of an alternating double-bond arrangement as seen in benzene.

Examination of the names of the preceding compounds indicates that, in addition to characteristic endings, there are general stem names related to the number of carbon atoms in the molecule. The stem names for systems up to C_6 are listed below.

GENERAL STEM NAMES

Carbons in chain	*Stem name*	*Carbons in chain*	*Stem name*
1 (C_1)	meth	4 (C_4)	but
2 (C_2)	eth	5 (C_5)	pent
3 (C_3)	prop	6 (C_6)	hex

A hydrogen atom (or atoms) in a hydrocarbon can be replaced by other atoms or groups of atoms. The hydrocarbon portion of the compound is called a *radical*. Alkane and aromatic radicals occur most frequently. Alkane-derived radicals are named by adding *-yl* to the stem name. From methane and ethane, we obtain methyl and ethyl radicals, respectively. The radical derived from benzene is called a phenyl radical:

```
     H              H  H                   H
     |              |  |                   |
  H—C—           H—C—C—              H\  //C\  /H
     |              |  |                  C     C
     H              H  H                  |     ||
                                          C     C
                                       H/  \\C/  \H
                                             |
   Methyl-          Ethyl-                Phenyl-
```

Methyl- **Ethyl-** **Phenyl-**

Two types of substituted hydrocarbons are alcohols and carboxylic acids. *Alcohols* are formed by the replacement of a hydrocarbon H atom with an —OH group. *Carboxylic acids* are characterized by the —C(=O)OH group, which contains a carbon to which a double-bonded oxygen (C═O bond) and an —OH group are attached (Table 1-10). Examples of these are ethyl alcohol and acetic acid. Note that in the examples below and in Table 1-10, only bonding electron pairs are shown.

```
     H  H                 H     O
     |  |                 |    //
  H—C—C—OH             H—C—C
     |  |                 |    \
     H  H                 H     OH
```

Ethyl alcohol **Acetic acid**

1.4 CHEMICAL REACTIONS

Writing equations

Chemical equations are shorthand representations of chemical reactions. They describe the relationship between *reactants* and *products*. For example, in equation 1.4, 1 mole of CH_4 and 2 moles of O_2 react to form 1 mole of CO_2 and 2 moles of H_2O as products:

$$CH_4 + 2O_2 \rightarrow CO_2 + 2H_2O \tag{1.4}$$

$$CH_4(g) + 2O_2(g) \rightarrow CO_2(g) + 2H_2O(l) \tag{1.5}$$

$$CH_4(g,\ 1\ \text{atm}) + 2O_2(g,\ 1\ \text{atm}) \rightarrow CO_2(g,\ 1\ \text{atm}) + 2H_2O(l) \tag{1.6}$$

Chemical equations can also be written in more detail, if needed, as in equations 1.5 and 1.6. The physical states of the reaction species can be specified: (s) for solid, (g) for gas, (l) for liquid, and (aq) for aqueous solution. The pressure, temperature, and concentration can also be included if important.

Table 1-10. HALIDES, ALCOHOLS, AND ACIDS

General formula	*General name*	*Characteristic group*	*Example compound*	*Name of example*
R—F	Fluoride	—F	C_2H_5F	Ethyl fluoride Fluoroethane
R—Cl	Chloride	—Cl	CH_3Cl	Methyl chloride Chloromethane
R—OH	Alcohol	—OH	C_2H_5OH	Ethanol Ethyl alcohol
R—C(=O)—OH	Carboxylic acid	—C(=O)—OH	CH_3CO_2H	Ethanoic acid (acetic acid)

Chemical equations in which the reactants and the products are shown completely are called *complete* chemical equations:

$$Cu(NO_3)_2 + Zn \rightarrow Zn(NO_3)_2 + Cu \quad (1.7)$$

When this reaction takes place in water, it is more useful to write $Cu(NO_3)_2$ and $Zn(NO_3)_2$ in their ionized forms as they actually occur in solution:

$$Zn(s) + Cu^{2+}(aq) + 2NO_3^-(aq) \rightarrow Cu(s) + Zn^{2+}(aq) + 2NO_3^-(aq) \quad (1.8)$$

This is a *complete ionic equation.* The physical and chemical state of the NO_3^- ion does not change in the reaction. We can show the species that do change, as

$$Zn(s) + Cu^{2+}(aq) \rightarrow Cu(s) + Zn^{2+}(aq) \quad (1.9)$$

The resulting abbreviated equation is called the *net ionic equation.*

For any chemical equation to be written completely, it must be balanced; the number of atoms of each element on the reactant side of the equation must equal and number on the product side. For simple equations, balance can be accomplished by inspection. Such is the case with equations 1.4 to 1.9.

Reaction stoichiometry

Reaction stoichiometry deals with the weight relationships of species involved in chemical reactions. To understand reaction stoichiometry, one must remember three important concepts: the mole; the law of conservation of mass; and the balancing of equations. The *law of conservation of mass* states that matter can never be created nor destroyed by chemical means. In a chemical reaction, this means that the total mass of the products must equal that of the reactants.

EXAMPLE **1.4**

How many moles of $KClO_3$ are needed to produce 1 mole of O_2 according to the reaction

$$2KClO_3 \rightarrow 2KCl + 3O_3$$

The equation, which is balanced as shown, tells us that for every 2 moles of $KClO_3$ reacting, 2 moles of KCl and 3 moles of O_2 are formed. Therefore, according to

$$\frac{2 \text{ moles } KClO_3}{3 \text{ moles } O_2} = \frac{x}{1 \text{ mole } O_2}$$

$$x = \frac{2 \text{ moles } KClO_3}{3 \text{ moles } O_2}(1 \text{ mole } O_2)$$

$$= 2/3 \text{ mole } KClO_3$$

$$= 0.67 \text{ mole } KClO_3$$

we determine that for every mole of O_2 that forms, 0.67 mole of $KClO_3$ is needed.

EXAMPLE **1.5**

How many moles of H_2 are formed when 10.0 g of Zn reacts with excess H_2SO_4 according to

$$Zn + H_2SO_4 \rightarrow ZnSO_4 + H_2$$

In this problem it is important to realize that the amount of Zn limits the amount of H_2 formed, since H_2SO_4 is stated to be present in excess. In this case, Zn is called the *limiting reagent*.

Since we want to know the answer in moles, we first determine the number of moles of Zn contained in 10.0 g:

$$\text{moles Zn} = \frac{10.0 \text{ g Zn}}{65.4 \text{ g Zn/mole Zn}} = 0.153 \text{ mole}$$

From the equation, we know that 1 mole of H_2 is produced per mole of Zn consumed. Thus, 10.0 g of Zn, in excess H_2SO_4, would yield 0.153 mole of H_2.

EXAMPLE **1.6**

What weight of $BaCl_2$ is needed to react with $AgNO_3$ to form 5.00 g of AgCl?

In this case, we must first write a balanced equation for the reaction that will occur:

$$BaCl_2 + 2AgNO_3 \rightarrow Ba(NO_3)_2 + 2AgCl$$

The number of moles in 5.00 g AgCl is 5.00/143.3 = 0.0349. The equation tells us that 1 mole of $BaCl_2$ yields 2 moles of AgCl. Therefore, we need $\frac{1}{2} \times 0.0349 = 0.0175$ mole of $BaCl_2$. The weight of $BaCl_2$ needed is then $0.0175 \times 208.2 = 3.64$ g.

Stoichiometry of solution

Many chemical reactions occur in solution. To deal with their stoichiometry we need to understand the commonly used systems for describing solution concentrations. Two of the most common systems of concentration units are mole fraction (X) and molarity (M). Later, other units will be introduced as needed.

Mole fraction. The mole fraction of a species is defined as the number of moles of species divided by the total number of moles in the solution. For a system of c components the number of moles of species 1, 2, . . . , c are given by n_1, n_2, . . . , n_c, and the mole fractions are defined by

$$X_i = \frac{n_i}{\sum_{i=1}^{c} n_i}$$

For a two-component system:

$$X_1 = \frac{n_1}{n_1 + n_2}, \quad X_2 = \frac{n_2}{n_1 + n_2}$$

Note that

$$\sum_{i=1}^{c} X_i = 1$$

EXAMPLE **1.7**

Determine the mole fraction of each component in a solution consisting of 0.1 mole ethanol, 8.4 moles methanol, and 1.5 moles water. The total number of moles in the solution is

$$\sum_{i=1}^{3} n_i = 0.1 \text{ mole ethanol} + 8.4 \text{ moles methanol} + 1.5 \text{ moles water}$$
$$= 10.0 \text{ moles}$$

The mole fractions of the components are

$$X_{C_2H_5OH} = \frac{\text{moles } C_2H_5OH}{\text{total moles}} = \frac{0.1}{10.0} = 0.01$$

$$X_{CH_3OH} = \frac{\text{moles } CH_3OH}{\text{total moles}} = \frac{8.4}{10.0} = 0.84$$

$$X_{H_2O} = \frac{\text{moles } H_2O}{\text{total moles}} = \frac{1.5}{10.0} = 0.15$$

Molarity. The molarity of a solution, or the molar concentration of a species in the solution, is defined as the number of moles of species per liter of solution:

$$\text{molarity } (M) = \frac{\text{moles of species}}{\text{liters of solution}}$$

For example, a solution that contains 0.1 mole of $BaCl_2$ in 1 liter of solution is 0.1 M in $BaCl_2$. However, since 1 mole of $BaCl_2$ yields 1 mole of Ba^{2+} and 2 moles of Cl^-, the solution can also be described as being 0.1 M in Ba^{2+} and 0.2 M in Cl^-. It is particularly important to understand this last point when doing solution stoichiometry problems.

EXAMPLE **1.8**

Calculate the molarity of a solution prepared by dissolving 25.0 g of NaCl in water to make a total of 0.5 liter of solution.

First, we need to determine how many moles are contained in 25.0 g of NaCl:

$$\text{moles NaCl} = \frac{25.0 \text{ g NaCl}}{58.4 \text{ g/mole}} = 0.43 \text{ mole}$$

$$\text{molarity NaCl} = \frac{0.43 \text{ mole}}{0.5 \text{ liter}} = 0.86\ M$$

EXAMPLE **1.9**

How many liters of 0.1 M H_2SO_4 are needed to exactly neutralize 2.0 liters of 0.6 M NaOH solution?

First we write the balanced equation for the neutralization reaction:

$$H_2SO_4 + 2NaOH \rightarrow 2H_2O + Na_2SO_4$$

Clearly, for every mole of H_2SO_4, we will need 2 moles of NaOH.
The number of moles of NaOH in the solution is

$$\begin{aligned}\text{moles NaOH} &= (\text{liters NaOH})(M\,\text{NaOH}) \\ &= (2.0 \text{ liters})(0.6 \text{ mole/liter}) \\ &= 1.2 \text{ moles}\end{aligned}$$

The 1.2 moles of NaOH will require 0.6 mole of H_2SO_4 for complete reaction. Since our H_2SO_4 solution is 0.1 M, the required number of liters of H_2SO_4 will be

$$\begin{aligned}\text{liters } H_2SO_4 \text{ required} &= \frac{0.6 \text{ mole}}{0.1 \text{ mole/liter}} \\ &= 6.0 \text{ liters}\end{aligned}$$

1.5 PROPERTIES OF GASES: IDEAL GAS LAW

One finds by experiment a general result, closely followed by all gases: 1 mole of a gas occupies 22.4 liters at a temperature of 273°K and a pressure of 1 atm. For example, 32 g of O_2 and 2 g of H_2 each occupy 22.4 liters at 273°K and 1 atm.

The ideal gas law, which simply relates the volume V, temperature T, pressure p, and number of moles n for gases, is

$$pV = nRT \tag{1.10}$$

where the gas law constant R is established from the preceding experimental results:

$$R = \frac{pV}{nT} = \frac{(1\text{ atm})\,(22.4\text{ liters})}{(1\text{ mole})\,(273\,°\text{K})} = 0.0821\,\frac{\text{liter-atm}}{\text{mole-deg}} \tag{1.11}$$

This law enables one to determine the number of moles in a given volume of a gas. An equation such as equation 1.10 is known as an *equation of state.*

EXAMPLE **1.10**

A sample of 5 g of an unknown gas occupies a volume of 1.2 liters at a temperature of 300°K and a pressure of 650 torr.* What is its molecular weight?

$$n = \frac{pV}{RT} = \frac{\left(\frac{650}{760}\text{atm}\right)(1.2\text{ liters})}{\left(0.0821\,\frac{\text{liter-atm}}{\text{mole-deg}}\right)(300\,°\text{K})} = 0.0417\text{ mole}$$

The molecular weight is then

$$MW = \frac{\text{grams of sample}}{n} = \frac{5.00}{0.0417} = 120$$

Another important calculation is finding the relation between p, V, and T for a fixed number of moles of a gas when these properties are changed between an initial (1) and a final (2) state. Since n and R are constant:

$$\frac{p_1V_1}{T_1} = \frac{p_2V_2}{T_2} \tag{1.12}$$

*One torr is defined as 1/760 of an atmosphere (atm) of pressure. For all practical purposes, a pressure of 1 torr equals 1 mm Hg.

EXAMPLE 1.11

Two liters of a gas, initially at 1 atm and 300°K, is compressed to 1 liter and reaches a final temperature of 600°K. What is the final pressure?

Using equation 1.12, we find

$$p_2 = p_1\left(\frac{V_1}{V_2}\right)\left(\frac{T_2}{T_1}\right) = 1 \text{ atm}\left(\frac{2 \text{ liter}}{1 \text{ liter}}\right)\left(\frac{600\,°\text{K}}{300\,°\text{K}}\right) = 4 \text{ atm}$$

When we have a mixture of ideal gases, the number of moles, n, is the sum of the moles of the c constituent gases:

$$n = \sum_{i=1}^{c} n_i \tag{1.13}$$

The pressure contribution of each constituent gas is called its partial pressure p_i:

$$p_i = n_i\left(\frac{RT}{V}\right) \tag{1.14}$$

We also have the total pressure as the sum of the partial pressures:

$$p = \Sigma p_i = \Sigma n_i\left(\frac{RT}{V}\right) = n\left(\frac{RT}{V}\right) \tag{1.15}$$

This gives the mole fraction X_i:

$$\frac{p_i}{p} = \frac{n_i}{n} = X_i \tag{1.16}$$

or

$$p_i = X_i p \tag{1.17}$$

EXAMPLE 1.12

Air contains N_2 and O_2 in a 4:1 ratio. For a total pressure of 650 torr, the partial pressures are

$$p_{O_2} = (1/5)\ (650) \text{ torr} = 130 \text{ torr}$$
$$p_{N_2} = (4/5)\ (650) \text{ torr} = 520 \text{ torr}$$

PROBLEMS

1. Define (a) atomic number; (b) mass number; (c) isotope; (d) saturated hydrocarbon; (e) atom; (f) ion; (g) molecule.
2. How many protons, neutrons, and electrons are there in (a) an atom of ^{238}U; (b) an atom of ^{28}Si; (c) a mole of ^{11}B?
3. Give the symbol, the values of Z and A, and the number of electrons for a species with (a) atomic number 10 and 12 neutrons; (b) atomic number 92 and mass number 238.
4. Calculate the atomic weight of naturally occurring boron, making use of the data in Table 1-2 and the fact that the atomic weights of the ^{10}B and ^{11}B isotopes are 10.012 and 11.009, respectively.
5. (a) What values of the angular momentum quantum number, ℓ, are permitted for an electron with principal quantum number $n = 5$? (b) What values of the magnetic quantum number, m_ℓ, are possible for an electron with $\ell = 4$?
6. How many electrons can be in (a) an s substate; (b) a p substate; (c) an f substate?
7. How many electrons can be placed in the $n = 3$ state of an atom?
8. Without referring to Table 1-6 write electronic configurations for H, B, N, and Ne.
9. List the elements of the third period (Na to Ar) that have (a) only one electron in a p state; (b) two electrons in a p state.
10. Give the symbol for the atoms that have the following ground-state electronic configurations: (a) $1s^2 2s^2 2p^4$; (b) $1s^2 2s^2 2p^6 3s^2$; (c) $1s^2 2s^2 2p^6 3s^2 3p^3$.
11. Give two examples of (a) halogens; (b) coinage metals; (c) transition metals; (d) alkali metals.
12. A sample of chlorine gas (Cl_2) is analyzed in a mass spectrometer. The mass spectrum shows peaks at $m/e = 70$, 72, and 74, of relative intensity 9:6:1. What is the ratio of ^{35}Cl to ^{37}Cl in the sample?
13. How many moles of atoms of each element are there in 1 mole of (a) $KMnO_4$; (b) PCl_3; (c) $B_{10}H_{14}$?
14. Determine the molecular weight of (a) C_6H_{14}; (b) PCl_5; (c) C_5H_5N; (d) $Ca(C_2H_3O_2)_2$.
15. Calculate the number of moles of each compound present in 100.0 g of (a) NaCl; (b) $Ca(C_2H_3O_2)_2$; (c) C_6H_6.
16. In the entire universe, approximately 93% of the atoms are H, and 7% are He. By weight, what percentage of the universe is hydrogen?
17. Chlorine is the most abundant element in ocean water. It is present as the Cl^- ion, at a concentration of about 19 g/kg of water. Given that the volume of ocean water is 1.4×10^{21} liters, how many moles of Cl_2 are potentially available from the oceans? (Assume the density of ocean water is 1.0 g/cm^3.)
18. Calculate the empirical formula for a compound that contains Mg, 20.2%; S, 26.6%; and O, 53.2%.
19. Nicotine, a constituent of tobacco, contains 74.0% C, 8.65% H, and 17.3% N. What is its empirical formula?
20. Calculate the percent composition (by weight) of the elements in (a) ZnI_2; (b) C_6H_5Cl; (c) Na_3PO_4.
21. The molecular weight of a certain hydrocarbon is found to be 100.2. It contains 84.0% C and 16.0% H by weight. What is its molecular formula?
22. Determine the number of valence electrons for (a) Mg; (b) Na; (c) C; (d) Si; (e) Cl; (f) P; (g) B; (h) H.
23. Draw electron dot formulas for (a) HF; (b) C_2H_6; (c) ICl; (d) NaCl.
24. Give electron dot formulas for (a) BH_4^-; (b) PCl_5; (c) HCO_3^-; (d) I_3^-; (e) ICl_3.

25. Predict whether the following compounds would contain ionic, polar-covalent, or covalent bonds: (a) NaF; (b) CO; (c) F_2; (d) $CaCl_2$; (e) N_2; (f) ICl.
26. Give the oxidation number of the element in boldface in the species that follow: (a) $\mathbf{Mn}O_4^-$; (b) $\mathbf{P}Cl_3$; (c) $\mathbf{P}Cl_3O$; (d) $H\mathbf{Cl}O$; (e) $\mathbf{Cl}O_3^-$; (f) $H\mathbf{I}$; (g) $Na_2\mathbf{S}_2O_3$; (h) $\mathbf{N}O_2^-$; (i) $\mathbf{Fe}_2O_3$.
27. Write a formula for compounds of each of the following types: (a) covalently-bonded; (b) binary inorganic; (c) binary organic; (d) oxyanion-containing; (e) hydrocarbon.
28. Give the formula for the potassium salts of (a) $HClO_3$; (b) H_3PO_4; (c) H_2SO_4.
29. Write formulas for (a) ammonium chloride; (b) sodium chromate; (c) calcium bromide; (d) barium chloride; (e) iron(II) chloride; (f) aluminum oxide; (g) potassium permanganate; (h) phosphoric acid; (i) calcium hydrogen sulfate; (j) copper(II) carbonate; (k) silver cyanide.
30. Write the formulas for (a) methane; (b) propane; (c) sodium acetate.
31. Name the following compounds: (a) $AgCl$; (b) Na_2CO_3; (c) $NaMnO_4$; (d) $FeCl_3$; (e) $Ca(OH)_2$; (f) $CoBr_3$; (g) Na_2O; (h) $SnCl_2$.
32. Give electron dot structural formulas for (a) cyclopropane; (b) chloroethane; (c) acetic acid; (d) methylalcohol.
33. Write net ionic equations for the following reactions:
    (a) $HCl(aq) + KOH(aq) \rightarrow KCl(aq) + H_2O(l)$
    (b) $Fe_2(SO_4)_3(aq) + Fe(s) \rightarrow 3FeSO_4(aq)$
    (c) $I_2(s) + 2Na_2S_2O_3(aq) \rightarrow Na_2S_4O_6(aq) + 2NaI(aq)$
34. Balance the following equations:
    (a) $PCl_3 + H_2O \rightarrow H_3PO_3 + HCl$
    (b) $NCl_3 + H_2O \rightarrow NH_3 + HOCl$
    (c) $Na_2CO_3 + HCl \rightarrow NaCl + CO_2 + H_2O$
    (d) $[Ag(NH_3)_2]Cl + HNO_3 \rightarrow AgCl + NH_4NO_3$
35. Calculate the weight of P_4O_{10} that would result from the reaction of 1.00 g of P_4 with 10.00 g of O_2.
36. Carbon dioxide, CO_2, can be removed from the atmosphere of a spaceship by NaOH according to the reaction

    $$2NaOH + CO_2 \rightarrow Na_2CO_3 + H_2O$$

    Calculate the weight of NaOH needed to remove CO_2 from the atmosphere of a spaceship carrying ten men for 10 days in space. Assume that the average human discharges about 900 g of CO_2 per day.
37. A 12.40 mg sample of an organic compound containing C, H, and O was burned in excess oxygen gas, yielding 17.60 mg CO_2 and 10.80 mg H_2O. Calculate the empirical formula of the compound.
38. A sample weighing 26.00 g contains $NaHCO_3$ and Na_2CO_3. When excess HCl is added to the sample, 22.0 g of NaCl is obtained. The reactions of HCl with $NaHCO_3$ and Na_2CO_3 are

    $$NaHCO_3 + HCl \rightarrow NaCl + CO_2 + H_2O$$
    $$Na_2CO_3 + HCl \rightarrow NaCl + CO_2 + H_2O$$

    (a) Balance the reactions. (b) Calculate the percentage of $NaHCO_3$ in the sample.
39. What is the mole fraction of benzene in a solution containing 0.10 mole benzene, 10.20 mole methanol, and 1.20 mole diethyl ether?
40. Determine the mole fraction of each component in a solution containing 2.00 g of C_2H_5OH (ethyl alcohol) in 26.00 g of water.

41. Calculate the weight of bromide ion in 1.00 liter of the following solutions: (a) 10.0% NaBr (density 1.10 g/ml); (b) 1.00 *M* NaBr.
42. Calculate the molarities of 1.00 liter aqueous solutions containing (a) 10.0 g NaCl; (b) 25.0 g C_2H_5OH; (c) 18.0 g $KMnO_4$.
43. What weight of aluminum sulfate is needed to prepare 100 ml of a 2.00 *M* solution?
44. What weight of $CaBr_2$ is needed to prepare 500 ml of a solution that is (a) 1.00 *M* in Ca^{2+} ion; (b) 4.00 *M* in Br^- ion?
45. How many milliliters of 0.500 *M* $KMnO_4$ solution will react completely with 20.0 g of $K_2C_2O_4$ in water according to the equation

$$16H^+ + 2MnO_4^- + 5C_2O_4^{2-} \longrightarrow 10CO_2 + 2Mn^{2+} + 8H_2O$$

46. Cyanogen is a gas used frequently as a fumigant. Its empirical formula is CN. If 3.46 g of the gas occupies 1.64 liter at 1 atm and 300°K, what is the molecular formula of the gas?
47. A 2.50-liter tank containing C_2H_6 gas at 27°C and 30.0 atm pressure develops a leak. By the time the leak is discovered, the tank has lost 66.0 g of C_2H_6. What is the pressure of the gas remaining in the tank at 27°C?
48. Using the appropriate conversion factors given in Appendix B, find the value of R in (a) calories/mole-deg; (b) joules/mole-deg.
49. Calculate the molecular weight of a gas, 0.30 g of which occupies a volume of 82 cm^3 at 3.0 atm pressure and 300°K.
50. Under what conditions could a sample of an ideal gas exhibit not only a pressure of 1 atm but also a concentration of 1 mole/liter?
51. A small automobile engine of a particular type has a cylinder displacement of 2000 cm^3. Assume that air fills the cylinders at 1 atm pressure and 27°C, and that air is one-fifth oxygen by volume. What weight of octane (C_8H_{18}) is necessary to combine with the oxygen, if combustion occurs according to

$$2C_8H_{18} + 25O_2 \longrightarrow 16CO_2 + 18H_2O.$$

52. A gaseous mixture of *n*-hexane (C_6H_{14}) and O_2 was placed in an evacuated vessel at 300°C. The mixture was ignited and reacted completely to form a mixture of gaseous CO, CO_2, and H_2O in a 4:8:14 ratio, respectively. Write a balanced equation for the combustion reaction.

2 THE SOLID STATE OF MATTER

Aggregation of matter occurs in the solid and liquid states. *Crystalline* solids occur when there is long-range ordering of constituent particles. Examples are salt and sugar. *Amorphous* solids are those in which long-range ordering is absent. Examples are Teflon and glass. Crystalline solids exhibit characteristic shapes (crystal habits); amorphous solids do not. Also, crystalline solids can be *anisotropic*, in which case a given property depends on direction in the solid. Graphite, for example, shows different abilities to conduct heat in different directions through the crystal. Amorphous solids are *isotropic*. Their properties are independent of direction. Liquids have no definite shape; they assume the shape of their container. Liquids lack long-range ordering of their constituent particles and, as a result, are generally isotropic.

The macroscopic properties of solids are a result of the structural and bonding characteristics of their constituent units (ions, atoms, or molecules). In the following sections we will examine structure and its relationship to some macroscopic properties.

2.1 TYPES OF CRYSTALLINE SOLIDS

Crystalline solids are characterized by the following types of properties:

lattice energy the energy* change that accompanies the formation of 1 mole of solid from infinitely separated gaseous constituent particles

melting point the temperature at which the solid-to-liquid phase-transition occurs

thermal and **electrical conductivity** the ease with which a solid can transfer heat or electricity

resistance to deformation the difficulty with which a solid is compressed, malled (malleability), or fractured (brittleness)

---

*The most common unit of energy for these purposes is the kilocalorie (kcal), which equals 1000 calories (cal). One calorie is approximately the energy required to raise 1 g of water 1°C. The calorie is precisely defined to be equal to 4.180 joules, which is defined by electrical measurements as shown in section 3.1.

These properties vary considerably from solid to solid. In general, they depend on the type, arrangement, and bonding of the constituent particles. Based on these differences, we differentiate four types of solids: ionic, covalent-network, metallic, and molecular.

Ionic solids are comprised of ions (cations and anions) held together by electrostatic interactions. Sodium chloride (Fig. 2-1, *A*) is an example. Electrostatic bonding forces are generally high as indicated by lattice energy (Table 2-1). As a result, ionic solids have high melting points, are brittle, and tend to fracture between specific planes called *cleavage planes*. In general, they are poor conductors of heat or electricity because of the immobility of the ions in the crystal lattice.

Covalent-network solids contain atoms bonded in a highly specific and directional way by covalent (shared-electron) bonds. Diamond (Fig. 2-1, *B*) is an example. Due to the directional character of the bonding forces, the lattices are difficult to distort or disrupt. Lattice energies and melting points are generally high. As with ionic

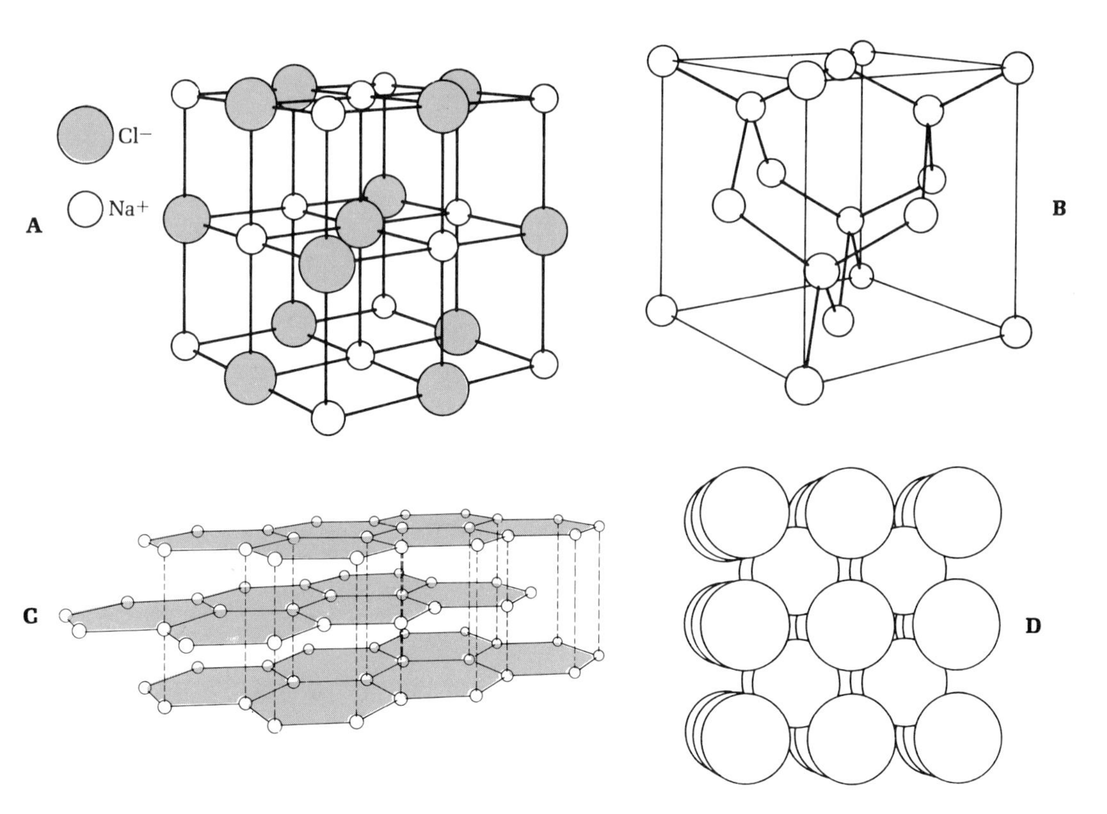

Fig. 2-1. Representative crystals. **A,** Sodium chloride. **B,** Diamond. **C,** Graphite. **D,** Sodium metal.

Table 2-1. PROPERTIES OF CRYSTALLINE SOLIDS

Crystal type	*Bonding in crystal*	*Lattice energy (kcal/mole)*	*Melting point (°C)*
IONIC	Electrostatic		
NaCl		186	801
CaF_2		500	1360
ZnO		964	1975
METALLIC	Metallic		
Li		38	179
Al		77	660
Fe		99	1535
COVALENT-NETWORK	Covalent		
C (diamond)		170	>3500
SiO_2 (quartz)		434	1610
MOLECULAR	van der Waals		
Ar		1.6	−189
Cl_2		4.9	−101
CO_2		6.0	−56.6

solids, the absence of mobile, charge-carrying units in the structures causes covalent-network solids to be poor conductors. Graphite (Fig. 2-1, *C*) is an exception because it has electrons between layers of the structure, thus providing a unique mechanism for conduction.

Metallic solids contain metal atoms bonded by highly mobile valence electrons. The structure of Na metal is shown in Fig. 2-1, *D*. Lattice energies (Table 2-1) are generally less than 100 kcal/mole. Metals show a wide variety of physical properties. Mercury melts at −39°C, while iron melts at 1535°C. Sodium is a soft, malleable metal, whereas tungsten is extremely hard and refractory. Aluminum and copper are excellent conductors; lead and bismuth are poor ones.

Molecular crystals are comprised of molecules. Examples are solid N_2, CO_2, and benzene (C_6H_6), shown in Fig. 2-2, *A* to *C*. The molecules are bonded by weak forces called *van der Waals* forces. Lattice energies and melting points are low, and the crystals are easily deformed. They are poor conductors.

The determination of solid-state structure is accomplished by X-ray diffraction studies. This technique is discussed in detail in section 14.1.

2.2 CRYSTAL LATTICES

Crystalline solids are characterized by an orderly, regularly repeating arrangement of their constituent units. This regular, three-dimensional arrangement of units is called the crystal lattice. A representative lattice is shown in Fig. 2-3. Each lattice point represents an equivalent position in the lattice. All lattice points need not be occupied by atoms or ions.

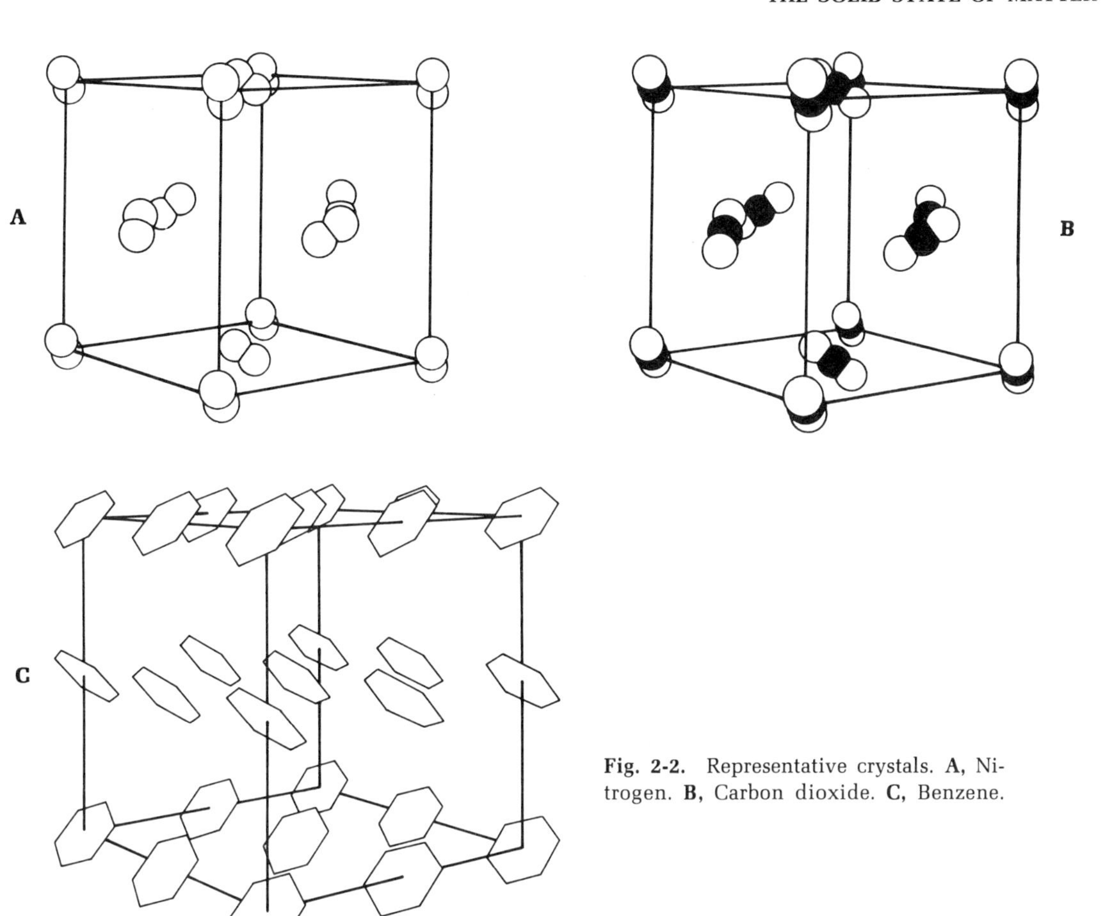

Fig. 2-2. Representative crystals. **A,** Nitrogen. **B,** Carbon dioxide. **C,** Benzene.

A crystal lattice is characterized by the three crystal axes, a, b, and c, and the angles between them, α, β, and γ. The convention followed in labeling angles and axes is shown in Fig. 2-3. The lattice shows a series of successive repeating units along each axis.

Unit cells

Any crystal lattice can be described in terms of a minimal-sized unit, the smallest unit in three dimensions that when repeated will generate the entire crystal. This is the unit cell, a parallelepiped with characteristic edge lengths and interaxial angles just like the lattice. A complete lattice is formed by taking unit cells and stacking them together in three dimensions. In Fig. 2-3 a unit cell of the lattice is outlined in black.

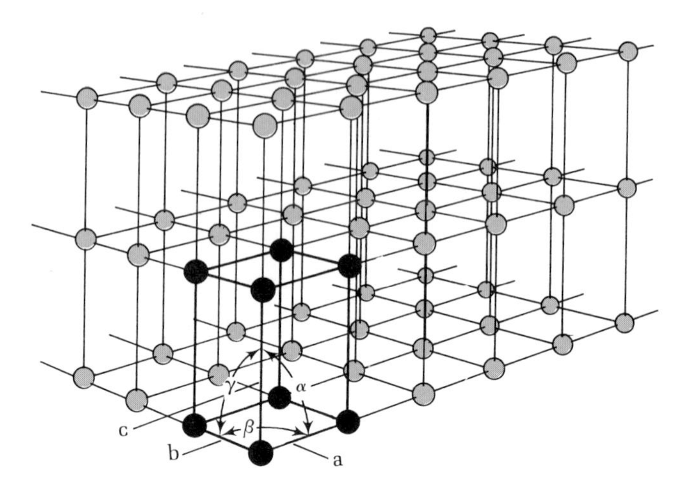

Fig. 2-3. Three-dimensional crystal lattice. Corner parallelepiped outlined in black is unit cell of lattice.

Lattice types

Theoretically, it can be shown that there are seven *crystal systems: cubic, tetragonal, orthorhombic, triclinic, monoclinic, rhombohedral,* and *hexagonal.* Associated with these seven crystal systems are 14 lattice arrangements, known as *Bravais lattices.* Unit cells of the 14 Bravais lattices are listed in Table 2-2 and shown in Fig. 2-4. For crystals that contain only one type of constituent particle, such as crystalline Na or Fe, the crystal lattices are simple, and the unit cells are those shown in Fig. 2-4.

Crystals that contain two types of basic units (for example, cations and anions) form *compound lattices.* Sodium chloride has Na^+ and Cl^- ions in the lattice. Silicon carbide, SiC, has Si and C atoms. The description of the positions of the atoms (or ions) in a unit cell of such compounds is more complex, as shown by the unit cell of NaCl in Figure 2-1, A. This cell is the smallest unit which duplicates the properties of the lattice. The face-centered cubic property of the overall lattice can be viewed as two interpenetrating face-centered cubic lattices.

Atoms in unit cells

In examining unit cells of simple or compound lattices, we see that, except for body-centered atoms, the atoms of the cell are common to more than one cell unit. A corner is shared among eight unit cells (Fig. 2-5, A). Each corner atom contributes $\frac{1}{8}$ atom to a given unit cell. Since each cell has eight corners, there are $8 \times \frac{1}{8}$ atoms due to corner atoms in one cubic cell. Similarly, an atom on a face is shared by two

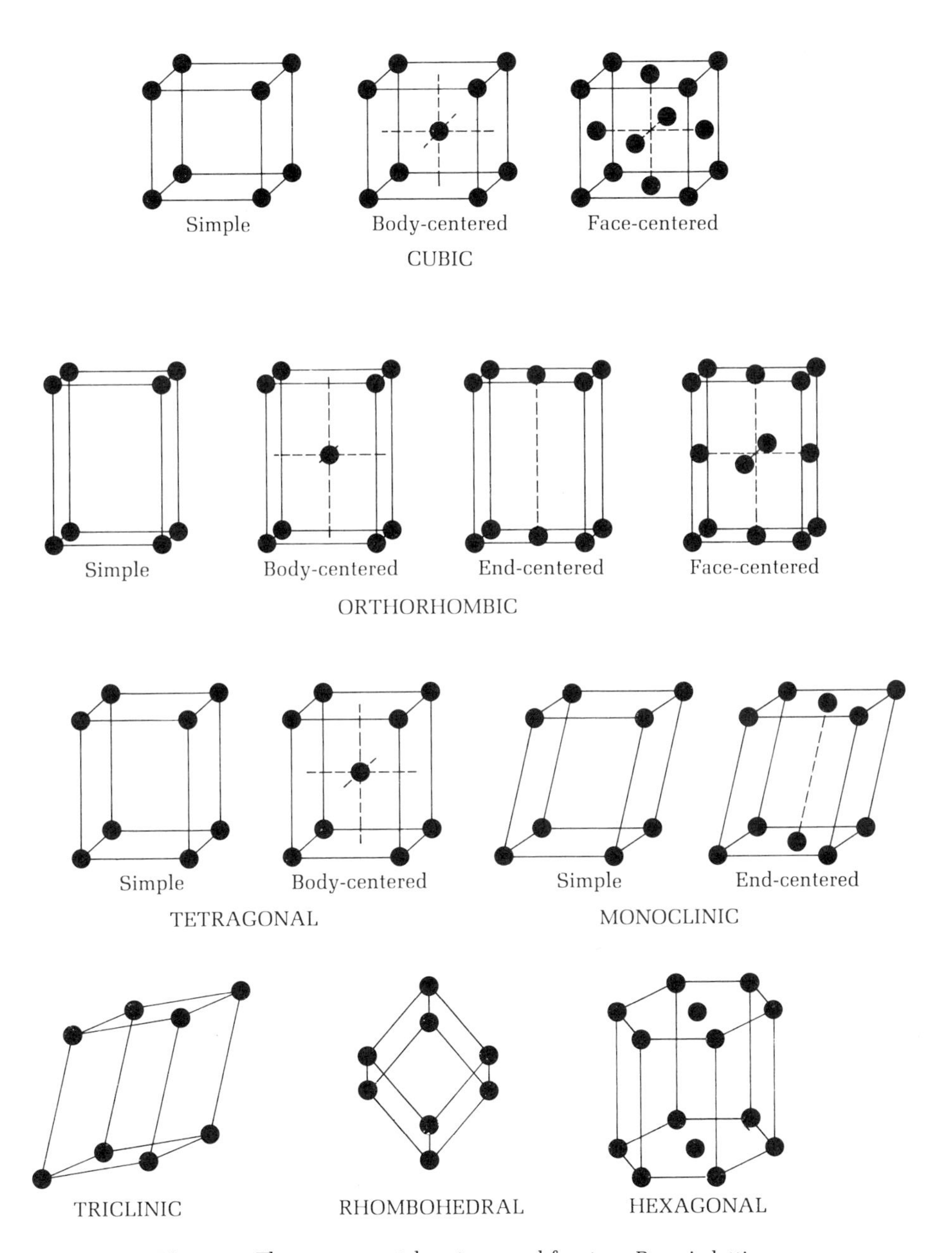

Fig. 2-4. The seven crystal systems and fourteen Bravais lattices.

Table 2-2. CRYSTAL SYSTEMS AND UNIT CELLS

System	*Unit cell parameters*		*Bravais lattice*
Cubic	$a = b = c$	$\alpha = \beta = \gamma = 90°$	Simple Body-centered Face-centered
Orthorhombic	$a \neq b \neq c$	$\alpha = \beta = \gamma = 90°$	Simple Body-centered End-centered Face-centered
Tetragonal	$a = b \neq c$	$\alpha = \beta = \gamma = 90°$	Simple Body-centered
Monoclinic	$a \neq b \neq c$	$\alpha = \gamma = 90°$ $\beta \neq 90°$	Simple End-centered
Triclinic	$a \neq b \neq c$	$\alpha \neq \beta \neq \gamma \neq 90°$	Simple
Rhombohedral	$a = b = c$	$\alpha = \beta = \gamma \neq 90°$	Simple
Hexagonal	$a = b \neq c$	$\alpha = \beta = 90°$ $\gamma = 120°$	Simple

cells ($\frac{1}{2}$ per cube), and an atom at the center of a cell is entirely in the cube (Fig. 2-5, *B* and *C*). Thus, *simple, face-centered,* and *body-centered* unit cells contain one, four, and two atoms per cell, respectively.

Generally, there are more atoms in the unit cell of a compound lattice than in the unit cell of a simple lattice. In NaCl (Figs. 2-1, *A* and 2-5, *D*), there are 8 ions at corners, 6 on faces, 12 on edges, and 1 at the center of the unit, for a total of 8 ions in the cell. Since each NaCl molecule contains two ions, there are four NaCl molecules in the unit cell.

Determination of Avogadro's number

Avogadro's number can be determined very precisely if the size and composition of the unit cell of a pure crystal is known from an X-ray crystallographic study as shown below.

EXAMPLE **2.1**

The edge lengths of the unit cell of a pure crystal of NaCl are found to be 5.638 $\times 10^{-8}$ cm. The density, ρ, is 2.164 g/cm^3. Referring to the NaCl unit cell shown in Fig. 2-1, *A*, calculate Avogadro's number.

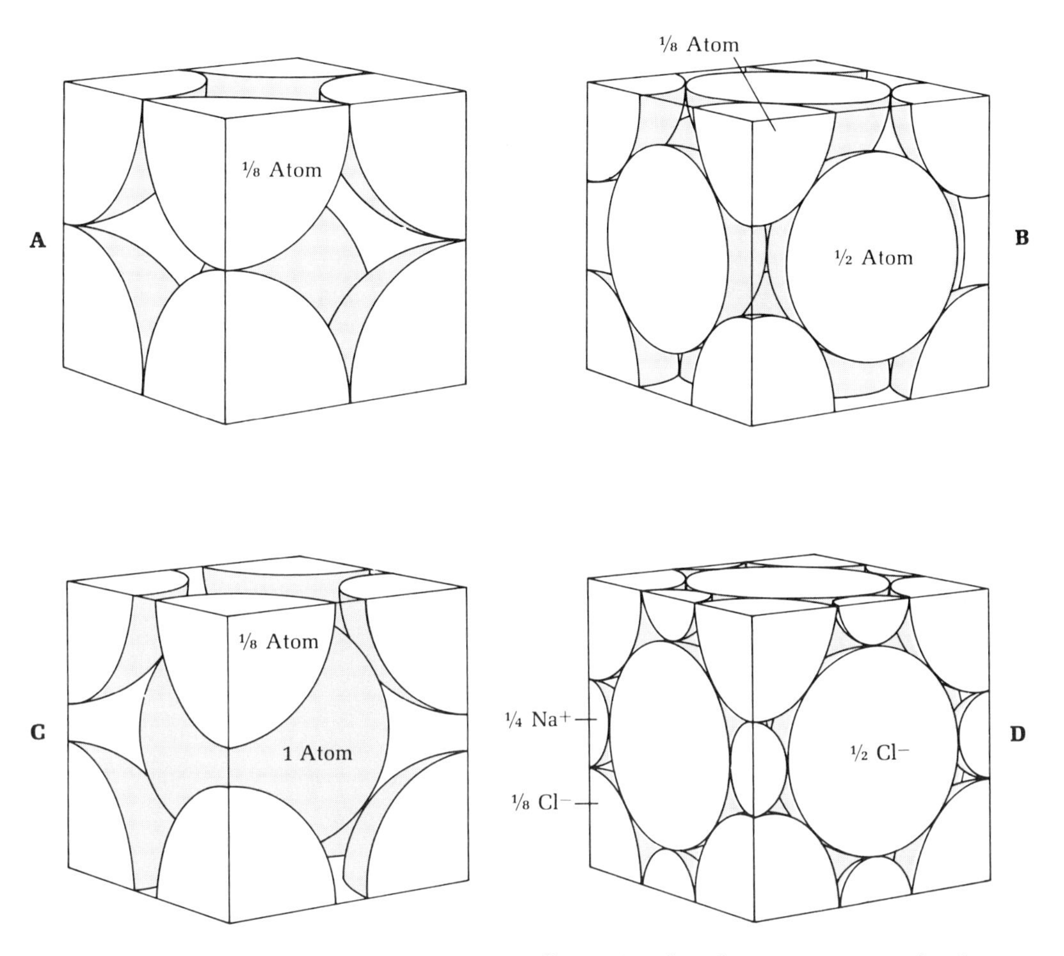

Fig. 2-5. Atoms in some representative unit cells. **A,** Simple cubic. **B,** Face-centered cubic. **C,** Body-centered cubic. **D,** Compound unit cell of NaCl.

The volume, V, of the unit cell is d^3, where $d = 5.638 \times 10^{-8}$ cm. There are four NaCl molecules per unit cell, each with a weight of MW/N, where the molecular weight, MW, is 58.44. The volume, d^3, is obtained by dividing the mass, $4MW/N$, by the density:

$$\frac{4MW/N}{\rho} = d^3$$

$$N = \frac{4MW}{\rho d^3} = 6.027 \times 10^{23}$$

2.3 CLOSEST PACKING IN THE SOLID STATE

The structures of many crystalline solids are the result of closest packing of identical-sized spheres. A large group of structural types show closest packing.

Closest packing is the most efficient way to fill space. Fig. 2-6 illustrates how close packing is achieved. In the initial layer (A) the spheres are arranged in a hexagonal pattern so that every sphere is surrounded by six others in the same plane. The second layer (B) is placed on top of A in such a way that every sphere of B sits in the triangular depressions of A. A third layer (C) is placed on top of B. The spheres of C can occupy two types of positions, one directly over atoms of A, the other over holes in A. The first type of pattern repeats as designated *ABABAB* . . . ; the second pattern repeats as designated *ABCABCABC* . . . (Fig. 2-6). The *ABCABCABC* pattern is called *cubic closest* packing (ccp). The *ABABAB* sequence is called *hexagonal closest* packing (hcp). Side views of ccp and hcp packing are shown in Fig. 2-7.

The origin of the names cubic closest and hexagonal closest packing is easy to see if we look at an expanded section of each packing arrangement. The placement of ccp spheres results in a cubic arrangement (Fig. 2-8, A and B) in which there is a sphere at each corner and at each face, forming a face-centered cube, one of the basic lattice patterns. In the hcp structure (Fig. 2-8, C and D) the atoms in the A layers occupy the corners of hexagonal prisms, giving rise to a hexagonal unit cell.

It is important to understand the relationships between the layers of packing spheres and the cubic unit cell. When the packing layers are located in horizontal planes, the cubic unit cell is located such that a diagonal through opposite cube corners is perpendicular to the planes. Conversely, when we look at a cubic structure oriented so that the unit cubes are sitting on their bases, the layers of the packing spheres are in the form of diagonal planes.

The ccp and hcp structures have several features in common:

1. The spheres occupy 74% of the available space.
2. The coordination number (CN) of every packing sphere in the system is 12. The *coordination number* of a given sphere is the number of spheres that surround it at an equal distance.

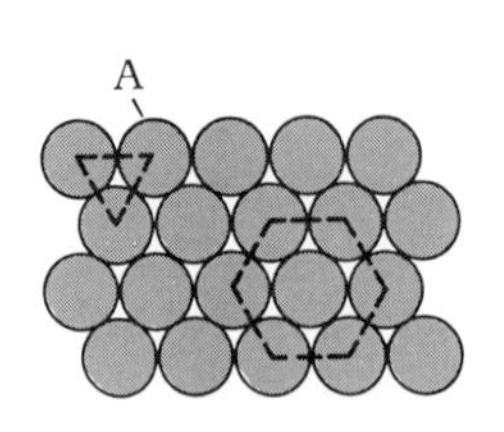

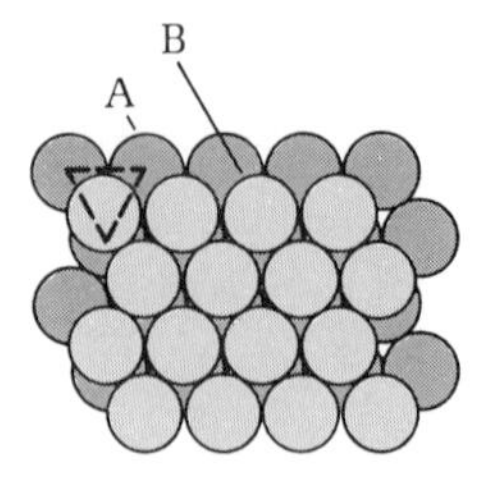

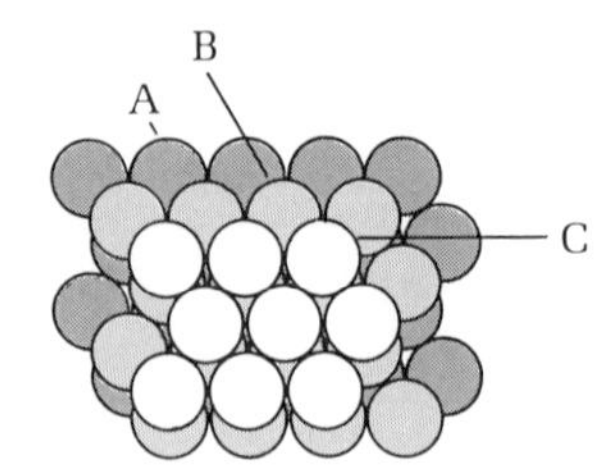

Fig. 2-6. Arrangement of layers in closest packing.

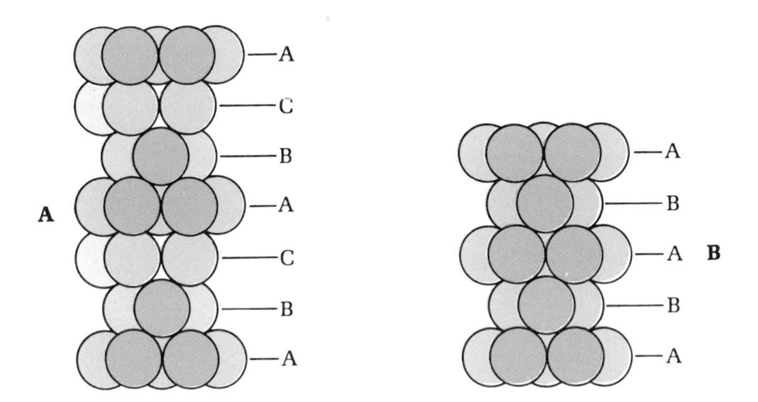

Fig. 2-7. Side view of closest-packed layers. **A,** Cubic closest packed. **B,** Hexagonal closest packed.

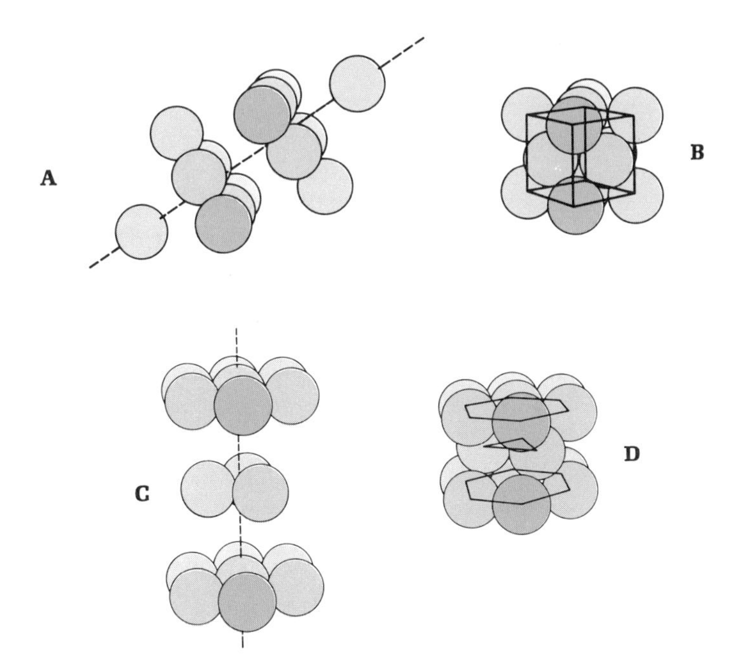

Fig. 2-8 Spheres in closest packing. **A** and **B,** Cubic arrangement of spheres in an *ABCABC* pattern. **C** and **D,** Hexagonal arrangement of spheres in an *ABAB* pattern.

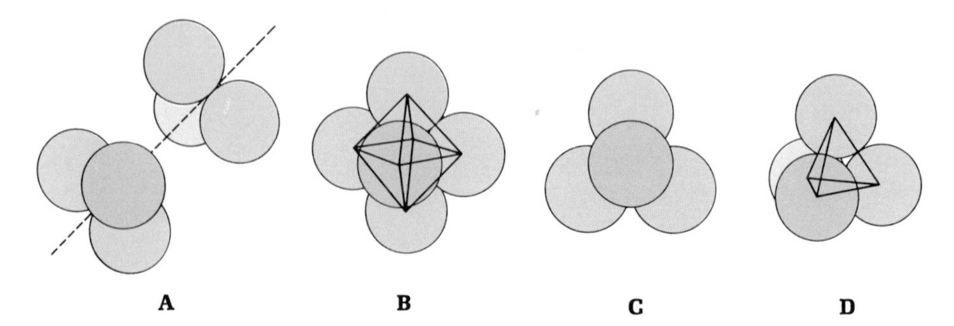

Fig. 2-9. **A** and **B**, Octahedral holes. **C** and **D**, Tetrahedral holes.

3. The structures contain spaces between the spheres called octahedral and tetrahedral holes. These holes are spaces where smaller spheres can be placed. *Octahedral* holes occur between groups of six packing spheres that form an octahedron, a six-pointed, eight-faced, regular polyhedron (Fig. 2-9, *A* and *B*). A sphere in an octahedral hole has a coordination number of 6. *Tetrahedral* holes (Fig. 2-9, *C* and *D*) arise among groups of four closest-packed spheres that lie at the corners of a tetrahedron, a four-pointed, four-faced, regular polyhedron. A sphere in a tetrahedral hole has a coordination number of 4.

2.4 THE CLOSEST-PACKING APPROACH TO GENERAL STRUCTURE CLASSIFICATION

Examination of a closest-packed structure (either hcp or ccp) reveals that there are as many octahedral (O) holes as there are packing spheres (P). The O holes lie midway between the packing layers (Fig. 2-10) and form a second lattice of the same type (ccp or hcp) as the initial packing atoms. Tetrahedral (T) holes lie in layers between the P and O layers. As a result, if there are n P spheres (where n is an integer) and n O sites, there are $2n$ T holes. The tetrahedral holes alternate in two types throughout the system; half are located above the O-hole plane (T'), and half are located below the O-hole plane (T''). The T' sites and the T'' sites each have the same lattice arrangement (ccp or hcp) as the P spheres and O holes. The relationship of the P, O, T', and T'' positions is shown in Fig. 2-11.

In a closest-packed structure, there is a system of four interpenetrating lattices, the P, O, T', and T'' lattices. Each of the four types of lattice sites have characteristic properties with regard to coordination number. Each site in each lattice has characteristically arranged neighbors. The coordination-number properties of the sites are shown in Table 2-3 and in Fig. 2-12. By placing atoms or ions in these positions in a selective, systematic way, one can describe many basic crystalline structures.

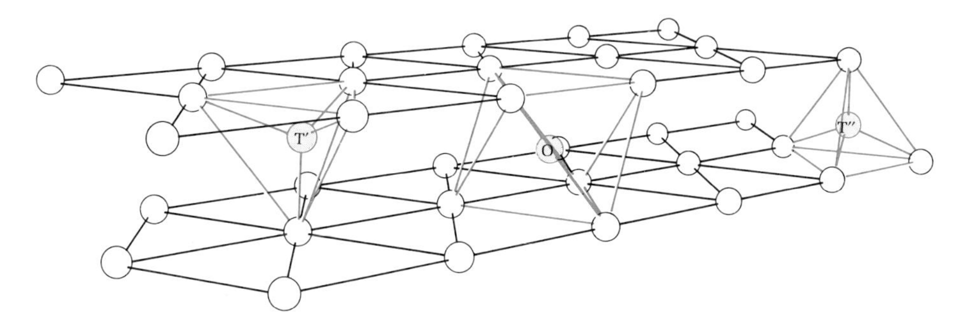

Fig. 2-10. Relative positioning of T', T'', and O holes between two closest-packed layers. For clarity, only one of each is shown.

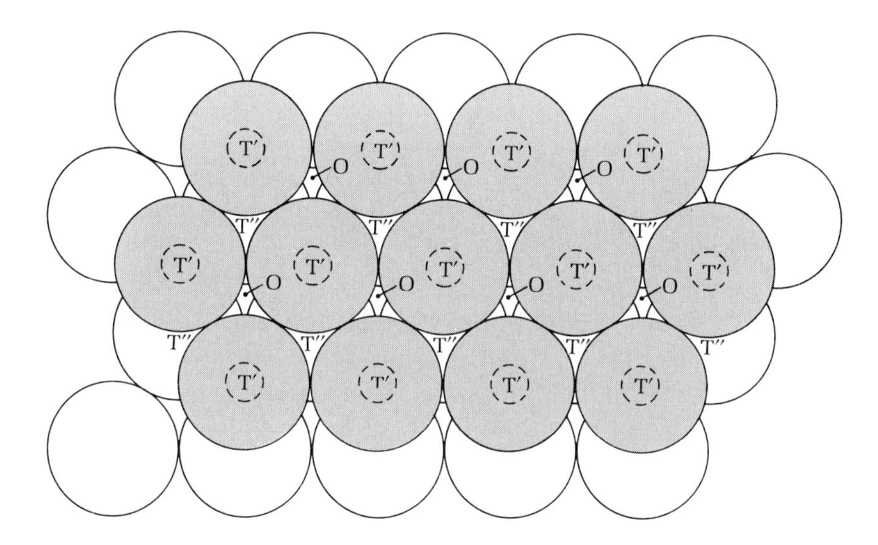

Fig. 2-11. Top view of relative positions of T', T'', and O sites between two P layers. Lower P layer is shown by large open circles, upper P layer by gray circles.

Crystalline solids generally assume the structure that yields the lowest potential energy for the system. Lowest energy generally is achieved when constituent units are as close as possible, thereby maximizing interionic, interatomic, or intermolecular bonding effects.

Ionic crystalline solids

The balance of two factors establishes the lowest energy arrangement for an ionic solid:

Table 2-3. COORDINATION NUMBERS OF SITES

ccp packing		hcp packing	
Site in question	*Number (type) and arrangement of neighbors*	*Site in question*	*Number (type) and arrangement of neighbors*
O	6 (P), octahedral 8 ($4T' + 4T''$), cubic	O	6 (P), trigonal prism* 6 ($3T' + 3T''$), layered
P	6 (O), octahedral 8 ($4T' + 4T''$), cubic	P	6 (O), trigonal prism 8 ($4T' + 4T''$), trigonal prism with one T site above each trigonal face
T' or T''	4 (O), tetrahedral 4 (P), tetrahedral	T' or T''	4 (P), tetrahedral 3 (O), tetrahedral

*A trigonal prism is a prism-shaped polyhedron that has parallel opposite triangular faces and rectangular sides.

1. The structure must provide sites in a ratio equal to the stoichiometric relationships of the constituent ions. Each ion must go into a site such that the coordination number and charge of each ion are balanced. In NaCl there are equal numbers of Na^+ and Cl^- ions with equal coordination numbers to maintain electrical neutrality. With calcium fluoride (CaF_2) the coordination number of Ca^{2+} is twice that of F^-.
2. The relative sizes of constituent ions are important in determining the possible coordination numbers that ions can assume (Fig. 2-13). The preferred coordination number is geometrically determined when the spheres, representing the ions, just touch. In A, $CN = 3$ for the central sphere. However, in B, a larger central sphere causes the outer spheres to move apart, so that $CN = 4$ (tetrahedral) is better, as in C.

The ratio of the size of cations to the size of anions is called the *radius ratio*, r_+/r_-. The radius ratio determines the preferred coordination number. Radius-ratio ranges for various coordination types can be calculated and are shown in Table 2-4. In each case an r_+/r_- range is given. Within this range a given coordination-number type is preferred.

In Table 2-5, radius ratios for some typical cations and anions are given, along with the theoretical and the observed coordination numbers for them.

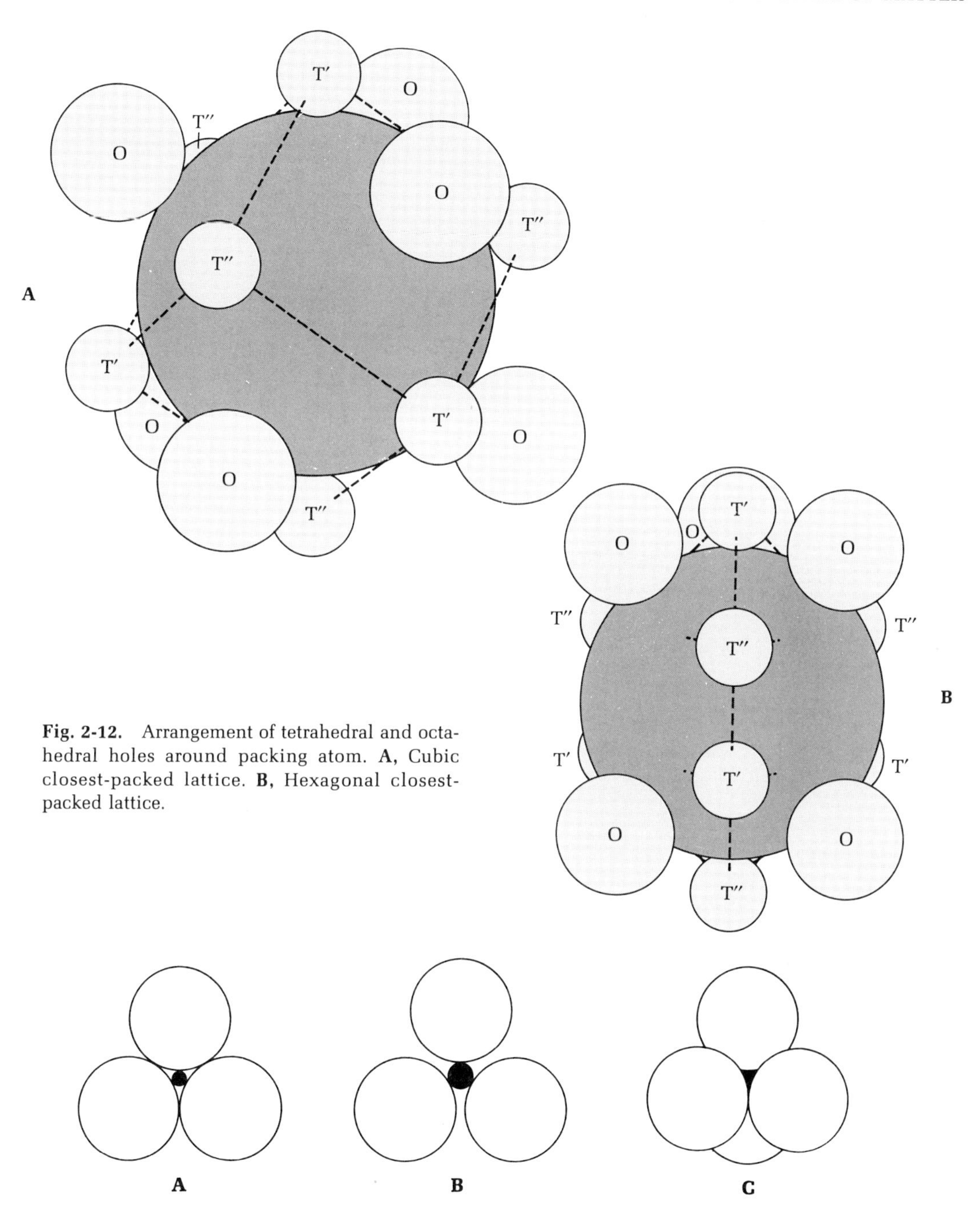

Fig. 2-12. Arrangement of tetrahedral and octahedral holes around packing atom. **A**, Cubic closest-packed lattice. **B**, Hexagonal closest-packed lattice.

Fig. 2-13. Radius-ratio effects. **A,** Largest possible cation (black sphere) that can be accommodated among three anions. Larger cation pushes the anions apart, **B**, and prefers $CN = 4$, **C.**

Table 2-4. RADIUS-RATIO RANGES

r_+/r_-	*Coordination number of smaller sphere*	*Arrangement*
<0.225	3	Trigonal
0.225-0.414	4	Tetrahedral
0.414-0.732	6	Octahedral
0.732-1.0	8	Cubic
1.0	12	Closest-packing (ccp or hcp)

Table 2-5. RADIUS RATIO IN PREDICTION

Compound	r_+/r_-	*Coordination numbers*			
		Theoretical		*Observed*	
		Cation	*Anion*	*Cation*	*Anion*
NaCl	0.540	6	6	6	6
CsI	0.744	8	8	8	8
ZnS	0.363	4	4	4	4
CaF_2	0.870	8	4*	8	4
RbCl	0.820	8	8	6	6

*Since the Ca^{2+} charge is double the F^- charge, we know the *CN* of F^- must be one-half that of Ca^{2+} to maintain electrical neutrality.

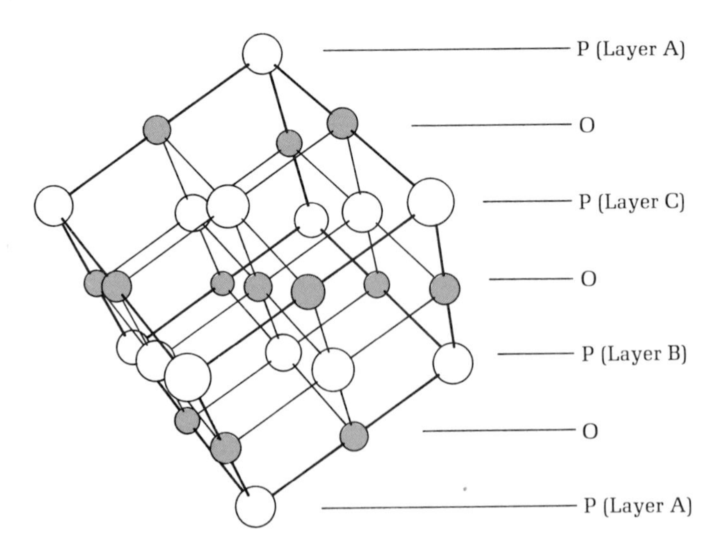

Fig. 2-14. NaCl unit cell oriented to show closest-packing layers.

For NaCl, CsI, and ZnS the radius ratios are in the expected ranges. Sometimes, however, a structure with a coordination number lower than that predicted by the theory occurs. Such is the case with RbCl. Large cations can be compressed somewhat and made to fit into a coordination space smaller than the one predicted.

Some ionic compounds whose structures are classed conveniently into the closest-packing picture are NaCl, ZnS (zinc-blende form), and ZnS (Wurtzite form). Sodium chloride (Fig. 2-14) requires a coordination number of 6 for both Na^+ and Cl^- ions. In closest-packing terms the Cl^- and Na^+ ions are in *P* positions and *O* holes, respectively, of a ccp structure. Thus, NaCl is a *PO* (ccp) structure. In Fig. 2-15, *A*, ZnS (zinc blende) has S^{2-} ions ($CN = 4$) in ccp *P* positions, and one half of the *T* holes (T') occupied by Zn^{2+} ions ($CN = 4$). Thus, it is a PT' (ccp) structure. ZnS (Wurtzite) requires $CN = 4$ for both Zn^{2+} and S^{2-} ions (Fig. 2-15, *B*); however, here the packing pattern is hcp. The S^{2-} ions are in *P* positions, the Zn^{2+} ions, in T' holes, to yield a PT' (hcp) structure.

Some ionic compounds in the major categories of classification are listed below:

IONIC-COMPOUND STRUCTURES

Closest-packing type	*Examples*	*Closest-packing type*	*Examples*
PO (ccp)	NaCl, KCl, AgCl, PbS	$PT'T''$ (ccp)	CaF_2, Na_2O
		$POT'T''$ (ccp)	CsCl, CsBr, NH_4Cl
PT' (ccp)	ZnS (zinc blende), BeO, HgS	PT' (hcp)	ZnS (Wurtzite), NH_4I, ZnO

Covalent-network solids

Covalent-network crystalline solids, like ionic solids, require structures in which atoms can be placed so as to balance stoichiometry. The highly directional properties of covalent bonding, however, severely limit which sites can be used.

Examples of network solids are diamond and SiC, shown in Fig. 2-16. Carbon in diamond and silicon in SiC form four covalent bonds tetrahedrally distributed around them. Because of this highly directional character, the carbon or silicon atoms must go into positions where tetrahedral bond distributions can be maintained. In diamond, half the carbon atoms are in ccp *P* positions, and half in tetrahedral holes. In SiC the Si atoms are in ccp *P* positions, the C atoms are in T' holes.

Metals

Pure metals assume cubic closest-packed (ccp), hexagonal closest-packed (hcp), or body-centered cubic (bcc) structures. The bcc structure is less dense than the

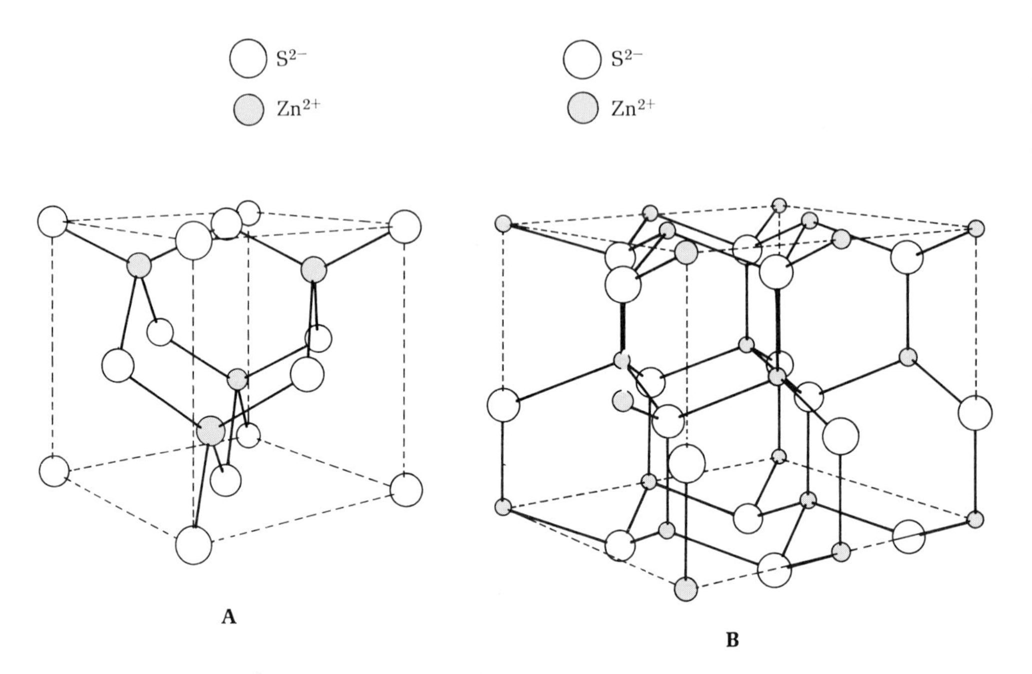

Fig. 2-15. Structures of **A,** ZnS, zinc blende; **B,** ZnS, Wurtzite.

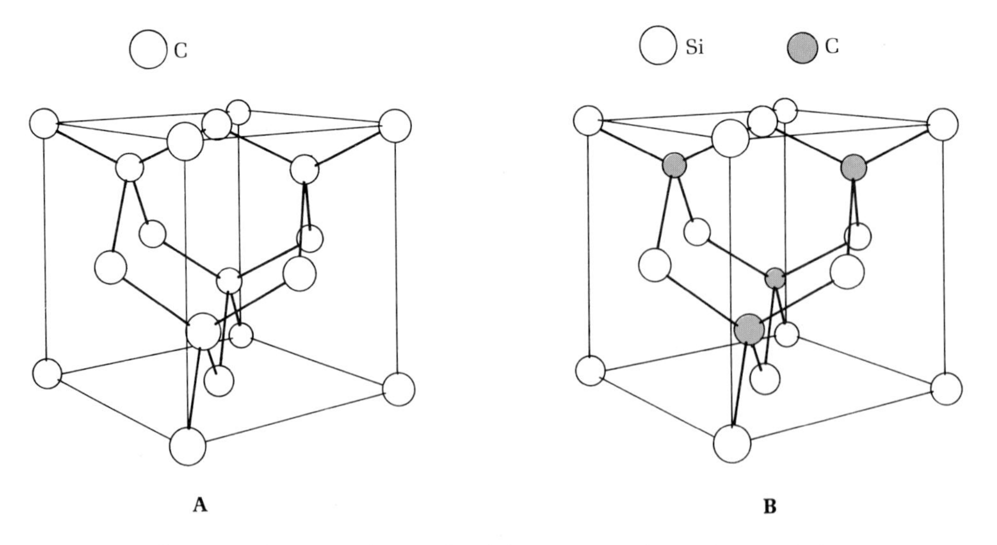

Fig. 2-16. Structure of network solids. **A,** Diamond. **B,** Silicon carbide.

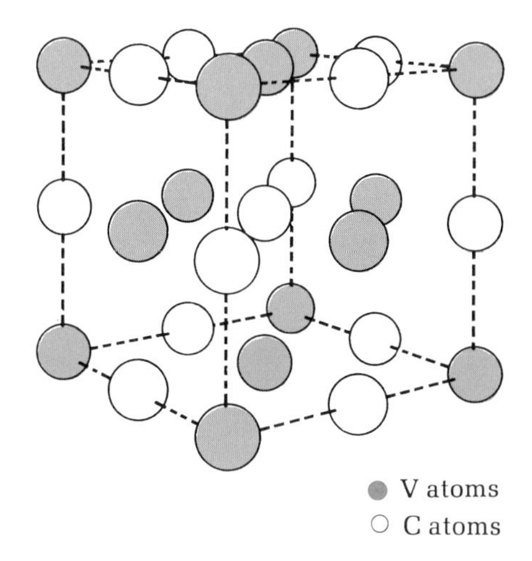

Fig. 2-17. Structure of vanadium carbide (VC) alloy.

Table 2-6. STRUCTURES OF COMMON METALS

Li bcc	Be hcp										
Na bcc	Mg hcp	Al ccp									
K bcc	Ca ccp	Sc hcp	Ti hcp	V bcc	Cr bcc	Mn bcc	Fe bcc	Co hcp	Ni ccp	Cu ccp	Zn hcp
Rb bcc	Sr ccp	Y hcp	Zr hcp	Nb bcc	Mo bcc	Tc hcp	Ru hcp	Rh ccp	Pd ccp	Ag ccp	Cd hcp

ccp and hcp structures and involves lower coordination numbers for the metal atoms, presumably because of the increased importance of directional forces between atoms. Table 2-6 shows the most stable structural types at room temperature and atmospheric pressure for several metals.

Alloys assume closest-packed structures in which the minor constituent occupies octahedral or tetrahedral lattice sites. For example, vanadium carbide (VC), shown in Fig. 2-17, has the V atoms in ccp *P* positions and the C atoms in the *O* holes; it is a *PO*(ccp) structure.

Pressure and temperature affect structure; a given metal or alloy, can assume different structures under different conditions of temperature and pressure.

2.5 BONDING IN IONIC CRYSTALS

In the model for ionic bonding in solids it is assumed the ions are held together by electrostatic attractions between the positively and negatively charged ions. In the simple theory each ion is considered spherical, with its entire charge concentrated at the center of the sphere. The spherical ions are viewed as point charges arranged in a three-dimensional lattice.

Ionic lattice energies

The lattice energy (U_0) of a solid is the energy involved in bringing infinitely separated ions to their lattice site positions to form 1 mole of solid. We examine lattice energy from an approach developed by Born. This theory provides a useful quantitative expression and gives insight into the bonding of ionic solids.

There are two main energy terms to consider in developing the Born equation: a coulombic energy term (U_c), which arises from the attraction or repulsion between point charges; and a repulsive energy term (U_R), which is due to strong, short-range repulsions between electron clouds. These energy terms and their dependence on the distance d between the ions are shown in Fig. 2-18. The energy is plotted vertically—the lower the position on the curve, the lower the energy or the greater the stability of the system. The coulombic energy term has the general form $Z_+Z_-e^2/d$, where Z_+ and Z_- are the charges on the ions, e is the standard unit of electrical charge,* and d is the interionic distance. The term U_R has the form B/d^n, where n is on the order of 7 to 10, and B is a constant, both n and B depending on the particular system. For large values of d, U_R is negligible; however, as d becomes small, U_R increases rapidly. The U_c term becomes increasingly negative at small d. At some distance, d_0, the sum of the potential energies

$$U_T = U_R + U_c \tag{2.1}$$

reaches a minimum, where the ion system is most stable.

The detailed form of the U_c term in an ionic crystal depends on the charges and geometrical properties of the lattice system. The NaCl structure illustrates this point. In Fig. 2-19, we arbitrarily choose a cation (Na^+) at the corner of a portion of the structure and sum the coulombic energies (attractive and repulsive) that the cation experiences. This cation is surrounded in three dimensions by eight similar structural units. Table 2-7 shows the total number of ions at specific distances from the corner ion. The cation's nearest neighbors are six Cl^- ions at a distance of d. The next nearest neighbors are 12 Na^+ ions at a distance of $\sqrt{2}d$. The overall coulombic

*The value of e is 4.80×10^{-10} esu, which, when inserted into the coulombic energy equation with d in cm, gives the energy in ergs. One erg is 10^{-7} joules or 2.39×10^{-11} kcal.

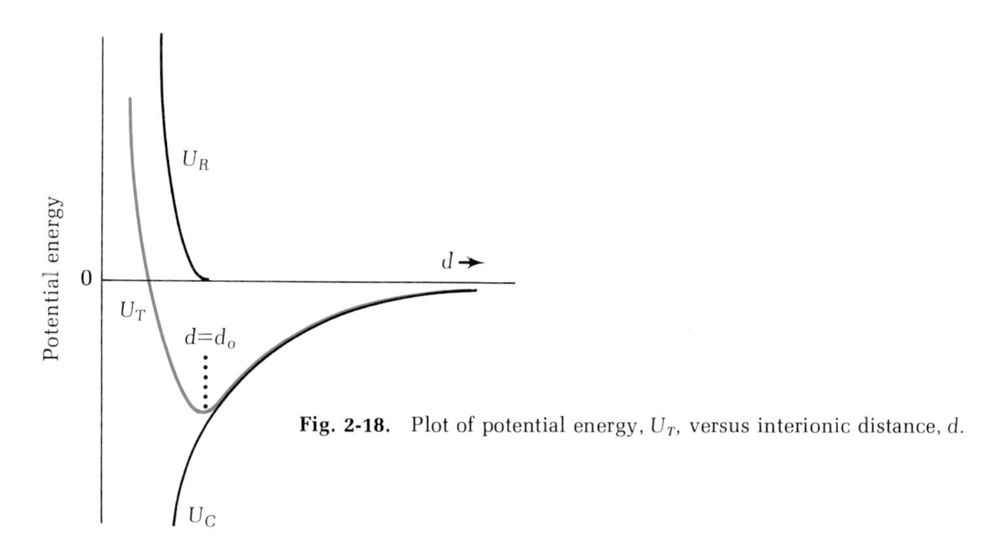

Fig. 2-18. Plot of potential energy, U_T, versus interionic distance, d.

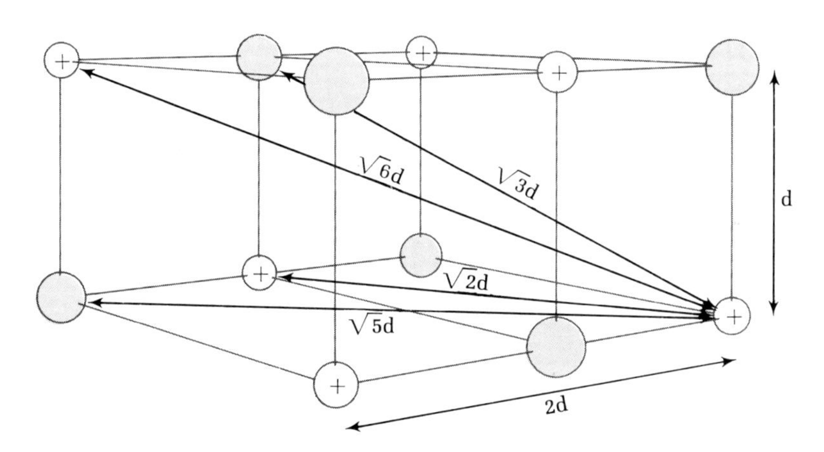

Fig. 2-19. Segment of NaCl structure showing geometric relationships between cations and anions in neighborhood of central cation (shown as the ion in lower-right corner).

Table 2-7. COULOMBIC TERMS IN TWO LAYERS

Attractive		*Repulsive*	
Number	*Distance*	*Number*	*Distance*
6	d	12	$\sqrt{2}d$
8	$\sqrt{3}d$	6	$2d$
24	$\sqrt{5}d$	24	$\sqrt{6}d$

energy is given by a series of terms that include the number of ions at a certain distance times the energy effect for that distance. The attractive terms have a negative sign; the repulsive terms have a positive sign. The magnitude of interacting charges Z_+ and Z_- is $|Z_+Z_-|$. Then

$$U_c = -\frac{|Z_+Z_-|e^2 6}{d} + \frac{|Z_+Z_-|e^2 12}{\sqrt{2}d} - \frac{|Z_+Z_-|e^2 8}{\sqrt{3}d} + \frac{|Z_+Z_-|e^2 6}{2d} - \frac{|Z_+Z_-|e^2 24}{\sqrt{5}d} + \frac{|Z_+Z_-|e^2 24}{\sqrt{6}d} \ldots \quad (2.2)$$

We factor $-|Z_+Z_-|e^2/d$ from the terms and obtain

$$U_c = -\frac{|Z_+Z_-|e^2}{d}\left(6 - \frac{12}{\sqrt{2}} + \frac{8}{\sqrt{3}} - \frac{6}{2} + \frac{24}{\sqrt{5}} - \frac{24}{\sqrt{6}} \ldots\right) \quad (2.3)$$

The quantity in parentheses is an infinite series that converges to 1.74756. This value represents a constant for the NaCl lattice system. It is called the *Madelung constant*, symbolized by *A*. Madelung constants for other important ionic crystal systems are given below.

MADELUNG CONSTANTS

Structure	*A*	*Structure*	*A*
NaCl, *PO* (ccp)	1.748	ZnS, *PT'* (hcp)	1.641
CsCl, *POT'T''* (ccp)	1.763	CaF_2, *PT'T''* (ccp)	2.519
ZnS, *PT'* (ccp)	1.638		

Equation 2.3 can be modified to take into account the geometry factor by including the Madelung constant

$$U_c = -\frac{|Z_+Z_-|e^2 A}{d} \quad (2.4)$$

From equation 2.1

$$U_T = -\frac{|Z_+Z_-|e^2 A}{d} + \frac{B}{d^n} \quad (2.5)$$

The expression can be simplified by eliminating *B*. At equilibrium ($d = d_0$), U_T is at a minimum; that is, the derivative of U_T is zero. Thus, at $d = d_0$

$$\frac{dU_T}{dd} = \frac{A|Z_+Z_-|e^2}{{d_0}^2} - \frac{nB}{{d_0}^{n+1}} = 0 \quad (2.6)$$

or

$$\frac{A|Z_+Z_-|e^2}{d_0^{\,2}} = \frac{nB}{d_0^{\,n+1}} \tag{2.7}$$

We then obtain an expression for B

$$B = \frac{d_0^{\,n-1}A|Z_+Z_-|e^2}{n} \tag{2.8}$$

Substitution of this expression for B in equation 2.5 yields

$$U_T = -\frac{A|Z_+Z_-|e^2}{d_0}\left(1 - \frac{1}{n}\right) \tag{2.9}$$

To account for the overall energy of 1 mole of ionic material we multiply equation 2.9 by the Avogadro number, N, and obtain

$$U_0 = -\frac{NA|Z_+Z_-|e^2}{d_0}\left(1 - \frac{1}{n}\right) \tag{2.10}$$

where U_0 is the lattice energy of 1 mole of crystalline solid. This is the Born equation for the lattice energy.

The parameter n is related to the short-range repulsion force that arises when ions come so close to one another that their electron clouds interpenetrate. The value of n is related to the compressibility of the solid; the harder it is to compress the solid, the larger the value of n. The n values vary from 5 to 12 as shown below,

n VALUES FOR RARE-GAS CONFIGURATIONS

n	*Configuration*
5	He
7	Ne
9	Ar
10	Kr
12	Xe

and the correct n is selected according to which rare-gas electron configuration the ions have. In NaF, both Na^+ and F^- have $1s^22s^22p^6$ configurations (Ne configurations); a value of $n = 7$ is used. If the configurations of the ions differ, such as Na^+ and Cl^- in NaCl ($1s^22s^22p^6$[Ne] and $1s^22s^22p^63s^23p^6$[Ar], respectively), it is customary to use the average n value.

EXAMPLE **2.2**

Calculate U_0 for CsI, using the Born equation, given that $d_0 = 3.95$ Å and that CsI assumes the NaCl (*PO*, ccp) structure.

For CsI, we use Z_+ and Z_- values of 1+ and 1−, so that $|Z_+Z_-| = 1$. The Madelung constant *A* is 1.748. The average *n* value is 10. Thus

$$U_0 = -\frac{NA|Z_+Z_-|e^2}{d_0}\left(1 - \frac{1}{n}\right)$$

$$= -\frac{(6.023 \times 10^{23}/\text{mole})\,(1.748)\,(1)\,(4.80 \times 10^{-10}\ \text{esu})^2}{3.95 \times 10^{-8}\ \text{cm}}\left(1 - \frac{1}{10}\right)$$

$$= -5.53 \times 10^{12}\ \text{erg/mole}$$

$$= -132\ \frac{\text{kcal}}{\text{mole}}$$

This model for lattice energy gives us insight into what factors primarily determine the magnitude of the lattice energies of different types of ionic solids. Several conclusions are clear. Lattice energy depends on $|Z_+Z_-|$, A, d_0, and n. Of these, $|Z_+Z_-|$ is the most important because it can range from 1, in a system like NaCl, to 4, in ZnS. Next in importance are A and d_0. The parameter A depends on geometry but does not vary by more than a factor of 2. The lattice energy U_0 depends inversely on d_0; as lattice dimensions increase, all else remaining constant, U_0 decreases. Finally, n has the least effect on U_0 because it appears in a $(1 - 1/n)$ term.

Ionic radii

Measurement of lattice dimensions and interionic distances in ionic crystals allows for the determination of the relative sizes of ions. We have seen that ionic radii are important in the consideration of properties of ionic crystals, such as radius ratios and lattice energies.

One method of establishing ionic radii in solids that contain large anions is to assume that the anions touch. The distance between anions can be halved to yield their radii. In NaI, for example, the I^- to I^- distance is 4.40 Å, and r_{I^-} is 2.20 Å (Fig. 2-20, *A*). In LiI and KI, similar values for r_{I^-} are obtained. We conclude that r_{I^-} of 2.20 Å is a consistent number. Once an anion radius is obtained, we look at other solids where larger cations are present. In CsI, which has a body-centered cubic structure, the I^- to I^- distance is 4.50 Å. From 2.20 Å for r_{I^-}, the radius of Cs^+ (r_{Cs^+}) is calculated to be 1.70 Å (Fig. 2-20, *B*).

Radii determined by this method vary somewhat due to differences in coordination numbers in solids. More refined methods of establishing radii are used also,

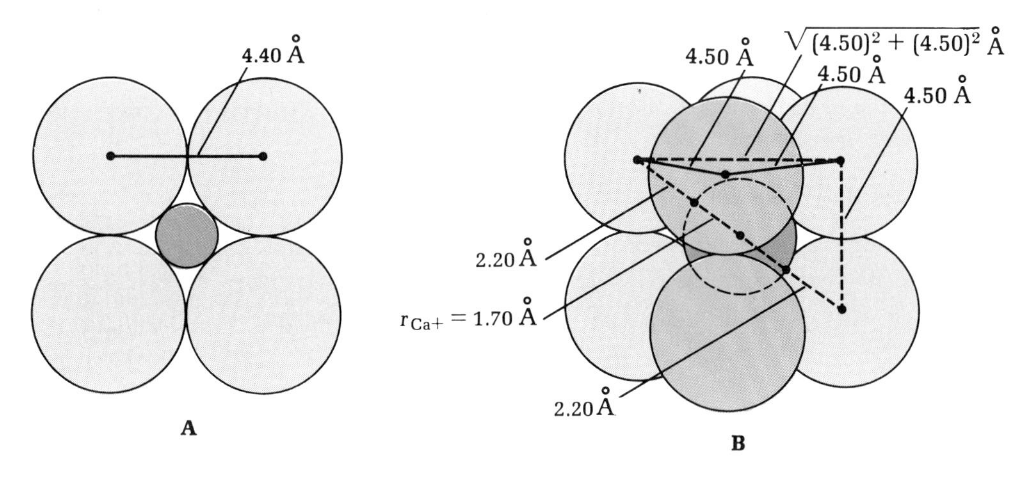

Fig. 2-20. Determination of ionic radius. **A,** I^- in NaI. **B,** Cs^+ in CsI.

Table 2-8. SOME REPRESENTATIVE IONIC RADII (Å)

Li^+ 0.68	Be^{2+} 0.35			O^{2-} 1.40	F^- 1.36
Na^+ 0.97	Mg^{2+} 0.67			S^{2-} 1.87	Cl^- 1.81
K^+ 1.33	Ca^{2+} 0.99	Cu^+ 0.95	Zn^{2+} 0.74	Se^{2-} 1.98	Br^- 1.95
Rb^+ 1.47	Sr^{2+} 1.12	Ag^+ 1.26	Cd^{2+} 0.97		I^- 2.16
Cs^+ 1.67	Ba^{2+} 1.34	Au^+ 1.37	Hg^{2+} 1.10		

but they go beyond the scope of this text. Some of the most important radii values are shown in Table 2-8. Most of them are established using refined methods.

2.6 DISORDER IN CRYSTALS

A completely ordered crystal is an idealized situation in which each particle (atom, ion, or molecule) has a well-defined place in the crystal lattice. Naturally occurring crystals contain varying types and degrees of disorder; most are somewhat imperfect. Defects in crystalline structures are a fortunate circumstance, however, because many mechanical, optical, and electrical properties of solids are dependent upon them.

Disorder effects can arise from mechanical stress, from vibrational or rotational motion of particles in the lattice, or from the presence of impurities. There are three classes of disordered systems: orientational disorder, positional disorder, and plane and line defects.

Orientational disorder

Orientational disorder is encountered in molecular crystalline solids and in ionic solids that contain complex ions. Orientational disorder occurs when the orientation varies for equivalent groups in a given lattice position. Consider the NH_4Cl lattice, shown in Fig. 2-21, *A* and *B*. The Cl^- ions are at cube corners, and the NH_4^+ ions are at cube centers. Two different orientations of the NH_4^+ ions are possible.

Positional disorder

Positional disorder occurs when particles are misplaced or absent from their normal lattice positions. These disorder effects are sometimes called *point defects*.

Disorder of atoms among the normal lattice sites is shown by the alloy FeAl. In its ordered form the alloy has a body-centered cubic structure in which each atom is surrounded by eight atoms of the other type (Fig. 2-22, *A*). If some atoms exchange lattice positions (Fig. 2-22, *B*), the perfect ordering is destroyed.

Point defects can arise from thermal vibrations of atoms or ions, from the presence of impurities, or from nonstoichiometry of a compound. If a particle in a lattice is displaced to an interstitial position, a *Frenkel defect* results (Fig. 2-23, *A*). This type of defect can occur only in lattices where there is sufficient space to accommodate a displaced species. If the structure is densely packed, a displaced atom must migrate to the surface. Vacancies created in this way are called *Schottky defects* (Fig. 2-23, *B*). If there are many Schottky defects, it is possible for the overall order of the lattice to be lost while localized ordered units persist. These smaller units are called *crystallites* (Fig. 2-23, *C*). This phenomenon occurs commonly in metals and accounts for their "grain" structures.

In Schottky defects in ionic crystals, cation and anion vacancies must occur in equal amounts (Fig. 2-24, *A*). The lattice ions in the immediate vicinity of a vacancy will move away from the empty site and create a bigger hole than normal. At high temperatures or in an external electric field, ions move between interstitial positions or lattice vacancies. This movement gives a defective ionic crystal a mechanism for current conduction that does not exist in an ideal crystal.

Because of their dense structures, alkali halides seldom form Frenkel defects; Schottky defects are formed almost exclusively. In less dense lattices like AgI, where the Ag^+ ions are small compared to the I^- ions, Frenkel defects (Fig. 2-24, *B*) are common.

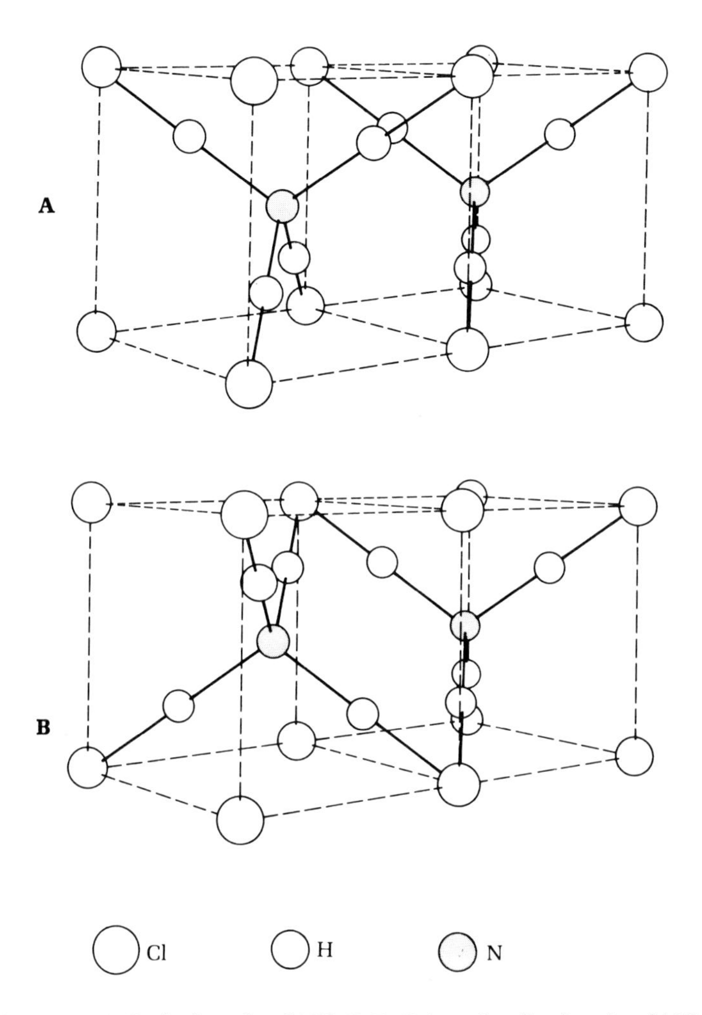

Fig. 2-21. A, Perfectly ordered NH_4Cl. B, Orientationally disordered NH_4Cl.

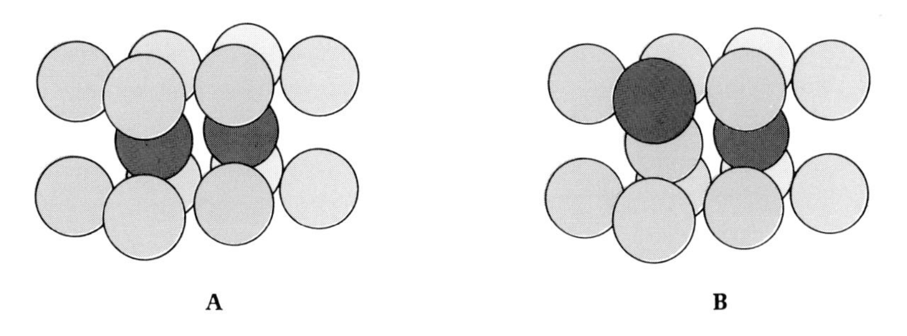

Fig. 2-22. A, Perfectly ordered FeAl. B, Positionally disordered FeAl.

Point defects commonly arise during precipitation of ionic materials. The precipitation of ZnS in the presence of Ni^{2+} ions results in Ni^{2+} entering the lattice in positions normally occupied by Zn^{2+} ions. Such substitutions occur when the size and charge of the substitutional ion are similar to those of the normal ion. Interstitial impurities often occur in metal systems. The introduction of impurities often

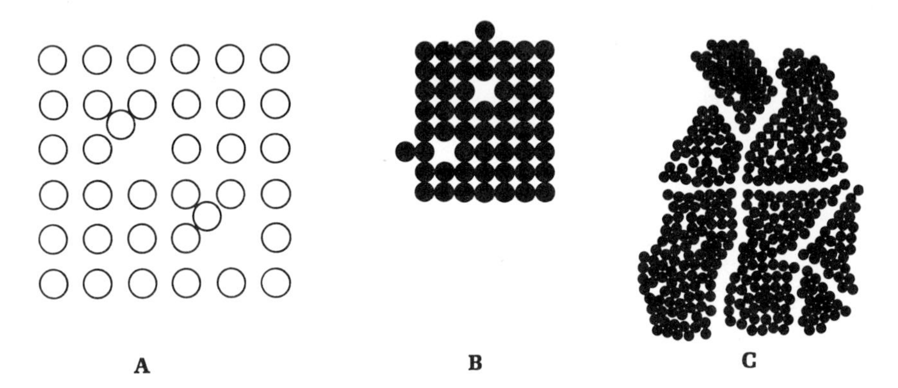

Fig. 2-23. Two-dimensional monatomic crystals with **A,** Frenkel defects; **B,** Schottky defects; **C,** crystallites.

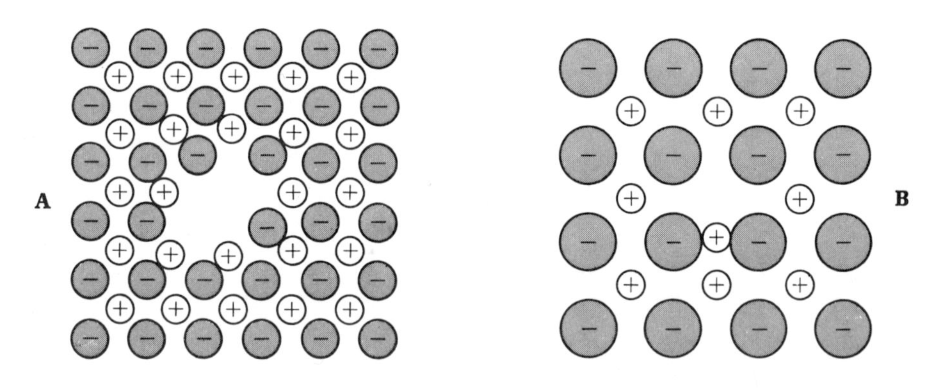

Fig. 2-24. Two-dimensional ionic lattices with **A,** Schottky defect, and **B,** Frenkel defect.

Fig. 2-25. Schematic representation of how interstitial atoms reduce ease of interplanar slippage.

is intentional (alloy production) in order to attain desired mechanical or electrical properties. If foreign metal atoms are put into the interstitial positions, the low-energy pathway for interplane slippage is made more difficult and the metal becomes less ductile and less pliable (Fig. 2-25).

Nonstoichiometry in ionic solids leads to disorder effects in lattice systems and involves the presence of excess cation or anion in the compound. If ZnO is heated, oxygen is driven off, and the Zn/O ratio becomes greater than 1.0. Certain changes in the crystal structure occur. Since the oxygen leaves as atoms rather than as O^{2-} ions, two electrons per atom are left in the lattice. These electrons either combine with Zn^{2+} ions to form Zn atoms or remain as free electrons in the lattice. The free electrons can carry heat and electricity. Many oxides and sulfides are insulators when pure but become semiconductors when made nonstoichiometric.

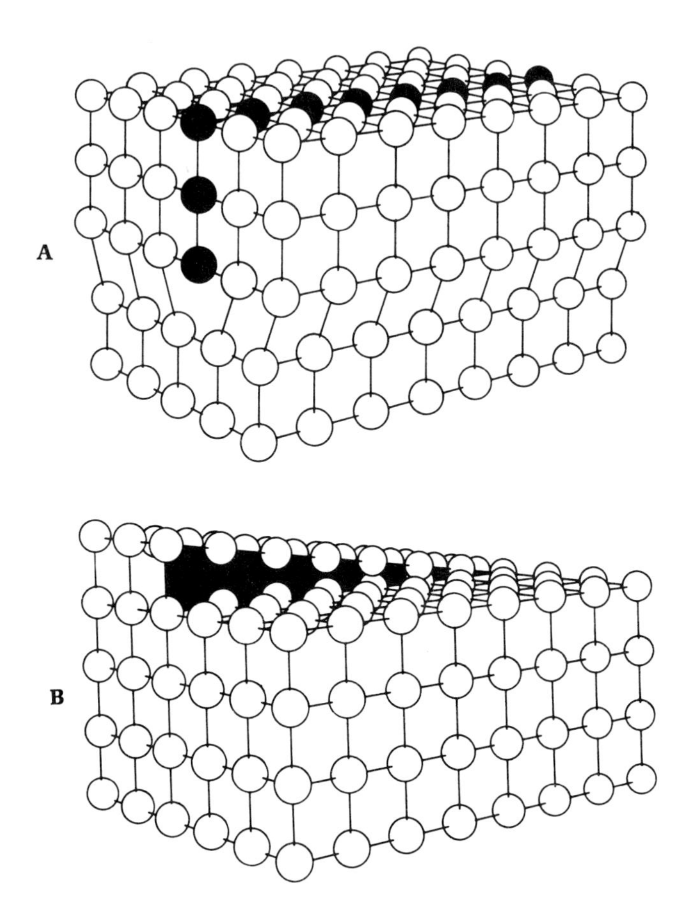

Fig. 2-26. Line and plane defects. **A,** Edge dislocation. **B,** Screw dislocation.

Line and plane defects

Line and plane defects differ from point defects in that they involve the cooperative effect of a large number of particles in a given lattice row or plane. Two types are important. An *edge dislocation* occurs when part of an extra plane is present (Fig. 2-26, *A*). The lattice expands to accommodate the extra plane, and the edges are dislocated or forced out. A *screw dislocation* occurs when part of a set of lattice planes is moved relative to its neighboring planes (Fig. 2-26, *B*).

Edge dislocations can have a tremendous effect on the mechanical properties of a solid. In a perfect structure the planes of atoms must be displaced over one another for shearing to take place. Edge dislocations, if present, can provide a low-energy pathway for shearing, reducing the force necessary to cause it by a factor of about 1000.

PROBLEMS

1. Give two examples of each of the following types of solids: (a) ionic; (b) covalent; (c) metallic; (d) molecular.
2. Define (a) unit cell; (b) lattice; (c) cubic -closest-packed system; (d) compound lattice; (e) tetrahedral hole.
3. Determine the two-dimensional unit cells of the arrays of dots below. Is there more than one way to represent any of these unit cells?

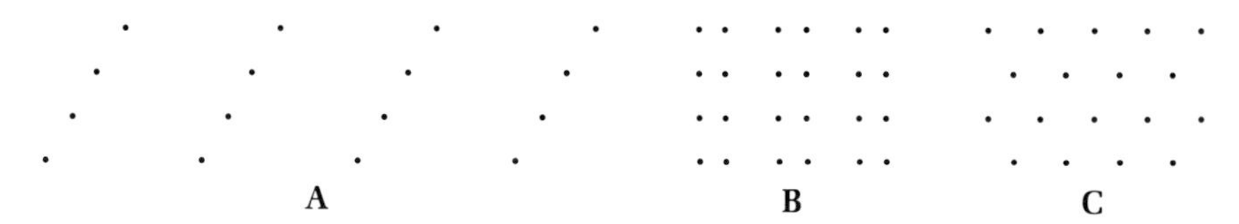

4. Calculate the number of atoms in the simple unit cells: (a) face-centered orthorhombic; (b) body-centered tetragonal; (c) end-centered monoclinic; (d) rhombohedral; (e) hexagonal.
5. In a simple cubic lattice there are eight spheres in contact at the corners of a cube. What percent of the volume of the cube is unoccupied?
6. Calculate the percent of the volume occupied by the spheres in a closest-packed structure. Assume that the spheres are of radius R and that they touch, as in Fig. 2-5, *B*.
7. What are the dimensions of the cubical box that will just enclose the centers of the 14 spheres of a compund face-centered cubic unit cell (Fig. 2-5, *D*)? Assume packing spheres (large spheres) are of radius R.
8. The minerals listed below have the unit cell parameters shown. To which crystal system does each belong?

Mineral	Relative axial lengths (Å) *a*	*b*	*c*	Angles (°) α	β	γ
Zircon, $ZrSiO_4$	1.000	1.000	0.640	90.0	90.0	90.0
Colemanite, $Ca_2B_6O_{11} \cdot 5H_2O$	0.775	1.000	0.541	90.0	69.5	90.0
Realgar, AsS	0.720	1.000	0.486	90.0	66.2	90.0

9. Tungsten metal (W) crystallizes in a body-centered cubic structure. Calculate the unit cell dimensions, assuming the density of W is 19.3 g/cm^3.
10. Lithium crystallizes in a cubic unit cell with edges of 3.50 Å. Given that the density of Li is 0.534 g/cm^3, calculate the number of atoms per unit cell. What type of cubic cell is represented?
11. The density of solid KCl is 2.000 g/cm^3. Assuming a face-centered cubic structure, calculate the dimensions of a cube that would contain 1.00 mole of KCl.
12. Show by means of a suitable sketch that the coordination number of the spheres in ccp and hcp structures is 12.
13. Show by a geometrical argument, employing mainly the Pythagorean theorem, that the cation to anion ratio (r_+/r_-) cannot be less than 0.73 in a body-centered cubic lattice without anion-anion overlap occurring.
14. Calculate the radius of the largest cation that can occupy a tetrahedral hole in a lattice of spherical packing anions of radius R, allowing the packing anions to just touch.
15. Consider a crystalline substance whose formula is A_xB_y, where x and y represent the relative number of atoms of A and B in the crystal. Let the coordination numbers of A and B be represented by a and b, respectively. Prove that $x/y = b/a$ and that the formula of the substance is A_bB_a.
16. Imagine that a 1000-liter beaker is filled with ice spheres with diameters of 10^{-4} cm, that a second 1000-liter beaker is filled with ice spheres with diameters of 10^{-5} cm, and that the spheres in both beakers are cubic closest packed. When the ice melts, which beaker will contain the most water?
17. Estimate ionic radii for A^+, B^+, X^-, and Y^- ions from the data for PO (NaCl) type crystals shown below.

	Internuclear distances	
	Anion-anion (Å)	*Cation-anion* (Å)
AX	1.63	1.15
AY	2.40	1.70
BX	2.09	1.40
BY	2.66	1.88

18. Utilizing the ionic radii given in Table 2-8, predict the coordination numbers of the ions in the crystal lattices (all cubic) of the following materials:
    (a) CsBr
    (b) ZnO
    (c) $CaBr_2$
    (d) Rb_2O
19. According to the system of closest packing used to designate crystalline solids, what classifications would you expect for
    (a) $ZnCl_2$ ($CN_{Zn^{2+}} = 4$, $CN_{Cl^-} = 8$)
    (b) CsCl ($CN_{Cs^+} = 8$, $CN_{Cl^-} = 8$)
    (c) KCl ($CN_{Na^+} = 6$, $CN_{Cl^-} = 6$)
    (Assume the basic packing pattern in each case is ccp.)
20. Derive a "Madelung constant" for a one-dimensional "crystal" consisting of a row of alternating, regularly spaced cations and anions:

$\oplus \quad \ominus \quad \oplus \quad \ominus \quad \oplus \quad \ominus \quad \oplus$ etc.

21. Derive an expression for the "lattice energy" of a two-dimensional square array of alternating, unipositive cations and anions.

$$\left.\begin{matrix} \oplus & \ominus & \oplus & \ominus \\ \ominus & \oplus & \ominus & \oplus \\ \oplus & \ominus & \oplus & \ominus \end{matrix}\right\} \text{etc.}$$

22. A sample of nickel oxide has the composition $Ni_{1.00}O_{1.04}$. What is the ratio of Ni^{2+} ions to Ni^{4+} ions in the lattice?

3 THE THERMAL PROPERTIES OF MATTER

An understanding of the chemical properties of matter depends on an understanding of several areas of scientific thought, such as structure, energy relationships, and bonding theories. An introduction to the concepts of structure, as they apply to solids, was given in the previous chapter. We now begin an examination of the energy properties of matter. The broad science that deals with this subject is called *thermodynamics*.

Thermodynamics applies to a wide variety of scientific situations. It is concerned with heat, work, and the energy of macroscopic (easily visible) amounts of materials. It is important to note that our understanding of thermodynamics is not governed by and does not depend on a knowledge of molecular theory; however, we will see later that the results can be interpreted in molecular terms.

3.1 THE MEASUREMENT AND DEFINITION OF HEAT

The thermal properties of all materials are based upon the measurement of heat. The modern method for defining a given quantity of heat involves passing an electric current of i amperes through a resistor of R ohms for an increment of time dt seconds. The increment of heat, dQ, generated in the resistor is

$$dQ = i\mathcal{E}dt \tag{3.1}$$

where $\mathcal{E}$ is the voltage drop across the resistor. The heat generated between 0 and t seconds is

$$Q = \int_0^t i\mathcal{E}dt \tag{3.2}$$

The unit of heat in these electrical terms is the joule. At one time another unit, the calorie, was used as the unit of heat. The calorie was defined as the amount of heat needed to raise the temperature of 1 g of water at 15°C by 1°C. The more precise and versatile electrical measurement is now used to define the calorie as 4.184 joules.

EXAMPLE **3.1**

An electrical heater of 100 ohms is connected to a voltage source of 100 volts for 1.0 hour. Assume the resistance and voltage are constant for this time period. The heat generated is

$$Q = i\mathscr{E}t$$

According to Ohm's law $i = \mathscr{E}/R$, so

$$Q = \frac{\mathscr{E}^2 t}{R} = \frac{(100 \text{ volts})^2 \, (3600 \text{ sec})}{100 \text{ ohms}}$$

$$= 3.6 \times 10^5 \text{ volt}^2\text{-sec-ohm}^{-1} = 3.6 \times 10^5 \text{ joules}$$

$$= (3.6 \times 10^5 \text{ joules}) \times \left(\frac{1 \text{ cal}}{4.18 \text{ joule}} \right) = 8.6 \times 10^4 \text{ cal}$$

What happens to the heat generated in the resistor in example 3.1? If the resistor is imbedded in another object, the heat flows through this combined system. The temperature of the object and the resistor rises. The heat lost from the resistor is gained by the object (Fig. 3-1). We can express this conservation of heat transfer by

$$Q_{\text{Resistor}} + Q_{\text{Object}} = 0 \tag{3.3}$$

The value of Q_{Resistor} must be equal in magnitude to Q_{Object} but of opposite sign. By convention, the heat gained is positive and the heat lost is negative. Since heat is lost from the resistor to the object in the above example, Q_{Resistor} is negative (-8.6×10^4 cal), and Q_{Object} is positive ($+8.6 \times 10^4$ cal).

3.2 TEMPERATURE AND TEMPERATURE SCALES

Intrinsically, temperature can be defined quantitatively by assigning a scale to sensations of hotness and coldness by means of an instrument called a *thermometer*.

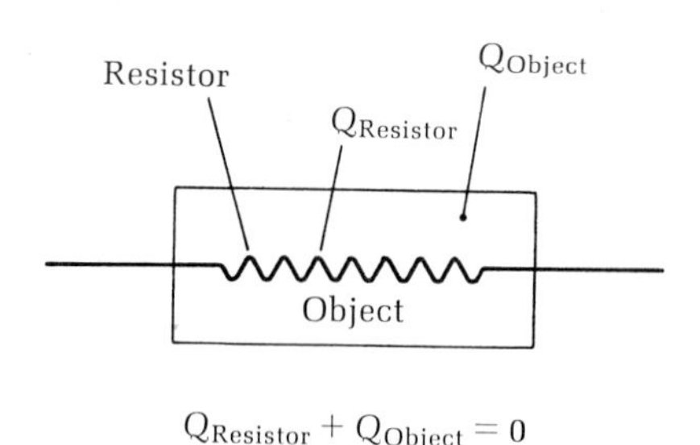

Fig. 3-1. Conservation of heat, Q, between resistor and object.

An expanding thread of a liquid in a marked capillary tube provides one means of temperature evaluation. Such a device gives a measure of temperature that depends on the expansion properties of the liquid. The scale of such thermometers is established by choosing end-point reference conditions, customarily the freezing and boiling points of water. The *centigrade scale* assigns a value of 0 to the freezing point and 100 to the boiling point.

It was of great significance when a thermometer was found that gives temperature readings independent of the material used. The low-pressure gas thermometer is such an instrument. The gas used is unimportant as long as it is at a temperature well above the point at which condensation to the liquid phase occurs.

The temperature scale obtained with the gas thermometer is called the *ideal gas temperature scale*. The freezing point of water is assigned a value of 273.16 in units the same size as those of the Centigrade scale. This defines the Kelvin temperature scale, denoted by the symbol T. The relationship between Kelvin and centigrade temperature scales is

$$T = 273.16 + t \tag{3.4}$$

where t is in degrees centigrade.

The practical, accepted standard for precise thermometry is the *platinum resistance thermometer*. The electrical resistance of platinum depends on temperature in a highly reproducible way; the thermometer makes use both of this consistency and of the preciseness of electrical measurements. The readings depend on the material used, so it is necessary to calibrate the platinum thermometer against the low-pressure gas thermometer.

3.3 HEAT CAPACITY

We have seen in the preceding sections that the specification of a given quantity of heat and the specification of temperature do not individually depend on the nature of a sample of matter. Thus we can add a given quantity (for example, 100 calories) of heat to any object and independently measure the object's temperature with a thermometer. Experimentally, it is found that the temperature increase of an object of given mass and composition is directly proportional to the amount of heat supplied to it. The factor that determines the proportionality constant is known as the heat capacity, C, of the object. Heat capacity depends on the nature of the object and is, therefore, a fundamental thermal property of matter.

The ratio of an increment of heat, dQ, to the increment of temperature rise, dT, in an object defines the heat capacity:

$$C = \frac{dQ}{dT} \tag{3.5}$$

Table 3-1. HEAT CAPACITY OF WATER*

Temperature °C	Heat capacity (C_p)	
	cal/g/°C	*joules/g/°C*
0	1.00738	4.2177
10	1.00129	4.1922
20	0.99888	4.1819
30	0.99802	4.1785
40	0.99804	4.1786
50	0.99854	4.1807
60	0.99943	4.1844

*Adapted from Osborn, N. S., H. F. Stimson, and D. C. Ginnings. 1939. Bur. Std. J. Research 23:238.

Table 3-2. CONSTANTS OF EMPIRICAL EQUATIONS FOR $\overline{C}_p$ (300 to 1500°K)

Substance	a	$10^3 b$	$10^7 c$
$O_2(g)$	6.148	3.102	− 9.23
$N_2(g)$	6.524	1.250	− 0.01
$H_2O(g)$	7.256	2.298	2.83
$CO_2(g)$	6.214	10.396	−35.45
$CO(g)$	6.420	1.665	− 1.96

In general, the heat capacity of a given sample of material will vary with temperature. Values of the heat capacity of water at several temperatures and at 1 atm pressure are shown in Table 3-1. The heat capacities in the table are given per gram of water. When the heat capacity is given for a gram of material, it is called the *specific heat capacity*. When specified for a mole of material it is called the *molar heat capacity*, $\overline{C}$.

The dependence of heat capacity on temperature is often expressed by a power series:

$$\overline{C} = a + bT + cT^2 + dT^3 + \ldots \tag{3.6}$$

Table 3-2 shows some experimental values for the constants a, b, c, and d for several substances at a constant pressure of 1 atm.

The simplest measurements of heat capacity are done with the sample at a fixed volume or pressure. The heat capacity depends on which constraint is imposed. At constant volume the heat capacity is defined as

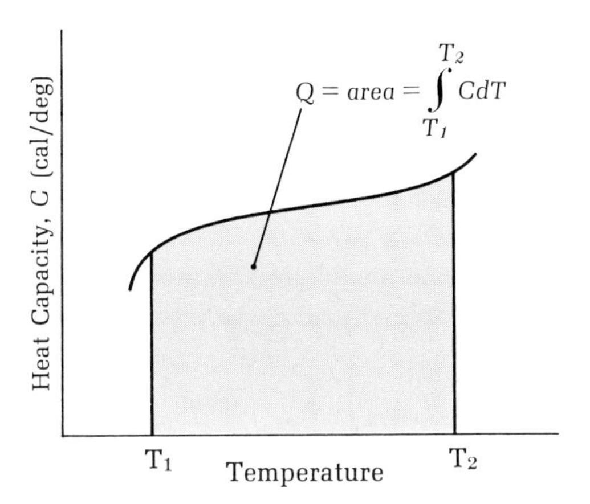

Fig. 3-2. Heat, Q, represented by area under curve of heat capacity versus temperature between T_1 and T_2.

$$C_V = \left(\frac{dQ}{dT}\right)_V \tag{3.7}$$

and at constant pressure, as

$$C_p = \left(\frac{dQ}{dT}\right)_p \tag{3.8}$$

Later we shall see how C_p and C_V are related to each other by additional experimentally determined derivatives.*

The amount of heat required to raise the temperature of a sample by an increment of temperature, dT, is

$$dQ = CdT \tag{3.9}$$

The heat required to raise the temperature from T_1 to T_2 is

$$Q = \int_{T_1}^{T_2} CdT \tag{3.10}$$

To evaluate this integral we need to know how C varies with T. The area under the C-versus-T curve gives Q (Fig. 3-2). If the sample is heated at constant volume or pressure, C_V or C_p, respectively, must be used.

---

*Students who are familiar with partial differential notation will realize that the heat capacities at constant volume and pressure could be written as $(\partial Q/\partial T)_V$ and $(\partial Q/\partial T)_p$, respectively.

EXAMPLE **3.2**

The heat capacity, $\overline{C}_p$, for liquid mercury is 6.6615 cal/deg-mole at 25°C and 6.5752 cal/deg-mole at 100°C. How much heat is needed to raise the temperature of 20.0 moles of mercury at 1 atm from 25°C to 100°C?

The heat capacity is nearly constant in this temperature interval; its average value is 6.62 cal/deg-mole. To a first approximation the integral $\int CdT$ will be

$$Q = (20.0 \text{ moles})\left(6.62 \frac{\text{cal}}{\text{mole-deg}}\right)\left(\int_{25}^{100} dT \text{ deg}\right) = 9930 \text{ cal}$$

Heat capacities can be used to calculate the results of various thermal processes. If two objects, A and B, at initially different temperatures, T_A and T_B, are placed in thermal contact with each other, the heat lost by one will be gained by the other. Thermal equilibrium is achieved at a final temperature T'. By the rule of conservation of heat (equation 3.3), we can express the heat transfer in terms of the appropriate heat capacities as

$$\int_{T_A}^{T'} C_A dT + \int_{T_B}^{T'} C_B dT = 0 \tag{3.11}$$

From equation 3.11, we then calculate the final equilibrium temperature.

EXAMPLE **3.3**

Suppose that a piece of copper at 500°K, whose heat capacity is 100 cal/deg, is placed in thermal contact with a piece of silver at 1000°K, whose heat capacity is 200 cal/deg. Assume that the heat capacities of both metals are constant. Calculate the final temperature reached.

According to equation 3.11

$$\int_{500}^{T'} 100dT + \int_{1000}^{T'} 200dT = 0$$

$$100\ (T' - 500) + 200\ (T' - 1000) = 0$$

$$T' = 833°\text{K}$$

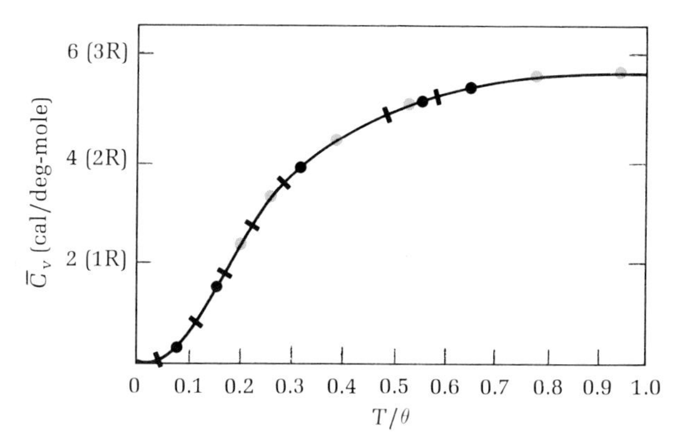

Fig. 3-3. Heat capacities of solid elements as function of T/θ, where bars are for Pb ($\theta = 88°$), black dots are for Cu ($\theta = 315°$), and green dots are for C (diamond, $\theta = 1830°$). The solid line is given by the Debye theory.

Heat capacities of solids

If the heat capacities of solids are measured as a function of temperature, a particularly interesting result is found. At low temperature, $\overline{C}_V$ of all solids approaches zero. At high temperature, $\overline{C}_V$ of all solid elements approaches $3R$, where $R = 1.987$ cal/deg-mole.* This behavior is shown in Fig. 3-3.

A theory for the temperature dependence of $\overline{C}_V$ of solids was developed by Debye. His theory gives the curve shown in Fig. 3-3, where the parameter θ, which is characteristic for each element, is needed to fit the curve. Debye showed that at low temperature

$$\overline{C}_V = \frac{12\pi^4}{5} (T/\theta)^3 \tag{3.12}$$

His theory shows that at high temperatures the value of $3R$ is approached.

EXAMPLE **3.4**

The heat required to raise the temperature of 1 mole of carbon (diamond, $\theta = 1830°$) from 0°K to 10°K at constant volume can be estimated from Debye's law as follows:

---

*We previously gave R as 0.0821 liter-atm/deg-mole (sec. 1-5). The unit of liter-atm is an energy unit that can be converted to calories or joules by the following relations: 1 liter-atm = 24.218 cal = 101.33 joules. Thus R in calories is 1.987 cal/deg-mole.

$$
\begin{aligned}
Q &= \int_0^{10} \bar{C}_V dT \\
&= \left(\frac{12\pi^4}{5\theta^3}\right) \int_0^{10} T^3 dT \\
&= \left(\frac{12\pi^4}{5(1830)^3}\right)\left(\frac{1}{4}\right)(10^4) \\
&= 9.56 \times 10^{-5} \text{ cal}
\end{aligned}
$$

Thus, only a tenth of a millicalorie of heat is needed to raise the temperature of 1 mole of diamond by 10° at this low temperature. In contrast, 14.6 cal is needed to raise the temperature of 1 mole of diamond from 298 °K to 308 °K.

Each atom in a solid element vibrates in three directions with respect to its neighbors, giving rise to three vibrational modes of motion (Fig. 3-4). According to solid-state theory, each mode contributes R to the total heat capacity, $3R$, of the solid. The dependence of the heat capacity on temperature can be interpreted as arising from a failure to completely activate a given motion at a given temperature. A high temperature would be needed to activate vibrational motions in a very rigid lattice, which explains why the value of $3R$ is achieved for diamond only at very high temperatures. The complete, exact theory of these effects requires the application of quantum statistical mechanics as shown by Debye's theory.

Molecular solids generally have heat capacities greater than $3R$ because intramolecular vibrations (motion within the molecules) as well as intermolecular vibrations (motion between molecules) are possible.

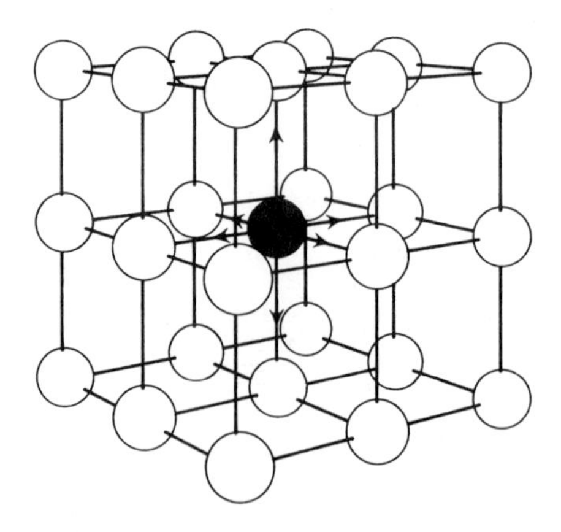

Fig. 3-4. Atom vibrating in three directions in representative crystal lattice.

3.4 HEATS OF PHASE TRANSITIONS

When heat is added to a substance and its temperature does not rise, a phase transition is occurring. The most familiar phase changes involve transitions between solid, liquid, and gas states. Phase changes can also occur between different solid phases and, in a few cases, between different liquid phases. The characteristic features of phase transitions are (1) they occur at a particular combination of temperature and pressure, (2) they are accompanied by absorption or release of a specific amount of heat, and (3) they involve a change in heat capacity. Table 3-3 shows some typical phase transitions.

EXAMPLE 3.5

Suppose a piece of copper at 100°C with a heat capacity of 10 cal/deg is put into a mixture of ice and water at 0°C. How much ice melts if we assume that the heat capacity of the copper is constant and that there is sufficient ice to maintain the system at 0°C?

It takes 80 cal to melt 1 g of ice. The basic heat-transfer equation is $Q_1 + Q_2 = 0$. Let Q_1 represent the heat lost by the copper in going from 100°C to 0°C:

$$Q_1 = \int_{100}^{0} 10\,dt = -1000 \text{ cal}$$

The heat added to melt ice is thus 1000 cal. The number of grams of ice melted will be 1000/80 = 12.5 g.

If the same piece of copper at 100°C is placed in contact with 10 g of ice at −10°C (ice has a heat capacity of 0.5 cal/deg-g; liquid water has a heat capacity of 1.0 cal/deg-g), what would be the final temperature?

Again we add all the heat effects and equate with zero. Let t' represent the final temperature:

$$\int_{100}^{t'} 10 dt + \int_{-10}^{0} 5 dt + 800 + \int_{0}^{t'} 10 dt = 0$$

The first term is the heat lost by copper; the second term, the heat gained by the 10 g of ice in going from −10° to 0°; the third term, the heat of fusion of 10 g of ice; the fourth term, the heat absorbed by the liquid water in going from 0°C to t'. Then

$$10\,(t' - 100) + 5\,(0 + 10) + 800 + 10\,(t' - 0) = 0$$
$$20t' = 150$$
$$t' = 7.5\text{°C}$$

Table 3-3. CHANGES OF STATE

Process	Name of heat effect	Example	$\Delta\bar{C}_p$* (cal/mole-deg)	Q* (kcal/mole)	Temperature (°K)
Melting	Heat of fusion	$H_2O(s) \rightarrow H_2O(l)$	8.91	1.436	273.16
Boiling	Heat of vaporization	$H_2O(l) \rightarrow H_2O(g, 1\ atm)$	−10.02	9.717	373.16
Sublimation	Heat of sublimation	$CO_2(s) \rightarrow CO_2(g, 1\ atm)$	†	6.03	194.7
Structure change	Heat of transition	S(s, rhombic) → S(s, monoclinic)	0.24	0.09	368.6

*At the temperature indicated.
†Data not available.

3.5 ENTROPY

Here we shall define the entropy, S, of a substance by an experimental procedure involving heat and temperature measurements. Later we will interpret entropy from a molecular point of view.

Heat is added in a small increment dQ to a substance at temperature T. We define the increase in the entropy of the substance by

$$dS = \frac{dQ}{T} \tag{3.13}$$

Since we measure finite changes, the entropy change is the sum of the heat additions divided by the temperature and is given by

$$\Delta S = S_2 - S_1 = \int \frac{dQ}{T} \tag{3.14}$$

The difference, ΔS, is the entropy added to the substance in going from some initial state with an entropy S_1 to some new state with an entropy S_2. The temperature generally changes as heat is added to the substance, in which case the initial and final states are at different temperatures. Such is the case when a substance is heated at constant volume or pressure and no phase change occurs.

Entropy changes from heat-capacity information

As we have seen, it is convenient to describe quantities of the heat in terms of the appropriate heat capacity and temperature change by

$$dQ = CdT \tag{3.15}$$

The entropy change in going from an initial temperature T_1 to a final temperature T_2 is given by

$$\Delta S = \int_{T_1}^{T_2} \frac{C\,dT}{T} \tag{3.16}$$

This integral is evaluated from a knowledge of the heat capacity in this temperature range. The integration can be performed graphically by plotting C/T versus T. The

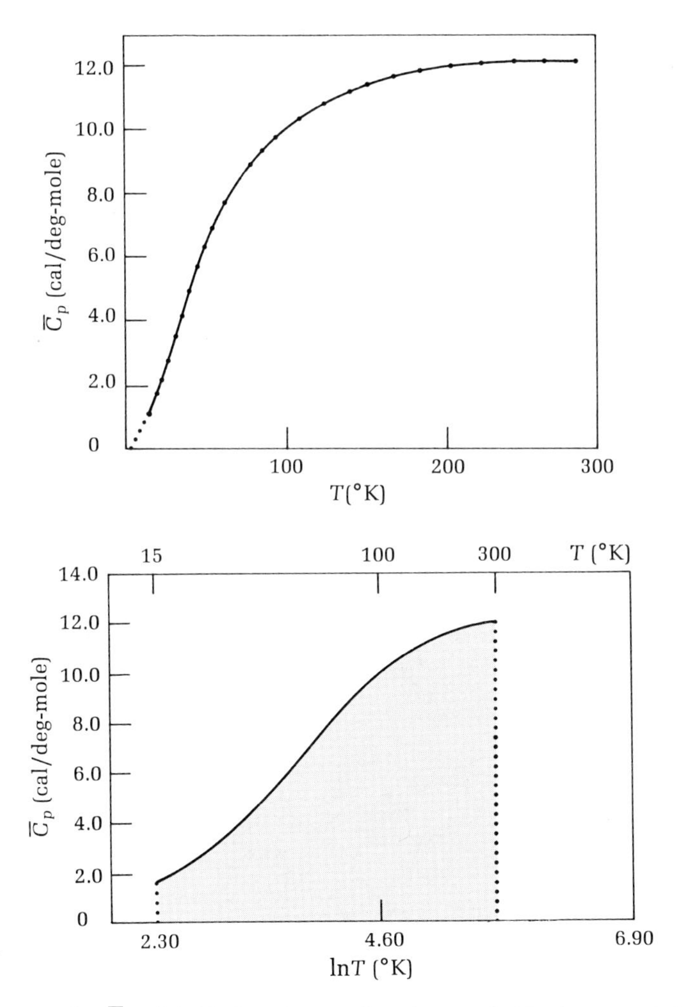

Fig. 3-5. Heat capacity, $\overline{C}_p$, of AgCl plotted versus T and versus ln T, where area between T_1 and T_2 gives ΔS.

area between T_1 and T_2 gives the value of the integral. A better way is to plot C versus ln T, in which case the area between ln T_1 and ln T_2 gives the value of the integral. This method recognizes that dT/T is equal to d ln T. Heat-capacity data and a plot of C versus ln T for AgCl(s) are shown in Fig. 3-5.

In general, the heat capacity is a function of temperature. This function must be known before we can evaluate these integrals. When C is a constant, the value of the integral is simply

$$\Delta S = C \ln (T_2/T_1) \tag{3.17}$$

We must still specify which C we are using, C_V or C_p.

It is important to understand why we can divide the heat increment dQ by a particular temperature T when the temperature varies as heat is added. Although a change in temperature occurs, it is infinitesimal compared to the average value of T. Each incremental addition of heat comes at a slightly higher average temperature, the temperature that applies for that portion of the experiment. The total entropy effect is the sum of all these additions, which, in the limit of incremental additions, is given by an integral.

Entropy changes in phase transitions

When a phase transition occurs, a quantity of heat, Q_t, is released or absorbed. The temperature is at a fixed value T_t, so the entropy change is simply found from equation 3.13:

$$\Delta S_t = \frac{Q_t}{T_t} \tag{3.18}$$

EXAMPLE 3.6

In Table 3-3, heats and temperatures are given for several processes. Calculate ΔS for the four phase transitions in the table.

The entropy changes for the four processes are

$$\Delta S_{\text{fusion}}\,(H_2O) = \frac{1436 \text{ cal/mole}}{273.2\,^\circ\text{K}} = 5.26 \text{ cal/mole-deg}$$

$$\Delta S_{\text{vap}}\,(H_2O) = \frac{9717 \text{ cal/mole}}{373.2\,^\circ\text{K}} = 26.16 \text{ cal/mole-deg}$$

$$\Delta S_{\text{sub}}\,(CO_2) = \frac{6030 \text{ cal/mole}}{194.7\,^\circ\text{K}} = 31.0 \text{ cal/mole-deg}$$

$$\Delta S_{\text{trans}}\,(\text{S, rhombic} \rightarrow \text{monoclinic}) = \frac{90 \text{ cal/mole}}{369\,^\circ\text{K}} = 0.244 \text{ cal/mole-deg}$$

General determination of entropy changes

By combining the results of the previous two sections we can evaluate ΔS for a substance between any two given states. For example, for the transition from ice at T_1 to gaseous water at T_2

$$S_2 - S_1 = \int_{T_1}^{273} \frac{C(\text{ice})}{T} dT + \frac{Q_{\text{fus}}}{273} + \int_{273}^{373} \frac{C(\text{liq water})}{T} dT + \frac{Q_{\text{vap}}}{373} + \int_{373}^{T_2} \frac{C(\text{gas water})}{T} dT \tag{3.19}$$

In general, then, we represent the entropy change by an equation of the form

$$\Delta S = \int \frac{C dT}{T} + \sum \frac{Q_t}{T_t} \tag{3.20}$$

Entropy-change measurements can be standardized if we fix the initial state at 0°K and 1 atm pressure. This low-temperature condition can only be approached, but, as noted earlier, at low temperatures the heat capacities of nearly all substances rapidly approach zero. There is therefore very little contribution to the entropy-determining integral at extremely low temperatures. We can see this from plots of C versus $\ln T$ (Fig. 3-5). We define the entropy of a substance as its entropy relative to its entropy value at 0°K.

An example of the experimental determination of entropy is shown in Table 3-4 for the organic material furan (C_4H_4O). The heat-capacity data used in Table 3-4 are shown in Fig. 3-6. Note that there are two crystal phases of furan. From 0°K to 12°K the Debye heat-capacity equation (equation 3.12) is used for the entropy contribution. From 12°K to 150.0°K the entropy of crystal II is determined by graphical integration. At 150.0°K the transition from crystal II to crystal I occurs, with a heat of transition of 489.2 cal. The entropy contribution is (489.2/150.0) cal/deg. The

Table 3-4. ENTROPY OF LIQUID FURAN*

T (°K)	*Evaluation procedure*	ΔS *(cal/deg-mole)*
0 to 12	Debye equation, $\theta = 95.5°$	0.347
12 to 150.0	Crystal II: graphical $\int C \, d \ln T$	18.076
150.0	Transition of crystal II to crystal I: 489.2/150.0	3.262
150.0 to 187.55	Crystal I: graphical $\int C \, d \ln T$	4.047
187.55	Fusion of crystal I: 908.8/187.55	4.846
187.55 to 298.15	Liquid: graphical $\int C \, d \ln T$	11.638
298.15	Total entropy of liquid (sum of above terms)	42.22

*Adapted from Guthrie and others. 1952. J. Am. Chem. Soc. 74:4662.

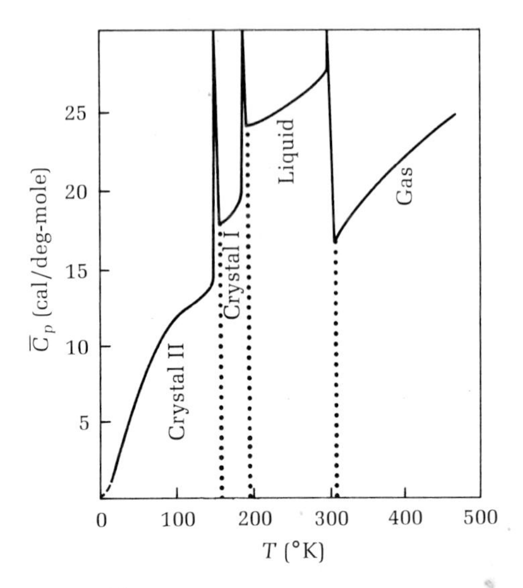

Fig. 3-6. Plot of heat capacity, $\overline{C}_p$, of furan versus temperature T. Spikes on curve represent transition regions.

entropy of crystal I is determined by graphical integration of its heat capacity to the fusion temperature, 187.55°K. The entropy of fusion at 187.55°K is determined from the heat of fusion, 908.8 cal/deg. The final liquid contribution from 187.55°K to 298°K is determined by graphical integration. The total value for the entropy of liquid furan at 298.15°K is 42.22 cal/mole-deg.

3.6 THE THIRD LAW OF THERMODYNAMICS

The third law of thermodynamics states that at 0°K all substances in perfect crystalline or ordered form have the same entropy, arbitrarily assigned a value of zero. This law is based on many experimental results. We shall briefly describe two verifications of the law and then consider the statistical meaning of entropy and its connection with the third law.

An experimental verification of the third law is obtained in studies of the thermal properties of sulphur. The heat capacities of the solid-phase forms of sulphur, rhombic and monoclinic, have been studied from the transition temperature of 368.6°K to very low temperatures. From these measurements the entropy difference between the monoclinic and rhombic forms from 0°K to 368.6°K has been determined to be 0.22 cal/deg-mole. This calculation assumes that each phase has the same entropy value at 0°K; that is, it assumes the third law is valid. The test of the third law depends on comparing the entropy difference at the transition temperature by an independent

Table 3-5. ENTROPIES OF MONATOMIC GASES AT 298.15°K

Material	S_{expt} *(cal/deg-mole)**	S_{calc} *(cal/deg-mole)*
Ne	35.01 ± 0.10	34.95 ± 0.01
Ar	36.95 ± 0.2	36.99 ± 0.01
Kr	39.17 ± 0.1	39.20 ± 0.01
Xe	40.7 ± 0.3	40.54 ± 0.01

*Adapted from Kelly, K. K. 1950. U.S. Bur. Mines Bull. 477:10.

experiment. By direct heat measurements it is found that 95 ± 10 cal/mole are required to convert rhombic sulfur to monoclinic sulfur at 368.6°K. Thus, the entropy difference for this phase transition is 0.26 ± 0.03 cal/deg-mole, which is comparable to the integrated heat capacity result of 0.22 cal/deg-mole.

A second verification of the third law comes from consideration of the molecular theory of entropy. It can be shown that the entropy of an ideal monatomic gas at 1 atm is given by

$$S = \tfrac{3}{2}R \ln MW + \tfrac{5}{2}R \ln T - 2.311 \text{ cal/deg-mole} \tag{3.21}$$

where MW is the molecular weight, and T, the temperature. This equation assumes that at 0°K the entropy of the system is zero. The entropy determined from measurements of heat can be compared to results calculated from this equation, as shown in Table 3-5. The experimental values agree with the values calculated from the theory.

3.7 ENTROPY OF IMPERFECT SOLIDS

It is found experimentally, that the entropy of a material depends on the state it is in. The entropy of a solid also depends on the specific arrangement of its molecules. The entropy associated with a random arrangement is higher than that associated with a perfectly ordered arrangement. For example, solid carbon monoxide can be prepared in two ways. If the liquid is very slowly frozen, a highly ordered arrangement of CO molecules results (Fig. 3-7, *A*); rapid freezing, on the other hand, forms a solid in which the CO molecules are randomly oriented in two directions (Fig. 3-7, *B*). Experimentally, it is found that at very low temperatures the entropy for the disordered CO is 1.0 cal/deg-mole higher than that observed for the ordered CO.

One of the most powerful theoretical means for interpreting disorder effects is the Boltzmann relation:

$$S = k \ln \Omega \tag{3.22}$$

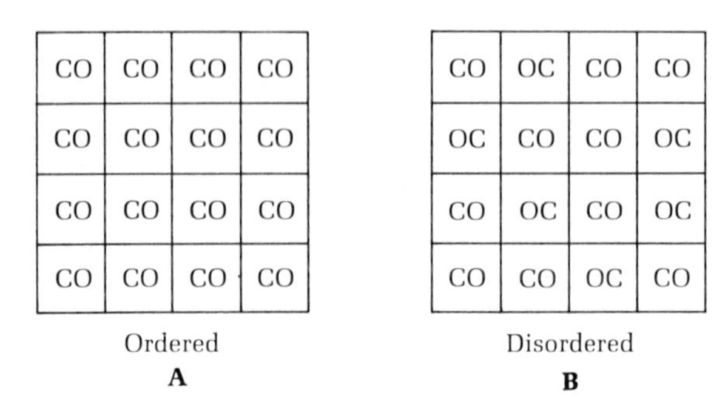

Fig. 3-7. Schematic representations of solid CO.

where k is the Boltzmann constant.* This equation relates the entropy, S, of a system to its number of microstates, Ω. A *microstate* is a molecular description of a particular state of the system.

Equation 3.22 can be used to calculate the entropy in a random crystal at 0°K. The number of microstates in a random crystal of CO with N molecules is 2^N since there are two orientations for each molecule. In the perfectly ordered crystal each of the N molecules has one specific orientation, and $\Omega = 1^N$. The entropy difference between ordered and disordered CO is

$$\begin{aligned}\Delta S = S_{\text{disordered}} - S_{\text{ordered}} &= k(\ln 2^N - \ln 1^N)\\ &= kN \ln 2\\ &= R \ln 2\\ &= 1.987 \ln 2 \text{ cal/deg-mole}\\ &= 1.377 \text{ cal/deg-mole}\end{aligned}$$

This theoretical calculation is close to the experimentally observed value of 1.0 cal/deg-mole. The deviation indicates that the order of the experimentally studied material was not completely random.

In general, if a molecule goes from a condition in which it has n_1 distinguishable orientations to a state in which it has n_2 distinguishable orientations, Ω_2/Ω_1 for N molecules is $(n_2/n_1)^N$. The entropy change per mole would be $R \ln (n_2/n_1)$.

That entropy is a reflection of the state of order or disorder can also be seen in various solid-state phase transitions. These can be experimentally observed for orientational order-disorder transitions.

The transition between crystalline forms depends on temperature and pressure. We shall assume the pressure is near 1 atm unless otherwise stated. The more ordered

*The Boltzmann constant, k, is given by $k = R/N$, where R is the gas constant and N is Avogadro's number. In energy units of ergs, $k = 1.3805 \times 10^{-16}$ erg/deg-molecule.

state is preferred at low temperatures. Order-disorder transitions occur in two ways.

In a *first-order transition* the addition of heat to a system at a given fixed temperature and pressure causes a change in state. For example, solid HCl at 98.41°K can undergo a transition from solid phase II to solid phase I. The structure changes from a face-centered orthorhombic (II) lattice in which the molecules are orientationally ordered, to a face-centered cubic (I) structure in which each molecule has a twelvefold orientational disorder. Entropy and volume changes are observed in this transition. In a first-order transition the heat capacity, C_p, is essentially infinite since the temperature does not change during the transition. This is seen as a spike on the experimental heat-capacity curves (see Fig. 3-6).

In a *λ-type transition* the change in state occurs gradually over a range of temperatures. The heat capacity, C_p, is not infinite in the transition region; rather, it appears as a λ-shaped blip on the experimental heat-capacity curves. The order-disorder transition in NH_4Cl (see Fig. 2-21) is observed to be of the λ-type. In the low-temperature form all NH_4^+ ions are oriented in one way, so that $n_1 = 1$; in the high-temperature disordered form two orientations are found, so that $n_2 = 2$. The entropy change for this transition is $R \ln 2 = 1.377$ cal/mole-deg. This agrees with the experimental value.

Liquid crystals: an application of the order-disorder properties of solid-to-liquid phase transitions

The distinction between liquids and solids cannot always be viewed as absolute. An amorphous solid has some properties of a liquid; for example, both are isotropic and have only limited, short-range order. Similarly, some liquids can show behavior that is not unlike that of solids. These materials are called liquid crystals.

Most solids melt sharply, at which point the crystal undergoes a phase transition from a crystalline solid to an isotropic liquid. However, certain organic compounds pass through an intermediate state known as the liquid-crystalline state:

$$\text{crystal} \rightarrow \text{liquid crystal} \rightarrow \text{liquid}$$

The intermediate state is a true liquid in that it flows and assumes the shape of its container. There are two broad classes of liquid crystals, smectic and nematic.

Smectic liquid crystals are the more highly ordered. The molecules are arranged in layers with the long axes of the molecules parallel to each other (Fig. 3-8, *A*). Smectic liquids crystals show anisotropic viscosity behavior; because a preferential sliding of layers of molecules can occur along the *xy* plane, viscosity is lower in the *x* and *y* directions than in the *z* direction. Smectic phases also show anisotropy in their indices of refraction in the *x*, *y*, and *z* directions.

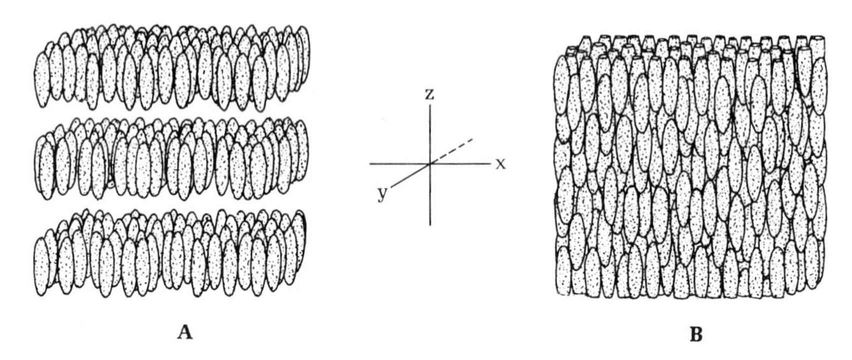

Fig. 3-8. Types of liquid crystals. **A,** Smectic. **B,** Nematic.

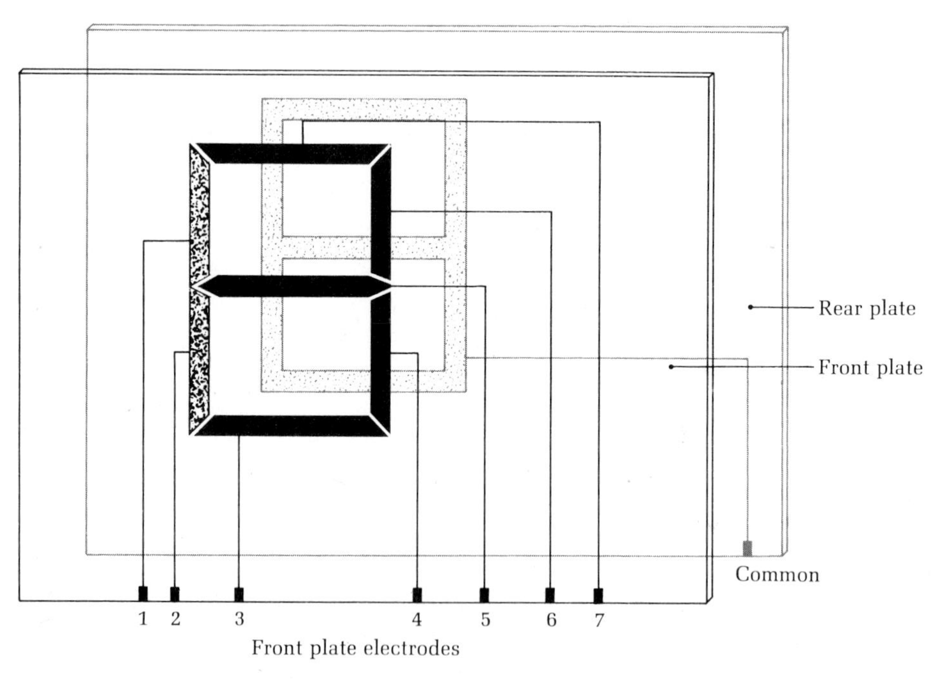

Fig. 3-9. Liquid-crystal digital display device. Device consists of nematic liquid-crystal layer sandwiched between two electrode-impregnated glass plates (shown in gray and black). Rear plate has one common electrode. Front plate is segmented, so that any digit from 0 to 9 can be produced by selectively applying voltage to electrodes 1 to 7. When electric field is applied to any segment, liquid crystal becomes turbid and opaque and scatters light. The digit 3 is shown here.

Nematic liquid crystals are less ordered. Their ordering involves the parallel alignment of molecules along their long axis (Fig. 3-8, *B*). Nematic liquid crystals exhibit a unique property: if ions are dissolved in them and a small current is applied, they scatter light and appear opaque as long as the current flows. This unusual light-scattering behavior finds use in new types of display devices, such as signs and digital clocks (Fig. 3-9).

Liquid crystals are generally formed by elongated aromatic molecules. Table 3-6 shows several examples, along with the types of liquid crystals they form. The last example is particularly interesting because it exhibits both nematic and smectic behavior. At the lower temperature range it is smectic, but at the higher temperature the less-ordered nematic liquid prevails.

Table 3-6. LIQUID-CRYSTAL COMPOUNDS

Compound formula	*Type of liquid crystal*	*Temperature range (°C)*
$CH_3O-C_6H_4-N{=}N(\rightarrow O)-C_6H_4-OCH_3$	Nematic	118–136
$C_2H_5-O-C_6H_4-CH{=}N-C_6H_4-C_4H_9$	Nematic	36–80
$C_5H_{11}O-C_6H_4-O_2C-C_6H_4-CO_2-C_6H_4-OC_5H_{11}$	Smectic	16–175
	Nematic	175–213

PROBLEMS

1. Calculate the heat produced from passing a fixed current of 1.35 amp through a 10.0-ohm resistor for 5.00 minutes.
2. The current in an electrolysis cell was found to vary with time according to $i = i_0/(1 + t)$. The initial current, i_0, equals 1.2 amp, and t is the time in seconds. The voltage applied to the system remains constant at 5.3 volts. Calculate the heat generated in 200 seconds from $t = 0$.
3. Calculate the absolute-zero temperature in °C for air whose density at 0°C and 100°C is 1.293 g/ml and 0.946 g/ml, respectively. Assume air behaves according to the ideal gas law.
4. The coefficient of thermal expansion, α, is defined as $\alpha = (1/V_0)(dV/dt)_p$, where V_0 is the volume of the material at 0°C. For ethanol, $\alpha = 1.0414 \times 10^{-3} + (1.567 \times 10^{-6})t + (5.148 \times 10^{-8})t^2$, where t is in °C.

(a) Derive an expression showing how the volume V depends on t.
(b) From this expression, use a linear relation of $\theta = [(V - V_0)/(V_{100} - V_0)](100)$ to derive a temperature scale, θ, for the alcohol thermometer. V_{100} is the volume of the ethanol at 100°C. Notice that the volumes V_0 and V_{100} are the reference points in developing a linear scale. There are 100 one-degree units in this particular case.
(c) Calculate the temperature given by the alcohol scale when an ideal gas thermometer reads 50°C.

5. Calculate the increase in temperature that occurs when 250 g of water initially at 10°C is heated at constant pressure by 15,030 cal. Assume the specific heat capacity of water is 1.000 cal/g.
6. Calculate the heat required to increase the temperature of 5.00 moles of O_2 from 300°K to 1000°K at constant pressure. (Note: Use data from Table 3-2.)
7. A solid object at 100°C with a constant heat capacity of 10 cal/deg is placed in a mixture of ice and water so that some, but not all, of the ice is melted in producing thermal equilibration of the object to 0°C. The heat of fusion of ice is 80 cal/gram. How much ice melts?
8. The object used in problem 7, at 100°C, is placed in contact with 10 g of ice at −10°C. What is the final temperature of this isolated system if the heat capacity of ice is 0.5 cal/deg, and that of water is 1.0 cal/deg?
9. How much heat must be added to a solid object at constant volume in order to change its temperature from 10°K to 100°K if its heat capacity at constant volume is equal to $0.05\ T^3$?
10. Show that the heat capacity of the air within a house of volume V can be expressed by an equation with the form of either

$$C = \frac{pV}{RT}\overline{C}_p$$

or

$$C = \frac{pV}{RT}\overline{C}_p\left[1 + \left(\frac{T_0 - T}{T}\right)\right]$$

depending on whether the temperature increases or decreases, and where $\overline{C}_p$ is the heat capacity per mole of the air at constant pressure. Assume ideal gas law behavior. T_0 is the temperature of the air outside the house. Note that if the pressure is to be kept constant, some of the air must escape through cracks in the house. Once air has escaped it is not involved in the heating process.

11. Using the appropriate result from problem 6, calculate the heat required to raise the temperature from 0°C to 25°C of a house whose volume is 10^5 liter if the heat capacity of the air within the house at constant pressure is 7 cal/deg-mole and if the pressure remains constant at 1 atm during the heating process.
12. Estimate the specific heat capacity of aluminum at high temperatures where $\overline{C}_V$ is approximately 6 cal/deg-mole.
13. Calculate the entropy change involved in heating 0.50 moles of argon at a fixed volume from 50°C to 100°C. Assume the heat capacity at constant volume is 3.0 cal/mole-deg.
14. Calculate the entropy increase for heating the solid in problem 9.
15. Calculate the increase in entropy upon heating 5.0 g of ice at −10°C to liquid water at

50 °C. Assume the specific heat capacities of ice and water are 0.50 cal/g-deg and 1.00 cal/g-deg, respectively. The heat of fusion of ice at 0 °C is 80 cal/g.

16. Calculate the entropy of 1 mole of helium at 1000 °K and 1 atm.
17. Benzthiophene is a planar molecule with the structure

```
        H     H
        |     |
        C     C
 H     // \  / \\
  \  C     C      \\
     |     ||      C—H
  /  C     C      /
 H     \\ / \   /
        C     S
        |
        H
```

At low temperatures a solid of this compound undergoes an order-disorder λ-transition upon heating. The entropy change is 2.75 cal/mole-deg.

(a) Calculate the number of orientations in the disordered state to account for this entropy change.

(b) Draw structures of the possible arrangements of benzthiophene in the disordered solid state.

18. Calculate the entropy change for the system defined in problem 7.

4 THE ENERGY OF CHEMICAL SYSTEMS

In the previous chapter we developed the ideas of the measurement of heat and the thermal properties of matter. We now turn to an examination of the broad relationships that exist among heat, work, and energy. These relationships provide a basis for understanding and discussing chemical reactions.

We begin examining some of the characteristics of work. A common feature of certain experimental processes is the lifing of a weight. A compressed gas confined by a cylinder and piston can lift a weight when it expands (Fig. 4-1, *A*). When a stretched spring contracts it can lift a weight (Fig. 4-1, *B*). Other devices can lift weights by less direct means. A chemical reaction can generate an electric current to drive a motor that lifts a weight (Fig. 4-2). A steam engine uses heat to lift a weight. The common feature of these processes is their ability to lift a weight. We can conclude that they are related to each other in some fundamental way.

4.1 DEFINITION OF WORK

Let us define the lifting of a weight as work. The amount of work, W, will be measured by multiplying the quantity of weight by the height through which it is lifted. Any process that does work is called a *work process*.

How much work can a specific process do? A gas can be expanded so that some maximum amount of weight is lifted. Under this condition the weight is just balanced by the force exerted by the gas pressure. Complete control of the work process exists. At the point of this balanced condition, the expansion process can be reversed by increasing the weight on the piston by an infinitesimal amount. This condition is called a *reversible process*.

Another example of a work process is the lifting of one weight by a second weight (Fig. 4-3). When the weights are equal, the process is reversible and the maximum amount of work is done.

What happens if an expansion work process is not reversible? If a gas expands into a vacuum, no weight is lifted, so no work is done. This is an *irreversible*

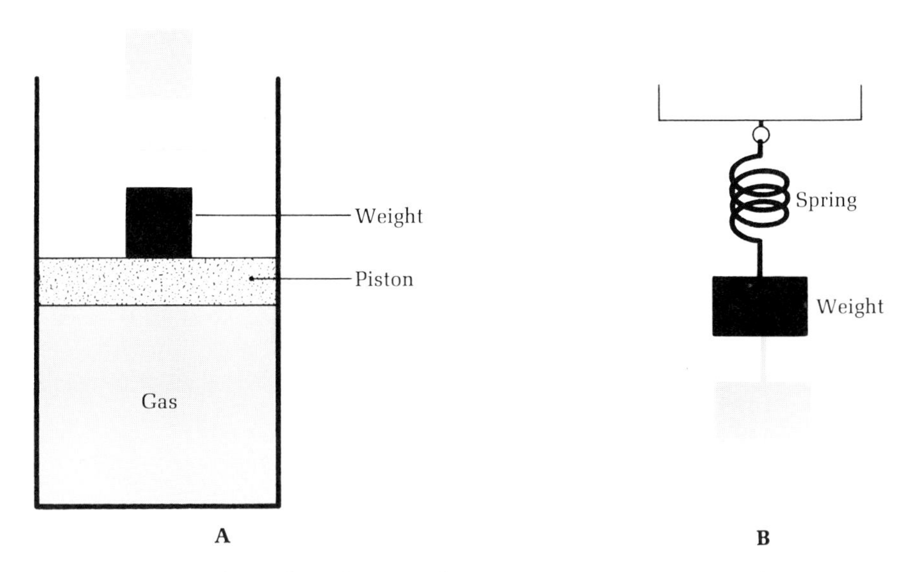

Fig. 4-1. Lifting of weights. **A,** Volume expansion. **B,** Spring contraction.

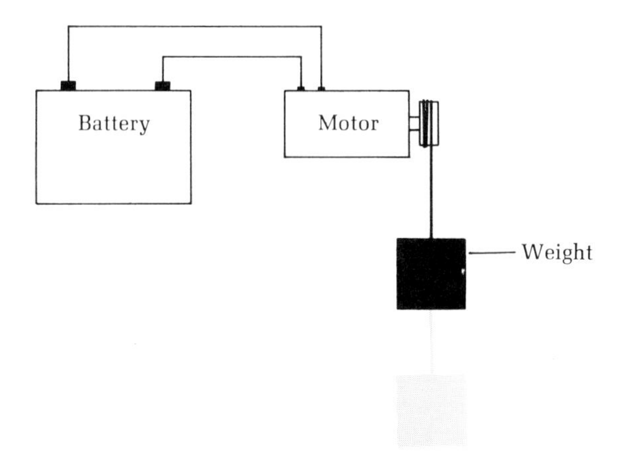

Fig. 4-2. Battery used to drive motor that lifts weight.

work process; the work that might have been done was not. In an experiment to analyze irreversible work, Joule studied the action of a falling weight attached by a string to a stirrer in a vessel of water (Fig. 4-4). He observed that the temperature of the water rose in proportion to the weight and the distance it fell. The effect of the irreversible work process was to produce a proportional amount

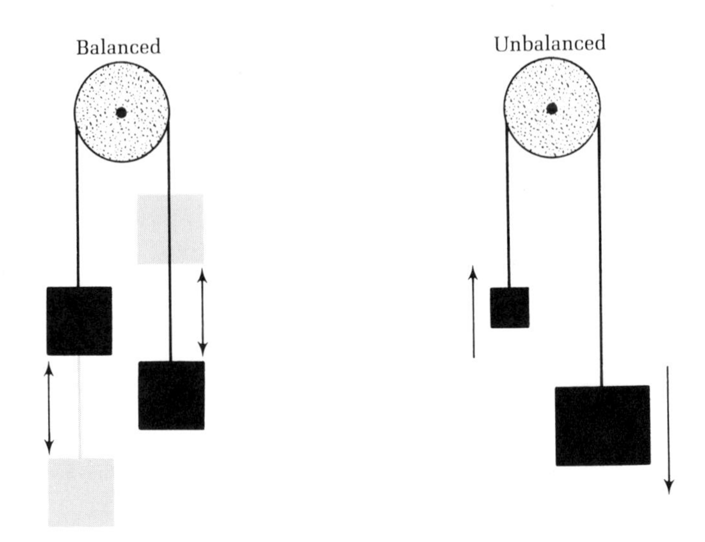

Fig. 4-3. Balanced and unbalanced work effects.

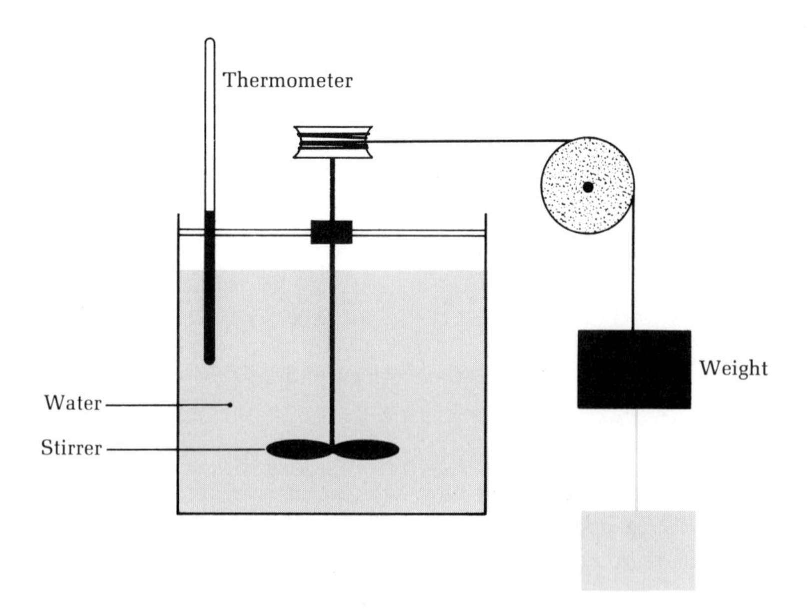

Fig. 4-4. Dissipation of work to produce heat.

of heat. This important result demonstrates the existence of a fundamental relationship between heat and work.

We previously used some of these ideas to describe the basic electrical measurement of a quantity of heat. In particular, the irreversible work process of passing an electric current through a voltage difference presented by a resistor produces a given amount of heat.

The units of work and heat are based on a feature of the basic work processes. If 1 kg is lifted 1 m in a gravitational field of 980 dynes/cm-sec, 9.80 joules of work is done. If this same weight is dropped 1 m to a resting point, 9.80 joules of heat is generated.

4.2 SYSTEMS, SURROUNDINGS, AND RESERVOIRS

Irreversible work results in the production of heat. To find other rules relating heat and work we must experimentally investigate a particular device or system and determine the important properties that affect the work process. In the expansion work process the important properties are the pressure of the system and its change in volume.

In a general experiment we consider the system, a region for work measurement outside the system, and a location for heat measurement outside the system. We shall always assume these three elements have distinct locations in space.

The regions outside the system are called the surroundings. We will designate the system (for example, a confined gas, a chemical reaction, a weight) by a circle, the work measuring device by a square, and the heat measuring device by a triangle (Fig. 4-5).

Heat and work are measured by changes that occur in the external heat and

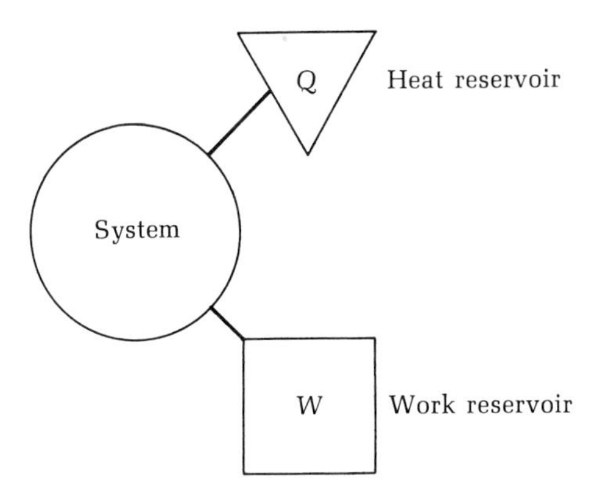

Fig. 4-5. Generalized representation of system and external heat and work reservoirs.

work devices, which are located in regions are called reservoirs. If heat is generated in the work reservoir, we imagine that this heat is transferred to the heat reservoir and measured there. In general, to study how system changes are related to heat and work we examine changes on the system resulting from interaction with the heat and work reservoirs.

Careful definition of the system is necessary. The system must have specific spacial boundaries, such as a gas confined by a piston and a cylinder. Heat and work are transmitted to or from the system by interaction at the boundaries. Heat can flow to the system from the heat reservoir. Work can be done in the external work reservoir if the gas expands to lift a weight. The work is indicated by the lifted weight, which functions as the work reservoir. If the gas expands into a vacuum, no external weight is lifted and no work is done. The expansion alone is not an indication of work being done outside the system.

Irreversible work processes produce heat. If an irreversible work process occurs within the system, an internal heat effect occurs that is not measured by changes in the heat and work reservoirs.

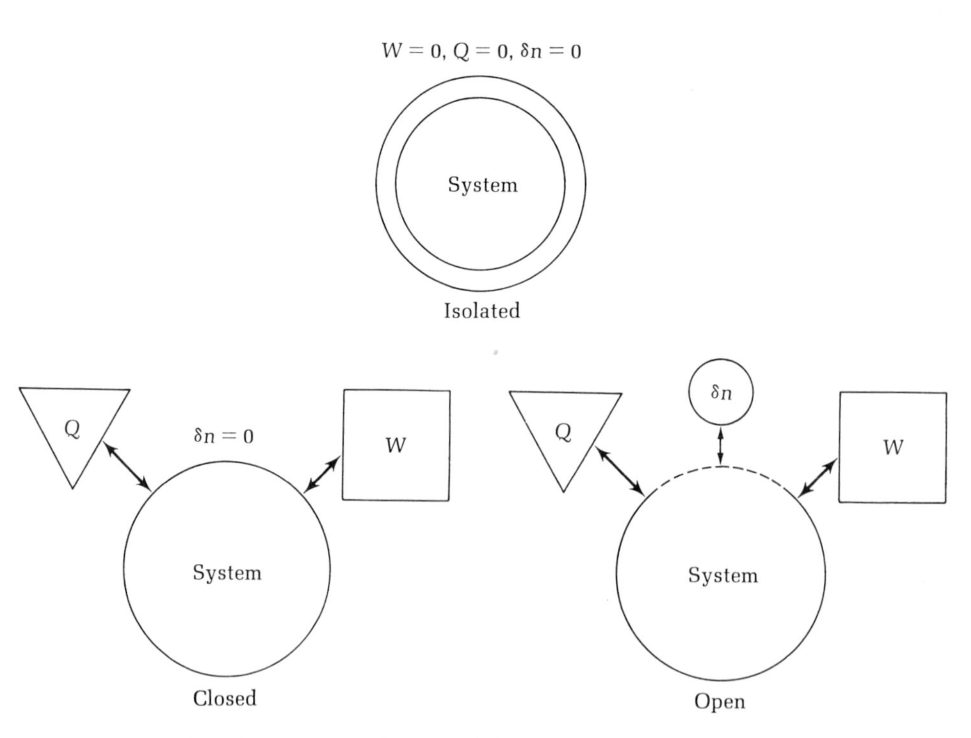

Fig. 4-6. Classification of thermodynamic systems.

Systems are categorized by the types of interaction they can have with their surroundings. In an *isolated* system there is no interaction with the surroundings, that is, no connection with the heat and work measuring reservoirs. In a *closed* system interaction with the heat and work reservoirs is permitted, but there is no material exchange between the system and its surroundings. In an *open* system heat, work, and material exchanges can occur. We denote measured effects in the heat and work reservoirs by Q and W respectively, and any material exchanges between the system and its surroundings by δn. For the three systems:

$$\begin{aligned} \text{Isolated:} &\quad Q = 0,\ W = 0,\ \delta n = 0 \\ \text{Closed:} &\quad Q \neq 0,\ W \neq 0,\ \delta n = 0 \\ \text{Open:} &\quad Q \neq 0,\ W \neq 0,\ \delta n \neq 0 \end{aligned} \tag{4.1}$$

where the symbol $\neq$ means "not necessarily equal to." These three conditions are represented pictorially in Fig. 4-6.

Before we can summarize the results found for various interacting systems, we must define the sign of the heat and work effects, Q and W, measured in the heat and work reservoirs. We assign Q or W a positive sign when heat or work is lost from the reservoir and delivered to the system. A negative sign for Q or W indicates that a reservoir has gained heat or work (Fig. 4-7). This bookkeeping scheme allows us to study any changes a system undergoes in terms of heat and

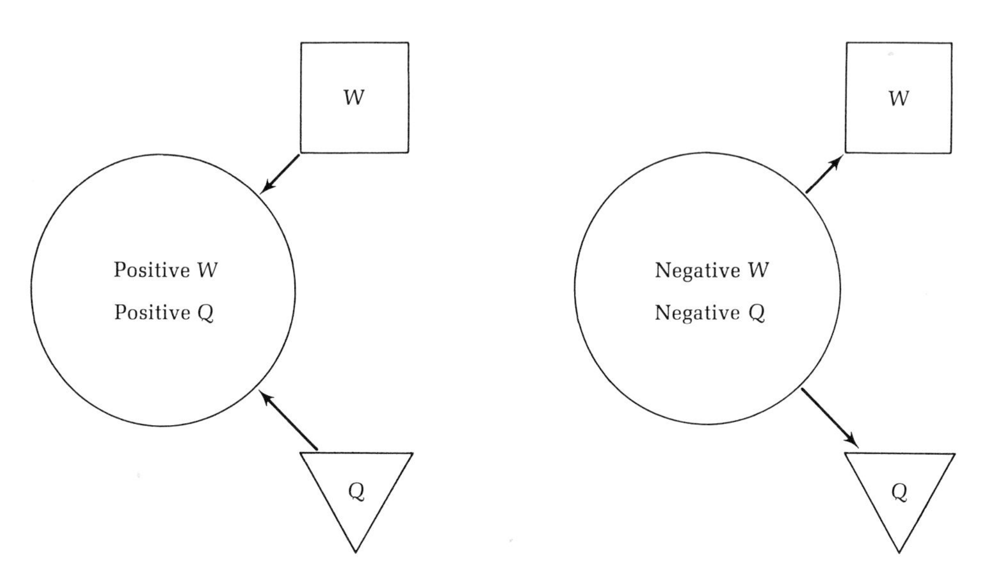

Fig. 4-7. Experimental significance of signs of W and Q.

work, regardless of whether these changes occur by reversible or irreversible processes.

4.3 INTERNAL ENERGY OF A SYSTEM

When a system interacts with the heat and work reservoirs, its properties change. When a gas expands, its volume changes. Its pressure and temperature change also, but in a way that depends on whether the expansion occurs reversibly. The properties of temperature, pressure, and volume are used to define the state of a system.

The state of a system can be changed by adding or removing heat, by changing the volume of the system, or by adding or removing material. Other properties, such as temperature and pressure, depend on how these processes occur. There are many different ways, called *paths*, for a system to go from some initial state to some final state of temperature, pressure, and volume. Each path involves the heat and work reservoirs in a characteristic way.

We denote the measurements of heat and work along path I as Q_{I} and W_{I}, and along any other path II as Q_{II} and W_{II} (Fig. 4-8). For paths with identical initial and identical final states:

$$Q_{\mathrm{I}} + W_{\mathrm{I}} = Q_{\mathrm{II}} + W_{\mathrm{II}} \tag{4.2}$$

Only the initial and final states of the system affect the result given by equation 4.2. The sum $Q + W$ measures a change in a property of the system. We define this

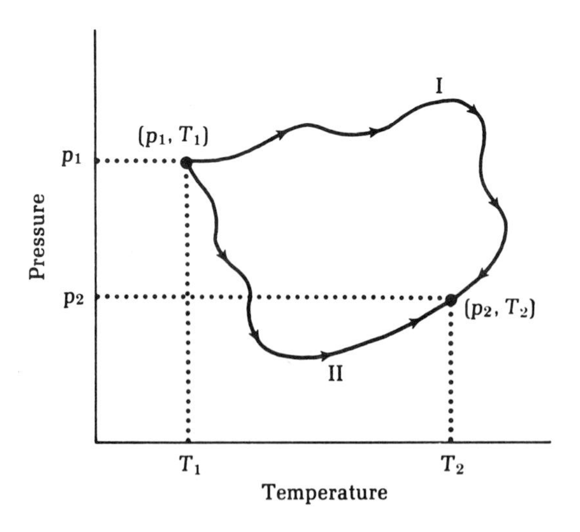

Fig. 4-8. Representation of change of state p_1, T_1 to state p_2, T_2 by two different paths.

property as the *internal energy* and denote it by the symbol E. A change in the internal energy of a system is given by

$$\Delta E = Q + W \tag{4.3}$$

This equation relates the three elements, the system and the two reservoirs, of our experimental set-up. It is completely general although for open systems with material exchange we would have to include appropriate material reservoirs.

4.4 FIRST LAW OF THERMODYNAMICS

Equation 4.3 summarizes a vast array of experience. It is the basis of the first law of thermodynamics, which may be stated as follows: The internal energy, E, is a property of the state of a system, and energy changes are measured by interactions with external reservoirs such that $\Delta E = Q + W$. The quantities of heat and work involved depend on the path followed in changing the state of the system, but the energy depends only on the state.

A quantity of heat can be represented by the integral of the heat capacity:

$$Q = \int C dT \tag{4.4}$$

The value of this integral depends on the path followed in going from the initial to the final state. Similarly, it is necessary to specify the path to calculate W. However, the internal energy change depends only on the initial and final states:

$$\Delta E = E_2 - E_1 \tag{4.5}$$

If one path is more convenient than another for calculating the difference in internal energy, then that path can be used. Calculations of this sort are expressed by integration of differential changes. If we can describe the state of our system by two variables such as volume and temperature, then the internal energy is a function $E(T, V)$. The differential* of E is given by

$$dE = \left(\frac{dE}{dT}\right)_V dT + \left(\frac{dE}{dV}\right)_T dV \tag{4.6}$$

The change, $E_2 - E_1$, is the integral of this expression:

$$E_2 - E_1 = \int \left(\frac{dE}{dT}\right)_V dT + \int \left(\frac{dE}{dV}\right)_T dV \tag{4.7}$$

Thus if we have values for $(dE/dT)_V$ and $(dE/dV)_T$, integration gives ΔE.

The derivatives, $(dE/dT)_V$ and $(dE/dV)_T$, express important relationships between the thermodynamic properties of a system.

*Those familiar with advanced calculus will recognize $(dE/dT)_V$ and $(dE/dV)_T$ as partial derivatives.

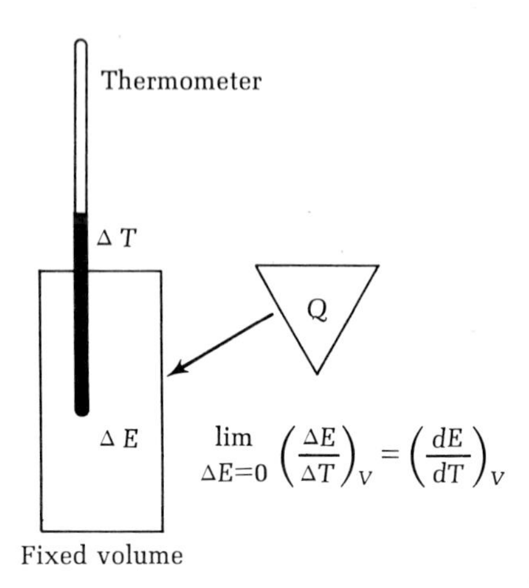

Fig. 4-9. Change of internal energy for constant-volume process gives $(dE/dT)_V$.

The derivative $(dE/dT)_V$ is determined in an experiment in which the volume of the system is fixed (Fig. 4-9), thus eliminating the possibility of expansion work. The change in the internal energy of the system is indicated by an increment of heat dQ added to the system to produce an increase in temperature dT. We previously called this the constant-volume heat capacity, C_V:

$$C_V = \left(\frac{dE}{dT}\right)_V \tag{4.8}$$

The derivative $(dE/dV)_T$ is determined by an experiment at a fixed temperature T in which the volume is changed and ΔE is measured. ΔE can be measured by the sum of the heat and work effects, $Q + W$. Constant temperature is maintained during the expansion process by adding an appropriate quantity of heat to the system as work is being done. For ideal gases held at constant temperature the heat and work effects cancel. There is no change in energy under these conditions, and $(dE/dV)_T$ is zero. One way of conducting this experiment was used by Joule and involves expanding a gas into a vacuum as shown in Fig. 4-10.

The zero value of $(dE/dV)_T$ for ideal gases means that the energy of such materials does not depend on volume but only on the temperature. The internal energy change can be expressed exclusively by the change in temperature. Only the first integral term of equation 4.7 is needed.

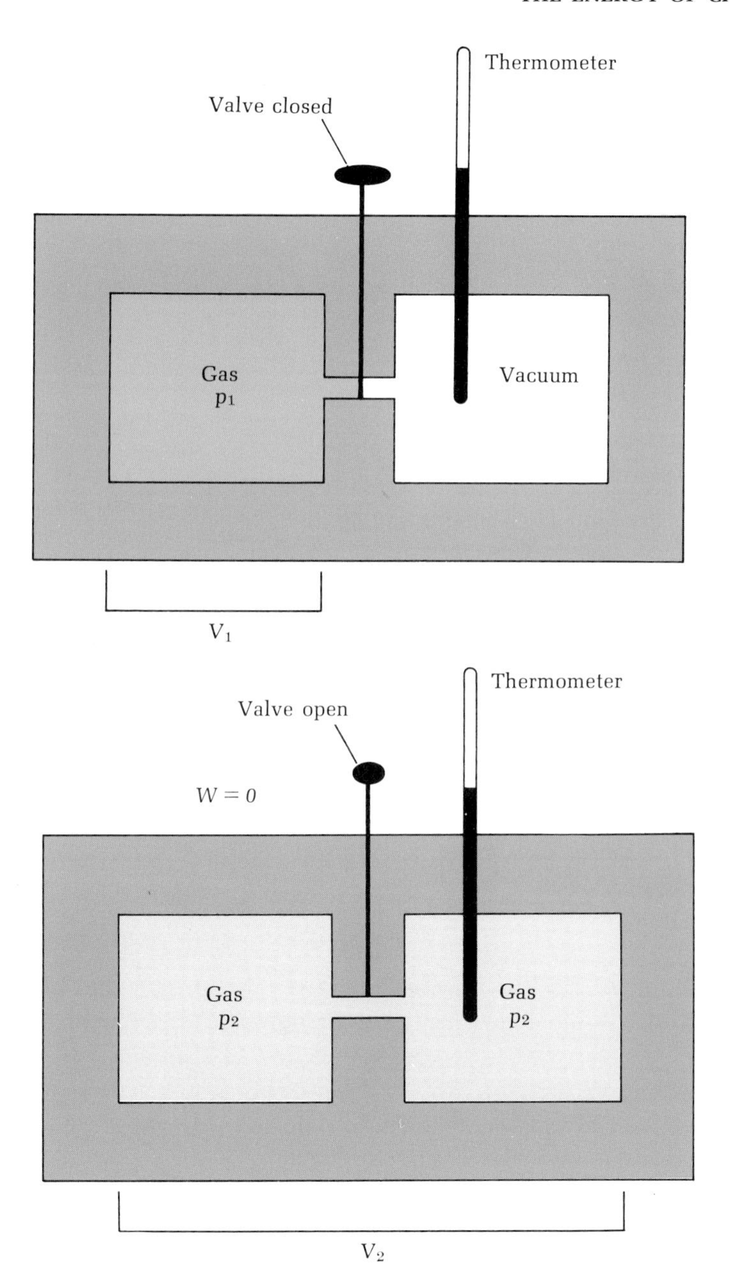

Fig. 4-10. Joule gas-expansion experiment. Joule found temperature did not change upon expansion of gas into vacuum. No work was done by system, so $W = 0$. He also observed that no heat was exchanged between system and surrounding heat reservoir, so $Q = 0$. Thus, the internal energy did not change, and $(dE/dV)_T = 0$ for ideal gases. For nonideal gases, small heat effects are found and $(dE/dV)_T \neq 0$.

EXAMPLE **4.1**

What is ΔE if 5.00 moles of an ideal gas is taken from an initial state of 25°C and 1 atm to a final state of 100°C and 10 atm? The heat capacity of the gas at constant volume is $\overline{C}_V = 7.00 + 0.010t$ cal/mole-deg, where t is in degrees Centigrade.

For an ideal gas, only the temperature change and the constant-volume heat capacity are needed.

$$\begin{aligned}\Delta E &= \int_{t_1}^{t_2} n\overline{C}_V dt \text{ cal} \\ &= \int_{25}^{100} 5.00\,(7.00 + 0.010t)dt \text{ cal} \\ &= 5.00\left[7.00\,(100-25) + \frac{0.010}{2}(100^2 - 25^2)\right] \text{ cal} \\ &= 2859 \text{ cal}\end{aligned}$$

From the information given, we do not know what path was followed in this change of state, so W and Q cannot be calculated.

4.5 WORK AND PROPERTIES OF A SYSTEM

Thus far we have purposefully operationally defined work as the lifting of a weight in an external work measuring reservoir, thereby emphasizing the specific location where the work W is measured. The work is calculated from

$$W = -mg\Delta h \tag{4.9}$$

where m is the mass, g is the gravitional constant,* and Δh is the height through which the weight is lifted. We can now examine the relation of W to specific properties and changes within the system under investigation.

When a system expands reversibly, the pressure of the system is balanced by the external force of the weight acting on the piston (Fig. 4-11). For a small displacement of the piston, we have

$$dW_r = -mgdh \tag{4.10}$$

There is a balance of forces:

$$pA = mg \tag{4.11}$$

*In this text we will assign g a value of 980 cm/sec^2.

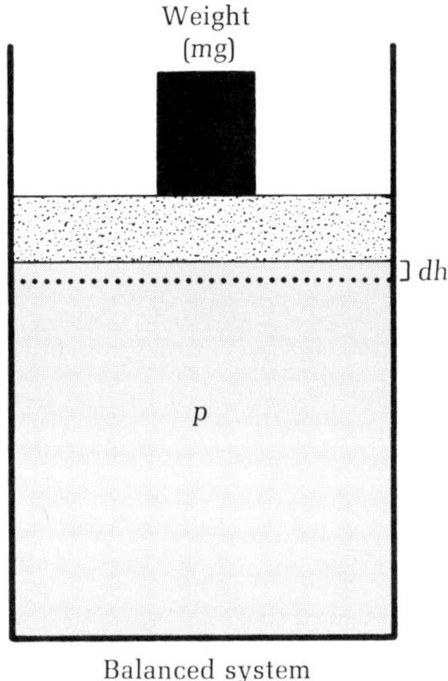

Fig. 4-11. Reversible work of expansion to lift maximum amount of weight.

where A is the area of the piston. Then

$$Adh = dV \tag{4.12}$$

so

$$dW_r = -pdV \tag{4.13}$$

Equation 4.13 is valid only under reversible conditions, denoted by the subscript r. If a smaller weight is placed on the piston, it can be lifted by expansion, but less work is performed even though the same system pressure conditions exist as before. In an irreversible work process, heat is generated internally in place of the full production of work. The total work in any reversible expansion process is the integral of equation 4.13:

$$W_r = -\int_{V_1}^{V_2} pdV \tag{4.14}$$

EXAMPLE **4.2**

If a system expands by the motion of a piston with an area of 5.0 cm^2 to lift a weight of 100 g a distance of 10.0 cm, how much work is done?

$$
\begin{aligned}
W &= -mg\Delta h \\
&= -(100\ \text{g})\ (980\ \text{cm/sec}^2)\ (10.0\ \text{cm}) \\
&= -9.8 \times 10^5\ \text{ergs} \\
&= -9.8 \times 10^{-2}\ \text{joules} \\
&= -\left(9.8 \times 10^{-2}\right)\left(\frac{1}{4.18}\right) \\
&= -2.34 \times 10^{-2}\ \text{cal}
\end{aligned}
$$

EXAMPLE **4.3**

If a system expands reversibly from a volume of 10 liters to a volume of 20 liters by a path given by

$$p = 5 + 3/V + 2V$$

where p is in atm and V is in liters, what is the work of expansion, W_r?

$$
\begin{aligned}
W_r &= -\int_{V_1}^{V_2} p dV \\
&= -\int_{10}^{20} (5 + 3/V + 2V) dV \\
&= -[5\ (20 - 10) + 3\ \ln 20/10 + (20^2 - 10^2)] \\
&= -352\ \text{liter-atm}
\end{aligned}
$$

Without further information, we can say nothing about Q or ΔE.

On a graph of p versus V, W_r is represented by the area under the curve describing the expansion path (Fig. 4-12). In a cyclic path, we return to the

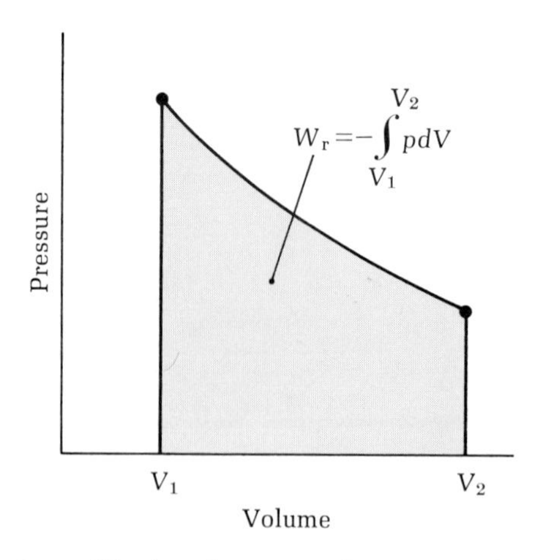

Fig. 4-12. W_r given by area under p-versus-V curve.

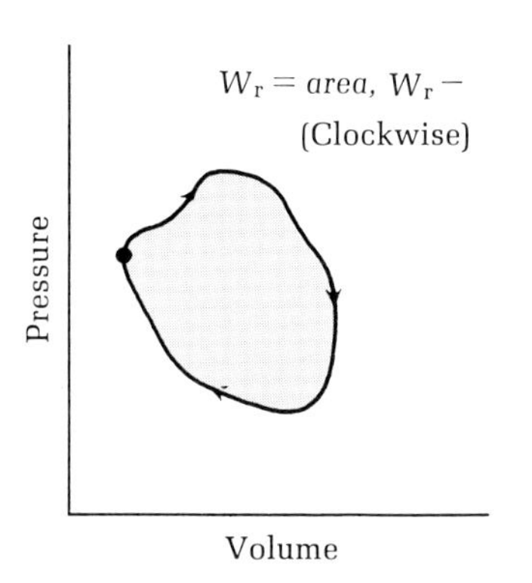

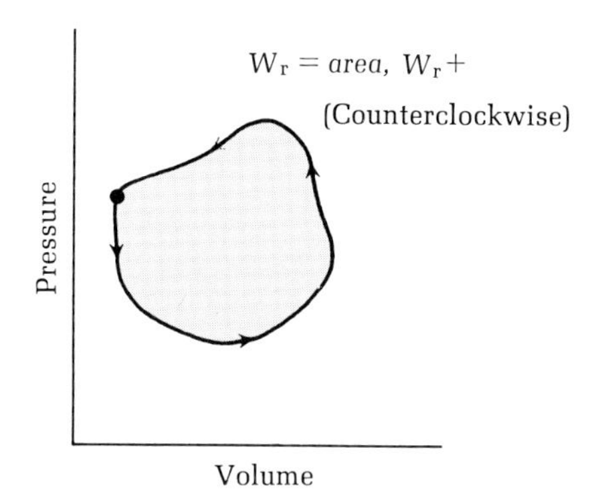

Fig. 4-13. Reversible work effects for cyclic paths on p-versus-V diagrams.

initial state and enclose an area that represents W_r, which in general is not zero (Fig. 4-13).

EXAMPLE 4.4

Suppose a cyclic reversible path is followed as shown in Fig. 4-14. Expansion first occurs at a pressure of 3 atm, resulting in the lifting of a large weight; that is, a large negative amount of work is done on the system. At a fixed volume of 20 liters the system is brought to a pressure of 1 atm. At 1 atm the system is compressed to 10 liters, and a positive amount of work is done on it. Finally, the system is brought to its initial state of 3 atm and 10 liters. Heat transfers have been required to execute these changes.

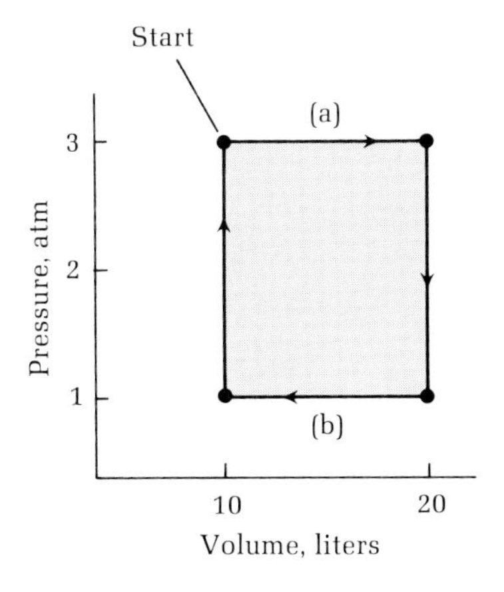

Fig. 4-14. Reversible cyclic path used in example 4.4.

The reversible work is due to the two steps, (*a*) and (*b*), in Fig. 4-14:

$$W_r = -\int_{10}^{20} 3dV - \int_{20}^{10} 1dV = -30 + 10 = -20 \text{ liter-atm}$$

This is equivalent to the area enclosed by all paths: $-(3-1) \times (20-10) = -20$ liter-atm. If the direction of the overall path is reversed, then W_r is $+20$ liter-atm. Since the initial and final states are the same, $\Delta E = 0$ and $Q = -W$.

The sign of W_r is negative for a clockwise cyclic path and positive for a counter-clockwise cyclic path. In considering these paths one should remember that heat exchanges are necessary to cause the system to change its state in the described manner. Expansion work is not the only way that a system can do work, but it is often the most pertinent for the study of the properties of materials.

4.6 CONSTANT-PRESSURE PROCESSES: ENTHALPY CHANGES

The development of specific thermodynamic equations is guided by practical considerations of experimental feasibility. For example, it is practical to conduct an experiment at fixed volume with gases, but not with solids or liquids; fixed volume is difficult to achieve for solids and liquids because whatever contains them would itself expand under the high pressures that result when the volume of a liquid or solid changes. Consequently, we usually consider what happens to solids and liquids under the condition of fixed pressure.

The first law for infinitesimal changes is written

$$dE = dQ + dW \tag{4.15}$$

In the case of reversible expansion work

$$dW_r = -pdV \tag{4.16}$$

So

$$dE = dQ - pdV \tag{4.17}$$

With the system at constant pressure we integrate and get

$$\Delta E = Q_p - p\Delta V \tag{4.18}$$

The heat Q_p as measured for changes on this system at constant pressure gives a measure of the combination of internal energy changes ΔE and expansion work:

$$Q_p = \Delta E + p\Delta V \tag{4.19}$$

This equation suggests that we define a property of the system given by

$$H = E + pV \tag{4.20}$$

We call H the enthalpy of the system. Since E and pV are state properties of a system, H also must be a state property. Changes in enthalpy at constant pressure are directly measured by Q_p as shown by equation 4.19, or:

$$Q_p = \Delta H_p \tag{4.21}$$

EXAMPLE **4.5**

What are ΔH and ΔE for the vaporization of 10.0 g of water at 100°C and 1.00 atm?

The heat required to vaporize 1 g of water is 540 cal. The heat required for 10 g is 5400 cal. Since the vaporization is done at constant pressure, ΔH is 5400 cal.

The change in energy is found by determining the expansion work, $-p\Delta V$. The volume change ΔV is $V_g - V_l$, where V_g is the volume of gas and V_l is the volume of liquid. For 10 g of water, V_g is given approximately by the ideal gas law. (Note: 10 g of water $\cong$ 10 ml.)

$$V_g = \frac{nRT}{p} = \frac{(10.0/18.0)\ (0.082\ \text{liter-atm/deg-mole})\ (373\,°\text{K})}{1.00\ \text{atm}} = 17.0\ \text{liter}$$

$$V_l = 0.010\ \text{liter}$$

$$p\Delta V = (1)\ (17.0 - 0.010) = 17.0\ \text{liter-atm} = 407\ \text{cal}$$

$$\Delta E = Q_p - p\Delta V = 5400 - 407 = 4993$$

The general method for calculating enthalpy changes begins by differentiation of equation 4.20:

$$dH = dE + pdV + Vdp \tag{4.22}$$

We replace dE with the internal energy differential of equation 4.17 to give

$$dH = dQ + Vdp \tag{4.23}$$

For finite changes

$$\Delta H = Q + \int Vdp \tag{4.24}$$

We already have discussed how heat measurements often can be expressed by temperature changes through the quantity called the heat capacity. At constant pressure for a simple system

$$Q_p = \int_{T_1}^{T_2} C_p dT = \Delta H_p \tag{4.25}$$

and at constant volume

$$Q_V = \int_{T_1}^{T_2} C_V dT = \Delta E_V \tag{4.26}$$

These equations summarize the way heat measurements determine enthalpy and internal energy changes under conditions of constant pressure and constant volume, respectively.

The differential forms of these results are

$$dH_p = C_p dT \tag{4.27}$$

and

$$dE_V = C_V dT \tag{4.28}$$

which means that

$$C_p = \left(\frac{dH}{dT}\right)_p \tag{4.29}$$

and

$$C_V = \left(\frac{dE}{dT}\right)_V \tag{4.30}$$

The general method for calculating ΔE and ΔH between initial and final states involves integration along a convenient path that connects the two states. Any path will do since only the initial and final states affect the result. The convenient variables for E are V and T, and the convenient variables for H are p and T. We form the differentials of E and H in terms of their variables and integrate to give the following results:

$$\Delta E = \int \left(\frac{dE}{dT}\right)_V dT + \int \left(\frac{dE}{dV}\right)_T dV \tag{4.31}$$

$$\Delta E = \int C_V dT + \int \left(\frac{dE}{dp}\right)_T dp \tag{4.32}$$

$$\Delta H = \int \left(\frac{dH}{dT}\right)_p dT + \int \left(\frac{dH}{dp}\right)_T dp \tag{4.33}$$

$$\Delta H = \int C_p dT + \int \left(\frac{dH}{dp}\right)_T dp \tag{4.34}$$

In obtaining the equations for ΔE and ΔH we have used the appropriate heat capacities C_V and C_p to express the temperature effects. In the actual execution of

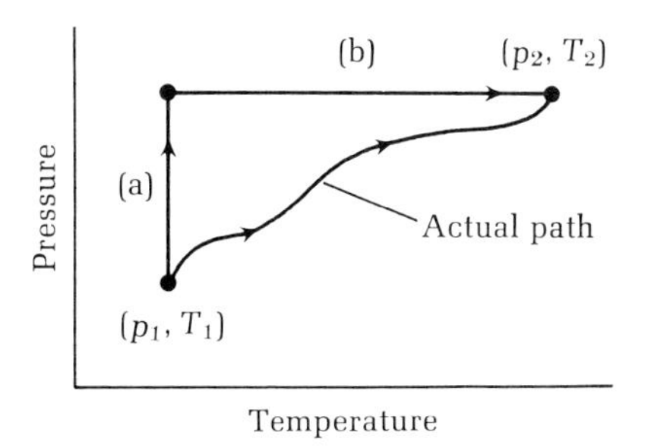

Fig. 4-15. The determination of ΔH by convenient paths, a and b, between initial and final states.

these integrations we follow the most convenient paths. For example, with ΔH we could go at constant pressure to the final temperature and then at constant temperature to the final pressure (Fig. 4-15).

In the following examples we consider in detail the manner in which these equations are used.

EXAMPLE 4.7

What is ΔE for 1.0 mole of CO_2 going from 10.0 liters at 300°K to 2.0 liters at 600°K? Experimentally, it is found that the heat capacity of CO_2 is $\overline{C}_V = 4.2 + 10.4 \times 10^{-3}T$ cal/deg, and that $(dE/dV)_T = 3.59$ atm.

We use equation 4.32 to find ΔE:

$$\begin{aligned}\Delta E &= \int_{300\,°\mathrm{K}}^{600\,°\mathrm{K}} (4.2 + 10.4 \times 10^{-3}T)dT + 24.2 \int_{10.0\text{ liters}}^{2.0\text{ liters}} 3.59dV \text{ cal} \\ &= (4.2)\,(600 - 300) + (5.2 \times 10^{-3})\,(600^2 - 300^2) + (24.2)\,(2.0 - 10.0)\,(3.59) \\ &= 1260 + 1400 - 700 \\ &= 1960 \text{ cal}\end{aligned}$$

Note that the factor 24.2 converts liter-atm to calories.

EXAMPLE 4.8

What is ΔH for 1 mole of CO_2 initially at 200°K and 1 atm and finally at 400°K and 40 atm? The necessary experimental factors are $\overline{C}_p = 6.2 + 10.4 \times 10^{-3}T$ cal/deg-mole and, at 400°K, $(dH/dp)_T = -6.65 + 0.02\,p$ cal/atm-mole.

The calculation then follows from equation 4.34:

$$\Delta H = \int_{200°K}^{400°K} (6.2 + 10.4 \times 10^{-3}T)dT + \int_{1 \text{ atm}}^{40 \text{ atm}} (-6.65 + 0.02p)dp$$
$$= 6.2\ (400 - 200) + 5.2 \times 10^{-3}\ (400^2 - 200^2)$$
$$+ 24.2\ [-6.65\ (40 - 1) + 0.01\ (40^2 - 1^2)]$$
$$= 1240 + 624 - 24.2\ [259 + 16]$$
$$= -4017 \text{ cal}$$

The path followed in this example consists of first changing the temperature from 200°K to 400°K at a fixed pressure (1 atm) and then, at a fixed temperature (400°K) where $(dH/dp)_T$ is known, changing the pressure from 1 atm to 40 atm.

4.7 JOULE-THOMPSON EXPERIMENT

As we have seen, $(dH/dp)_T$ is an important derivative. Numerical values for it can be derived from the Joule-Thompson experiment (Fig. 4-16). Gas flows through a pipe that contains a porous plug. This plug restricts gas flow so that $p_1 > p_2$. In the ideal experiment the gas is unable to gain heat from the surroundings so that $Q = 0$.

Analysis of this experiment in terms of the first law equation (equation 4.3) leads us to consider what happens when a given quantity of gas originally on the left side of the plug goes to the right side. The original state is described by E_1, V_1, T_1, p_1, and H_1; the final state, by E_2, V_2, T_2, p_2, and H_2. Expansion work is required to move the gas from left to right. We can imagine pistons at the dotted lines in Fig. 4-16 moving in the same direction as the flowing gas. The compression work on the left is

$$W_1 = p_1V_1 \tag{4.35}$$

and the expansion work on the right side is

$$W_2 = -p_2V_2 \tag{4.36}$$

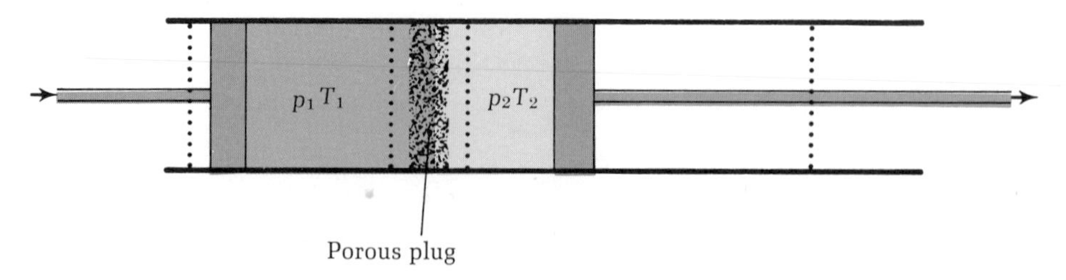

Fig. 4-16. Representation of Joule-Thompson experiment.

Table 4-1. JOULE-THOMPSON COEFFICIENTS, $(dT/dp)_H$ (°K/ATM)

Gas	*273°K*	*373°K*
H_2	−0.013	−0.039
N_2	+0.333	+0.159
O_2	+0.366	+0.193

The energy change when $Q = 0$ is

$$E_2 - E_1 = p_1V_1 - p_2V_2 \tag{4.37}$$

or

$$E_2 + p_2V_2 = E_1 + p_1V_1 \tag{4.38}$$

and

$$H_2 = H_1 \tag{4.39}$$

or

$$\Delta H = 0 \tag{4.40}$$

The enthalpy is constant in this experiment.

We can study the derivative $(dT/dp)_H$ by measuring the ratio of temperature change ΔT to pressure change Δp. For an ideal gas no temperature change is found; $(dT/dp)_H = 0$. In general, for real gases a finite value is found. For some gases the temperature increases, for others it drops, as shown in Table 4-1. The relation between $(dH/dp)_T$ and $(dT/dp)_H$ is given by calculus as

$$\left(\frac{dH}{dp}\right)_T = -C_p\left(\frac{dT}{dp}\right)_H \tag{4.41}$$

The Joule-Thompson effect can be used to produce low temperatures in cryogenic refrigerators. For example, the Joule-Thompson coefficient of O_2 at room temperature is 0.30 °K/atm. If the pressure of O_2 is decreased from 100 atm to 1 atm by a porous-plug expansion, the temperature drops by about 30°C, equivalent to about 210 calories per mole of oxygen. If this cooling effect is repeated, extremely low temperatures can be reached, and eventually the gas can be liquefied.

EXAMPLE 4.9

What is the difference in enthalpy at 1 atm and 100 atm for H_2 at 273°K? The Joule-Thompson coefficient for H_2 at 273°K is −0.013°C/atm. The heat capacity of H_2 at 273°K is 6.85 cal/deg-mole.

For one mole

$$\Delta H = -\int_{1}^{100} C_p \left(\frac{dT}{dp}\right)_H dp$$
$$= -(99)(6.85)(-0.013)$$
$$= 8.8 \text{ cal}$$

Liquefaction of gases by adiabatic expansion: an application of the Joule-Thompson effect

A process for the liquefaction of gases depends on the cooling effect of a Joule-Thompson expansion. By such means, liquid nitrogen, oxygen, and hydrogen can be obtained. When in the liquid state, hydrogen and oxygen can be efficiently stored.

The expansion occurs in a heat-exchanger tube (Fig. 4-17). The gas is cooled not only by the expansion process but also by the counterflow of cooled gas. This is a constant enthalpy process. One mole of gas at initial temperature and pressure p_1, T_1 is converted to x moles of liquid at p_2, T_2 and $1 - x$ moles of gas at p_2, T_2. The initial enthalpy of the gas, $H^G(p_1, T_1)$, is equal to the fraction of gas, $(1 - x)$, times $H^G(p_2, T_1)$ plus the fraction of liquid, x, times $H^L(p_2, T_2)$. Note that the final gas state is at a pressure p_2 and returns from the liquefier apparatus at its original temperature T_1.

$$H^G(p_1, T_1) = (1 - x)H^G(p_2, T_1) + xH^L(p_2, T_2)$$

or

$$x = \frac{H^G(p_2, T_1) - H^G(p_1, T_1)}{H^G(p_2, T_1) - H^L(p_2, T_2)}$$

The numerator is given by equation 4.34. The denominator includes the enthalpy of heating the gas from T_2 to T_1 plus the enthalpy of vaporization, ΔH_{vap}:

$$x = \frac{\int_{p_1}^{p_2} \left(\frac{dH^G}{dp}\right) dp}{\int_{T_2}^{T_1} C_p dT + \Delta H_{\text{vap}}} = \frac{-\int_{p_1}^{p_2} C_p \left(\frac{dT}{dp}\right)_H dp}{\int_{T_2}^{T_1} C_p dT + \Delta H_{\text{vap}}}$$

If oxygen originally at 0°C is expanded from 100 atm to 1 atm, what fraction is liquefied? The boiling point of oxygen at 1 atm is 90°K, and ΔH_{vap} is 1600 cal/mole. Assume that $\bar{C}_p$ for O_2 is 7 cal/deg-mole. The Joule-Thompson coefficient is 0.30°K/atm.

Then

$$x = \frac{\int_1^{100} (0.30)\,(7)dp}{\int_{90}^{273} 7dT + 1600} = \frac{208}{1281 + 1600} = 0.072$$

indicating that 7% of the gas could be converted to liquid in this idealized expansion process. The expelled gas can be compressed, cooled to 0°C, and expanded again in a second cycle.

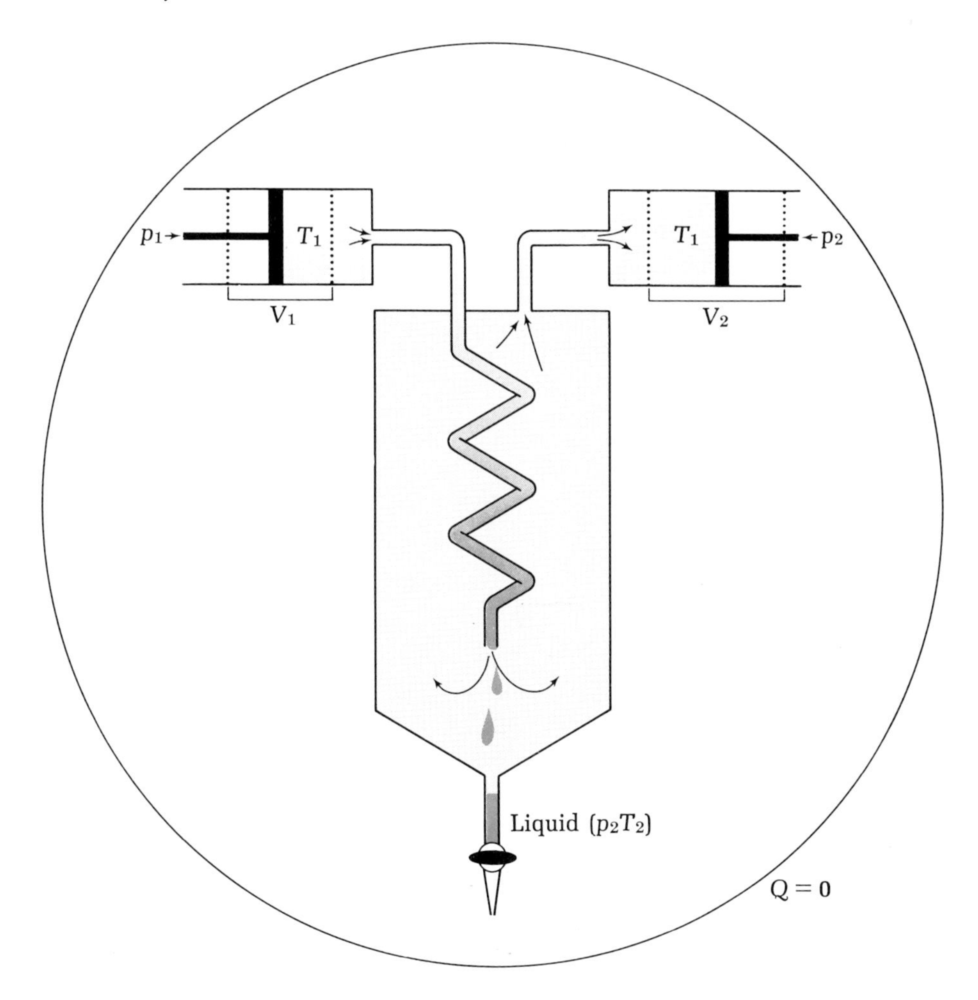

Fig. 4-17. Schematic diagram of apparatus for liquefaction of gases by adiabatic expansion.

4.8 HEATS OF REACTION

In the preceding section we showed how the properties (such as T, p, and V) of a closed simple system can be changed by processes involving heat and work. This led us to the concept of internal energy E. We now extend these arguments to cases where the chemical composition of the system changes.

Let us examine a chemical reaction in a closed system. For example, suppose H_2 and O_2 are initially present as a mixture in a closed vessel. Ignition by a spark causes them to react to produce H_2O:

$$H_2(g) + \tfrac{1}{2}O_2(g) \rightarrow H_2O(g) \tag{4.42}$$

Since this system is closed, there is no involvement of external material reservoirs, although the composition changes. There may be heat and work effects for the process. If the system is to maintain its initial temperature, heat has to be removed. In general, we would record Q and W and determine ΔE. It is important to understand that when writing a chemical equation we are considering a process going from an initial state (reactants) on the left to a final state (products) on the right. We need not specify how this change is accomplished. It might be spontaneous, or it might require external action with the heat and work reservoirs.

Internal energy and enthalpy changes in reactions

For practical reasons we measure heat under the simplest external conditions, at constant volume or at constant pressure. The heats accompanying a reaction under these conditions give either ΔE_V or ΔH_p:

$$\Delta E_V = Q_V \tag{4.43}$$

$$\Delta H_p = Q_p \tag{4.44}$$

Usually additional conditions are specified. For example, the adiabatic condition, where no heat is transferred to the surroundings ($Q = 0$), can be imposed. If we require adiabatic conditions, then by equations 4.43 and 4.44, $\Delta E_V = 0$ and $\Delta H_p = 0$.

It is more common to require constant temperature conditions. At a fixed temperature, the heat accompanying a chemical reaction is measured by the quantity of heat that must be added or removed to maintain constant temperature. If heat is added to the system (positive Q), the reaction is *endothermic;* if heat is removed (negative Q), it is *exothermic* (Fig. 4-18). If the heat of reaction in an exothermic reaction is not removed, the temperature rises.

Heats of reaction for the formation of compounds from their constituent elements are known as *heats of formation*. When the reactants and products are at 1 atm and 298°K, they are said to be in their *standard states*. At constant pressure the heat

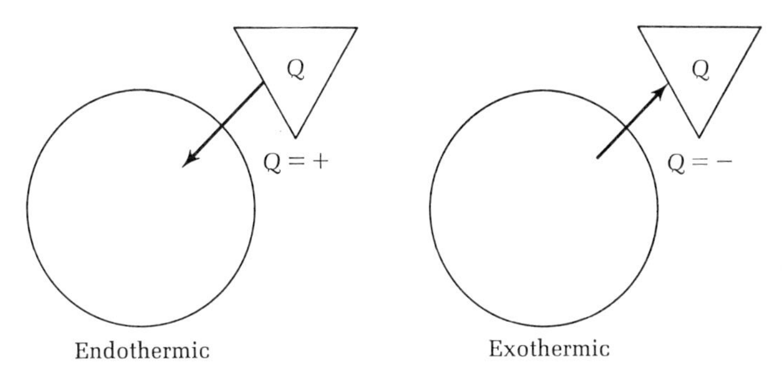

Fig. 4-18. Endothermic and exothermic heat effects.

of reaction corresponds to the enthalpy change (equation 4.44). Enthalpy changes for formation reactions in which the reactants and products are in standard states are designated by ΔH_f^0. Typical examples are

$$H_2(g) + \tfrac{1}{2}O_2(g) \rightarrow H_2O(l) \qquad \Delta H_f^0 = -68.32 \text{ kcal}$$
$$C(\text{graphite}) + O_2(g) \rightarrow CO_2(g) \qquad \Delta H_f^0 = -94.05 \text{ kcal}$$

Enthalpy changes, like energy changes (sec. 4.3), depend on only the initial and final states of the system. The initial and final states of a chemical reaction are specified by the reactants and products, respectively. Thus, we can add or subtract chemical reactions and their enthalpy changes to obtain the enthalpy change for the combined reaction.

For example, if we want the heat of reaction of diamond with oxygen and we have information on graphite and diamond reactions, we can combine the information to obtain the desired result:

$$C(\text{diamond}) \rightarrow C(\text{graphite}) \qquad \Delta H_f^0 = -0.45 \text{ kcal}$$
$$C(\text{graphite}) + O_2(g) \rightarrow CO_2(g) \qquad \Delta H_f^0 = -94.05 \text{ kcal}$$
$$C(\text{diamond}) + O_2(g) \rightarrow CO_2(g) \qquad \Delta H^0 = -94.05 - 0.45 = -94.50 \text{ kcal}$$

A somewhat more involved use of algebraic addition of chemical reactions and their enthalpies is needed to determine ΔH^0 for the combustion of $CH_4(g)$ with oxygen to form $H_2O(l)$ and $CO_2(g)$. The balanced equation is

$$CH_4(g) + 2O_2(g) \rightarrow CO_2(g) + 2H_2O(l)$$

To obtain the desired overall reaction we make use of the following reactions:

$$(a)\ C(s) + O_2(g) \rightarrow CO_2(g) \qquad \Delta H_f^0 = -94.1 \text{ kcal}$$
$$(b)\ H_2(g) + \tfrac{1}{2}O_2(g) \rightarrow H_2O(l) \qquad \Delta H_f^0 = -68.3 \text{ kcal}$$
$$(c)\ C(s) + 2H_2(g) \rightarrow CH_4(g) \qquad \Delta H_f^0 = -17.9 \text{ kcal}$$

We multiply (*b*) by 2 and reverse the direction of (*c*), which is the same as multiplying by -1. We add these two results to (*a*). The algebraic manipulation is $2(b) - (c) + (a)$:

$2(b)$: $2H_2(g) + O_2(g)$	$\rightarrow$	$2H_2O(l)$	$\Delta H^0 = -136.6$ kcal
$-(c)$: $CH_4(g)$	$\rightarrow$	$C(s) + 2H_2(g)$	$\Delta H^0 = 17.9$ kcal
(a): $C(s) + O_2(g)$	$\rightarrow$	$CO_2(g)$	$\Delta H^0 = -94.1$ kcal
$CH_4(g) + 2O_2(g)$	$\rightarrow$	$CO_2(g) + 2H_2O(l)$	$\Delta H^0 = -212.8$ kcal

The sign of ΔH^0 depends on the direction in which the reaction is written; the magnitude of ΔH^0 depends on the amount of material reacted.

Only changes of enthalpy are measured by heat; we cannot measure the absolute enthalpy of a subtance. For convenience, we can arbitrarily assign a value of zero to the enthalpy of elements in their standard states. When we do this, the standard-state enthalpies of compounds are given as H_f^0, where $H_f^0 = \Delta H_f^0$. The enthalpy of 1 mole of a compound is expressed by $\overline{H}_f^0$. A tabulation of useful $\overline{H}_f^0$ data is given in Appendix E.

The general expression used for calculating the enthalpy change ΔH^0 for any reaction under standard state conditions from $\overline{H}_f^0$ data is

$$\Delta H^0 = \Sigma H_f^0(\text{products}) - \Sigma H_f^0(\text{reactants}) \tag{4.45}$$

For example, we calculate ΔH^0 for the preceding reaction of methane with oxygen from the following $\overline{H}_f^0$ values ($\overline{H}_f^0$ is shown below each compound):

$$\begin{array}{lccccc} & CH_4(g) & + \; 2O_2(g) & \rightarrow & CO_2(g) & + \; 2H_2O(l) \\ \overline{H}_f^0(\text{kcal/mole}): & (-17.9) & (0) & & (-94.1) & (-68.3) \end{array}$$

$$\begin{aligned} \Delta H^0 &= [(-94.1) + 2\,(-68.3)] - [(-17.9) + 2(0)] \\ &= -212.8 \text{ kcal} \end{aligned}$$

Another example of such a calculation is as follows:

$$\begin{array}{lcccc} & CaO(s) & + \; CO_2(g) & \rightarrow & CaCO_3(s) \\ \overline{H}_f^0(\text{kcal/mole}): & (-151.9) & (-94.1) & & (-288.5) \end{array}$$

$$\begin{aligned} \Delta H^0 &= (-288.5) - (-151.9 - 94.1) \\ &= -42.5 \text{ kcal} \end{aligned}$$

Since the enthalpy change depends on the amount of material involved, the enthalpies of reactants and products are calculated by multiplying their $\overline{H}_f^0$ values by their coefficients in the balanced reaction equation.

Enthalpy changes for reactions between ions in aqueous solution can also be calculated from tabulated $\overline{H}_f^0$ data. A scale of ion enthalpies of formation is established relative to the hydrogen ion. We arbitrarily assign an enthalpy value of zero to H^+ at one molar concentration and standard state conditions. The standard state

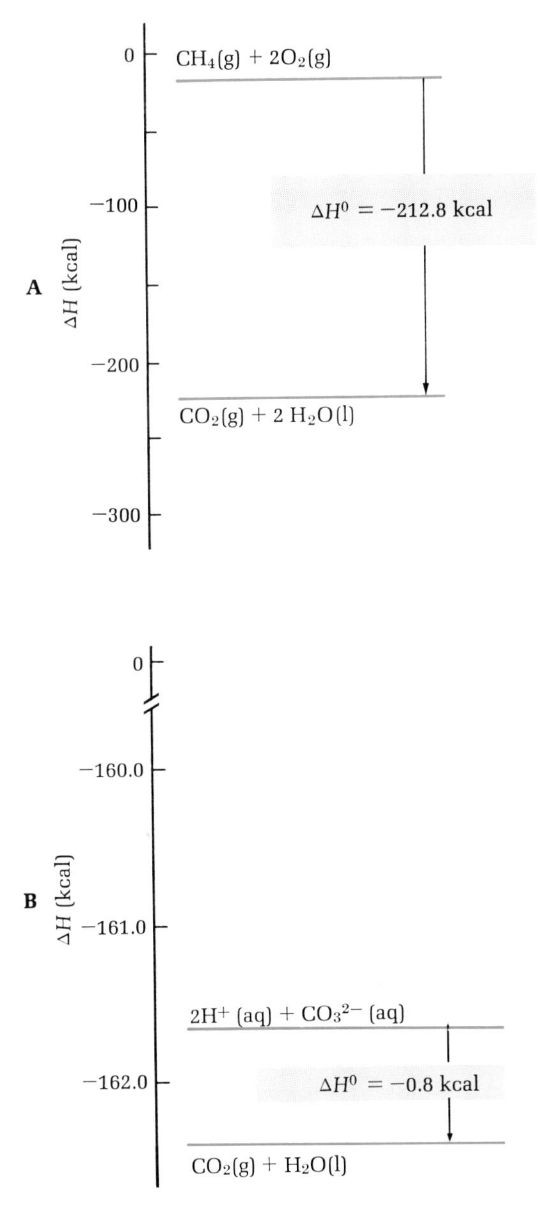

Fig. 4-19. Enthalpy diagrams. **A,** Enthalpy change for reaction of CH_4(g) and O_2(g) to form CO_2(g) and $2H_2O$(g). **B,** Enthalpy change for reaction of $2H^+$(aq) and CO_3^{2-}(aq) to yield CO_2(g) and H_2O(l).

enthalpies of other ions at one molar concentration are expressed relative to the H^+ ion. For example, to calculate ΔH^0 for the reaction

$$\begin{array}{lcccc} & 2H^+(aq) & + \; CO_3^{2-}(aq) & \rightarrow \; CO_2(g) & + \; H_2O(l) \\ \overline{H}_f{}^0(\text{kcal/mole}): & (0) & (-161.6) & (-94.1) & (-68.3) \end{array}$$

$$\begin{aligned} \Delta H^0 &= [(-94.1) + (-68.3)] - [2\,(0) + (-161.6)] \\ &= -0.8 \text{ kcal} \end{aligned}$$

The enthalpy change ΔH^0 can be depicted on a diagram in terms of the numerical values of the enthalpies of formation of the reactants and the products. The enthalpy diagram for the combustion of $CH_4(g)$ with $O_2(g)$ is shown in Fig. 4-19, *A*. This

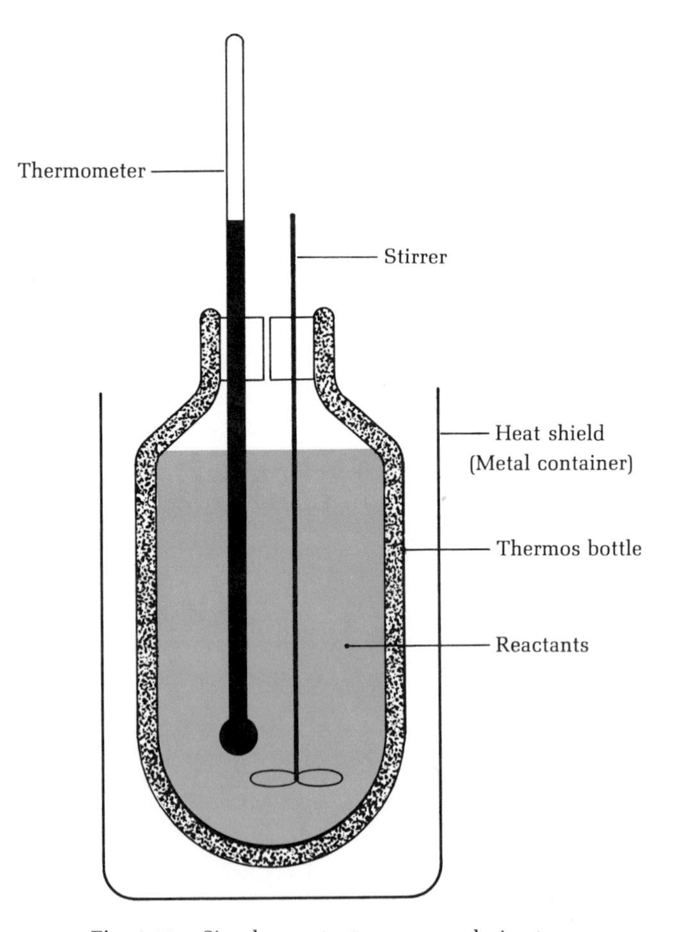

Fig. 4-20. Simple constant-pressure calorimeter.

reaction is exothermic; the products have much lower enthalpies than the reactants. ΔH^0 for the reaction between $H^+(aq)$ and $CO_3^{2-}(aq)$ is depicted in Fig. 4-19, *B*. The zero value in these figures corresponds to the elements in their standard states.

As indicated by equation 4.44, enthalpy changes of chemical reactions are determined by heat measurements at constant pressure. Heat is measured by the use of an instrument called a *calorimeter* (Fig. 4-20). The heat of a reaction is measured by multiplying the temperature change by the heat capacity of the calorimeter. The device shown in Fig. 4-20 is open to the atmosphere during the reaction to insure constant pressure conditions.

4.9 TEMPERATURE EFFECT ON ΔH AND ΔE

Internal energy or enthalpy changes of reactions are tabulated at a specific temperature, for example, at 25°C. However, it is not difficult to calculate the enthalpy changes of reactions at other temperatures. The following scheme serves as a guide for such calculations:

$$
\begin{array}{ccc}
\text{Reactants at } T_2 & \xrightarrow{\Delta H_2} & \text{Products at } T_2 \\
\uparrow \Delta H_R & & \uparrow \Delta H_P \\
\text{Reactants at } T_1 & \xrightarrow{\Delta H_1} & \text{Products at } T_1
\end{array}
$$

where

$$\Delta H_R = \int_{T_1}^{T_2} C_p(\text{reactants})\, dT \tag{4.46}$$

and

$$\Delta H_P = \int_{T_1}^{T_2} C_p(\text{products})\, dT \tag{4.47}$$

C_p(reactants) and C_p(products) are the heat capacities of the reactants and products, and ΔH_2 and ΔH_1 are the heats of reaction at temperatures T_2 and T_1. We know from the first law that enthalpy is a state property. Thus, the enthalpy changes along any two paths between the same initial and final states are equal.

There are two paths in going from reactants at T_1 to products at T_2 in the above scheme. This gives

$$\Delta H_R + \Delta H_2 = \Delta H_1 + \Delta H_P \tag{4.48}$$

or

$$\Delta H_2 = \Delta H_1 + \int_{T_1}^{T_2} [C_p(\text{products}) - C_p(\text{reactants})]\, dT \tag{4.49}$$

This gives ΔH_2 at T_2 in terms of ΔH_1 and the heat capacity difference between products and reactants.

The heat capacities of products and reactants depend on the reaction equation. For example, in the reaction

$$2H_2(g) + O_2(g) \rightarrow 2H_2O(l)$$

the heat capacity of product is $2\overline{C}_p(H_2O)$, where $\overline{C}_p(H_2O)$ is the molar heat capacity of liquid water. The heat capacity of the reactants is $2\overline{C}_p(H_2) + \overline{C}_p(O_2)$. In general, at constant pressure the difference in heat capacity ΔC_p is

$$\Delta C_p = \Sigma C_p(\text{products}) - \Sigma C_p(\text{reactants}) \tag{4.50}$$

For the preceding reaction

$$\Delta C_p = 2\overline{C}_p(H_2O) - 2\overline{C}_p(H_2) - \overline{C}_p(O_2)$$

The analogous equations for calculating the effect of T on ΔE would depend on C_V values:

$$\Delta E_2 = \Delta E_1 + \int_{T_1}^{T_2} \Delta C_V dT \tag{4.51}$$

where

$$\Delta C_V = \Sigma C_V(\text{products}) - \Sigma C_V(\text{reactants}) \tag{4.52}$$

EXAMPLE **4.10**

What is ΔH at 398°K for the following reaction:

$$2C(s, \text{graphite}) + O_2(g) \rightarrow 2CO(g)$$

At 298°K, $\Delta H^0 = -52.8$ kcal, $\overline{C}_p(CO) = 6.96$ cal/deg-mole, $\overline{C}_p(O_2) = 7.02$ cal/deg-mole, and $\overline{C}_p(C) = 2.07$ cal/deg-mole. Then

$$\begin{aligned} \Delta C_p &= 2\,(6.96) - [2\,(2.07) + 7.02] \\ &= 2.76 \text{ cal/deg} \\ \Delta H^{398} &= \Delta H^{298} + \int_{298}^{398} \Delta C_p dT \\ &= -52{,}800 + 2.76\,(398 - 298) \\ &= -52{,}800 + 276 \\ &= -52{,}524 \text{ cal} \end{aligned}$$

Flame temperatures: an application of heats of reaction

Heats of reaction and heat capacities are used to predict the maximum temperatures reached in various reactions. The design of rocket exhaust systems and the calculation of temperatures of metal-cutting flames are two examples where this information is needed. These reactions occur at fixed pressure, so enthalpy changes form the basis of our analysis. We shall assume the entire enthalpy change of such a reaction goes into heating the products. This is the adiabatic condition for which $\Delta H_p = 0$. In general, the temperature changes drastically.

The overall reaction can be considered by two equivalent paths: (1) it occurs adiabatically ($\Delta H_p = 0$) or (2) it proceeds in two steps, reactants first going to products at a fixed temperature T_1 with enthalpy ΔH_1, the system then being heated to T_2 with an enthalpy change of ΔH_2. We depict these two paths by the scheme:

$$\text{Reactants at } T_1 \begin{cases} \xrightarrow{\Delta H_p = 0} \text{Products at } T_2 \\ \qquad\qquad\qquad \uparrow \Delta H_2 \\ \xrightarrow{\Delta H_1} \text{Products at } T_1 \end{cases}$$

Since both paths from reactants at T_1 to products at T_2 involve the same overall enthalpy change, we have

$$\Delta H_p = 0 = \Delta H_1 + \Delta H_2$$

where ΔH_2 is given by

$$\Delta H_2 = \int_{T_1}^{T_2} C_p(\text{products} +)\,dT$$

where C_p(products +) is the heat capacity of the system after the reaction has occurred—including products, uncombined reactants, and inert materials.

In a torch that uses air and propane, the reaction is

$$C_3H_8(g) + 5O_2(g) \quad \rightarrow \quad 3CO_2(g) + 4H_2O(g)$$

with $\Delta H^0 = -488.53$ kcal at 298°K. The heat capacities of the products, $CO_2(g)$ and $H_2O(g)$, are 9 cal/deg-mole and 8 cal/deg-mole, respectively, giving the products a total heat capacity of 3(9) + 4(8) = 59 cal/deg (for simplicity, we neglect the effect of temperature on heat capacity). We assume all the propane is burned by just enough oxygen to produce CO_2 and H_2O exclusively. If this were not the case, the final state would include other materials and the product heat capacity would have to include their heat capacities. For example, if just enough air was used to react with 1 mole of propane, nitrogen would be among the product gases. For each mole of O_2 there would be 4 moles of N_2 with an additional heat capacity of approximately (7)(4)(5) = 140 cal/deg to be added to the heat capacities of CO_2

and H_2O (59 cal/deg) to give a total product heat capacity of 199 cal/deg. The temperature increase of these gases upon absorbing 489,000 cal of reaction heat would be

$$\Delta T = \frac{489,000}{199}\,^{\circ}\mathrm{K} = 2457\,^{\circ}\mathrm{K}$$

One of the hottest flames is that of the hydrogen-oxygen torch. The reaction is

$$H_2(g) + \tfrac{1}{2}O_2(g) \rightarrow H_2O(g) \qquad \Delta H^0 = -57.80 \text{ cal}$$

The heat capacity of the product $H_2O(g)$ is approximately 8 cal/deg-mole; the predicted temperature rise would be about 7200°K. A flame involving the reaction of the atomic species

$$2H(g) + O(g) \rightarrow H_2O(g)$$

with $\Delta H^0 = -218.4$ kcal would have a potential temperature rise of approximately 20,000°K. At these temperatures the water molecule is not very stable and a more probable reaction would be the formation of the radical species HO. To answer such questions as which reaction is important we need additional thermodynamic tools to enable us to calculate how much water dissociates at high temperatures. Consequently, for most practical applications flame-temperature calculations need to be assessed with some additional information. However, the simple calculation can often suffice to give a rough estimate of reaction temperatures.

4.10 BOND ENTHALPIES

The enthalpy of a molecule can be regarded as the sum of the enthalpies of the bonds in the molecule. To establish values for bond enthalpies one considers reactions where specific bonds are broken, such as

$$H_2(g) \rightarrow 2H(g) \qquad \Delta H^0 = 104.18 \text{ kcal}$$

The enthalpy of dissociation for the H—H bond is 104.18 kcal. When several bonds are broken, as in the reaction

$$CH_4(g) \rightarrow C(g) + 4H(g) \qquad \Delta H^0 = 347.95 \text{ kcal}$$

the average dissociation enthalpy of the C—H bond is 397.95/4 = 99.5 kcal. The dissociation enthalpy of bonds is represented by the symbol D.

The average bond enthalpies shown below are the best average values obtained from measurements on many compounds. These values are used (1) to estimate the enthalpy of a given compound relative to its isolated constituent atoms, and (2) to estimate ΔH^0 for a reaction.

REPRESENTATIVE BOND ENTHALPIES (kcal/mole)*

H—H	104.2	C—Cl	78.5
H—C	98.8	C—Br	65.9
H—N	93.4	C—I	57.4
H—O	110.6	Si—O	88.2
H—F	134.6	N—N	38.4
H—Cl	103.2	N=N	100
H—Br	87.5	N≡N	226.2
H—I	71.4	O—O	33.2
C—C	83.1	O=O	119.2
C=C	147	F—F	36.6
C≡C	194	F—Cl	60.6
C—N	69.7	Cl—Cl	58.0
C=N	147	Cl—Br	52.3
C≡N	213	Cl—I	50.3
C—O	84.0	Br—Br	46.1
C=O	173	Br—I	42.5
C—F	105	I—I	36.1

*Adapted from Pauling, L. 1964. College Chemistry, 3rd ed. W. H. Freeman and Co. Publishers, San Francisco.

EXAMPLE **4.11**

Calculate the enthalpy of dissociation of ethylene to its constituent atoms.

$$\mathrm{H{-}\overset{\displaystyle H}{\overset{|}{C}}{=}\overset{\displaystyle H}{\overset{|}{C}}{-}H(g)} \rightarrow 2\mathrm{C}(g) + 4\mathrm{H}(g)$$

$$\begin{aligned}\Delta H^0 &= 4D_{\mathrm{H—C}} + D_{\mathrm{C=C}} = 4(98.8) + 147 \\ &= 395 + 147 = 542 \text{ kcal}\end{aligned}$$

The enthalpy change for forming ethylene from its constituent atoms is −542 kcal. This is the enthalpy of the compound relative to its constituent atoms.

In a reaction between molecules we compute the overall enthalpy change as shown in the following example.

EXAMPLE **4.12**

Calculate ΔH^0 for the hydrogenation of ethylene:

$$\mathrm{H_2C{=}CH_2} + \mathrm{H_2} \rightarrow \mathrm{H_3C{-}CH_3}$$

We begin by considering the enthalpies of dissociation for each compound according to the following scheme:

$$\mathrm{H_2C{=}CH_2} + \mathrm{H_2} \xrightarrow{\Delta H^0} \mathrm{H_3C{-}CH_3}$$

ΔH_a ΔH_b ΔH_c

$$4\mathrm{H(g)} + 2\mathrm{C(g)} + 2\mathrm{H(g)}$$

$$\begin{aligned}
\Delta H_a &= 4D_{\mathrm{C-H}} + D_{\mathrm{C=C}} &&= 542 \text{ kcal} \\
\Delta H_b &= D_{\mathrm{H-H}} &&= 104 \text{ kcal} \\
\Delta H_c &= 6D_{\mathrm{C-H}} + D_{\mathrm{C-C}} &&= 593 + 83 = 676 \text{ kcal} \\
\Delta H^0 &= \Delta H_a + \Delta H_b - \Delta H_c &&= 542 + 104 - 676 = -30 \text{ kcal}
\end{aligned}$$

Thus, the heat of hydrogenation of ethylene is -30 kcal/mole.

4.11 GIBBS FREE ENERGY: CHEMICAL ENERGY

Internal energy is determined by the state of the system. Changes in E are indicated by specific changes in the properties of volume, entropy, and material content. The change in internal energy as determined by the first law is measured by the heat and work interactions between the system and the surroundings. As we saw in Chapter 3, the heat increment dQ equals TdS, where dS is the change in the entropy of the system and T is the absolute temperature. We have also seen (sec. 4.4) that reversible expansion work, dW_r, is determined by $-pdV$. If we change the material content of a system from one form to another, by a chemical reaction or by adding material to the system, there is a change in the chemical energy of the system.

Let G represent the chemical energy. The change in chemical energy is given by the product of the change in number of moles, dn, and a new property called the chemical potential, μ: $dG = \mu dn$.

According to the first law, the overall internal energy change dE of the system, including the change in chemical energy, is

$$dE = dQ + dW + dG \qquad (4.53)$$

In terms of the properties of a system that is undergoing reversible change

$$dE = TdS - pdV + \mu dn \qquad (4.54)$$

The condition of reversibility is needed to identify dQ, dW, and dG, as measured in the external reservoirs, with their corresponding values in terms of properties of the system.

Equation 4.54 applies to a system of one chemical species. When there are many chemical species in the system, a chemical energy term must be written for each. For a chemical species i, the chemical energy change may be written $\mu_i dn_i$. The energy change for a system of many chemical species is thus

$$dE = TdS - pdV + \Sigma\mu_i dn_i \qquad (4.55)$$

The chemical potentials are the key factors affecting a variety of chemical events.

Let us examine the internal energy of a system that has a temperature T, an entropy S, a pressure p, a volume V, n_1 moles of species 1 with chemical potential μ_1, and so on. We can think of building this system in increments of material with the same temperature, pressure, and chemical potentials as the total system. Each of these increments has an entropy dS, a volume dV, and an amount of chemical species dn_1, and so on. Each increment has a fraction, ϵ, of the property in the total system. Thus

$$dS = \epsilon S,\ dV = \epsilon V,\ dn_1 = \epsilon n_1,\ \text{etc.} \qquad (4.56)$$

The energy contained in each increment is $dE = \epsilon E$. If we insert these terms into equation 4.55, we get

$$\epsilon E = T\epsilon S - p\epsilon V + \Sigma\mu_i \epsilon n_i \qquad (4.57)$$

or

$$E = TS - pV + \Sigma\mu_i n_i \qquad (4.58)$$

This same result can be obtained from integration of equation 4.55 at constant T, p, and μ_i. Equation 4.58 allows us to interpret the internal energy of any system in terms of its thermal energy TS, its internal expansion energy $-pV$, and its chemical energy $\Sigma\mu_i n_i$.

The chemical energy, as we will see, is of great importance in understanding chemical phenomena. It is given in terms of the chemical potentials μ_i and the number of moles n_i of species i as

$$G = \Sigma \mu_i n_i \tag{4.59}$$

Willard Gibbs was the first to draw attention to this energy factor, and G is called the Gibbs free energy. In these symbols equation 4.58 becomes

$$E = TS - pV + G \tag{4.60}$$

In terms of the enthalpy ($H = E + pV$), equation 4.60 can be rearranged to

$$G = H - TS \tag{4.61}$$

This form provides a direct way to measure changes in G, as ΔG, from practical experimental measurements on substances and chemical reactions.

Determination of ΔG of reactions from heat measurements

At constant temperature and pressure

$$\Delta G = \Delta H_p - T\Delta S_p \tag{4.62}$$

where ΔH_p is the heat of reaction and ΔS_p is the entropy change upon going from reactants to products at constant pressure. As we have seen from the third law (sec. 3.7), we can evaluate the entropies of reactants and products by measuring heat capacities and transition heats from 0°K to the temperature of interest. The difference between the entropies of products and reactants is

$$\Delta S = \Sigma S(\text{products}) - \Sigma S(\text{reactants}) \tag{4.63}$$

In this way ΔS_p, the entropy change for the reaction at constant pressure, can be evaluated. Superscript ^{0} is used to denote the standard condition of 1 atm and 25°C. The value of ΔH_p is found from heats of reaction at constant T and p, as we have seen in section 4.6. We thus have the experimental means for determining ΔG, the change in Gibbs free energy of a reaction.

ΔG is important in determining whether a reaction will occur spontaneously. We will establish this connection in Chapter 5.

EXAMPLE **4.13**

Calculate ΔG^0 for the conversion of diamond to graphite.

The conversion of diamond to graphite is represented by

$$C(\text{diamond}) \rightarrow C(\text{graphite})$$

The enthalpy change ΔH^0 at 25°C as determined from heats of combustion is -0.450 kcal/mole. At 25°C the entropies of diamond and graphite as determined from heat capacity measurements at low temperatures are 0.58 cal/mole-deg and 1.36 cal/mole-deg, respectively. The entropy change is $\Delta S^{\circ} = 1.36 - 0.58 = 0.78$ cal/deg-mole. The Gibbs free energy change is

$$\begin{aligned}\Delta G^0 &= \Delta H^0 - T\Delta S^0 \\ &= -450 - (298)(0.78) \\ &= -450 - 232 \\ &= -682 \text{ cal/mole}\end{aligned}$$

The standard-state free-energy change for forming a compound from its constituent elements is indicated by ΔG_f^0. Like standard-state enthalpies of formation, the standard-state free energy of an element in its most stable form is defined as zero. The standard free energies of formation per mole $\overline{G}_f^0$ are then tabulated as shown in Appendix E. Changes in free energies for reactions can be calculated from the relation

$$\Delta G^0 = \Sigma G_f^0(\text{products}) - \Sigma G_f^0(\text{reactants}) \tag{4.64}$$

EXAMPLE **4.14**

Calculate ΔG^0 for the reaction

$$\begin{array}{lcccc} & C_2H_2(g) + \tfrac{5}{2}O_2(g) & \rightarrow & 2CO_2(g) + & H_2O(g) \\ \overline{G}_f^0(\text{kcal/mole}): & (50.00) \qquad (0) & & (-94.3) & (-54.64)\end{array}$$

$$\begin{aligned}\Delta G^0 &= -54.64 + 2(-94.3) - 50.00 - 0 \\ &= -293.2 \text{ kcal}\end{aligned}$$

PROBLEMS

1. Calculate the work done in the following processes. The system under consideration is in italics.
   (a) A 15 kg *weight* is lifted 10 m.
   (b) A *spring* whose force F is described the equation

   $$F = -kx$$

   where k is the Hooke's law constant, equal to 300 dynes/cm, and x is the distance stretched from equilibrium. The spring is stretched from $x = 0$ to $x = 10$ cm.
   (c) An *ideal gas* expands against a fixed external pressure of 1 atm from an initial volume of 5.0 liters to a final volume of 15.0 liters.

(d) A 10.0 kg *weight* is dropped (irreversibly) 5.0 m.

(e) In an apparatus as shown in Fig. 4-3, a large weight (10.0 kg) is connected to a small weight (5.0 kg) such that the *large weight* drops 5.0 m and the small weight rises 5.0 m. Consider the large weight as the system and the small weight as the work-measuring reservoir.

(f) An *ideal gas* goes from an initial volume of 5 liters to a final volume of 10 liters by expanding into an originally evacuated 5-liter vessel.

(g) Five moles of an *ideal gas* is compressed isothermally and reversibly at 25°C from an initial volume of 15 liter to a final volume of 3 liter.

(h) Derive an expression for the work involved in reversibly compressing n moles of an *ideal gas* from volume V_1 to volume V_2 if the temperature varies along the compression path by $T = T_1 \ln 10V$, where T_1 is a constant.

2. (a) Calculate the heat generated internally when a 10 kg weight moves through a height of 5 m causing a stirrer to stir 1 kg of water initially at 25°C.

   (b) Assuming the heat capacity of this system is 1200 cal/deg, how much does the temperature increase?

3. One mole of an ideal gas at 27°C and 5.0 atm is expanded isothermally and irreversibly against an outside pressure of 1 atm until the gas pressure equals 1 atm. Find W, Q, ΔE, ΔH, and ΔS.

4. (a) Two moles of an ideal gas at 27°C and 10 atm is expanded adiabatically and irreversibly against a constant pressure of 1 atm such that the volume goes to 10.0 liters. Calculate W, Q, ΔE.

   (b) Assume the heat capacity of the gas, $\overline{C}_V$, is 5 cal/deg-mole. Calculate ΔH and the final temperature of the gas.

5. Calculate the change in temperature that occurs if hydrogen initially at 25°C and 100 atm is expanded through a porous plug to a final pressure of 1 atm.

6. A mole of liquid water is evaporated reversibly at 1 atm and 100°C. The heat of vaporization is 539.4 cal/g. Calculate W, Q, ΔE, ΔH, and ΔS.

7. Using data from Appendix E, calculate ΔH^0, ΔS^0, and ΔG^0 for the following reactions:

   (a) $Ag^+(aq) + Cl^-(aq) \rightarrow AgCl(s)$

   (b) $Mg^{2+}(aq) + 2Cl^-(aq) \rightarrow MgCl_2(s)$

   (c) $C_2H_5OH(l) + \frac{1}{2}O_2(g) \rightarrow CH_3COOH(l) + H_2(g)$

   (d) $C_2H_5OH(l) + 3O_2(l) \rightarrow 2CO_2(g) + 3H_2O(l)$

   (e) $C_2H_4(g) + H_2(g) \rightarrow C_2H_6(g)$

   (f) $CaCO_3(s) + 2H^+(aq) \rightarrow Ca^{2+}(aq) + CO_2(g) + H_2O(l)$

8. From

$$S(\text{rhombic}) + O_2(g) \rightarrow SO_2(g) \qquad \Delta H^0 = -70.96 \text{ kcal}$$
$$S(\text{rhombic}) + \tfrac{3}{2}O_2(g) \rightarrow SO_3(g) \qquad \Delta H^0 = -94.45 \text{ kcal}$$

calculate ΔH^0 for

$$SO_3(g) \rightarrow \tfrac{1}{2}O_2(g) + SO_2(g).$$

9. Calculate ΔH^0 for the reaction

$$2C(\text{graphite}) + 2H_2(g) + H_2O(g) \rightarrow C_2H_5OH(l)$$

from the ΔH^0 values of the following combustion reactions:

$$C_2H_5OH(l) + 3O_2(g) \rightarrow 2CO_2(g) + 3H_2O(g) \qquad \Delta H^0 = -258.4\,\text{kcal}$$
$$2C(\text{graphite}) + 2O_2(g) \rightarrow 2CO_2(g) \qquad \Delta H^0 = -188.1\,\text{kcal}$$
$$2H_2(g) + O_2(g) \rightarrow 2H_2O(g) \qquad \Delta H^0 = -136.6\,\text{kcal}$$

10. Calculate ΔH for the following reaction at 500°K:

$$CO(g) + \tfrac{1}{2}O_2(g) \rightarrow CO_2(g)$$

Obtain the necessary $\overline{H}_f{}^0$ and ΔC_p values from Appendix E.

11. Calculate the highest temperature expected for the following reaction (the acetylene torch) at constant pressure:

$$C_2H_2(g) + \tfrac{5}{2}O_2(g) \rightarrow 2CO_2(g) + H_2O(g)$$

Look in Appendix E for $\overline{H}_f{}^0$ and $\overline{C}_p$ values.

12. Calculate the maximum temperature of a Bunsen burner that burns propane in air. Assume air consists of O_2 and N_2 in the molar ratio 1:4. Assume the burner uses propane as follows:

$$C_3H_8(g) + 5O_2(g) \rightarrow 3CO_2(g) + 4H_2O(g)$$

Hint: Remember the products also consist of a certain amount of $N_2(g)$.

13. One mole of nitroglycerine is confined to a volume of 200 ml. Assume the reaction at 25°C is

$$C_3H_5N_3O_9(l) \rightarrow 3CO_2(g) + \tfrac{5}{2}H_2O(g) + \tfrac{3}{2}N_2(g) + \tfrac{1}{4}O_2(g) \qquad \Delta H^0 = -337\ \text{kcal}$$

The $\overline{C}_V$ values in cal/mole-deg are $CO_2(g)$, 7.0; $H_2O(g)$, 7.0; $N_2(g)$, 5.0; and $O_2(g)$, 5.0.
(a) Calculate the maximum temperature expected for this reaction.
(b) If the gaseous products behave ideally, what is the pressure at this maximum temperature?

14. From bond enthalpy data on p. 115, estimate ΔH for the following reactions:
(a) $C_2H_2(g) + 2H_2(g) \rightarrow C_2H_6(g)$
(b) H—N=N—H(g) + $H_2(g)$ → H_2N—NH_2(g) (drawn with two H on each N)
(c) $C_3H_8(g) + 5O_2(g) \rightarrow 3CO_2(g) + 4H_2O(g)$
(d) $3H_2(g) + N_2(g) \rightarrow 2NH_3(g)$

5 THE CRITERIA OF SPONTANEITY

The *second law of thermodynamics* states that when spontaneous events occur in an isolated system, the entropy of the system always increases. The law is based on the experimental observation that whenever irreversible work processes occur, heat is generated. When a weight is dropped to the floor or when electric current flows through a resistor, heat is generated. Both processes could have produced work if they had been carried out reversibly. Only in the case of irreversible work processes is heat generated. We have discussed these features of heat and work in section 4.1. Now we will examine the properties of a system that affect work and heat, particularly the thermal property of entropy. To study these properties we must consider reversible processes where work can be measured in an external work reservoir. We will summarize the results of such studies in the following sections. Then we will examine the detailed features of irreversible processes.

5.1 ENTROPY AND THE CARNOT CYCLE

As we saw in the discussion of the third law, the entropy of any system is a measurable property. Adding or removing heat from an object is equivalent to increasing or decreasing its entropy. The incremental change in the entropy of the system is related to the incremental quantity of heat in the surroundings by $dS = dQ/T$. For this relation to be true, no irreversible work processes may occur within the system.

Any object can be used as a device to transfer entropy. We can think of such an object as an entropy "elevator." The operation of a conventional elevator consists of increasing its mass load at a certain initial height h_{ini} by an amount dm, shutting its door, lowering the elevator to a height h_{fin} where the mass dm is removed, and finally returning the elevator to the initial height h_{ini}. The elevator is then in its initial state; however, an increment of work $-dW$ has been performed for the mass transport according to $(h_{\text{ini}} - h_{\text{fin}})gdm$.

The entropy "elevator" functions in an analogous way: the entropy corresponds to the mass; the temperature, to the height. Consider four steps of a cycle starting with the system at an initial temperature T_{ini}. (1) The entropy content of the system is increased by dS by adding heat at constant temperature T_{ini}; (2) without changing the entropy of the system, the temperature is changed to T_{fin} (for example, if the system is a gas, a reversible adiabatic expansion of the gas lowers its temperature); (3) at T_{fin}, a quantity of heat with entropy dS is removed; and (4) the system is returned to its initial temperature without changing its entropy. The overall result of this cyclical process is to transfer an amount of entropy dS from an initial temperature T_{ini} to a final temperature T_{fin}. The work, $-dW$, measured in the external work reservoir, is found to be $(T_{ini} - T_{fin})dS$, which describes the relation between work and the properties T and S of the system.

We have used the important fact that entropy is a property of any object. This means that for the system to return to the same initial state the amount of entropy added in the first stage of the cycle has to equal the amount removed in the later stage.

The entropy elevator cycle was first analyzed by Carnot. The entropy and temperature of the object system during the cycle is shown in Fig. 5-1. The work performed is the area enclosed by the rectangular path.

At the same time the temperature-entropy state of the system is following this rectangular path, other variables of the system are being changed. The simultaneous pressure-volume path for an ideal-gas system is shown in Fig. 5-2; the force-length path for a rubber-band system is shown in Fig. 5-3. Any material can be used to transport entropy between two temperatures.

It is always possible to analyze cyclic paths in terms of a series of rectangular path increments. The overall work done is the area enclosed by the cyclic path (Fig. 5-4). The direction in which the path is traveled determines the sign of the work done on the work reservoir $(-W)$; a clockwise path gives a positive value.

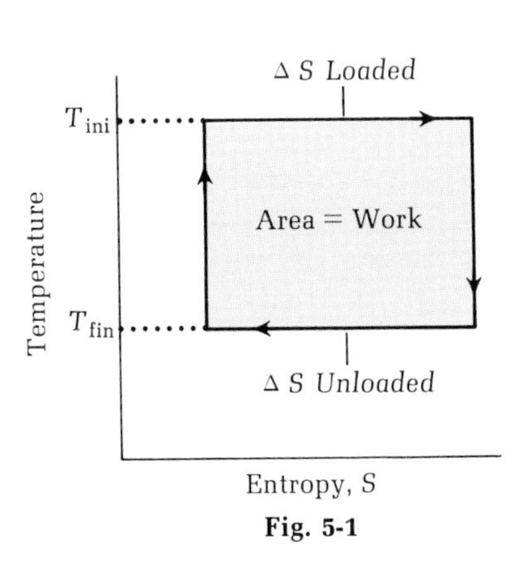

Fig. 5-1

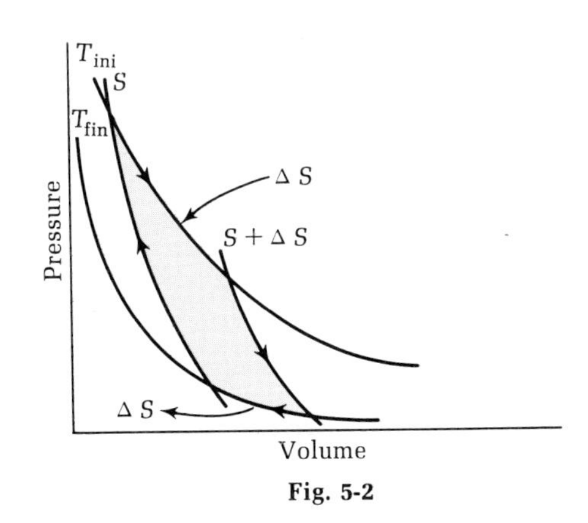

Fig. 5-2

Fig. 5-1. T-versus-S diagram for operation of entropy elevator.
Fig. 5-2. p-versus-V diagram of ideal gas used in Carnot cycle to transport entropy ΔS from T_{ini} to T_{fin}. Constant entropy paths denoted by S and $S + \Delta S$.

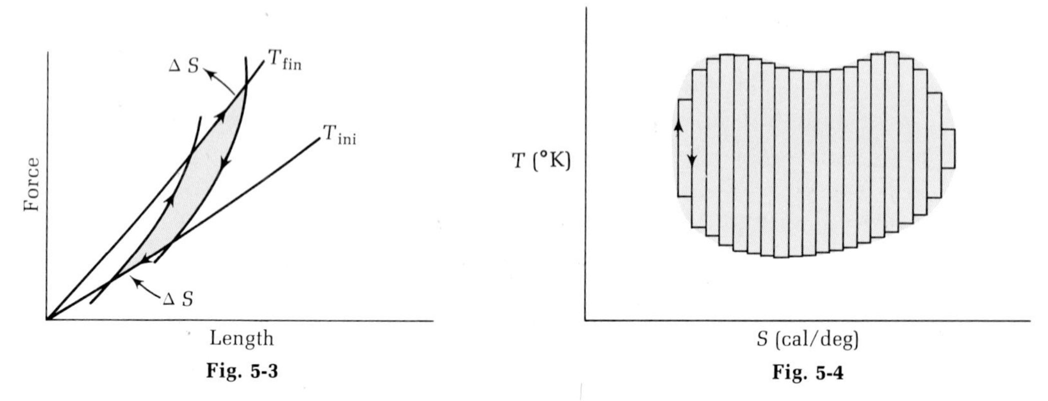

Fig. 5-3. Force-versus-length diagram of rubber band in Carnot cycle.
Fig. 5-4. Representation of complex cyclic path by series of incremental Carnot cycles.

EXAMPLE **5.1**

The diagrams in Fig. 5-5 show three different paths where entropy is transferred between different temperatures. Calculate the work done on the work reservoir in these processes.

$-W$ = area of TS diagram (A clockwise path gives a positive result; a counterclockwise path gives a negative result.)

For Fig. 5-5, *A:*

$-W = (500 - 200)\ 6 = 1800$ cal. A clockwise path is followed, so work is obtained in reservoir; that is, work is done on the reservoir.

For Fig. 5-5, *B:*

$-W = \frac{1}{2} \times 300 \times 6 = -900$ cal. A counterclockwise path is followed, so work is done on the system. The area is given by calculation of the area of a triangle.

For Fig. 5-5, *C:*

$-W = \pi \times 150 \times 3 = 1416$ cal. A clockwise path is followed, so work is done by the system. The area is given by calculation of the area of an ellipse.

In the reversible transfer of entropy from one temperature to another we obtain work if the transfer occurs from a higher to a lower temperature. This is called the *natural direction.* The ideal steam engine functions in this way. The reverse

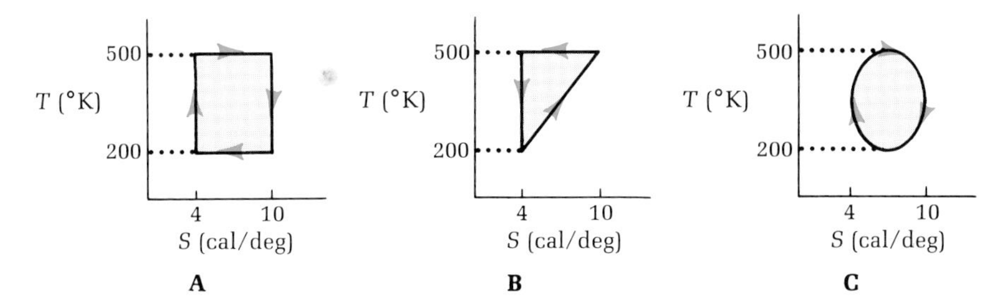

Fig. 5-5. Cyclic paths used in example 5.1.

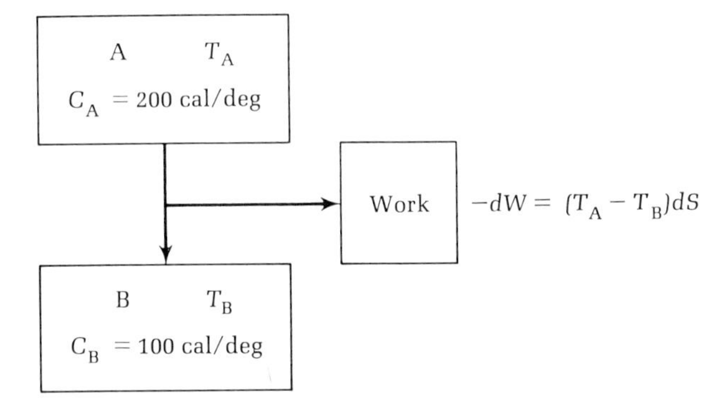

Fig. 5-6. Thermal objects A and B used in example 5.3.

situation, in which entropy is transferred from a lower to a higher temperature, requires the input of work. This is called the *unnatural direction*. A refrigerator works in this way.

EXAMPLE 5.2

Calculate the maximum work that can be done by entropy transfer between objects A and B, whose initial temperatures are $T_A{}^0 = 1000\,°K$ and $T_B{}^0 = 500\,°K$, and whose heat capacities are $C_A = 200$ cal/deg and $C_B = 100$ cal/deg.

We can express the increment of work done, $-dW$, in an incremental transfer of entropy dS from T_B to T_A in terms of the heat capacities of the two objects (Fig. 5-6):

$$-dW = (T_A - T_B)dS$$

By adding all work increments as the temperature of the objects change, we obtain the total work. The entropy transferred, dS, equals the specific changes of entropy in objects A and B:

$$dS = -dS_A = dS_B$$

In terms of heat capacities,

$$dS = \frac{-C_A dT_A}{T_A} = \frac{C_B dT_B}{T_B}$$

This last equation can be integrated to calculate the final temperature reached by both objects, T^*:

$$\int_{T_A{}^0}^{T^*} \frac{-C_A dT_A}{T_A} = \int_{T_B{}^0}^{T^*} \frac{C_B dT_B}{T_B}$$

or

$$C_A \ln \frac{T^*}{T_A{}^0} + C_B \ln \frac{T^*}{T_B{}^0} = 0$$

and

$$T^* = [(T_A{}^0)^{C_A} (T_B{}^0)^{C_B}]^{1/(C_A + C_B)}$$

In this example

$$T^* = (1000)^{2/3} (500)^{1/3} = 794\,°\text{K}$$

The work can now be calculated:

$$-W = \int (T_A - T_B) dS = -\int_{T_A{}^0}^{T^*} T_A dS_A - \int_{T_B{}^0}^{T^*} T_B dS_B$$

or

$$\begin{aligned} -W &= -\int_{T_A{}^0}^{T^*} C_A dT_A - \int_{T_B{}^0}^{T^*} C_B dT_B \\ &= -(794 - 1000)\ 200 - (794 - 500)\ 100 \\ &= 11{,}800 \text{ cal} \end{aligned}$$

5.2 ENTROPY GENERATION

Whenever an irreversible work process occurs, heat is generated, resulting in an increase in the entropy of the system, which we shall denote by ΔS_i.

EXAMPLE 5.3

Suppose a 5 kg weight is dropped 10 m into a bucket of ice and water at 273 °K. How much entropy is generated, and how much ice is melted?

The irreversible work is converted to heat. The amount of entropy generated is reflected by the melting ice. The work lost equals the heat generated:

$$(h_{\text{ini}} - h_{\text{fin}})mg = (980)\,(10^3)\,(5 \times 10^3)\,(2.39 \times 10^{-8})\ \text{cal}$$
$$= 117.1$$

The heat generated, Q_{i}, is related to the generated entropy, ΔS_{i}, at constant temperature by

$$T\Delta S_{\text{i}} = Q_{\text{i}}$$

or

$$\Delta S_{\text{i}} = \frac{Q_{\text{i}}}{T} = \frac{117.1}{273} = 0.429\ \text{cal/deg}$$

This amount of entropy is generated in the system, so the entropy of the system has increased by this amount.

It takes 80 cal to melt 1 g of ice, so 117.1/80 = 1.46 g of ice are melted.

The irreversible expansion of a gas is an irreversible work process in which heat or entropy is generated internally.

EXAMPLE **5.4**

Calculate the entropy generated when an ideal gas expands irreversibly from V_1 to V_2.

The irreversible work lost for an increment of expansion dV is pdV. This irreversible work generates heat dQ_{i}, or TdS_{i}. Thus we have

$$pdV = TdS_{\text{i}}$$

or

$$\Delta S_{\text{i}} = \int dS_{\text{i}} = \int_{V_1}^{V_2} \frac{p}{T}\, dV$$

For the ideal gas, $p/T = nR/V$ and

$$\Delta S_i = \int_{V_1}^{V_2} \frac{nR}{V}\, dV = nR \ln \frac{V_2}{V_1}$$

What happens when heat flows irreversibly from one temperature region to another? The irreversible work lost by this entropy transfer generates an internal heat effect. Thus, more entropy arrives at the region of the lower temperature than is taken from the region of the higher temperature.

EXAMPLE 5.5

Two objects, A and B, with heat capacities, $C_A = 200$ cal/deg and $C_B = 100$ cal/deg, at initial temperatures, $T_A{}^0 = 1000\,°K$ and $T_B{}^0 = 500\,°K$, are placed in contact. What temperature is reached, and how much entropy is generated?

An increment of entropy dS is taken from region A, so the entropy change of A is dS_A:

$$dS = -dS_A$$

Furthermore

$$-dS_A = \frac{-C_A dT_A}{T_A}$$

since

$$dQ_A = C_A dT_A$$

Also

$$dQ_A = -dQ_B$$

or

$$C_A dT_A = -C_B dT_B$$

The entropy generated, dS_{i}, in the region of the lower temperature, T_B, where the irreversible work is lost, is given by

$$(T_A - T_B)dS = T_B dS_{\mathrm{i}}$$

so that

$$dS_{\mathrm{i}} = \left(\frac{T_A - T_B}{T_B}\right) dS$$

or

$$dS_{\mathrm{i}} = \frac{C_A dT_A}{T_A} + \frac{C_B dT_B}{T_B}$$

This last equation shows that the entropy generated is the sum of entropy changes in objects A and B. Integration gives the total entropy generated:

$$\Delta S_{\mathrm{i}} = \int_{T_A{}^0}^{T^*} \frac{C_A dT_A}{T_A} + \int_{T_B{}^0}^{T^*} \frac{C_B dT_B}{T_B}$$

where T^* is the final temperature. In our example, T^* is found by integrating $C_A dT_A = -C_B dT_B$ as follows:

$$\int_{1000}^{T^*} 200 dT_A = -\int_{500}^{T^*} 100 dT_B$$

or

$$T^* = 833\,^\circ\mathrm{K}$$

The entropy generated is then

$$\Delta S_{\mathrm{i}} = C_A \ln \frac{T^*}{T_A{}^0} + C_B \ln \frac{T^*}{T_B{}^0}$$

$$\Delta S_{\mathrm{i}} = 200 \ln \frac{833}{1000} + 100 \ln \frac{833}{500} = 14.5 \text{ cal/deg}$$

This generated entropy represents the total entropy change of the entire system.

In example 5.2, for the case of the reversible transfer of entropy, no entropy was generated. Work was produced externally. In example 5.5, irreversible work is lost with the consequent generation of entropy.

5.3 ENTROPY CHANGES IN A SYSTEM

The entropy content of any system can be changed by two general methods (Fig. 5-7). First, the entropy may be changed by heat transfer, dQ, between the system and the external heat reservoir. The entropy change for such an external transfer is symbolized dS_{e}. The quantity dS_{e} may result in an increase or a decrease in the entropy of the system, depending on whether heat is supplied or removed, respectively. The second way in which the entropy of the system can be changed is by an irreversible work process in the system. As we have seen, an irreversible work process always generates entropy, the incremental change being symbolized by dS_{i}. Note that dS_{i} is always positive, whereas dS_{e} can be positive or negative.

In general, a change in the entropy of a system, dS, is given by the sum

$$dS = dS_{\mathrm{e}} + dS_{\mathrm{i}} \tag{5.1}$$

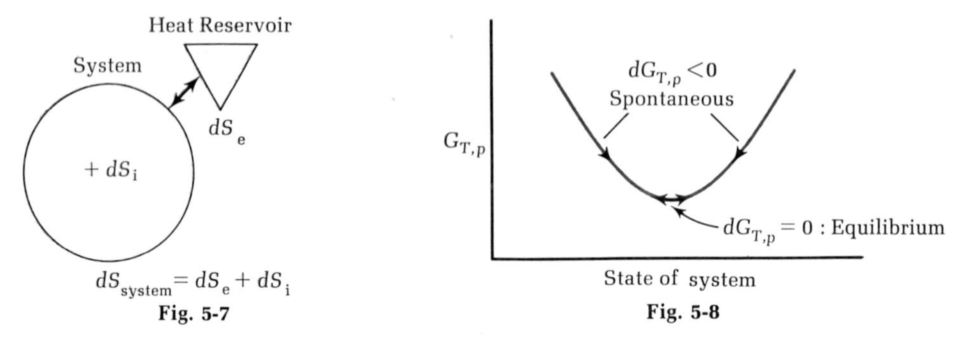

Fig. 5-7. Diagram showing ways entropy of system can be changed: (1) by external transfer dS_e and (2) by spontaneous internal work processes with creation of entropy dS_i.
Fig. 5-8. State of system as function of $G_{T,p}$. At equilibrium, $dG_{T,p} = 0$.

In an isolated system, $dS_e = 0$, so that $dS = dS_i$. In a system where no irreversible work processes occur, $dS_i = 0$, so that $dS = dS_e$.

5.4 GIBBS FREE ENERGY CRITERION OF SPONTANEOUS PROCESSES

If the temperature and pressure are held constant, equation 5.1 relates to the change in Gibbs free energy. By multiplying equation 5.1 by T, we get

$$TdS = TdS_e + TdS_i \tag{5.2}$$

At constant pressure, $TdS_e = dQ_p = dH_p$. Inserting this result into equation 5.2 and rearranging, we have

$$-TdS_i = dH_p - TdS \tag{5.3}$$

We have already seen that

$$dG_{T,p} = dH_p - TdS_p \tag{5.4}$$

so from equation 5.3

$$dG_{T,p} = -TdS_i \tag{5.5}$$

Thus, $dG_{T,p}$ must be a negative quantity for irreversible work processes, which are called *spontaneous processes*.

$$dG_{T,p} < 0, \text{ spontaneous processes} \tag{5.6}$$

If $dG_{T,p}$ is zero, no irreversible work process can occur within the system, and the system is said to be at *equilibrium*.

$$dG_{T,p} = 0, \text{ equilibrium} \tag{5.7}$$

The Gibbs free energy of a system under constant T and p, $G_{T,p}$, will therefore decrease spontaneously to a minimum value at which the system is at equilibrium (Fig. 5-8).

The entropy generated, ΔS_i, in a spontaneous chemical reaction at constant temperature T is given from equation 5.5 as

$$\Delta S_i = -\frac{\Delta G_{T,p}}{T} \tag{5.8}$$

The entropy change of the reaction, ΔS, is given by the difference between the entropies of products and reactants as calculated by equation 4.62. The entropy exchanged with the surroundings, ΔS_e, is determined by integrating equation 5.1 to give

$$\Delta S = \Delta S_e + \Delta S_i \tag{5.9}$$

We can calculate ΔS_e from the following equation:

$$\Delta S_e = \Delta S - \Delta S_i \tag{5.10}$$

or

$$\Delta S_e = \Delta S - \frac{\Delta G_{T,p}}{T} \tag{5.11}$$

This last equation is valid only for a totally irreversible reaction where equation 5.8 can be used. Under these circumstances we can identify the terms on the right of equation 5.11 with $-\Delta H_{T,p}/T$.

5.5 GENERAL WORK EFFECTS IN TERMS OF SYSTEM PROPERTIES

All work processes can be described in terms of transporting between two states an incremental quantity, dK, that represents various properties of the system. The states are described by appropriate properties P associated with the quantities K (Table 5-1). The incremental work for reversible transport of dK between initial and final states, P_{ini} and P_{fin}, is

$$-dW = (P_{ini} - P_{fin})dK \tag{5.12}$$

If an irreversible work process occurs, the amount of heat generated is

$$(P_{ini} - P_{fin})dK = TdS_i \tag{5.13}$$

Because spontaneous processes occur in the direction in which entropy is generated, the quantity K always must go from a higher P state to a lower P state (Fig. 5-9). Consequently, where spontaneous work processes occur, there is a continual generation of entropy. Thus, in 1850 Clausius described the second law by saying the entropy of the universe continually increases.

Table 5-1. PROPERTIES ASSOCIATED WITH QUANTITIES K FOR COMMON WORK PROCESSES

Work process	*P (properties)*	*K (quantity)*
Weight	h (height)	mg (weight)
Expansion	$-p$ (pressure)	V (volume)
Thermal	T (temperature)	S (entropy)
Chemical	μ (chemical potential)	n (moles)
Electrical	ψ (electrostatic potential)	q (charge)

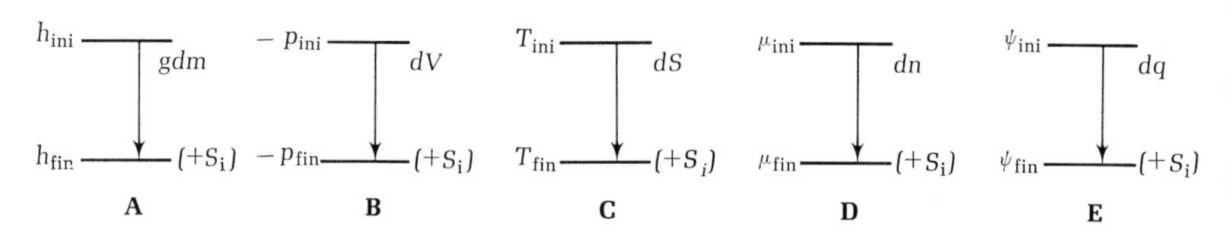

Fig. 5-9. Natural direction of transfer of quantity dK between property states P for **A**, weight; **B**, volume; **C**, entropy; **D**, moles; **E**, charge.

Any system will continue to generate entropy until the property states of all regions in the system are equal, that is, until the equilibrium state is reached. Temperature, pressure, chemical potentials, and so on will be constant throughout any system at equilibrium.

PROBLEMS

1. Calculate the work obtained in transferring 220 cal/deg of entropy from a constant temperature reservoir at 500°K to a constant temperature reservoir of 273°K.
2. Calculate the work obtained in executing the cycle shown below:

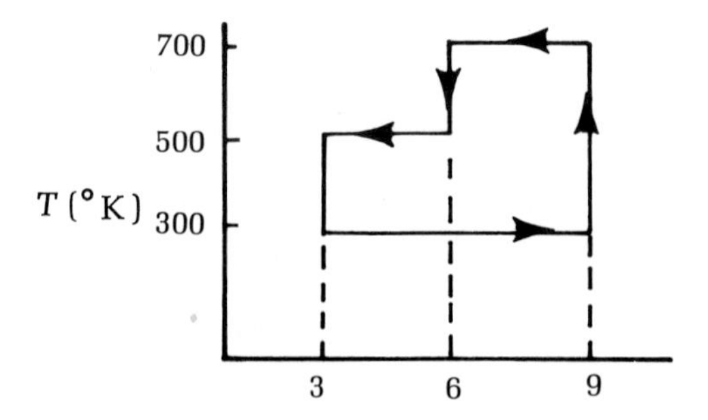

3. Calculate the maximum amount of work that could be obtained from a system of 1.0 kg of liquid water at 100°C and a mixture of 1.0 kg of ice and 1.0 kg of water at 0°C. Hint:

Follow example 5.5, but recognize that the lower and final temperatures are fixed at 0 °C.

4. Calculate the entropy generated in the following irreversible processes:
   (a) A 15 kg weight at 0 °C is dropped 10 m into a bucket of ice and water at 0 °C. What effect does the generated entropy produce?
   (b) One mole of an ideal gas at 25 °C expands adiabatically from 10 liters to 25 liters into a vacuum.
   Hint: From the properties of an ideal gas, what is the final temperature?
   (c) It takes 10 joules of work to wind the spring of an alarm clock. The clock is placed in a swimming pool full of water at 30 °C. Three days later the clock has completely run down. How much entropy was generated?
   (d) A lead bullet weighing 10 g traveling 1000 m/sec is stopped abruptly by hitting a plank. Assume the temperature of the bullet and the plank stay constant at 25 °C.
5. Over a waterfall 100 m in height flows water at a rate of 10^4 kg/sec. The temperature at the top of the fall is 20 °C.
   (a) If all the heat generated in falling is retained in the water, what is the temperature of the water at the bottom?
   (b) Estimate the entropy generated per second.
6. A power plant discharges 10^5 kg of water per second at 60 °C into a river that flows at 10^6 kg of water per second. Upstream from the discharge the temperature of the river is 20 °C.
   (a) Calculate the temperature downstream from the discharge, assuming no heat is lost.
   (b) Calculate the entropy generated per second.
   Hint: See example 5.5.
7. Calculate the entropy generated per second when an electrical current of 5 amps flows through a 1000-ohm resistance heater that is maintaining the temperature of a swimming pool at 30 °C.
8. (a) If we consider the resistance heater in problem 7 to be the system and the pool to be the surroundings, what is the entropy change in the heater and in the pool?
   (b) If we consider the system to be the resistance heater and the pool, and the system is isolated, what is the entropy change of the system?
9. Calculate the entropy generated (ΔS_i), the entropy difference between products and reactants (ΔS), and the entropy exchanged with the surroundings (ΔS_e) in the following spontaneous chemical reactions at 25 °C:
   (a) $\frac{1}{2}O_2(g) + C(\text{graphite}) \rightarrow CO(g)$
   (b) $CH_4(g) + 2O_2(g) \rightarrow CO_2(g) + 2H_2O(l)$
   (c) $Na(s) + \frac{1}{2}Cl_2(g) \rightarrow NaCl(s)$
10. Calculate ΔH^0 for the reactions in problem 9 and then compare the values of ΔS_e calculated in problem 9 with $\Delta H^0/T$.
11. Calculate ΔS, ΔS_i, ΔS_e, and $\Delta H^0/T$ for the reactions in problem 9. Assume the reactions are conducted reversibly.

6 THE CHEMICAL-POTENTIAL PROPERTIES OF MATTER

In order to deal with practical problems of chemical interest, let us examine how chemical potentials, μ_i, affect the Gibbs free energy for simple systems. We have previously seen two definitions of the Gibbs free energy:

$$G = H - TS = E + pV - TS \tag{6.1}$$

and

$$G = \Sigma \mu_i n_i \tag{6.2}$$

Equation 6.1 is most useful in relating changes in ΔG to thermal effects ΔH and ΔS. Equation 6.2 relates G to the chemical potentials of a system.

6.1 SINGLE-COMPONENT SYSTEMS

Let us examine the thermodynamic interrelationships among the properties of a single-component system. The energy change is

$$dE = TdS - pdV + \mu dn \tag{6.3}$$

From the definition of G in equation 6.1:

$$dG = dE + d(pV) - d(TS) \tag{6.4}$$

$$dG = dE + pdV + Vdp - TdS - SdT \tag{6.5}$$

Combining the results of equations 6.3 and 6.5 we obtain

$$dG = -SdT + Vdp + \mu dn \tag{6.6}$$

Equation 6.6 shows that G is directly affected by changes in T, p, and n.

Using the second definition of G, equation 6.2, we obtain for a one-component system

$$G = \mu n \tag{6.7}$$

where n is the total number of moles in the system. The differential of this is

$$dG = \mu dn + n d\mu \tag{6.8}$$

so that by combining equations 6.6 and 6.8 we find

$$n d\mu = -SdT + Vdp \tag{6.9}$$

In terms of molar quantities, where $\overline{S} = S/n$ and $\overline{V} = V/n$, we have

$$d\mu = -\overline{S}dT + \overline{V}dp \tag{6.10}$$

This relation shows how the chemical potential is affected by changes in T and p. An increase in T causes a decrease in μ, whereas an increase in p causes an increase in μ. The actual numerical effect of T and p depends on the value of $\overline{S}$ and $\overline{V}$.

6.2 CONDITIONS FOR PHASE EQUILIBRIUM

The thermodynamic properties of a system at equilibrium show no tendency to change. The properties (T, p, and μ_i) that describe the state of a chemical system must be the same throughout.

Spontaneous processes can occur when the properties T, p, and μ are not constant throughout a system. For example, if the value of the chemical potential of a substance differs between two regions of the system, the substance will spontaneously flow from the region of higher chemical potential to the region of lower chemical potential until the chemical potentials are the same throughout the system.

The *homogeneous regions* of a system are called *phases* (gas, liquid, and solid). Because gases mix completely, a mixture of gases is always a single-phase system. However, more than one liquid or solid phase can coexist. For our purposes, each phase will be identified by a superscript symbol α, β, γ, . . .

A system of P phases is described as shown in Fig. 6-1, *A*. The temperature in phase α is labeled T^α, the pressure in phase β is p^β, and so on. The chemical potential of component 1 in phase α is $\mu_1{}^\alpha$, and so on. If there are C different chemical species in the system, then the equilibrium conditions are

$$\begin{aligned}
T^\alpha &= T^\beta = T^\gamma = \ldots = T^P \\
p^\alpha &= p^\beta = p^\gamma = \ldots = p^P \\
\mu_1{}^\alpha &= \mu_1{}^\beta = \mu_1{}^\gamma = \ldots = \mu_1{}^P \\
\mu_2{}^\alpha &= \mu_2{}^\beta = \mu_2{}^\gamma = \ldots = \mu_2{}^P \\
&\cdot \quad \cdot \quad \cdot \quad \cdots \quad \cdot \\
\mu_C{}^\alpha &= \mu_C{}^\beta = \mu_C{}^\gamma = \ldots = \mu_C{}^P
\end{aligned} \tag{6.11}$$

We apply these equilibrium conditions to some specific situations in the sections that follow.

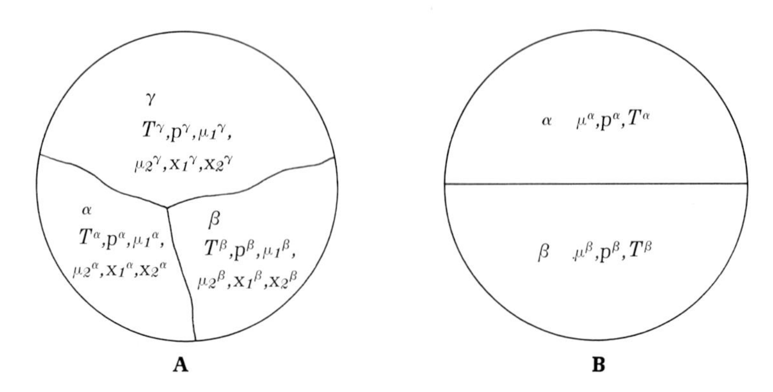

Fig. 6-1. **A,** General description of system with phases $\alpha, \beta, \gamma, \ldots$, chemical species $1, 2, 3, \ldots$, and mole fractions X_i^α in phase α, and so on. **B,** Two-phase, one-component system, α and β at equilibrium.

6.3 EQUILIBRIUM IN TWO-PHASE SYSTEMS

The simplest case of phase equilibrium occurs for a two-phase system consisting of a single substance. One phase is denoted by α, and the other, by β. The equilibrium conditions (Fig. 6-1, *B*) are

$$\begin{aligned} T^\alpha &= T^\beta \\ p^\alpha &= p^\beta \\ \mu^\alpha &= \mu^\beta \end{aligned} \tag{6.12}$$

Changes in μ, T, and p for phases α and β are related to each other by equation 6.10 as

$$d\mu^\alpha = -\overline{S}^\alpha dT^\alpha + \overline{V}^\alpha dp^\alpha \tag{6.13}$$

and

$$d\mu^\beta = -\overline{S}^\beta dT^\beta + \overline{V}^\beta dp^\beta$$

With the system at equilibrium, from equation 6.12 we have the differentials

$$\begin{aligned} dT^\alpha &= dT^\beta = dT \\ dp^\alpha &= dp^\beta = dp \\ d\mu^\alpha &= d\mu^\beta \end{aligned} \tag{6.14}$$

From equation 6.13 we then have

$$-\overline{S}^\alpha dT^\alpha + \overline{V}^\alpha dp^\alpha = -\overline{S}^\beta dT^\beta + \overline{V}^\beta dp^\beta \tag{6.15}$$

or

$$(\overline{S}^\beta - \overline{S}^\alpha)dT = (\overline{V}^\beta - \overline{V}^\alpha)dp \tag{6.16}$$

which gives

$$\frac{dp}{dT} = \frac{\overline{S}^{\beta} - \overline{S}^{\alpha}}{\overline{V}^{\beta} - \overline{V}^{\alpha}} = \frac{\Delta S}{\Delta V} \tag{6.17}$$

The entropy difference is related to the enthalpy change by

$$\overline{S}^{\beta} - \overline{S}^{\alpha} = \frac{\Delta H}{T} \tag{6.18}$$

where ΔH is the heat of transition between α and β phases at temperature T. We also let

$$\overline{V}^{\beta} - \overline{V}^{\alpha} = \Delta V \tag{6.19}$$

Equation 6.17 can then be written in the form known as the *Clausius equation:*

$$\frac{dp}{dT} = \frac{\Delta H}{T \Delta V} \tag{6.20}$$

EXAMPLE **6.1**

The effect of pressure on the freezing point of ice (273 °K) can be assessed from equation 6.20. The heat of fusion ΔH is 1440 cal/mole; the volume change ΔV upon fusion is -1.64 cm^3/mole. Thus

$$\frac{dp}{dT} = \frac{1440 \text{ cal}}{(273\,°\text{K})(-1.64 \text{ cm}^3)} \left(41.3 \frac{\text{atm-cm}^3}{\text{cal}}\right)^*$$
$$= -133 \text{ atm}/°\text{K}$$

An increase in pressure of 400 atm will thus depress the freezing point of ice by 3 °K. Water (ice) is unusual; the freezing point of most materials increases with pressure.

A positive value for dp/dT means ΔS and ΔV have the same sign; a negative value means they have different signs. For the transition of water from solid to liquid, dp/dT is negative since ΔS is positive and ΔV is negative. An increase in pressure requires a decrease in temperature to maintain the coexistence of both phases. In Fig. 6-2, *A*, the p, T conditions for the coexistence of ice and liquid water are shown by the line between regions *S* and *L*. The line for liquid-gas phase equilibrium (*L-G*) has a positive slope dp/dT since ΔS and ΔV are both positive.

*Since 1.987 cal equals 0.0821 liter-atm, 1 cal = 41.3 atm-cm^3.

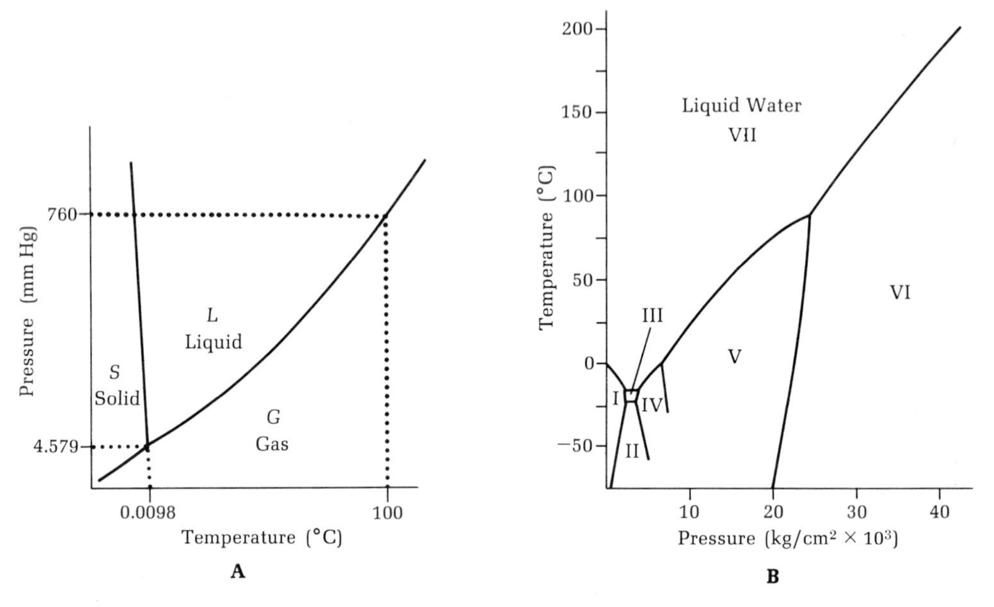

Fig. 6-2. **A,** Low-pressure and **B,** high-pressure phase diagrams of water. In **B** the solid phases are labeled I to VI.

Similarly, for solid-gas equilibrium (*S-G*) a positive slope is expected. At high pressures other solid phases of water exist (Fig. 6-2, *B*).

The pressure-temperature relationship for equilibrated two-phase systems can be found by integration of dp/dT. If the liquid molar volume $\overline{V}^{L}$ is negligible compared to the gas molar volume $\overline{V}^{G}$, $\Delta\overline{V} \cong \overline{V}^{G}$. If we assume the ideal gas law is applicable, then

$$\overline{V}^{G} = \frac{RT}{p} \tag{6.21}$$

With equation 6.20 we have

$$\frac{dp}{dT} = \frac{p\Delta H}{RT^{2}} \tag{6.22}$$

which can be rearranged to

$$\frac{dp}{p} = \frac{\Delta H}{RT^{2}}\, dT \tag{6.23}$$

and integrated if we assume ΔH is a constant. The result is

$$\ln p = -\frac{\Delta H}{RT} + \text{constant} \tag{6.24}$$

called the *Clausius-Clapeyron equation.* A plot of ln p versus $1/T$ gives a straight line with a slope of $-\Delta H/R$.

EXAMPLE **6.2**

Carbon tetrachloride boils at 350.0°K at 760 torr. At 298.2°K it has a vapor pressure of 115 torr. Calculate the molar heat of vaporization.

The Clausius-Clapeyron equation (6.24) can be written as

$$\ln \frac{p_2}{p_1} = -\frac{\Delta H}{R}\left(\frac{1}{T_2} - \frac{1}{T_1}\right)$$

Converting ln to log and solving for ΔH, we get

$$\begin{aligned}\Delta H &= \frac{2.303RT_2T_1}{T_2 - T_1}\log\frac{p_2}{p_1}\\ &= \frac{(2.303)(1.987)(298)(350)}{51.8}\log\frac{760}{115}\text{ cal/mole}\\ &= 7560\text{ cal/mole}\end{aligned}$$

From equation 6.13 it can be seen that an increase in temperature decreases the values of μ^α and μ^β according to the molar entropies of the α and β phases. An increase in pressure increases μ^α and μ^β in proportion to the molar volumes of α and β. At equilibrium the chemical potentials of the α and β phases are equal.

To discover what happens to the system if only the pressure or only the temperature is changed, let us consider solid and liquid water at equilibrium. Ice has a greater molar volume than liquid water. The molar entropy of the liquid is greater than that of ice. If only the pressure on the ice-liquid water system is increased, the chemical potentials become unequal (Fig. 6-3, *A*), creating an unstable situation in which material will be transformed from the high chemical potential form to the low chemical potential form. Thus, ice will be transformed to liquid water, resulting in the disappearance of the solid phase. If only the temperature is increased, the chemical potentials of the solid and the liquid decrease (Fig. 6-3, *B*). The solid is again unstable with respect to the liquid.

Most materials have larger liquid molar volumes than solid molar volumes; an increase in pressure increases the liquid chemical potential more than the solid chemical potential, and a spontaneous conversion to the solid phase occurs.

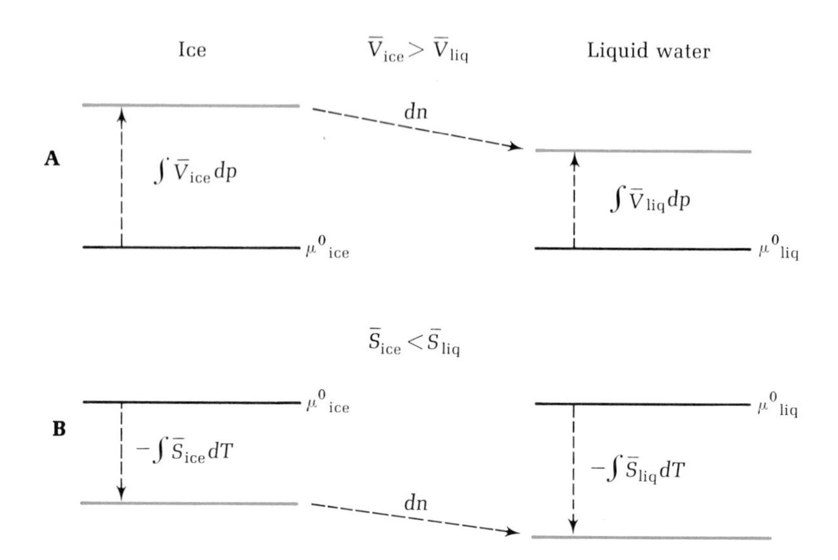

Fig. 6-3. Effects on chemical potentials of ice and water, originally at 1 atm, 0°C. **A,** Effect of increasing p. **B,** Effect of increasing T.

Synthesis of diamonds: an application of chemical potentials

At 25°C and 1 atm the chemical potential of diamond is 685 cal/mole, and that of graphite, 0 cal/mole.* Under these conditions diamond is thermodynamically unstable with respect to graphite, but the conversion of diamond to graphite is too slow to be detected. The determination of conditions for the reverse process, conversion of graphite to diamond, is of considerable commercial importance.

We can assess the thermodynamic conditions needed for this process by examining the effect of pressure and temperature on the chemical potentials of graphite and diamond. Use is made of equation 6.13 given as

$$d\mu = -\bar{S}dT + \bar{V}dp$$

The molar volumes for graphite and diamond at 25°C and 1 atm are 5.33 cm^3/mole and 3.41 cm^3/mole, respectively, and the molar entropies are 1.360 cal/deg-mole and 0.583 cal/deg-mole, respectively. The relative effect of increasing temperature and pressure is depicted by the arrows on the diagrams in Fig. 6-4, *B* and *C* for the chemical potentials of diamond and graphite initially at 25°C and 1 atm. Increas-

*Chemical potentials of pure substances in their standard states are equal to their $\bar{G}_f^0$ values (given in Appendix E).

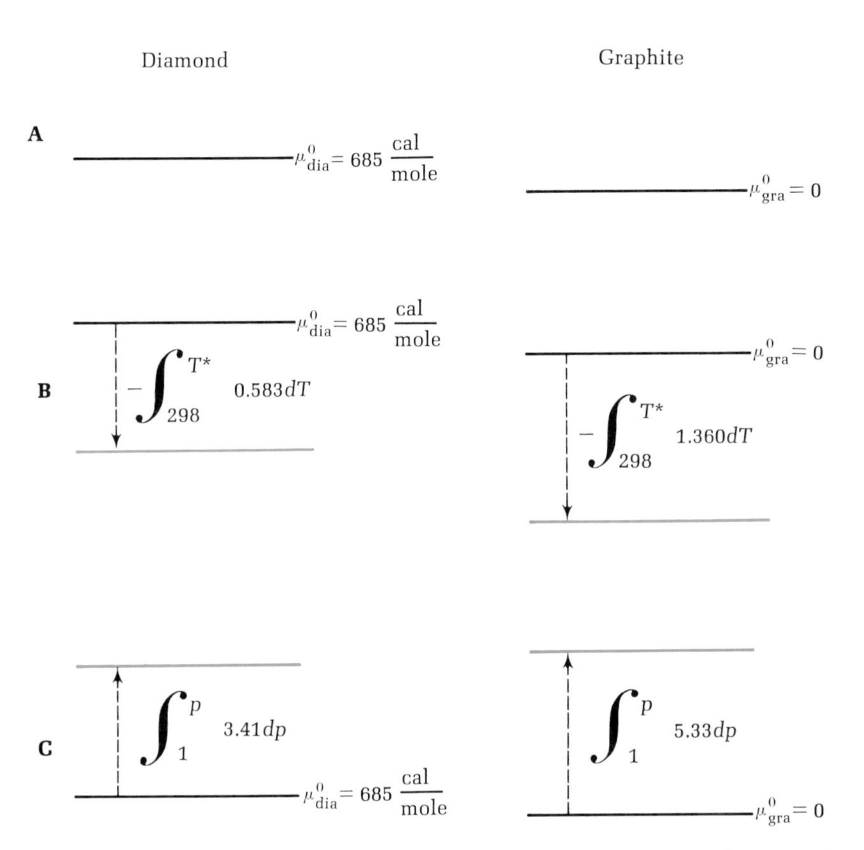

Fig. 6-4. Chemical potentials of diamond and graphite. **A,** 1 atm, 25° C. **B,** After increasing T. **C,** After increasing p.

ing the temperature to T^* (Fig. 6-4, *B*) only increases the instability of diamond relative to graphite. Increasing the pressure (Fig. 6-4, *C*), however, produces a situation in which the chemical potential of graphite equals that of diamond. Equality of the two chemical potentials occurs when

$$\int_1^p \overline{V}_{\text{graphite}} dp = 685 \text{ cal/mole} + \int_1^p \overline{V}_{\text{diamond}} dp$$

In terms of the properties of graphite and diamond, this equation gives, assuming constant molar volumes,

$$[5.33\,(p-1)]\,(2.42 \times 10^{-2}) \text{ cal} = 685 \text{ cal} + [3.41\,(p-1)]\,(2.42 \times 10^{-2}) \text{ cal}$$

where p is in atm. Thus

$$p - 1 = \frac{685}{(1.92)(2.42 \times 10^{-2})} = 1.47 \times 10^4 \text{ atm}$$

The conversion reaction is too slow to be practical at 25°C. It is necessary to increase the temperature. For example, if the temperature is raised by 1000°C, and if we assume the entropies of graphite and diamond do not change with temperature, then

$$\mu_{\text{graphite}} = 0 - \int_{298}^{1298} 1.36 dT = -1360 \text{ cal/mole}$$

$$\mu_{\text{diamond}} = 685 - \int_{298}^{1298} 0.583 dT = 102 \text{ cal/mole}$$

If we now apply a pressure p to bring these potentials to the same value we find

$$-1360 + \int_1^p \overline{V}_{\text{graphite}} dp = 102 + \int_1^p \overline{V}_{\text{diamond}} dp$$

The numerical calculation is:

$$-1360 + [5.33 (p - 1)] (2.42 \times 10^{-2}) = 102 + [3.41 (p - 1)] (2.42 \times 10^{-2})$$

$$p = 1 + \frac{1462}{1.92 \times 2.42 \times 10^{-2}} = 3.15 \times 10^4 \text{ atm}$$

The results of such calculations for different values of T and p are shown by the phase diagram in Fig. 6-5.

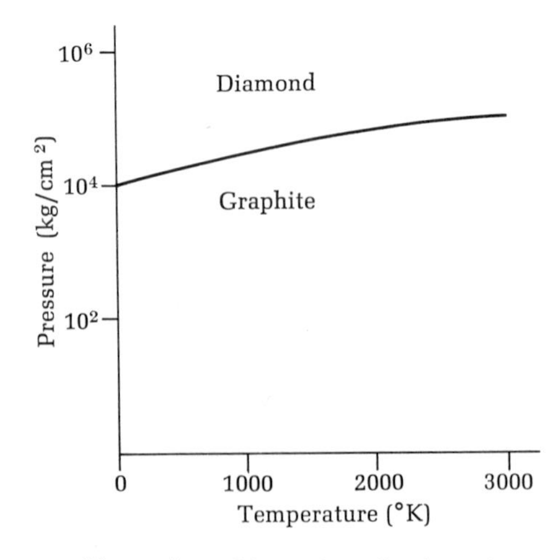

Fig. 6-5. Diamond-graphite region of carbon phase diagram.

Apparatus capable of producing very high pressures is needed to promote the conversion of graphite to diamond. Scientists have developed high-pressure, high-temperature equipment that is now used in the commercial production of diamonds from graphite.

6.4 CHEMICAL POTENTIALS OF PURE SUBSTANCES

In dealing with pure gases we are interested primarily in the effect of pressure on their chemical potentials. Therefore, the temperature is held constant. Integration of equation 6.1 gives

$$\int d\mu = \int \overline{V} dp \tag{6.25}$$

For an ideal gas

$$\overline{V} = \frac{RT}{p} \tag{6.26}$$

If we integrate equation 6.25 between $p = 1$ atm and $p = p$ atm, we obtain

$$\mu = \mu^0(T) + RT \ln p \tag{6.27}$$

where $\mu^0(T)$ is the value of the chemical potential when $p = 1$ atm. Equation 6.27 shows that the chemical potential of an ideal gas increases logarithmically with pressure. A plot of this function is shown in Fig. 6-6. For non-ideal gases, a term, μ^E, that corrects the ideal gas result is added to equation 6.27. The μ^E is called the excess chemical potential.

$$\mu = \mu^0(T) + RT \ln p + \mu^E \tag{6.28}$$

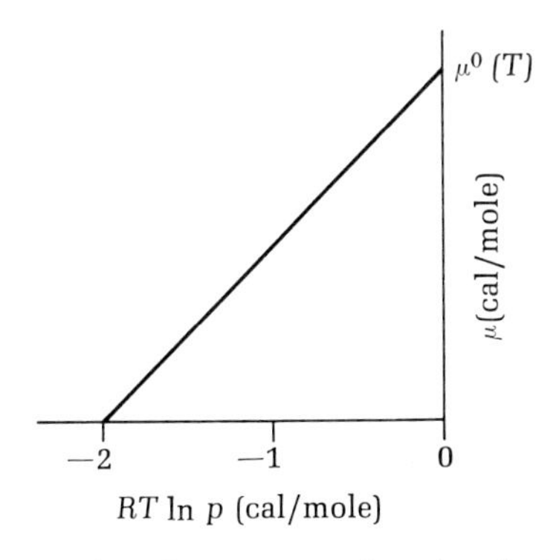

Fig. 6-6. Plot of μ versus $RT \ln p$ for ideal gas.

At low pressure μ^E becomes zero, and for all gases the equation for the chemical potential follows that for ideal gases.

The deviation from ideal-gas behavior is often expressed by the fugacity coefficient, γ, where

$$\mu^E = RT \ln \gamma \tag{6.29}$$

With equation 6.28 this gives the expression

$$\mu = \mu^0(T) + RT \ln \gamma p \tag{6.30}$$

The term γp is called the fugacity, f, a corrected type of pressure. We can write the general result for non-ideal gases as

$$\mu = \mu^0(T) + RT \ln f \tag{6.31}$$

The fugacity parameter allows us to use the simple ideal-gas form of the equation for the chemical potential even though the gas is non-ideal.

The effect of pressure on the chemical potential of any pure substance is given by equation 6.11. For liquids and solids, $\overline{V}$ is virtually constant over pressure ranges of several atmospheres, and the increase in μ is given by the product of $\overline{V}\Delta p$:

$$\mu = \mu^0 + \overline{V}(p - 1) \tag{6.32}$$

where μ^0 is the chemical potential at 1 atm.

6.5 CHEMICAL POTENTIALS OF MIXTURES

Mixtures of gases

We have seen that the chemical potential of an ideal gas at temperature T is affected by the pressure p according to equation 6.27. Let us now consider a mixture of ideal gases consisting of n_1 moles of gas 1, n_2 moles of gas 2, and so on. The total pressure p of the mixture is the sum of the partial pressures of the components. The partial pressures p_i are determined by multiplying the mole fraction, X_i^G, of component i in the gas mixture by the total pressure p:

$$p_i = X_i^G p \tag{6.33}$$

This equation provides a definition of p_i in terms that can be measured experimentally. We can obtain X_i^G from an analysis of the chemical composition of the gas and the pressure p.

We assume each component in a mixture of ideal gases behaves as though the other gases of the mixture were not present. Each gas behaves as a pure gas with partial pressure p_i; its chemical potential, μ_i^G, is

$$\mu_i^G = \mu_i^{0G} + RT \ln p_i \tag{6.34}$$

The term μ_i^{0G} stands for the chemical potential of i at temperature T and 1 atm.

Liquid-state chemical potentials from gas measurements

To measure the chemical potentials of substances in a liquid solution we allow the solution to become equilibrated with its gaseous components. At equilibrium the chemical potentials of the gas and liquid phases of component i are equal:

$$\mu_i^{\mathrm{L}} = \mu_i^{\mathrm{G}} \tag{6.35}$$

Thus the liquid-phase chemical potential of i can be found if we know the partial pressure of i in the gas phase.

EXAMPLE **6.3**

Water at 27°C has a vapor pressure of 0.035 atm. Calculate the chemical potential of liquid water. The chemical potential $\mu_{H_2O}^{0G}$ of gaseous water at 27°C and 1 atm is −54.6 kcal/mole.

The calculation is as follows:

$$\begin{aligned}
\mu_{H_2O}^{L} &= \mu_{H_2O}^{G} \\
\mu_{H_2O}^{G} &= \mu_{H_2O}^{0G} + RT \ln p_{H_2O} \\
p_{H_2O} &= 0.035 \text{ atm} \\
\mu_{H_2O}^{G} &= [-54{,}600 + (1.987)(300) \ln 0.035] \text{ cal/mole} \\
&= [-54{,}600 - 2000] \text{ cal/mole} \\
&= -56{,}600 \text{ cal/mole}
\end{aligned}$$

The study of liquid solutions in equilibrium with their gas phases leads to two general experimental laws used for describing the behavior of solutions.

Chemical potentials of ideal solutions

The partial pressure p_i of component i is determined by multiplying the mole fraction of i in the liquid phase (X_i^{L}) times the partial pressure of i above the pure liquid phase p_i^0:

$$p_i = X_i^{\mathrm{L}} p_i^0 \tag{6.36}$$

A solution that follows this law, known as *Raoult's law*, is called an *ideal solution*. Equation 6.36 is graphically represented in Fig. 6-7.

Few solutions follow Raoult's law over all concentrations. Two typical situations are shown in Fig. 6-8. Deviations from Raoult's law are positive or negative at low concentration, but as X_i^{L} approaches unity (concentrated solution in i) Raoult's law is always followed for component i.

In the region where Raoult's law holds, the chemical potential of the liquid, μ_i^{L}, is given by combining equations 6.34, 6.35, and 6.36. This gives the chemical potential for an ideal solution, $\mu_i^{\mathrm{L,ideal}}$, as

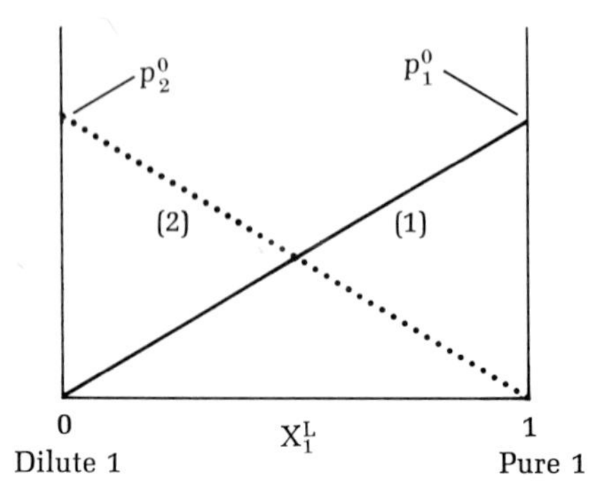

Fig. 6-7. Graph of ideal solution following Raoult's law for components 1 and 2.

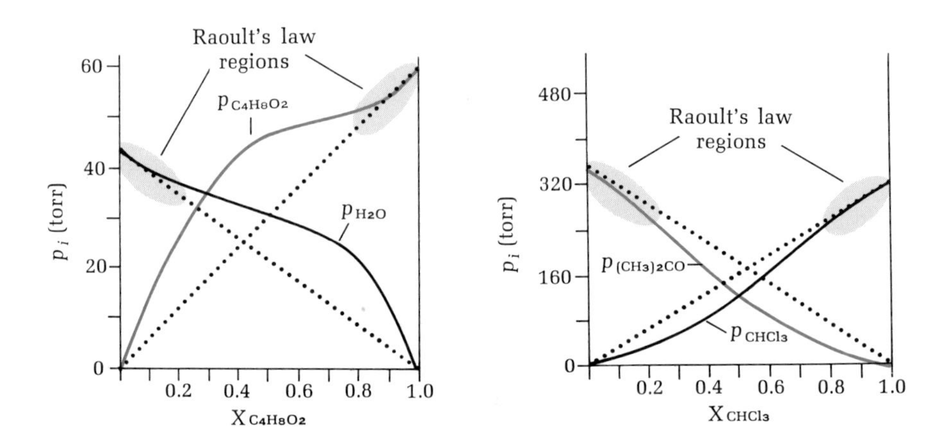

Fig. 6-8. Deviation from Raoult's law. **A,** Water-dioxane system at 35° C showing positive deviation. **B,** Acetone-chloroform system at 35° C showing negative deviation. (Raoult's law shown by dashed straight lines.)

$$\mu_i^{\mathrm{L,ideal}} = \mu_i^{0\mathrm{G}} + RT \ln p_i^0 + RT \ln X_i^{\mathrm{L}} \tag{6.37}$$

This expression combines gas and liquid phase properties. If we denote $\mu_i^{0\mathrm{L}}$ as the chemical potential for the pure liquid phase, that is, when $X_i^{\mathrm{L}} = 1$, then we write

$$\mu_i^{0\mathrm{L}} = \mu_i^{0\mathrm{G}} + RT \ln p_i^0 \tag{6.38}$$

The chemical potential of the liquid phase of an ideal solution, obtained by combining equations 6.37 and 6.38, is

$$\mu_i^{\mathrm{L,ideal}} = \mu_i^{0\mathrm{L}} + RT \ln X_i^{\mathrm{L}} \tag{6.39}$$

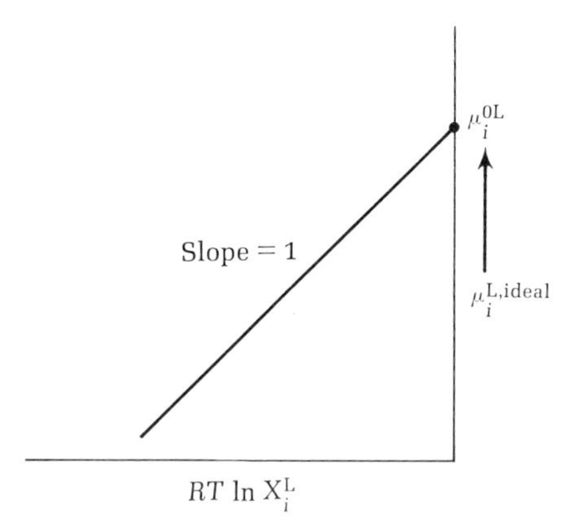

Fig. 6-9. Diagram of $\mu_i^{L,\text{ ideal}}$ versus $RT \ln X_i^L$ for ideal solution.

The important result is that the chemical potential of the liquid depends on its mole fraction. A plot of equation 6.39 is shown in Fig. 6-9.

A solution that does not obey Raoult's law (equation 6.36) is called a *non-ideal solution.* A correction factor μ_i^E can be added to the expression for the chemical potential of an ideal solution, given by equation 6.39, to give μ_i^L, the chemical potential of the non-ideal solution:

$$\mu_i^L = \mu_i^{L,\text{ ideal}} + \mu_i^E \tag{6.40}$$

Similar to the way non-ideal gas corrections were described, we use the factor γ_i where

$$\mu_i^E = RT \ln \gamma_i \tag{6.41}$$

Combining equations 6.39, 6.40, and 6.41, we have

$$\mu_i^L = \mu_i^{0L} + RT \ln \gamma_i X_i^L \tag{6.42}$$

The term $\gamma_i X_i^L$ is called the *activity,* a_i, and γ_i is called the *activity coefficient.* The activity is a corrected concentration that satisfies the ideal solution law. Equation 6.42 is written conveniently as

$$\mu_i = \mu_i^0 + RT \ln a_i \tag{6.43}$$

For an ideal solution

$$\mu_i^E = 0, \ \gamma_i = 1, \text{ and } a_i = X_i^L \tag{6.44}$$

Chemical potentials of dilute solutions

Dilute solutions show the other extreme region of solution behavior. Examination of Fig. 6-8 reveals that for very dilute solutions, where X_i^L approaches zero, p_i is proportional to X_i^L:

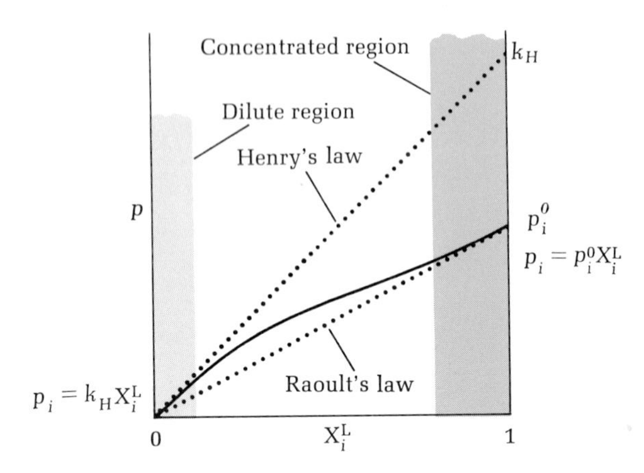

Fig. 6-10. Representation of dilute and concentrated regions of solution with positive deviations where Henry's law and Raoult's law hold.

$$p_i = k_H X_i^{\mathrm{L}} \tag{6.45}$$

This equation is called *Henry's law*, and k_H, the proportionality constant, is called the Henry's-law constant. Henry's law is a valid representation of p_i versus X_i^{L} for most solutions only in the dilute region (Fig. 6-10). The constant k_H is graphically described by the intercept where $X_i^{\mathrm{L}} = 1$. The factor k_H in Henry's law is fundamentally different from p_i^0 in Raoult's law. The p_i^0 is the partial pressure above the pure condensed phase of compound *i;* it is independent of the other components. In comparison, k_H depends on the various components in the mixture and must be measured for each mixture.

For dilute solutions we can express the chemical potential given by equations 6.34 and 6.35 by using Henry's law (equation 6.45):

$$\mu_i^{\mathrm{L,dil}} = \mu_i^{0\mathrm{G}} + RT \ln k_H + RT \ln X_i^{\mathrm{L}} \tag{6.46}$$

It is convenient to denote $\mu_i^{0\mathrm{G}} + RT \ln k_H$ by the symbol μ_i^*, so that for dilute solutions

$$\mu_i^{\mathrm{L,dil}} = \mu_i^* + RT \ln X_i^{\mathrm{L}} \tag{6.47}$$

Again the chemical potential is affected logarithmically by the mole fraction composition of the solution. Experimental deviations from this law can be treated by the use of activity coefficients in a way similar to that outlined by equation 6.42. In a dilute solution the mole fraction X_i^{L} is proportional to the molarity M_i. Thus equation 6.47 can be written in the abbreviated form

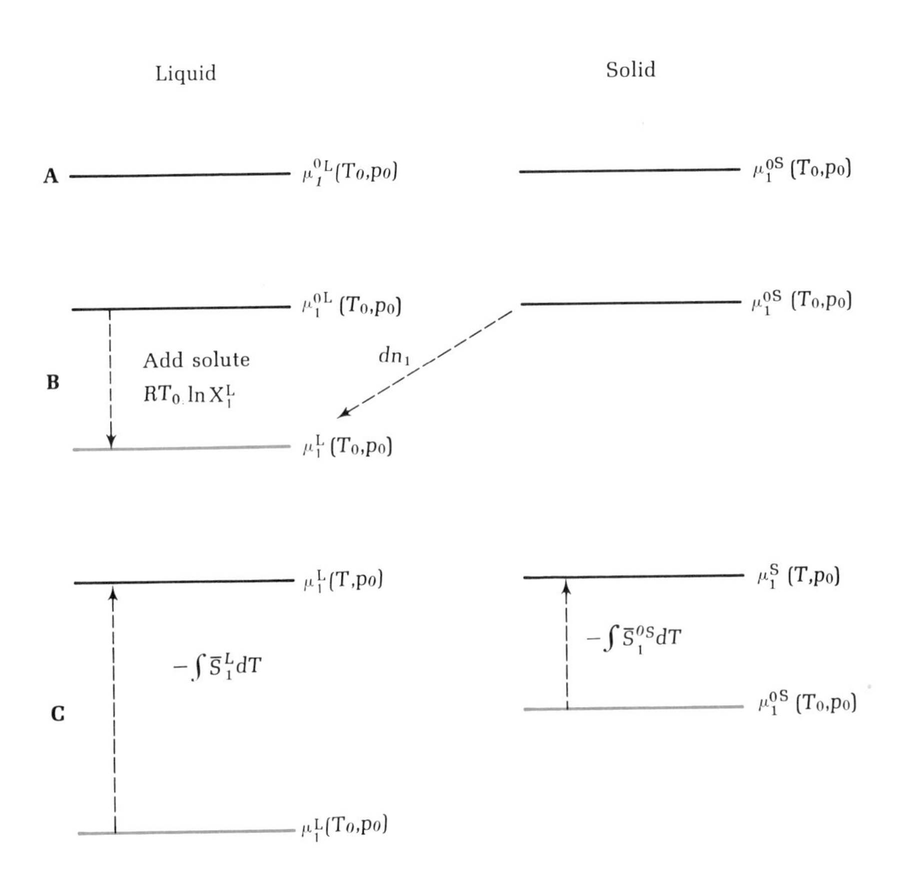

Fig. 6-11. **A,** Pure liquid and pure solid chemical potentials at equilibrium, T_0, p_0. **B,** Added solute depresses chemical potential of liquid component 1. **C,** Equilibrium is restored by lowering temperature to T, which raises chemical potentials of liquid and solid phases to equal each other.

$$\mu_i = \mu_i^0 + RT \ln M_i \tag{6.48}$$

where μ_i^0 is the hypothetical chemical potential for a "dilute" 1 molar solution.

6.6 FREEZING-POINT DEPRESSION

The freezing point of a solution is lower than that of the pure solvent. This effect is called freezing-point depression and has important applications: determination of molecular weights, interpretation of phase diagrams, and description of non-ideal solution behavior.

Consider a two-phase system with a pure solid phase and a liquid solution phase. For this system consider two equilibrium states: (1) the solid is equilibrated with the pure liquid and (2) the solid is equilibrated with a liquid solution.

In the first state, equilibrium between the pure solid and pure liquid occurs at temperature T_0 and pressure p_0. The chemical potentials are equal (Fig. 6-11, *A*).

Now let us dissolve a solute in the liquid phase. We assume it forms an ideal solution, and, for the moment, that no change in temperature or pressure occurs. The chemical potential of solvent, component 1, is given by equation 6.49:

$$\mu_1{}^{\mathrm{L}} = \mu_1{}^{0\mathrm{L}}\ (T_0, p_0) + RT_0 \ln X_1{}^{\mathrm{L}} \tag{6.49}$$

The symbol $\mu_1{}^{0\mathrm{L}}\ (T_0, p_0)$ is the chemical potential of pure liquid at T_0 and p_0. Since $X_1{}^{\mathrm{L}}$ is less than 1, $\mu_1{}^{\mathrm{L}}$ must be less than $\mu_1{}^{0\mathrm{L}}(T_0, p_0)$, as shown in Fig. 6-11, *B*. In this assumed situation, the solid-phase chemical potential is higher than the chemical potential of the solvent in the solution. Component 1 would therefore change from solid to liquid until equality of the levels or disappearance of the solid phase occurs.

The chemical potentials can be restored to equality by changing the temperature or pressure of the system. The relation for the change of chemical potential of component 1 due to a change in temperature is

$$d\mu_1 = -\bar{S}_1 dT \tag{6.50}$$

Since the entropy of component 1 is greater in the liquid phase than in the solid phase, the chemical potential of the liquid phase is more affected by a temperature change. It is necessary to lower the temperature of both phases to raise their chemical potentials to equal values (Fig. 6-11, *C*). The lengths of the arrows representing the various changes are described by the appropriate factors next to each arrow. From Fig. 6-11 we can see that

$$-\int_{T_0}^{T} \bar{S}_1{}^{0\mathrm{S}} dT = -\int_{T_0}^{T} \bar{S}_1{}^{\mathrm{L}} dT + RT_0 \ln X_1{}^{\mathrm{L}} \tag{6.51}$$

or

$$RT_0 \ln X_1{}^{\mathrm{L}} = \int_{T_0}^{T} (\bar{S}_1{}^{\mathrm{L}} - \bar{S}_1{}^{0\mathrm{S}}) dT \tag{6.52}$$

The entropy of component 1 in the liquid solution is*

$$\bar{S}_1{}^{\mathrm{L}} = \bar{S}_1{}^{0\mathrm{L}} - R \ln X_1{}^{\mathrm{L}} \tag{6.53}$$

With this result, equation 6.52 becomes

$$RT_0 \ln X_1{}^{\mathrm{L}} = \int_{T_0}^{T} (\bar{S}_1{}^{0\mathrm{L}} - \bar{S}_1{}^{0\mathrm{S}}) dT \tag{6.54}$$

We can make some simplifying assumptions in order to integrate equation 6.54.

---

*The entropy $\bar{S}_1$ can be identified with the differential $-(d\mu_1/dT)_p$, so from equation 6.39 we can easily derive the result of equation 6.53.

The entropy difference between pure solid and pure liquid equals $\Delta H_f^0/T_0$. If we assume this difference is independent of temperature, equation 6.54 becomes

$$RT_0 \ln X_1^{\mathrm{L}} = \frac{\Delta H_f^0}{T_0}(T - T_0) \tag{6.55}$$

The depression of the freezing point is then

$$\Delta T = T - T_0 = \frac{RT_0^2}{\Delta H_f^0} \ln X_1^{\mathrm{L}} \tag{6.56}$$

For dilute solutions, the following series approximation may be used:

$$\ln X_1^{\mathrm{L}} = \ln(1 - X_2^{\mathrm{L}}) = -\left[X_2^{\mathrm{L}} + \frac{(X_2^{\mathrm{L}})^2}{2} + \ldots \right] \tag{6.57}$$

where X_2^{L} is the mole fraction of solute. Equation 6.56 is given to the first order term by

$$\Delta T \cong \frac{-RT_0^2}{\Delta H_f^0}(X_2^{\mathrm{L}}) \tag{6.58}$$

The freezing-point depression is expressed in terms of molality m, that is, the number of moles of solute in 1000 g of solvent. In dilute solutions the mole fraction X_2^{L} is nearly equal to the ratio of moles of solute to moles of solvent, n_2/n_1. In terms of molality and molecular weight of solvent, MW_1, we have

$$X_2^{\mathrm{L}} \cong \frac{n_2}{n_1} \cong \frac{m}{1000/MW_1} \cong \frac{MW_1 m}{1000} \tag{6.59}$$

The freezing-point depression equation, 6.58, becomes

$$\Delta T = -\left(\frac{RT_0^2}{\Delta H_f^0}\right)\left(\frac{MW_1 m}{1000}\right) \tag{6.60}$$

$$= -K_{fp} m \tag{6.61}$$

where K_{fp} is the freezing-point constant. Selected values of K_{fp} are given in Table 6.1. Experimentally, the determination of ΔT can be used to find m for a solution containing a solute of unknown molecular weight. The molecular weight of the solute can then be found from m and the known weight of solute in solution.

Table 6-1. FREEZING-POINT AND BOILING-POINT CONSTANTS

Solvent	*Melting point (°K)*	*K_{fp} (°/molal)*	*Boiling point (°K)*	*K_b (°/molal)*
Water	273.2	1.862	373.2	0.51
Benzene	278.7	5.12	353.3	2.53
Camphor	448.7	37.7		

EXAMPLE **6.4**

Suppose a solution comprised of 0.522 g of camphor and 0.0386 g of an unknown solute has a freezing point of 429.0°K. The freezing point of pure camphor is 448.7°K, so the freezing-point depression is −19.7°K. Calculate the molecular weight, MW_2, of solute.

The molality m of the solution is

$$m = -\frac{\Delta T_{\mathrm{fp}}}{K_{\mathrm{fp}}} = \frac{(19.7°\mathrm{K})}{(37.7\ °\mathrm{K/molal})} = 0.523 \text{ molal}$$

The molecular weight MW_2 of solute is

$$MW_2 = \left(\frac{w_2}{w_1}\right)\left(\frac{1000}{m}\right)$$

where w_2 and w_1 are the weights of solute and solvent, respectively. Thus

$$MW_2 = \left(\frac{0.0386}{0.522}\right)\left(\frac{1000}{0.523}\right)$$
$$= 141$$

6.7 BOILING-POINT ELEVATION

The boiling-point behavior of solutions can be examined in a manner analogous to that used for freezing-point behavior. The boiling point of a solution is higher than that of the pure solvent. This effect is called boiling-point elevation. The temperature increase is affected by the entropy of vaporization, $\Delta H_{\mathrm{vap}}/T_0{}^{\mathrm{b}}$, the boiling-point temperature, $T_0{}^{\mathrm{b}}$, and the mole fraction of solute in solution, $X_2{}^{\mathrm{L}}$.

The equation for the boiling-point elevation is analogous to equation 6.61:

$$T = \left(\frac{R(T_0{}^{\mathrm{b}})^2}{\Delta H_{\mathrm{vap}}{}^0}\right)\left(\frac{MW_1}{1000}\right)m = K_{\mathrm{b}}m \tag{6.62}$$

where K_{b} is the boiling-point constant. Selected values of K_{b} are shown in Table 6-1.

6.8 OSMOTIC PRESSURE

Fig. 6-12 shows a pure solvent separated from a solution by a semipermeable membrane. The properties of the membrane are such that it can freely transmit solvent molecules (component 1) but not solute molecules (component 2). Suppose both sides initially are filled with pure solvent. The chemical potentials are equal (Fig. 6-12, A). Adding solute to the left side lowers the chemical potential of

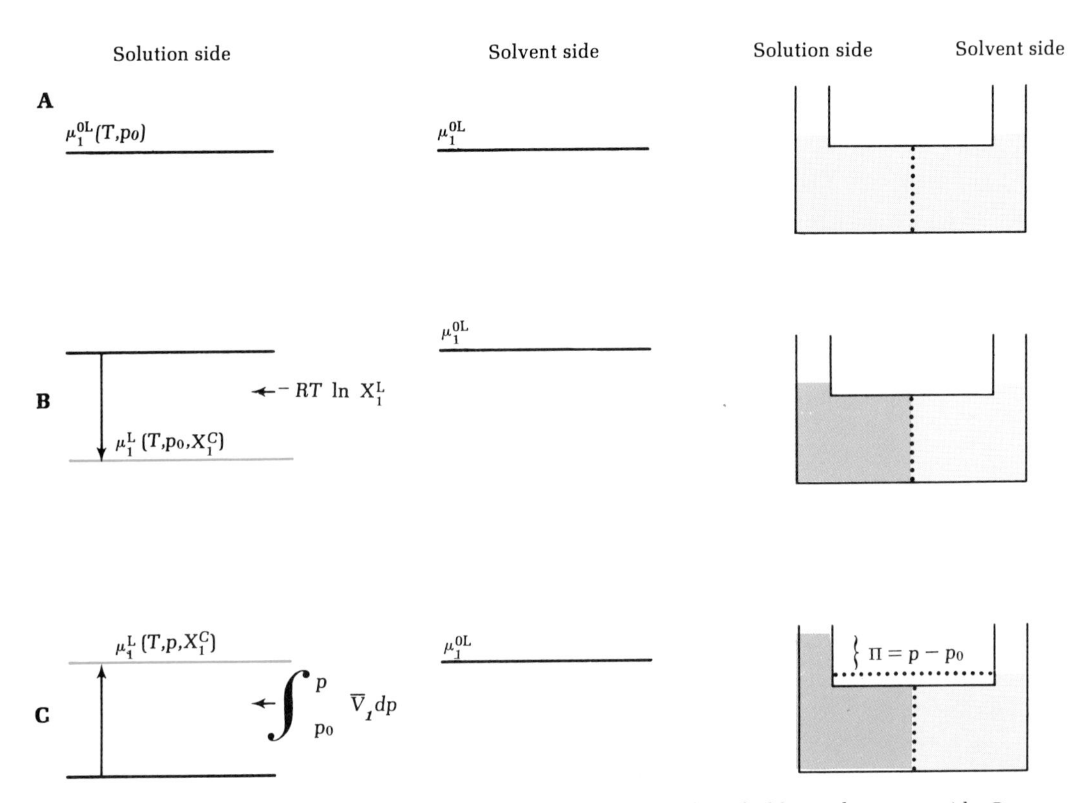

Fig. 6-12. **A,** Chemical potentials of separated pure solvent. **B,** Effect of adding solute to one side. **C,** Effect of pressure on solution side to restore equilibrium.

component 1 (Fig. 6-12, *B*). To restore equilibrium we apply pressure to the solution side. The result is expressed by

$$-RT \ln X_1{}^{L} = \int_{p_0}^{p} \overline{V}_1 dp \tag{6.63}$$

where p_0 is the pressure on the solvent side, and p, the pressure on the solution side. The osmotic pressure, Π, is defined as

$$\Pi = p - p_0 \tag{6.64}$$

In Fig. 6-12, *C* the value of Π is measured from the column height and is given in dynes/cm^2. The molar volume $\overline{V}_1$ of component 1 (solvent) may be regarded as nearly constant, so the integration of equation 6.63 gives

$$-RT \ln X_1{}^{L} = \overline{V}_1 \Pi \tag{6.65}$$

For dilute solutions we use the first term of the series expansion in equation 6.57, and equation 6.65 becomes

$$X_2^{L}RT \cong \Pi\overline{V}_1 \quad (6.66)$$

In a dilute solution

$$X_2^{L} \cong \frac{n_2}{n_1} \quad (6.67)$$

and the volume of solution is

$$V \cong n_1\overline{V}_1 \quad (6.68)$$

Equation 6.65 becomes

$$n_2RT = \Pi V \quad (6.69)$$

In this form the osmotic pressure is expressed by an equation analogous to that used for an ideal gas, although the bases of the two are entirely different.

The osmotic pressure provides a means to measure the number of moles of solute (n_2) in a solution and thereby provides a way to measure molecular weights. Osmotic-pressure measurements are especially useful for the study of polymeric materials because the osmotic pressure in solutions of such materials is measurably large even for solutions of low molar concentration.

The relative effect of solute molecules on various properties of a solution can be illustrated for a solution with a concentration of 1% by weight of a polymer of molecular weight 10,000 in benzene solvent. At 26.1°C, the vapor pressure of pure benzene is 100 torr, and the vapor pressure of benzene above the solution is 99.9922 torr. The addition of the polymer elevates the boiling point of the benzene solution by only 0.0025°C; the freezing point of the solution is depressed by only 0.0051°C. The osmotic pressure is 25×10^3 dynes/cm^2. This is equivalent to a benzene liquid column 28 cm high. From these values we can see that osmotic pressure is particularly sensitive to the number of solute molecules in solution.

Purification of water by reverse osmosis: an application of osmosis

The principles of osmosis provide a route to an important method of water purification known as reverse osmosis. An example of a simple reverse-osmosis apparatus is shown in Fig. 6-13. Saline (salt-containing) water is circulated through chamber *b* under pressure. At a sufficiently high pressure the normal osmotic process is reversed, and water molecules diffuse from chamber *b* into chamber *a*, leaving the solute (impurities) behind. The pure water in *a* can be removed and used for human consumption.

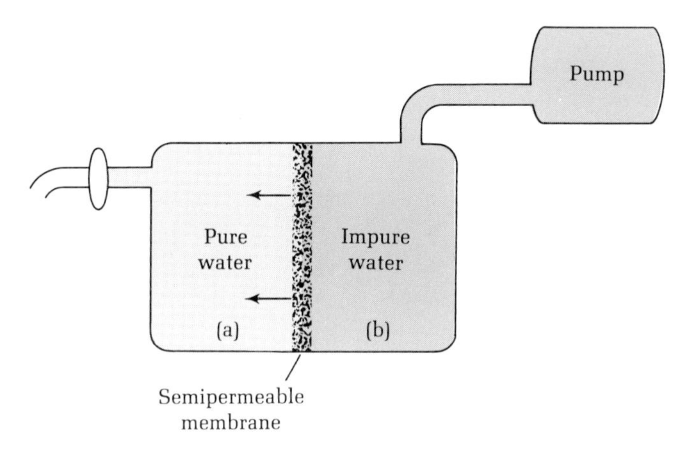

Fig. 6-13. Reverse-osmosis apparatus. Pump maintains hydrostatic pressure greater than Π in chamber *b*, causing a flow of water from chamber *b* into chamber *a*.

We can readily calculate what pressure, Π, is required to cause reverse osmosis of a given solution to occur. Consider a 0.40 *M* NaCl solution at 298 °K in chamber *b*. One liter of 0.40 *M* NaCl solution contains 0.80 moles of total solute. Thus $n_2 = 0.80$. From equation 6.69

$$\Pi = \frac{nRT}{V} = \frac{(0.80)(0.0821)(298)}{1}$$
$$= 19.6 \text{ atm}$$

We see that a hydrostatic pressure of 19.6 atm or greater in chamber *b* would maintain the reverse osmotic flow and consequently bring about the purification of the salt water.

PROBLEMS

1. Estimate the chemical potential of liquid water at 50 °C and 100 atm. Assume the entropy of 1 mole of water is constant at 16.7 cal/mole when the temperature is between 25 °C and 50 °C and the pressure is between 1 atm and 100 atm. Also assume the molar volume of liquid water is constant.
   Hint: Use equation 6.10.
2. The melting point of CCl_4 at 1 atm is −22.6 °C. The volume change and entropy change of fusion (ΔV_{fusion} and ΔS_{fusion}) are 3.97 cm³/mole and 2.45 cal/mole-deg, respectively. Calculate the melting point at 1000 atm.
3. Calculate ΔH^0, ΔG^0, and ΔS^0 for the vaporization of liquid gallium at 1154 °C from the following equilibrium data:

t, °C	1029	1154	1350
p, torr	0.0100	0.100	1.00

4. Calculate the heat of fusion of sodium at 1000 atm using the following equilibrium data:

$$Na(s) \rightarrow Na(l)$$

p, atm	1	2000
t, °C	97.6	114.2
ΔV, cm^3/gram	0.0279	0.0236

5. Calculate $\Delta H_{vap}{}^0$ for acetaldehyde, CH_3CHO, whose vapor pressure is described as a function of temperature by

$$\log p(\text{torr}) = -\frac{1447.14}{T} + 7.8206$$

6. From the entropy data in Appendix E, calculate the chemical potentials of Sn(white, s) and Sn(gray, s) at 1 atm as a function of T. From plots of $\mu_{\text{Sn(white)}}$ and $\mu_{\text{Sn(gray)}}$ versus T, determine the temperatures at which Sn(white) and Sn(gray) are stable.
7. Calculate the chemical potential of CO at 10 atm and 25°C, assuming ideal-gas behavior. Remember that $\mu^0 = \overline{G}_f{}^0$ for pure substances.
8. Calculate the fugacity of a gas whose pressure is 100 atm and whose excess chemical potential, μ^E, is 50 cal/mole at 25°C.
9. Calculate ΔG for the transformation of supercooled water at −5°C to solid water at −5°C according to

$$H_2O(l, -5°C) \rightarrow H_2O(s, -5°C)$$

The equilibrium vapor pressures at −5°C of H_2O(l) and H_2O(s) are 3.163 torr and 3.012 torr, respectively.
Hint: First express the chemical potentials of the liquid and solid forms in terms of the chemical potentials of gaseous water at their respective pressures.
10. Calculate the chemical potentials of N_2 and O_2 in air at 0.90 atm and at 25°C. The composition of air in terms of mole percentages may be taken as 20% O_2 and 80% N_2.
11. Calculate the composition and total pressure of the gas phase above a liquid solution of n-heptane and n-hexane at 50°C. The mole fraction of n-hexane in the liquid phase is 0.600. The vapor pressures of pure liquid n-hexane and n-heptane at 50°C are 408 torr and 141 torr, respectively. Assume Raoult's law holds.
12. Determine the solubility (in moles) of oxygen from air in 1 gram of water at 0°C. The air is at 1 atm pressure. The Henry's-law constant, k_H, by equation 6.45 is 1.93×10^7 torr.
13. Express the chemical potentials in terms of appropriate concentrations (or pressures) for a mixture of AgCl(s) in water at 298°K. The species involved are AgCl(s), Ag^+(aq), Cl^-(aq), H_2O(l), and H_2O(g). Refer to Appendix E for the appropriate μ^0 values.
14. Calculate the chemical potential of Ag^+(aq) in a solution of 0.0100 M Ag^+ at 25°C.
15. Calculate the standard-state chemical potential, μ^0, of Br_2 in water solution. Assume the dilute solution laws hold. Pure liquid Br_2 at 25°C is in equilibrium with an aqueous solution of Br_2 whose concentration is 0.193 M.
16. Calculate the molecular weight of 10.0 g of a nonvolatile substance dissolved in 200 g of water at 25°C. The vapor pressure of pure water at this temperature is 23.756 torr, and that of the solution is 23.400 torr.

17. Calculate the molecular weight of glucose from the knowledge that 3.6 g of glucose dissolved in 100 g of water depresses the freezing point by 0.372°C.
18. Calculate the molecular weight of hemoglobin from the determination that the osmotic pressure at 0°C of a solution that contains 22.1 g of hemoglobin per liter of solution is 6.2 torr.
19. Calculate the vapor pressure of water in blood at 40°C, where the osmotic pressure is 7.7 atm and the vapor pressure of pure water at 40°C is 55.32 torr. Assume the ideal-solution law can be used.
20. Calculate the osmotic pressure that results from a 4.0 *m* solution of sucrose at 0°C. Assume the ideal solution law holds. If this solution is in a tree that functions as an osmotic cell, how high will the liquid column rise in the tree? Assume the density of the solution is 1.0 gm/cm^3 and the molar volume, $\overline{V}_1$, is the same as that of pure water.

7 CHEMICAL REACTIONS: GIBBS FREE ENERGY AND EQUILIBRIUM

Chemical potentials or Gibbs free energy data have a very important application in understanding chemical reactions. The values of the Gibbs free energy allow us to predict whether and to what extent a reaction will occur under specific conditions. However, the rate at which a reaction takes place cannot be predicted from free energy information. We will examine reaction rates in Chapter 13.

7.1 GIBBS FREE ENERGY AND EXTENT OF REACTION

The general form of a reaction equation is

$$aA + bB + \ldots \quad \rightarrow \quad cC + dD + \ldots \tag{7.1}$$

where $a, b, \ldots$ and $c, d, \ldots$ are the stoichiometric coefficients of the reaction, and $A, B, \ldots$ and $C, D, \ldots$ are the reactant and product species. A factor called the extent of reaction, designated by ξ, is used to describe how many moles of reactants and products are involved. If $\xi = 1$, a moles of A, b moles of B, etc., are converted to c moles of C, d moles of D, etc. If $\xi = 2$, twice the number of moles is involved. A negative value of ξ means that reactants (A, B) are formed at the expense of products (C, D). If a fractional extent of reaction occurs, the fraction is given by the increment of reaction $d\xi$. The amounts of $A, B, \ldots$ that disappear and of $C, D, \ldots$ that form will be given by the product of $d\xi$ and the stoichiometric coefficients. The molar changes of $A, B, \ldots$ and $C, D, \ldots$ are related to the extent of reaction as

$$\begin{aligned} dn_A &= -a\,d\xi \\ dn_B &= -b\,d\xi \\ dn_C &= c\,d\xi \\ dn_D &= d\,d\xi \end{aligned} \tag{7.2}$$

The materials whose amounts decrease are shown with a negative sign. When $\xi = 1$, the changes in quantities of species are as follows: for A, $\Delta n_A = -a$; for B, $\Delta n_B = -b$; for C, $\Delta n_C = c$; and for D, $\Delta n_D = d$.

When a reaction occurs, properties of the system change due to differences in properties between reactants and products. Usually the volume, entropy, enthalpy, and free energy change. For a unit extent of reaction ($\xi = 1$) these changes are denoted by ΔV, ΔS, ΔH, and ΔG. For example, the change in volume for unit extent of reaction is

$$\Delta V = c\overline{V}_C + d\overline{V}_D - a\overline{V}_A - b\overline{V}_B \tag{7.3}$$

where $\overline{V}_C$ is the volume per mole of compound C, and so on. For a small extent of reaction, $d\xi$, the incremental volume change dV is given by

$$dV = \Delta V d\xi = (c\overline{V}_C + d\overline{V}_D - a\overline{V}_A - b\overline{V}_B)d\xi \tag{7.4}$$

Any change in property for a reaction can be expressed in this way. The Gibbs free energy for c moles of C and d moles of D from equation 4.59 is

$$\Sigma\, G(\text{products}) = c\mu_C + d\mu_D \tag{7.5}$$

and for a moles of A and b moles of B is

$$\Sigma\, G(\text{reactants}) = a\mu_A + b\mu_B \tag{7.6}$$

The change ΔG for $\xi = 1$ is then

$$\Delta G = c\mu_C + d\mu_D - a\mu_A - b\mu_B \tag{7.7}$$

and for an increment of reaction $d\xi$

$$dG = \Delta G d\xi \tag{7.8}$$

The Gibbs free energy per mole of a substance A, $\overline{G}_A$, is the same as the chemical potential for that substance, μ_A.

EXAMPLE **7.1**

Consider the reaction

	$2SO_2(g)$ +	$O_2(g)$	→	$2SO_3(g)$
$\overline{G}_f{}^0$(kcal/mole):	(−71.8)	0		(−88.5)

The Gibbs free energies at 25°C and 1 atm (from Appendix E) are shown beneath each substance. Let us calculate $\Sigma G_f{}^0$(reactants), $\Sigma G_f{}^0$(products), and ΔG^0:

$$\Sigma G_f^0(\text{reactants}) = 2(-71.8 + 0) = -143.6 \text{ kcal}$$
$$\Sigma G_f^0(\text{products}) = 2(-88.5) = -167.0 \text{ kcal}$$
$$\Delta G^0 = -23.4 \text{ kcal}$$

This is the Gibbs free energy change for $\xi = 1$ under standard-state conditions.

7.2 CONDITIONS FOR SPONTANEOUS DIRECTION OF CHEMICAL REACTIONS

The Gibbs free energies of reactants and products can be used in predicting the spontaneous direction of chemical reactions under specific conditions. The change in the Gibbs free energy for a small extent of reaction $d\xi$ is given by equation 7.8. At constant temperature and pressure the Gibbs free energy of a system decreases for spontaneous processes (sec. 5.4). There is no change in Gibbs free energy if the system is at equilibrium; the equilibrium condition for a chemical reaction is

$$\Delta G = 0 \tag{7.9}$$

The above situations may be shown by drawing the values of ΣG(reactants) and ΣG(products) on a free energy diagram (Fig. 7-1, *A* to *C*). Spontaneous reactions occur whenever the Gibbs free energies of reactants and products are unequal. The reaction is directed toward the side with the lower Gibbs free energy. A positive direction, from left to right, with $d\xi$ positive, occurs when $\Delta G < 0$. A

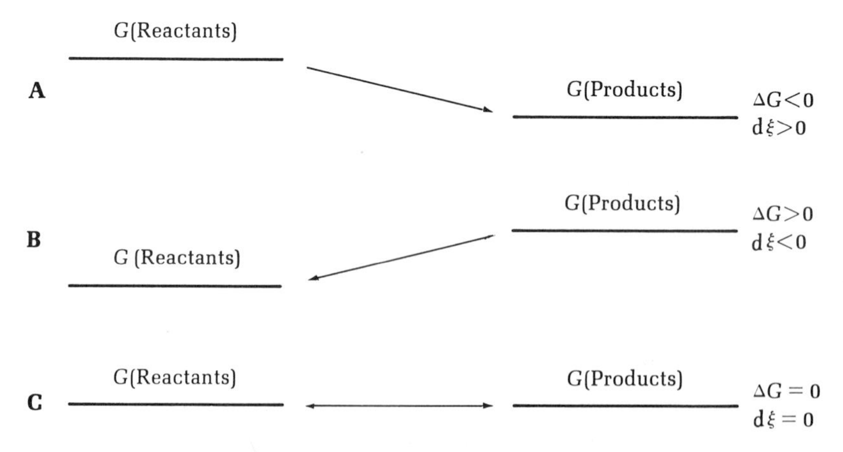

Fig. 7-1. **A,** Gibbs free energy of reactants is higher than that of products; reaction proceeds from left to right. **B,** Gibbs free energy of products is higher than that of reactants; reaction proceeds from right to left. **C,** Gibbs free energy of reactants and products is equal; reaction is at equilibrium.

negative direction, from right to left, with $d\xi$ negative, occurs when $\Delta G > 0$. No reaction occurs when $\Delta G = 0$.

7.3 GIBBS FREE ENERGY CHANGE AND EQUILIBRIUM CONSTANTS

Reactions of gases

We now examine how the Gibbs free energies of gaseous reactants and products are determined by their partial pressures. Assume all components in the reaction in equation 7.1 are ideal gases. The chemical potentials of these components are given by

$$\begin{aligned} \mu_A &= \mu_A{}^0(T) + RT \ln p_A \\ \mu_B &= \mu_B{}^0(T) + RT \ln p_B \end{aligned} \tag{7.10}$$

$$\begin{aligned} \mu_C &= \mu_C{}^0(T) + RT \ln p_C \\ \mu_D &= \mu_D{}^0(T) + RT \ln p_D \end{aligned} \tag{7.11}$$

The Gibbs free energy of reactants is

$$\Sigma G(\text{reactants}) = a\mu_A + b\mu_B$$

and with equation 7.10 we obtain

$$\Sigma G(\text{reactants}) = a\mu_A{}^0 + b\mu_B{}^0 + RT[a \ln p_A + b \ln p_B] \tag{7.12}$$

This may be arranged to give

$$\Sigma G(\text{reactants}) = a\mu_A{}^0 + b\mu_B{}^0 + RT \ln [(p_A)^a(p_B)^b] \tag{7.13}$$

The Gibbs free energy of products is

$$\Sigma G(\text{products}) = c\mu_C{}^0 + d\mu_D{}^0 + RT \ln [(p_C)^c(p_D)^d] \tag{7.14}$$

Increasing the partial pressures of the components increases the Gibbs free energy. Thus, by a suitable selection of partial pressures the free energies of reactants or products can be made higher or lower relative to one another. The difference between the free energy of products and that of reactants is

$$\Delta G = \Sigma G(\text{products}) - \Sigma G(\text{reactants}) \tag{7.15}$$

and from equations 7.13 and 7.14 we have

$$\Delta G = c\mu_C{}^0 + d\mu_D{}^0 - a\mu_A{}^0 - b\mu_B{}^0 + RT \ln \frac{(p_C)^c(p_D)^d}{(p_A)^a(p_B)^b} \tag{7.16}$$

The set of standard-state values is abbreviated by ΔG^0:

$$\Delta G^0 = c\mu_C{}^0 + d\mu_D{}^0 - a\mu_A{}^0 - b\mu_B{}^0 \tag{7.17}$$

Equation 7.16 is written as

$$\Delta G = \Delta G^0 + RT \ln Q \tag{7.18}$$

where Q is the ratio of partial pressures for the reaction equation. The value of ΔG is controlled by ΔG^0 and the values of the partial pressures that are being considered.

If we assume that chemical equilibrium is achieved, a particular set of partial pressures, determined by the equilibrium condition, $\Delta G = 0$, will be found. From equation 7.18

$$0 = \Delta G^0 + RT \ln \frac{[(p_C)^c(p_D)^d]_{\text{eq}}}{[(p_A)^a(p_B)^b]_{\text{eq}}} \tag{7.19}$$

where the subscript *eq* has been added as a reminder that these partial pressures apply for the reaction at equilibrium. Any set of partial pressures that satisfies equation 7.19 describes the equilibrium state.

Equation 7.19 provides a method by which ΔG^0 can be determined using the partial pressures measured in an equilibrated system. From its definition in terms of standard-state chemical potentials, ΔG^0 is a function of temperature only. The particular combination of partial pressures in equation 7.19 must then be a function of temperature alone. One defines this function K as the equilibrium constant:

$$K = \frac{[(p_C)^c(p_D)^d]_{\text{eq}}}{[(p_A)^a(p_B)^b]_{\text{eq}}} \tag{7.20}$$

From equation 7.19

$$\Delta G^0 = -RT \ln K \tag{7.21}$$

In broad terms, the magnitude of K expresses whether the partial pressures of the products are greater or less than the partial pressures of the reactants. Thus K indicates how far the reaction naturally proceeds from left to right.

As an example of the use of equilibrium constants, let us consider the dissociation of oxygen molecules into oxygen atoms. The reaction equation* is

$$O_2(g) \leftrightarrows 2O(g) \tag{7.22}$$

If the fractional amount of O_2 dissociated is α, the fraction remaining will be $1 - \alpha$. The fraction of O atoms will be 2α. The total moles of O_2 and O in the system is the sum, $1 + \alpha$. The mole fractions of O_2 and O are $(1 - \alpha)/(1 + \alpha)$ and $2\alpha/(1 + \alpha)$, respectively. We summarize these results as follows:

*We will use a double arrow when we wish to emphasize the equilibrium properties of a reaction.

	O_2	$\leftrightarrows$	$2O$
Moles:	$1-\alpha$		2α
Mole fractions:	$\dfrac{1-\alpha}{1+\alpha}$		$\dfrac{2\alpha}{1+\alpha}$
Partial pressures:	$\left(\dfrac{1-\alpha}{1+\alpha}\right)p$		$\left(\dfrac{2\alpha}{1+\alpha}\right)p$

The partial pressures have been calculated from the equation $p_i = X_i p$, where p is the total pressure in the system.

The equilibrium constant can be formulated as

$$K = \frac{(p_O)^2}{p_{O_2}} = \frac{\left(\dfrac{2\alpha}{1+\alpha}\right)^2 p^2}{\left(\dfrac{1-\alpha}{1+\alpha}\right)p} = \frac{4\alpha^2 p}{1-\alpha^2} \qquad (7.23)$$

If we know the equilibrium constant, as measured directly or as calculated from ΔG^0, we can evaluate the fraction of dissociation, α, as a function of p.

The above formulation of the equilibrium constant is in terms of partial pressures and is valid as long as the ideal gas approximation holds. When this assumption is inadequate, the corrected partial pressures, or fugacities, are required.

EXAMPLE **7.2**

Calculate the degree of dissociation of O_2 at 25°C.

The standard-state chemical potentials at 25°C for O_2(g) and O(g) are 0 and 55.00 kcal/mole. Therefore, ΔG^0 for the reaction given by equation 7.22 is

$$\Delta G^0 = 2 \times 55.00 - 0 = 110.00 \text{ kcal}$$

The equilibrium constant from equation 7.21 is

$$K = e^{-\Delta G^0/RT} = 10^{-110{,}000/(2.30)\,(1.987)\,(298)} = 10^{-80.7} \text{ atm}$$
$$= 10^{0.3} \times 10^{-81} \text{ atm} = 2 \times 10^{-81} \text{ atm}$$

Since the standard state is at 1 atm, K is in units of atmospheres. For O_2(g) at 1 atm the degree of dissociation is calculated from equation 7.23:

$$K = \frac{4\alpha^2 p}{1-\alpha^2}$$

Solving for α^2 gives

$$\alpha^2 = \left(\frac{4p}{K} + 1\right)^{-1} = 5 \times 10^{-82}$$

$$\alpha = 2.2 \times 10^{-41}$$

This value represents a fantastically low degree of dissociation. If we had 10^{18} moles of oxygen at 25°C, only one molecule would be dissociated. At high temperatures the situation would be modified drastically.

The state of equilibrium for reactions that involve both gases and pure liquids or pure solids is described by an equilibrium constant defined by the partial pressures of the gaseous components. The chemical potentials of pure solids and pure liquids are relatively insensitive to pressures (sec. 6.4); for most purposes they may be regarded as constant at atmospheric pressures. However, the chemical potentials of gases are very sensitive to their partial pressures. Thus, the equilibrium constant K is effectively determined by the partial pressures.

EXAMPLE **7.3**

What is the fraction of methane that decomposes at 1000°K if the total pressure is 1 atm?

$$CH_4(g) \rightleftarrows C(s, \text{graphite}) + 2H_2(g)$$

At 1000°K

$$\Delta G^0(1000°K, 1 \text{ atm}) = -4610 \text{ cal/mole}$$

The equilibrium constant is given in terms of partial pressures

$$K = \frac{(p_{H_2})^2}{p_{CH_4}}$$

Since C(s, graphite) is a solid, its concentration does not appear in the equation for K. From equation 7.21

$$K = e^{-\frac{\Delta G^0}{RT}} = e^{-\frac{-4610}{(1.987)(1000)}} = 10.18 \text{ atm}$$

The fraction decomposed is α, so

	$CH_4(g)$	$\rightleftarrows$	$C(s, \text{graphite}) + 2H_2(g)$
Fraction:	$1 - \alpha$		2α

Partial pressure: $\left(\frac{1-\alpha}{1+\alpha}\right)p$ $\left(\frac{2\alpha}{1+\alpha}\right)p$

$$K = \frac{\left(\frac{2\alpha}{1+\alpha}\right)^2 p}{\frac{1-\alpha}{1+\alpha}} = \left(\frac{4\alpha^2}{1-\alpha^2}\right)p$$

For $p = 1$ atm

$$10.18 = \frac{4\alpha^2}{1-\alpha^2}$$

$$10.18 = 14.16\alpha^2$$

$$\alpha^2 = \frac{10.18}{14.16} = 0.719$$

$$\alpha = 0.848$$

Solution reactions

The chemical potential of an ideal solution (sec. 6.5) is given by

$$\mu_i = \mu_i^0 + RT \ln X_i \tag{7.24}$$

where X_i is the mole fraction of species in solution. We shall drop the special superscripts on $\mu_i^{\text{L, ideal}}$ used earlier and simplify the notation to μ_i. The standard-state value, μ_i^0, is determined by the condition where $RT \ln X_i$ is zero, in this case, when $X_i = 1$. For dilute aqueous solutions the mole fraction is approximated in terms of molarity M_i by

$$X_i \cong \frac{M_i}{55.5}$$

where 55.5 is the number of moles of water per 1000 ml of a dilute solution. The chemical potential can be expressed as

$$\mu_i = \mu_i^0 + RT \ln M_i \tag{7.25}$$

where here μ_i^0 represents the chemical potential of the substance in a 1 molar solution. The derivation of the equilibrium-constant expression for solution reactions is analogous to the derivation shown in equations 7.15 to 7.18. The equilibrium constant is expressed in terms of the molarities of the various reaction species at equilibrium. For a general solution reaction

$$K = \frac{(M_C)^c(M_D)^d}{(M_A)^a(M_B)^b} \tag{7.26}$$

Again the general expression for ΔG is given as shown by equation 7.18:

$$\Delta G = \Delta G^0 + RT \ln Q$$

where Q is the ratio of non-equilibrium concentrations expressed in the same form as the equilibrium constant expression.

Gases, liquids, solids, and dissolved species may all be involved in a chemical reaction. By convention we represent the concentrations of gases in partial pressures (atm) and of dissolved species in moles per liter. Liquids or solids in the pure or nearly pure state (such as the solvent) do not change their concentrations and are omitted from the Q or K ratio. However, the chemical potentials of solids and liquids in chemical reactions do affect the value of ΔG^0. For example, consider the reaction

$$Mn^{2+}(aq) + Cl_2(g) + 6H_2O(l) \rightarrow 4H_3O^+(aq) + MnO_2(s) + 2Cl^-(aq)$$

$$\begin{aligned}\Delta G &= 4\mu_{H_3O^+} + \mu_{MnO_2} + 2\mu_{Cl^-} - \mu_{Mn^{2+}} - \mu_{Cl_2} - 6\mu_{H_2O} \\ &= 4\mu^0_{H_3O^+} + \mu^0_{MnO_2} + 2\mu^0_{Cl^-} - \mu^0_{Mn^{2+}} - \mu^0_{Cl_2} - 6\mu^0_{H_2O} \\ &\quad + 4RT \ln [H_3O^+] + 2RT \ln [Cl^-] - RT \ln [Mn^{2+}] - RT \ln p_{Cl_2} \\ &= \Delta G^0 + RT \ln \frac{[H_3O^+]^4[Cl^-]^2}{[Mn^{2+}]p_{Cl_2}}\end{aligned}$$

Note that ΔG^0 is expressed in terms of the standard-state chemical potentials of all reaction species. Since $MnO_2(s)$ and $H_2O(l)$ are effectively pure materials, they do not appear in the concentration-ratio expression.

7.4 EFFECT OF T AND p ON ΔG OF REACTIONS

The effect of temperature and pressure on the chemical potential or Gibbs free energy of a single substance is given by

$$d\mu_i = -\bar{S}_i dT + \bar{V}_i dp \tag{7.27}$$

The differential of the Gibbs free energy of reactants for species in equation 7.1 is

$$d\Sigma\, G(\text{reactants}) = -\Sigma\, S(\text{reactants})dT + \Sigma\, V(\text{reactants})dp \tag{7.28}$$

where

$$\Sigma\, S(\text{reactants}) = a\bar{S}_A + b\bar{S}_B \tag{7.29}$$

$$\Sigma\, V(\text{reactants}) = a\bar{V}_A + b\bar{V}_B \tag{7.30}$$

The effect of temperature and pressure on the Gibbs free energy of products in equation 7.1 is

$$d\Sigma\, G(\text{products}) = -\Sigma\, S(\text{products})dT + \Sigma\, V(\text{products})dp \tag{7.31}$$

The difference between product and reactant free energies gives

$$d\Delta G = -\Delta S dT + \Delta V dp \tag{7.32}$$

The explicit effects of temperature and pressure on ΔG are seen in equation 7.32 to be

$$\left(\frac{d\Delta G}{dT}\right)_p = -\Delta S \tag{7.33}$$

and

$$\left(\frac{d\Delta G}{dp}\right)_T = \Delta V \tag{7.34}$$

A particularly useful result is obtained by considering the temperature differential of $\Delta G/T$ at a fixed pressure. Differentiation of $\Delta G/T$ gives

$$\left(\frac{d\Delta G/T}{dT}\right)_p = \frac{1}{T}\left(\frac{d\Delta G}{dT}\right)_p - \frac{\Delta G}{T^2} \tag{7.35}$$

With equation 7.33 and $\Delta G = \Delta H - T\Delta S$, we find

$$\left(\frac{d\Delta G/T}{dT}\right)_p = -\frac{\Delta H}{T^2} \tag{7.36}$$

The effect of temperature on the equilibrium constant is then found from

$$\Delta G^0/T = -R \ln K$$

with equation 7.36, to give the *van't Hoff equation*

$$\left(\frac{d \ln K}{dT}\right)_p = \frac{\Delta H^0}{RT^2} \tag{7.37}$$

The integrated form of equation 7.37 is

$$\ln\left(\frac{K_2}{K_1}\right) = \int_{T_1}^{T_2} \frac{\Delta H^0}{RT^2}\, dT \tag{7.38}$$

If ΔH^0 is assumed constant

$$\ln\left(\frac{K_2}{K_1}\right) = -\frac{\Delta H^0}{R}\left(\frac{1}{T_2} - \frac{1}{T_1}\right) \tag{7.39}$$

EXAMPLE **7.4**

Calculate the ratio of equilibrium constants at 25°C and 100°C for the reaction

$$2NO_2(g) \rightleftarrows N_2O_4(g)$$

From the data in Appendix E

$$\Delta H^0 = [2.31 - 2\,(8.09)] = -13.87 \text{ kcal}$$

Using equation 7.39

$$\ln\left(\frac{K_2}{K_1}\right) = -\frac{\Delta H^0}{R}\left(\frac{1}{T_2} - \frac{1}{T_1}\right)$$

$$\log\left(\frac{K_2}{K_1}\right) = \frac{13{,}870}{(2.303)\,(1.987)}\left(\frac{1}{373} - \frac{1}{298}\right)$$

$$= -2.05$$

$$\frac{K_2}{K_1} = 8.91 \times 10^{-3}$$

We see that raising the temperature of an exothermic reaction shifts the equilibrium to the left. An increase in temperature shifts the equilibrium of an endothermic reaction to the right.

An explanation for the change of the equilibrium constant upon increasing the temperature can be made in terms of the effects of temperature on the chemical potentials. The sums of the chemical potentials for the reactants and for the products are shown for equilibrium conditions at 25°C in Fig. 7-2, A. The effect of temperature on the Gibbs free energy depends on the entropies of reactants and products

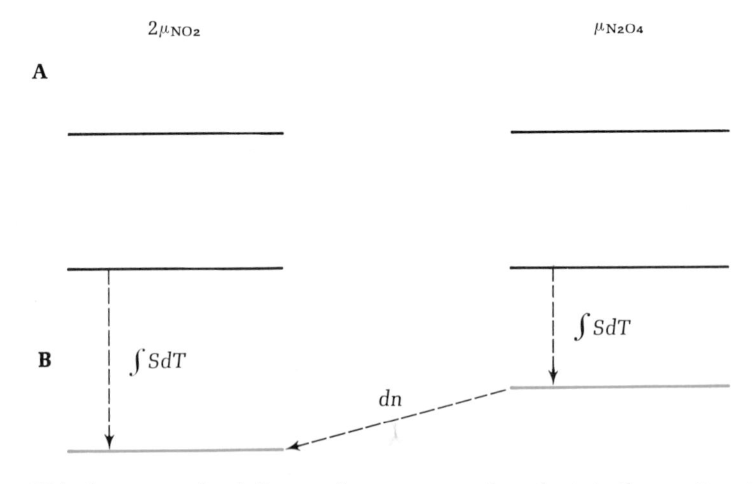

Fig. 7-2. Gibbs free energy level diagram for reactants and products in the reaction: $2NO_2$ (g) → N_2O_4 (g). **A,** Energy levels at equilibrium. **B,** Effect on free energy levels of increasing temperature.

by equation 7.27. In example 7.4, the entropy of the reactants ($2NO_2$) is 2 (57.47) = 104.94 cal/deg; the entropy of the products (N_2O_4) is 72.73 cal/deg. Thus an increase in temperature depresses the Gibbs free energy of NO_2 more than that of N_2O_4 (Fig. 7-2, *B*). This produces a non-equilibrium situation that requires a shift of material from the form of N_2O_4 to that of NO_2 until the free energies become equal.

7.5 LE CHATELIER'S PRINCIPLE

Le Chatelier's principle states that if stress is applied to a system at equilibrium, the equilibrium position will shift in the direction that reduces the stress. This important qualitative statement summarizes the general effects of changes in temperature, pressure, and concentration on the position of equilibrium in chemical reactions. We have already discussed these effects in quantitative terms expressed by the change in the Gibbs free energy. To illustrate the basis for Le Chatelier's principle we consider the effects of pressure and temperature on the equilibrium position of a chemical reaction.

Fig. 7-3, *A* and *B* shows the effect of increasing pressure on the Gibbs free-energy levels of products and reactants when $\Delta V > 0$ and when $\Delta V < 0$. The increase of pressure (stress) produces a non-equilibrium state for the reaction. In reattaining equilibrium the reaction shifts in direction toward a lower free energy level. The shift is always toward the state of smaller volume; this shift will relieve the stress of increased pressure.

In a similar way, increasing the temperature decreases the Gibbs free-energy levels of reactants and products (shown when $\Delta S > 0$ and when $\Delta S < 0$ in Fig. 7-3, *C* and *D*). At equilibrium, $\Delta H = T\Delta S$. Thus when $\Delta S > 0$, the reaction is endothermic ($\Delta H+$), and when $\Delta S < 0$, the reaction is exothermic ($\Delta H-$). The increase in temperature (stress) produces a non-equilibrium state that goes to equilibrium in the appropriate direction. The reaction always shifts toward the state of higher entropy, a state that relieves the stress of temperature. Thus an increase of temperature shifts endothermic reactions to the right and exothermic reactions to the left.

7.6 IONIC EQUILIBRIUM : ACID-BASE REACTIONS

Definitions of acids and bases

Any discussion of compounds makes frequent reference to acids, bases, and salts. We will classify acids and bases according to the Brönsted and Lewis definitions.

According to the Brönsted definition, an acid is a substance that donates a proton, and a base is a substance that accepts a proton. Some examples of Brönsted acid-base reactions are

$$HCl(aq) + NH_3(aq) \rightleftarrows NH_4^+(aq) + Cl^-(aq) \tag{7.40}$$

$$HCl(aq) + H_2O \rightleftarrows H_3O^+(aq) + Cl^-(aq) \tag{7.41}$$

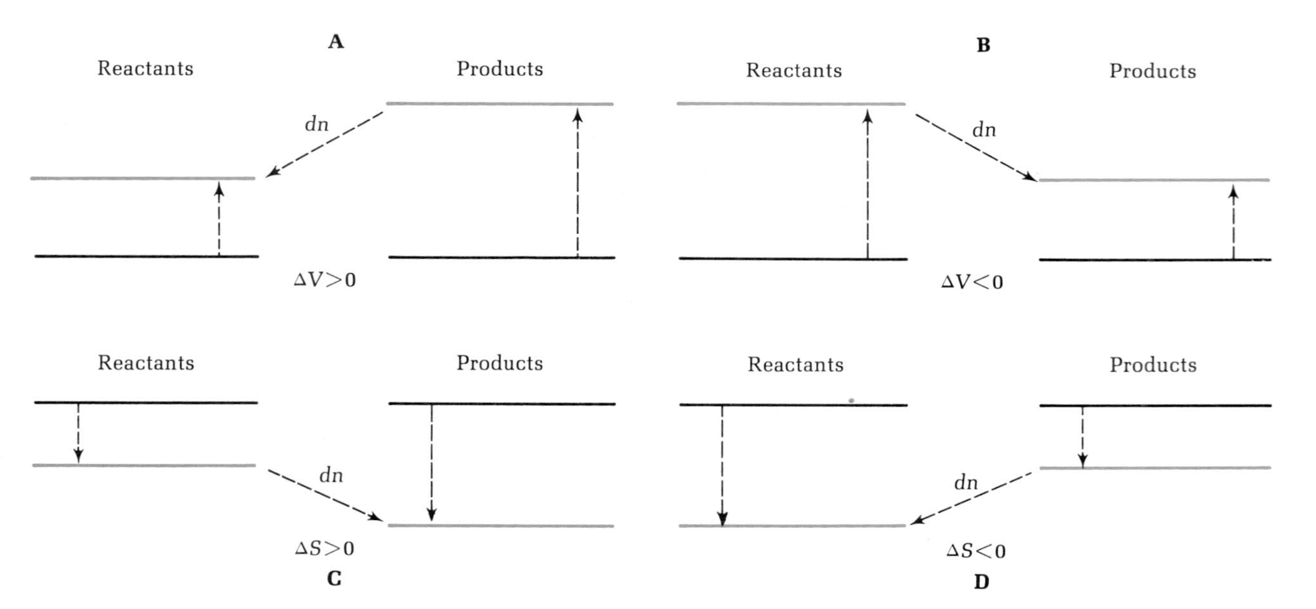

Fig. 7-3. Free energy level, diagrammatic representations of Le Chatelier's principle. **A,** If $\Delta V > 0$, increasing pressure shifts equilibrium to left. **B,** If $\Delta V < 0$, increasing pressure shifts equilibrium to right. **C,** If $\Delta S > 0$, increasing temperature shifts equilibrium to right. **D,** It $\Delta S < 0$, increasing temperature shifts equilibrium to left.

$$H_2O + NH_3(aq) \rightleftarrows NH_4^+(aq) + OH^-(aq) \qquad (7.42)$$

$$\text{Acid}_1 + \text{Base}_2 \rightleftarrows \text{Acid}_2 + \text{Base}_1 \qquad (7.43)$$

Equation 7.43 shows the general features of Brönsted acid-base reactions. A proton is donated from Acid_1 to Base_2 to form Acid_2 and Base_1. Each acid has its *conjugate base*. In equation 7.40, the conjugate base of the acid HCl(aq) is Cl^-(aq). In every case we are dealing with ionic equilibria. In the Brönsted system, water can function as an acid or as a base.

A broader definition of acids and bases, one that includes a greater number of compounds than the Brönsted method, is often extremely useful. The Lewis definition accomplishes this. A Lewis acid is a species that accepts electrons (generally an electron pair); a Lewis base is a species that donates electrons. Examples are shown in the reactions below (equations 7.44 and 7.45). In both cases, NH_3 has a lone pair of electrons that it donates. Ag^+ and BF_3 are acids because they accept the electron pair.

$$2\left(\begin{array}{c} \text{H} \\ | \\ \text{H—N:} \\ | \\ \text{H} \end{array}\right) + Ag^+ \rightarrow \left(\begin{array}{c} \text{H} \qquad\quad \text{H} \\ | \qquad\qquad | \\ \text{H—N—Ag—N—H} \\ | \qquad\qquad | \\ \text{H} \qquad\quad \text{H} \end{array}\right)^+ \qquad (7.44)$$

$$\begin{array}{c} \text{H} \\ | \\ \text{H—N:} \\ | \\ \text{H} \end{array} + \begin{array}{c} \text{F} \\ | \\ \text{B—F} \\ | \\ \text{F} \end{array} \rightarrow \begin{array}{c} \text{H} \quad \text{F} \\ | \quad\;\; | \\ \text{H—N—B—F} \\ | \quad\;\; | \\ \text{H} \quad \text{F} \end{array} \qquad (7.45)$$

Some additional examples of Lewis acid-base reactions are given in equations 7.46 to 7.48. They all involve electron-pair acceptors (acids) and electron-pair donors (bases).

$$NH_3 + H^+ \rightarrow NH_4^+ \qquad (7.46)$$

$$6Cl^- + Cr^{3+} \rightarrow CrCl_6^{3-} \qquad (7.47)$$

$$Ag^+ + Cl^- \rightarrow AgCl \qquad (7.48)$$

Strengths of acids and bases

The strengths of acids and bases are expressed quantitatively by the extent of reaction with a reference material such as water. The equilibrium constant conveniently gives the extent of reaction at equilibrium.

For an acid, HA, the reaction is

$$HA(aq) + H_2O \leftrightarrows H_3O^+(aq) + A^-(aq) \qquad (7.49)$$

$$K_a = \frac{[H_3O^+(aq)][A^-(aq)]}{[HA(aq)]} \tag{7.50}$$

The K_a is the acid dissociation constant. Strong acids have large values of $K_a(>1)$, and weak acids have small values of $K_a(<1)$. Strong acids are virtually completely dissociated whereas weak acids are partially dissociated.

Similarly, the strength of a base, B, is defined by the reaction

$$B(aq) + H_2O \leftrightarrows HB^+(aq) + OH^-(aq) \tag{7.51}$$

$$K_b = \frac{[HB^+(aq)][OH^-(aq)]}{[B(aq)]} \tag{7.52}$$

In the expressions for both K_a and K_b the solvent concentration is effectively constant and is therefore not included. Strong bases have large values for K_b, and weak bases have small values for K_b. Typical values of K_a and K_b are shown in Table 7-1.

An examination of the dissociation-constant data in Table 7-1 shows that acid strengths vary over a range of many powers of ten. However, some generalizations about acid behavior and acid strengths for inorganic and organic acids can be made.

Inorganic acids that have more than one acid proton (polyprotic acids) generally lose the first proton much more readily than subsequent protons. Equations for the successive dissociation reactions of H_3PO_4 are

Table 7-1. DISSOCIATION CONSTANTS OF ACIDS AND BASES AT 25°C

Acid	*Formula*	K_a
Hydriodic	HI	10^{10}
Hydrochloric	HCl	10^{7}
Nitric	HNO_3	2.4×10^{1}
Phosphoric	H_3PO_4 (1st proton)	7.5×10^{-3}
	$H_2PO_4^-$ (2nd proton)	6.2×10^{-8}
	HPO_4^{2-} (3rd proton)	4.8×10^{-13}
Nitrous	HNO_2	4.5×10^{-4}
Acetic	CH_3CO_2H	1.8×10^{-5}
Propanoic	$CH_3CH_2CO_2H$	1.3×10^{-5}
Chloroacetic	$ClCH_2CO_2H$	1.4×10^{-3}
Trichloroacetic	Cl_3CCO_2H	2.8×10^{-1}
Carbonic	H_2CO_3 (1st proton)	4.2×10^{-7}
	HCO_3^- (2nd proton)	4.8×10^{-11}
Hydrosulfuric	H_2S (1st proton)	1.0×10^{-7}
	HS^- (2nd proton)	1.0×10^{-14}
Base	*Formula*	K_b
Ammonia	NH_3	1.8×10^{-5}
Methylamine	CH_3NH_2	4.4×10^{-4}

$$\mathrm{H{-}O{-}P({=}O)(OH){-}O{-}H} + H_2O \rightleftharpoons \left(\mathrm{H{-}O{-}P({=}O)(OH){-}O}\right)^{-} + H_3O^+ \qquad K_a = 7.5 \times 10^{-3}$$

$$\left(\mathrm{H{-}O{-}P({=}O)(OH){-}O}\right)^{-} + H_2O \rightleftharpoons \left(\mathrm{O{-}P({=}O)(OH){-}O}\right)^{2-} + H_3O^+ \qquad K_a = 6.2 \times 10^{-8}$$

$$\left(\mathrm{O{-}P({=}O)(OH){-}O}\right)^{2-} + H_2O \rightleftharpoons \left(\mathrm{O{-}P({=}O)(O){-}O}\right)^{3-} + H_3O^+ \qquad K_a = 4.8 \times 10^{-13}$$

Each successive dissociation constant is lower than the previous one by a factor of nearly 10^5. We can readily understand this if we note that as the negative charge of the acid species increases, more work (free energy) is required to remove a proton.

Generally, the organic carboxylic acids are weak. They are differentiated from one another by the different groups (R groups) that are attached to the $—CO_2H$ group. The dissociation reaction for a carboxylic acid in water is

$$R{-}C({=}O){-}OH + H_2O \rightleftharpoons \left(R{-}C({=}O){-}O\right)^{-} + H_3O^+$$

The magnitudes of the dissociation constants of acids with similar R groups are about the same. For acetic acid ($R = CH_3—$) and propanoic acid ($R = CH_3CH_2—$), in which the R groups are simple hydrocarbon radicals, the values of K are about 10^{-5}. However, if R groups contain highly electronegative atoms, the strength of the acid is markedly increased. In the series CH_3CO_2H, $ClCH_2CO_2H$, and Cl_3CCO_2H, the dissociation constants increase from about 10^{-5} to about 10^{-1} because the highly electronegative Cl atoms withdraw electrons from the $—CO_2H$ group, making the proton of the acid progressively easier to remove as progressively less work is required to do so.

A reaction between a strong acid and a strong base (such as NaOH) yields water and the salt of the acid as products. For example, the reaction of HI and NaOH in aqueous solution is

$$HI + NaOH \rightarrow H_2O + NaI \tag{7.53}$$

The product NaI is called a *salt*. It is the sodium salt of hydriodic acid. The reaction in aqueous solution also can be written

$$H_3O^+(aq) + I^-(aq) + Na^+(aq) + OH^-(aq) \rightarrow 2H_2O + Na^+(aq) + I^-(aq) \tag{7.54}$$

because HI is a strong acid, NaOH is a strong base, and NaI is completely dissociated in water.

Similarly, a reaction between a weak acid and a weak base yields water and the salt of the weak acid. For the reaction of NH_3 with CH_3CO_2H (acetic acid), the salt ammonium acetate is formed:

$$NH_3 + CH_3CO_2H \rightarrow NH_4CH_3CO_2 + H_2O \tag{7.55}$$

In water, the ammonium acetate salt is completely dissociated, so the above reaction could be written

$$NH_3(aq) + CH_3CO_2H(aq) \rightarrow NH_4^+(aq) + CH_3CO_2^-(aq) + H_2O \tag{7.56}$$

In the above reactions, the predominate species are indicated in the equations. However, as we will see later, the complete description of all species in the reaction requires consideration of additional reactions and reaction components whose concentrations are relatively low.

pH, pOH, and pK

Concentrations of H_3O^+ and OH^- and values of K_a and K_b frequently are expressed in logarithmic terms, defined as follows:

$$pH = -\log [H_3O^+] \tag{7.57}$$

$$pOH = -\log [OH^-] \tag{7.58}$$

$$pK_a = -\log K_a \tag{7.59}$$

$$pK_b = -\log K_b \tag{7.60}$$

These terms are convenient because of the wide range of values found for the concentrations of H_3O^+ and OH^- and for the equilibrium constants.

EXAMPLE **7.5**

Calculate K_a, pK_a, and pH for a 0.1000 *M* solution of acetic acid in water at 25°C where $[H_3O^+] = 1.34 \times 10^{-3}$ *M*.

The reaction we consider is

$$CH_3CO_2H + H_2O \leftrightarrows H_3O^+ + CH_3CO_2^-$$

For this reaction

$$K_a = \frac{[H_3O^+][CH_3CO_2^-]}{[CH_3CO_2H]}$$

From the stoichiometry of this reaction

$$[H_3O^+] = [CH_3CO_2^-] = 1.34 \times 10^{-3} \quad M$$

Then

$$\begin{aligned}[CH_3CO_2H] &= 0.1000 - [CH_3CO_2^-] \\ &= 0.1000 - 0.0013 \\ &= 0.0987\ M\end{aligned}$$

Thus

$$K_a = \frac{(1.34 \times 10^{-3})^2}{0.0987} = 1.82 \times 10^{-5}$$

$$\begin{aligned}pK_a &= -\log K_a &&= -[(\log 1.82) - 5] = -(0.26 - 5) = 4.74 \\ pH &= -\log [H_3O^+] &&= -[(\log 1.34) - 3] = -(0.13 - 3) = 2.87\end{aligned}$$

Autoionization of water

Water dissociates according to

$$H_2O + H_2O \leftrightarrows H_3O^+ + OH^- \tag{7.61}$$

and thus functions as both a Brönsted acid and a Brönsted base. The equilibrium constant is written

$$K = \frac{[H_3O^+][OH^-]}{[H_2O]^2} \tag{7.62}$$

Since the water concentration, $[H_2O]$, is essentially constant for aqueous solutions, we define a new constant K_w, as

$$K_w = K[H_2O]^2 \tag{7.63}$$

$$K_w = [H_3O^+][OH^-] \tag{7.64}$$

At 25°C, K_w has the value 1.0×10^{-14}. The units of K_w are molar^2. Equation 7.64 tells us that for any aqueous solution, if the concentration of either H_3O^+ or OH^- is known, the concentrations of the other species can always be calculated.

In aqueous solutions, the pH and the pOH are related by taking negative logarithms of equation 7.64, to give, at 25°C:

$$\text{pH} + \text{pOH} = \text{p}K_w = 14 \qquad (7.65)$$

EXAMPLE **7.6**

Calculate the pH of pure water at 25°C.

According to equation 7.61, equal amounts of H_3O^+ and OH^- are formed in pure water. Thus

$$[H_3O^+] = [OH^-] = x$$

From equation 7.63

$$10^{-14} = x^2$$

so

$$x = 10^{-7} = [H_3O^+]$$

Thus the pH of pure water is

$$\text{pH} = -\log [H_3O^+] = 7$$

The pH and pOH of neutral solutions both are equal to 7. The pH of acidic solutions is less than 7, and the pH of basic solutions is greater than 7.

Solutions of weak acids, weak bases, and their salts

We have expressed the dissociation behavior of acids and bases in water in equations 7.40 to 7.42. In following examples we consider some of the simpler methods for calculating the concentrations of all species in solutions of (1) weak monoprotic acids and bases and (2) the salts of weak monoprotic acids or bases.

EXAMPLE **7.7**

Calculate the $[H_3O^+]$ for (a) 1.0 *M*, (b) 0.01 *M*, and (c) 0.0001 *M* acetic acid ($HC_2H_3O_2$) solutions. Let HO*Ac* be the abbreviation for $HC_2H_3O_2$.

The equilibrium reaction is

$$HOAc + H_2O \leftrightarrows H_3O^+ + OAc^-$$

with $K_a = 1.8 \times 10^{-5}$ at 25°C.

a. Let x represent the concentrations of H_3O^+ and OAc^- that arise upon dissociation of HO*Ac*. For the 1.0 *M* solution the concentrations of species at equilibrium will be

$$[HOAc] = 1.0 - x$$
$$[H_3O^+] = x$$
$$[OAc] = x$$

giving

$$K_a = \frac{x^2}{1.0 - x} = 1.8 \times 10^{-5}$$

This equation can be solved with the quadratic formula, but it is much easier to use successive approximations. We can see that $x^2/(1.0 - x)$ is a very small number (1.8×10^{-5}). This means that x must be very small and to a first approximation can be neglected in the term $1.0 - x$. Thus for the first approximation we have

$$\frac{x^2}{1.0} \cong 1.8 \times 10^{-5}$$
$$x = 4.2 \times 10^{-3}\ M$$

Since x is very small compared to 1.0, the procedure was reasonable. We can check further by placing the first value for x in the place where it was first neglected to arrive at a second approximation:

$$\frac{x^2}{1.0 - 0.0042} \cong 1.8 \times 10^{-5}$$
$$x = 4.2 \times 10^{-3}\ M = [H_3O^+] = [OAc^-]$$

Since the same value to two significant figures is obtained, we conclude that the answer is suitable. The concentration of HO*Ac* is then

$$[HOAc] = 1.0 - 0.0042 = 0.996\ M$$

b. For the 0.01 M solution the concentrations of species at equilibrium will be

$$[HOAc] = 0.01 - x$$
$$[H_3O^+] = x$$
$$[OAc^-] = x$$

giving

$$K_a = \frac{x^2}{0.01 - x} = 1.8 \times 10^{-5}$$

First approximation:

$$\frac{x^2}{0.01} = 1.8 \times 10^{-5}$$
$$x = 4.2 \times 10^{-4}\ M$$

Second approximation:

$$\frac{x^2}{0.01 - 0.0004} = 1.8 \times 10^{-5}$$
$$\mathrm{x} = 4.2 \times 10^{-4}\ M$$

so

$$[H_3O^+] = [OAc^-] = 4.2 \times 10^{-4}\ M$$
$$[HOAc] = 9.6 \times 10^{-3}\ M$$

c. For the 0.0001 M solution we have

$$K_a = 1.8 \times 10^{-5} = \frac{x^2}{0.0001 - x} = 1.8 \times 10^{-5}$$

First approximation:

$$\frac{x^2}{0.0001} = 1.8 \times 10^{-5}$$
$$x = 4.2 \times 10^{-5}$$

Second approximation:

$$\frac{x^2}{0.0001 - 0.000042} = 1.8 \times 10^{-5}$$
$$x = 3.2 \times 10^{-5}$$

Third approximation:

$$\frac{x^2}{0.0001 - 0.000032} = 1.8 \times 10^{-5}$$
$$x = 3.5 \times 10^{-5}$$

Fourth approximation:

$$\frac{x^2}{0.0001 - 0.000035} = 1.8 \times 10^{-5}$$
$$x = 3.4 \times 10^{-5}$$

This value satisfies our equation. Thus

$$[H_3O^+] = [OAc^-] = 3.4 \times 10^{-5}\ M$$
$$[HOAc] = 6.5 \times 10^{-4}\ M$$

In the preceding calculations we neglected the contribution to the concentration of H_3O^+ that arises from the ionization of water. The largest value of $[H_3O^+]$ that the ionization of water can contribute is $10^{-7}\ M$, which for the above solutions is small enough to be neglected.

To calculate the concentrations of all species in a solution made from a salt of a weak acid or base, we need to consider the reactions that occur between such salts and water. These reactions are called *hydrolysis reactions*. For the salt of a weak acid, we write the reaction of water with the acid anion (A^-) as

$$A^-(aq) + H_2O \leftrightharpoons HA(aq) + OH^-(aq) \tag{7.66}$$

The expression for the equilibrium constant is

$$K_h = \frac{[HA][OH^-]}{[A^-]} \tag{7.67}$$

in which the concentration of H_2O is included in K_h. Values for K_h can be obtained from a knowledge of K_a and K_w as follows. From equation 7.64:

$$[OH^-] = \frac{K_w}{[H_3O^+]} \tag{7.68}$$

Substituting this into equation 7.67, we obtain

$$K_h = \frac{[HA]K_w}{[A^-][H_3O^+]} \tag{7.69}$$

This can be written in the form of equation 7.50 as

$$K_a = \frac{[H_3O^+][A^-]}{[HA]} = \frac{K_w}{K_h} \tag{7.70}$$

Thus

$$K_h = \frac{K_w}{K_a} \tag{7.71}$$

EXAMPLE **7.8**

Calculate the pH of a solution of 1.0 M NaCN at 25°C. K_a of HCN is 7.2×10^{-10}. The concentrations of species at equilibrium are shown beneath the reaction:

$$\underset{1.0-x}{CN^-} + H_2O \leftrightarrows \underset{x}{HCN} + \underset{x}{OH^-}$$

giving

$$K_h = \frac{K_w}{K_a} = \frac{1.0 \times 10^{-14}}{7.2 \times 10^{-10}} = 1.4 \times 10^{-5}$$

$$K_h = 1.4 \times 10^{-5} = \frac{x^2}{1.0 - x}$$

First approximation:

$$\frac{x^2}{1.0} = 1.4 \times 10^{-5}$$

$$x = 3.7 \times 10^{-3}$$

Second approximation:

$$\frac{x^2}{1.0 - 0.0037} = 1.4 \times 10^{-5}$$

$$x = 3.7 \times 10^{-3}$$

Thus

$$[OH^-] = 3.7 \times 10^{-1}\ M$$

$$pOH = 2.43$$

and

$$pH = 14 - 2.43$$
$$= 11.57$$

We treat the hydrolysis of a salt of a weak base cation BH^+ (such as NH_4^+ in NH_4Cl) in an analogous manner:

$$BH^+(aq) + H_2O \leftrightarrows B(aq) + H_3O^+(aq) \quad (7.72)$$

$$K_h = \frac{[B][H_3O^+]}{[BH^+]} \quad (7.73)$$

We eliminate $[H_3O^+]$ by using $K_w = [H_3O^+][OH^-]$ and obtain

$$K_h = \frac{K_w}{K_b} \tag{7.74}$$

where K_b is given by equation 7.52. Typical base dissociation constants are given in Table 7-1.

EXAMPLE 7.9

Calculate the pH of a 1.0 M NH_4Cl solution.

$$NH_4^+ + H_2O \leftrightarrows NH_3 + H_3O^+$$

The equilibrium concentrations are: $[NH_4^+]$, $1.0 - x$; $[NH_3]$, x; $[H_3O^+]$, x. Thus

$$K_h = \frac{1.0 \times 10^{-14}}{1.8 \times 10^{-5}} = \frac{x^2}{1.0 - x} = 5.6 \times 10^{-10}$$

First approximation:

$$\frac{x^2}{1.0} = 5.6 \times 10^{-10}$$

$$x = 2.4 \times 10^{-5}\,M$$

$$\mathrm{pH} = -\log x = -(0.37 - 5)$$

$$= 4.63$$

Buffer solutions

In many practical applications it is necessary to have a solution whose pH remains essentially constant even though reactions that produce or consume large amounts of H_3O^+ are taking place. A convenient way of stabilizing pH is through the use of a buffer solution. A buffer solution is prepared from a mixture of a weak acid or base and its salt.

The theory of a buffer solution of a weak acid and its salt is based on the reaction of equation 7.50, where

$$K_a = \frac{[H_3O^+][A^-]}{[HA]} \tag{7.75}$$

This can be expressed in logarithmic form as

$$\log K_a = \log\,[H_3O^+] + \log \frac{[A^-]}{[HA]} \tag{7.76}$$

or as

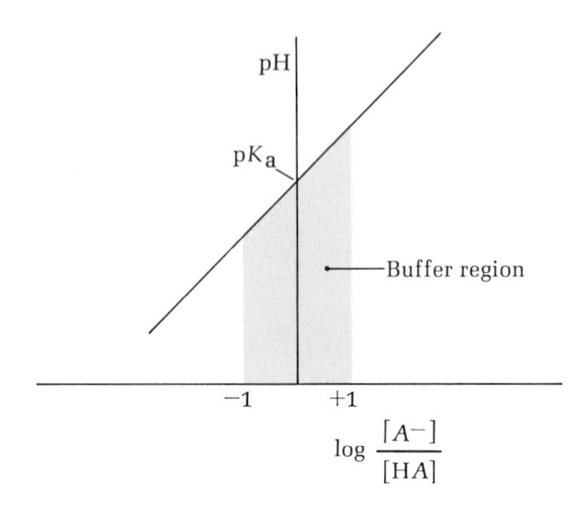

Fig. 7-4. Plot of pH versus log ([A^-]/[HA]) for weak acid with dissociation constant K_a.

$$pH = pK_a + \log \frac{[A^-]}{[HA]} \tag{7.77}$$

A plot of pH versus log ([A^-]/[HA]) is shown in Fig. 7-4. The intercept on the pH axis is pK_a, and the slope is unity. When the pH differs from pK_a by ± 1 unit, the concentration ratio [A^-]/[HA] varies from $\frac{1}{10}$ to 10. In this range of pH values the solution is said to function as a buffer. The pH change is relatively small compared to the change in number of moles of hydrogen ion involved in the reaction of A^- going to HA.

Consider 1 liter of a solution with a pH of 7 that is 1.0 *M* in A^- and 1 *M* in HA. [A^-]/[HA] = 1. If 0.1 moles of H_3O^+ are added to this solution, [A^-]/[HA] becomes 0.9/1.1 = 0.82, or log ([A^-]/[HA]) = −0.087. This is the change in pH for the buffered solution; that is, the pH goes from 7.00 to 6.91. This change in pH is small compared to the large amount of H_3O^+ added. If the same amount of acid were added to 1 liter of unbuffered pure water with a pH of 7, the water-acid solution would have a final pH of 1. The amount of acid a buffer can absorb without changing its pH by more than a given amount depends on the concentrations of HA and A^-.

EXAMPLE 7.10

Let us consider the preparation of a buffer solution with a pH of 4.00. To make this buffer we need a material with a pK_a close to 4. Table 7-1 shows that acetic acid has a $pK_a = 4.75$. From equation 7.77

$$\mathrm{pH} = \mathrm{p}K_a + \log \frac{[\mathrm{O}Ac^-]}{[\mathrm{HO}Ac]}$$

or

$$4.00 = 4.75 + \log \frac{[\mathrm{O}Ac^-]}{[\mathrm{HO}Ac]}$$

$$\log \frac{[\mathrm{O}Ac^-]}{[\mathrm{HO}Ac]} = -0.75$$

$$\frac{[\mathrm{O}Ac^-]}{[\mathrm{HO}Ac]} = 0.18$$

Thus we might prepare the buffer from 1 *M* HO*Ac* and 0.18 *M* NaO*Ac* or from any other combination of concentrations that gives the ratio 0.18. The higher the concentrations, the greater the buffer capacity.

Indicators

A special class of weak acids (or weak bases) has the interesting property of having different colors in the acid (H*Ind*) form than in the anionic (Ind^-) form. The equilibrium reaction is

$$\mathrm{H}Ind + \mathrm{H_2O} \leftrightarrows Ind^- + \mathrm{H_3O^+} \tag{7.78}$$

$$\text{one color} \leftrightarrows \text{different color}$$

$$K_{Ind} = \frac{[Ind^-][\mathrm{H_3O^+}]}{[\mathrm{H}Ind]} \tag{7.79}$$

This is the same type equilibrium reaction as seen for other weak acids. The pH of a solution is related to the concentrations of indicator species as

$$\mathrm{pH} = \mathrm{p}K_{Ind} + \log \frac{[Ind^-]}{[\mathrm{H}Ind]} \tag{7.80}$$

Table 7-2. pH RANGE AND COLORS OF TYPICAL INDICATORS

Indicator	*pH range*	*Color change*
Methyl orange	2.8–3.8	Red to orange
Methyl red	3.8–6.1	Red to yellow
Litmus	5.0–8.1	Pink to blue
Phenol red	6.8–8.6	Yellow to red
Phenolphthalein	8.0–9.6	Colorless to red
Thymolphthalein	10.2–11.7	Colorless to blue

When the pH changes ±1 unit from pK_{Ind}, the ratio of $[Ind^-]/[HInd]$ changes from $\frac{1}{10}$ to 10, easily recognized by a significant change in the color of the solution. The pH ranges for significant color changes of several indicators are shown in Table 7-2.

Indicators have many practical uses since they provide a direct means for assessing the approximate pH of solutions.

7.7 MULTISTAGE EQUILIBRIA

Polyprotic acids

Acids that can dissociate in water to give more than one H_3O^+ ion are called polyprotic acids. Several (H_2CO_3, H_3PO_4, H_2S) are listed in Table 7-1 along with the dissociation constants for the successive steps. For example, with H_2CO_3:

$$H_2CO_3 + H_2O \leftrightarrows HCO_3^- + H_3O^+ \qquad K_1 = 4.2 \times 10^{-7} \tag{7.81}$$

$$HCO_3^- + H_2O \leftrightarrows CO_3^{2-} + H_3O^+ \qquad K_2 = 4.8 \times 10^{-11} \tag{7.82}$$

where

$$K_1 = \frac{[HCO_3^-][H_3O^+]}{[H_2CO_3]} \tag{7.83}$$

$$K_2 = \frac{[CO_3^{2-}][H_3O^+]}{[HCO_3^-]} \tag{7.84}$$

In carbonate solutions there are always two equilibrium reactions. Often it is useful to consider an overall reaction as the sum of successive reactions. For the above two reactions

$$H_2CO_3 + 2H_2O \leftrightarrows CO_3^{2-} + 2H_3O^+ \tag{7.85}$$

where K_3 is the product of the constants K_1 and K_2:

$$K_3 = K_1K_2 = \frac{[CO_3^{2-}][H_3O^+]^2}{[H_2CO_3]} \tag{7.86}$$

To evaluate the concentrations of all species in carbonate solutions, we need a set of independent equations equal in number to the number of unknown species. The equilibrium-constant expressions provide one set of independent relations. Another equation that can be written is the *equation of mass balance*, which expresses the sum of the various carbonate species. If C_0 is the total concentration of carbonate species, we can write

$$C_0 = [H_2CO_3] + [HCO_3^-] + [CO_3^{2-}] \tag{7.87}$$

Finally, since the solution must be electrically neutral, an equation can be written to represent the balance of charge. The sum of the anion concentrations weighted according to charge must equal the sum of the charge-weighted cation concentrations. For a solution of carbonic acid

$$[OH^-] + [HCO_3^-] + 2[CO_3^{2-}] = [H_3O^+] \tag{7.88}$$

The factor of 2 before CO_3^{2-} occurs because CO_3^{2-} is doubly charged. We have also included $[OH^-]$ since water dissociates according to

$$H_2O + H_2O \leftrightarrows H_3O^+ + OH^- \tag{7.89}$$

$$K_w = [H_3O^+][OH^-] \tag{7.90}$$

thereby providing a source of OH^- ions. In this carbonate example, we have five species concentrations, $[H_2CO_3]$, $[HCO_3^-]$, $[CO_3^{2-}]$, $[OH^-]$, and $[H_3O^+]$, and five equations relating these species, 7.83, 7.84, 7.87, 7.88, and 7.90.

There are various ways to solve these equations. We shall develop an equation which gives the H_3O^+ concentration in terms of the equilibrium constants, K_1, K_2, K_w, and the amount of material, C_0. To obtain this equation we eliminate all other species by algebraically combining the equations that contain them. $[HCO_3^-]$ and $[CO_3^{2-}]$ in terms of H_2CO_3 and H_3O^+ are found from equations 7.83 and 7.86:

$$[HCO_3^-] = K_1 \frac{[H_2CO_3]}{[H_3O^+]} \tag{7.91}$$

$$[CO_3^{2-}] = \frac{K_1K_2[H_2CO_3]}{[H_3O^+]^2} \tag{7.92}$$

Substituting these terms into the mass-balance equation (7.87) we obtain

$$C_0 = [H_2CO_3] + \frac{K_1[H_2CO_3]}{[H_3O^+]} + \frac{K_1K_2[H_2CO_3]}{[H_3O^+]^2} \tag{7.93}$$

from which $[H_2CO_3]$ can be expressed in terms of C_0, K_1, K_2, and $[H_3O^+]$:

$$[H_2CO_3] = \frac{C_0}{1 + \dfrac{K_1}{[H_3O^+]} + \dfrac{K_1K_2}{[H_3O^+]^2}} \tag{7.94}$$

Using equations 7.91 and 7.92, we can write the concentrations of HCO_3^- and CO_3^{2-} in terms of $[H_3O^+]$, K_1, and K_2:

$$[HCO_3^-] = \frac{C_0 \dfrac{K_1}{[H_3O^+]}}{1 + \dfrac{K_1}{[H_3O^+]} + \dfrac{K_1K_2}{[H_3O^+]^2}} \tag{7.95}$$

and

$$[CO_3^{2-}] = \frac{C_0 \dfrac{K_1K_2}{[H_3O^+]^2}}{1 + \dfrac{K_1}{[H_3O^+]} + \dfrac{K_1K_2}{[H_3O^+]^2}} \tag{7.96}$$

These charged-species concentrations can now be substituted into the charge-balance equation (7.88) along with the expression for OH^- given by equation 7.90 to give

$$\frac{K_W}{[H_3O^+]} + \frac{C_0\left(\dfrac{K_1}{[H_3O^+]} + 2\dfrac{K_1K_2}{[H_3O^+]^2}\right)}{1 + \dfrac{K_1}{[H_3O^+]} + \dfrac{K_1K_2}{[H_3O^+]^2}} = [H_3O^+] \tag{7.97}$$

Using successive approximations, we can solve this equation for $[H_3O^+]$ at any given concentration of C_0. Then $[H_2CO_3]$, $[HCO_3^-]$, $[CO_3^{2-}]$, and $[OH^-]$ can be found from the preceding equations.

EXAMPLE **7.11**

Set up an equation for the calculation of $[H_3O^+]$ in 1 liter of solution prepared from 0.01 mole Na_2CO_3 and 0.011 mole HCl.

The total carbonate concentration is 0.01 *M*, distributed as species H_2CO_3, HCO_3^-, and CO_3^{2-}. The concentrations of Na^+ and Cl^- are 0.02 *M* and 0.011 *M*, respectively, since these ions are present as free ions in water. The charge-balance equation is

$$[OH^-] + [Cl^-] + [HCO_3^-] + 2[CO_3^{2-}] = [H_3O^+] + [Na^+]$$

and from the equations developed above we have

$$\frac{K_W}{[H_3O^+]} + [Cl^-] + \frac{C_0\left(\dfrac{K_1}{[H_3O^+]} + \dfrac{2K_1K_2}{[H_3O^+]^2}\right)}{\dfrac{K_1}{[H_3O^+]} + \dfrac{K_1K_2}{[H_3O^+]^2}} = [H_3O^+] + [Na^+]$$

We now insert the values for $[Na^+]$, $[Cl^-]$, C_0, K_1, K_2, and K_W to obtain

$$\frac{10^{-14}}{[H_3O^+]} - 0.009 + \frac{0.01\left(\dfrac{4.2 \times 10^{-7}}{[H_3O^+]} + \dfrac{4 \times 10^{-17}}{[H_3O^+]^2}\right)}{1 + \dfrac{4.2 \times 10^{-7}}{[H_3O^+]} + \dfrac{2 \times 10^{-17}}{[H_3O^+]^2}} - [H_3O^+] = 0$$

The value of $[H_3O^+]$ can be found by successive approximations.

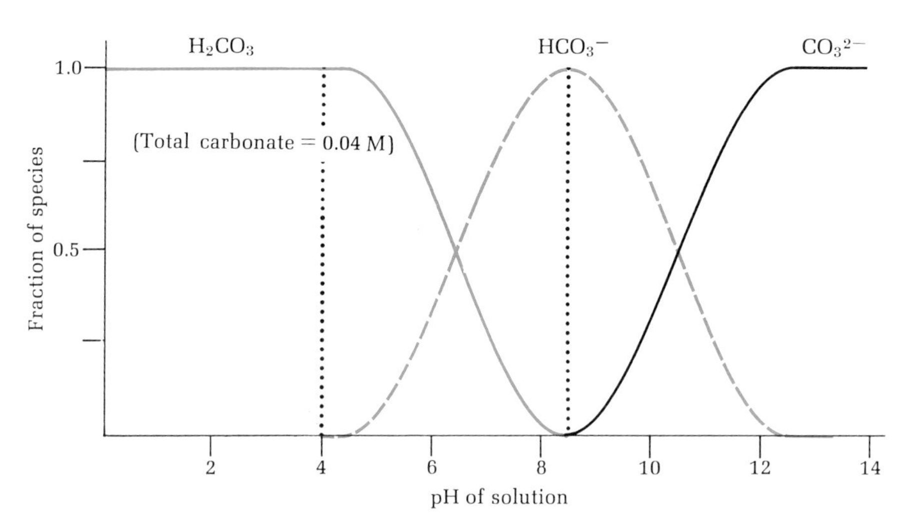

Fig. 7-5. Fraction of carbonate species (H_2CO_3, HCO_3^-, and CO_3^{2-}) present in solution containing 0.04 *M* total carbonate, as function of pH.

The calculation of the concentrations of various species of H_2CO_3, HCO_3^-, and CO_3^{2-} for different solution conditions has been indicated by the preceding example and by equations 7.94, 7.95, and 7.96. The results, expressed in terms of the fractional amounts of species as a function of pH, are shown in Fig. 7-5 for $C_0 = 0.04$. At pH values below 8 the important species in the solution are H_2CO_3 and HCO_3^-. For such solutions the second dissociation reaction, equation 7.82, can be ignored. At pH values above 8 the important species are HCO_3^- and CO_3^{2-}; the first dissociation reaction, equation 7.81, can be ignored. This situation arises because the dissociation constants, K_1 and K_2, differ by a factor of 10^4.

To calculate the pH of carbonate solutions when the above situation occurs, we can use a simple method that involves the consideration of only a single appropriate equilibrium reaction. For example, the pH of a solution of H_2CO_3 prepared by adding CO_2(g) to water can be calculated by using equation 7.81 in a calculation of the type shown for weak monoprotic acids in example 7.7. Similarly, the pH of a Na_2CO_3 solution can be calculated using equation 7.82 in the hydrolysis-reaction equations given in equation 7.71. A hydrolysis calculation was illustrated in example 7.8. The calculation of the pH of a solution prepared by adding only $NaHCO_3$ to water can be done easily. In this situation we consider the reaction

$$2HCO_3^-(aq) \rightleftarrows CO_3^{2-}(aq) + H_2CO_3(aq) \tag{7.98}$$

Thus, the concentrations of CO_3^{2-}(aq) and H_2CO_3(aq) must be equal. By equation 7.86, this means

$$[H_3O^+]^2 = K_1K_2 \qquad (7.99)$$

or

$$pH = \tfrac{1}{2}(pK_1 + pK_2) \qquad (7.100)$$

Thus, the pH of a $NaHCO_3$ solution would be

$$pH = \tfrac{1}{2}(6.38 + 10.32) = 8.35 \qquad (7.101)$$

Complex-ion equilibria

An important feature of the chemistry of metal ions is that they often bond to other molecules or ions, called *ligands*, to form complex ions. Examples of three complex ions are shown below:

A	B	C
$Ag(NH_3)_2^+$	$Cr(H_2O)_6^{3+}$	$CoCl_6^{3-}$
$(H_3N—Ag—NH_3)^+$	Cr bonded to six H_2O / OH_2 ligands, overall charge 3+	Co bonded to six Cl ligands, overall charge 3−

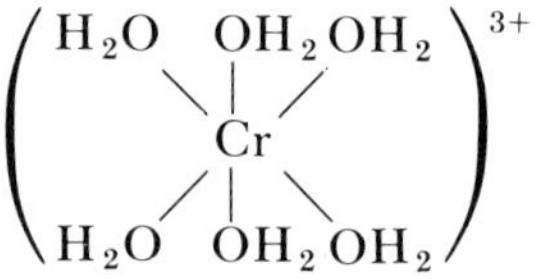

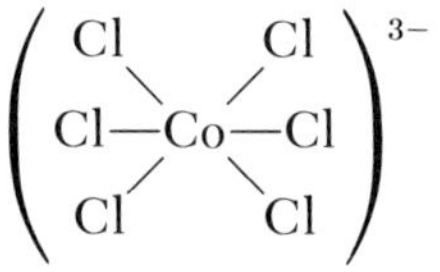

The metals function as Lewis acids, and the ligands function as Lewis bases. Each ligand provides an electron pair that is shared with the metal ion to form coordinate-covalent bonds. In *A* and *B*, since the ligands are neutral, the complex ion has the same charge as the metal ion. In *C*, there are six Cl^- ligands on Co^{3+}, giving the complex ion an overall charge of 3−. The structural features of complex ions are dealt with in Chapter 9. Here we are concerned only with the ionic equilibrium reactions in which the complex ions are formed.

Metal ions in water are present as *aquated* complex ions. The number of water molecules coordinated to a metal depends on the metal and its charge. Examples of some aquated metal ions are shown below.

Other ligands, when added to a solution containing aquated metal ions, often replace the H_2O molecules and form new complex ion species. For example, if aqueous NH_3 is added to a solution containing $Ag(H_2O)_4^+$ ions, the stepwise replacement of H_2O by NH_3 occurs according to

$$Ag(H_2O)_4^+ + NH_3(aq) \rightleftharpoons Ag(NH_3)(H_2O)_3^+ + H_2O \qquad (7.102)$$

$$Ag(NH_3)(H_2O)_3^+ + NH_3(aq) \rightleftharpoons Ag(NH_3)_2(H_2O)_2^+ + H_2O \qquad (7.103)$$

Since the reactions occur in a water solution, it is convenient to simplify the equations to

AQUATED METAL IONS

Transition metals	*Non-transition metals*
$Cu(H_2O)_6^{2+}$	$Li(H_2O)_4^{+}$
$Cr(H_2O)_6^{3+}$	$Na(H_2O)_6^{+}$
$Co(H_2O)_6^{3+}$	$Be(H_2O)_4^{2+}$
$Ni(H_2O)_6^{2+}$	$Mg(H_2O)_6^{2+}$
$Zn(H_2O)_6^{2+}$	$Al(H_2O)_6^{3+}$

$$Ag^+(aq) + NH_3(aq) \leftrightarrows Ag(NH_3)^+(aq) \qquad K_1 = 1.58 \times 10^3 \tag{7.104}$$

$$Ag(NH_3)^+(aq) + NH_3(aq) \leftrightarrows Ag(NH_3)_2^+(aq) \qquad K_2 = 6.75 \times 10^3 \tag{7.105}$$

with the equilibrium constants, K_1 and K_2, as shown.

For our purposes it is sufficient to consider only the overall equilibrium reaction, which for the above equations is

$$Ag^+(aq) + 2NH_3(aq) \leftrightarrows Ag(NH_3)_2^+(aq) \tag{7.106}$$

The overall equilibrium constant, K_0, for the reactions is obtained by combining K_1 and K_2:

$$K_0 = K_1K_2 = \frac{[Ag(NH_3)_2^+(aq)]}{[Ag^+(aq)][NH_3(aq)]^2} = 1.07 \times 10^7 \tag{7.107}$$

That K_0 is large means that the $Ag(NH_3)_2^+$ complex is the favored species in an aqueous ammonia solution containing the Ag^+ ion.

EXAMPLE 7.12

Calculate the ratio of $Ag^+(aq)$ to $Ag(NH_3)_2^+(aq)$ in a solution prepared by adding 0.001 moles of $AgNO_3$ to 1 liter of 1.0 M aqueous ammonia.

The reaction and the equilibrium concentrations of the species are

$$\begin{array}{ccccc} Ag^+(aq) & + 2NH_3(aq) & \leftrightarrows & Ag(NH_3)_2^+(aq) \\ 0.001 - x & 1.0 - 2x & & x \end{array}$$

The equilibrium expression is

$$K_0 = \frac{x}{(0.001 - x)\,(1.0 - 2x)^2} = 1.07 \times 10^7$$

First approximation:

$$\frac{x}{(0.001 - x)} = 1.07 \times 10^7$$

$$x \cong 10^{-3}$$

$$0.001 - x = 0.94 \times 10^{-10}$$

The ratio of $Ag^+(aq)/Ag(NH_3)_2^+(aq)$ is

$$\frac{0.94 \times 10^{-10}}{10^{-3}} = 0.94 \times 10^{-7}$$

which indicates that the Ag^+ concentration is extremely low in this solution.

A variety of metal ion complexes and their overall formation constants are shown below.

FORMATION CONSTANTS OF COMPLEX IONS

MX_2	K_0	MX_4	K_0	MX_6	K_0
$AgCl_2^-$	1×10^6	$CdCl_4^{2-}$	2×10^2	$Cr(OH)_6^{3-}$	1×10^{38}
$Ag(NH_3)_2^+$	1×10^7	$Cu(NH_3)_4^{2+}$	5×10^{12}	$Co(NH_3)_6^{3+}$	1×10^{35}
$Ag(CN)_2^+$	1×10^{22}	$Cu(CN)_4^{2-}$	1×10^{25}	$Co(CN)_6^{3-}$	1×10^{64}
$CuCl_2^-$	3×10^5	$Ni(CN)_4^{2-}$	1×10^{14}		
$Cu(NH_3)_2^+$	1×10^7	$Zn(OH)_4^{2-}$	3×10^{15}		

Note that the K_0 values differ immensely for complexes with different ligands. The cyanide complexes (ligand = CN^-) are notably stable.

7.8 PRECIPITATION REACTIONS: THE SOLUBILITY PRODUCT

When a slightly soluble solid is present in water, an equilibrium reaction is established that governs the concentration of the dissolved ions. For example, the equation that describes the solubility reaction for AgCl(s) would be

$$AgCl(s) \leftrightarrows Ag^+(aq) + Cl^-(aq) \tag{7.108}$$

where the expression for the equilibrium constant is

$$K = [Ag^+][Cl^-] \tag{7.109}$$

Since AgCl(s) is a pure substance, it does not appear in equation 7.109. This K is called K_{sp}, the solubility product. For the reaction in equation 7.108

$$K_{sp} = [Ag^+][Cl^-] \tag{7.110}$$

When AgCl(s) dissolves in pure water, the concentrations of Ag^+ and Cl^- are then $(K_{sp})^{1/2}$.

Values of K_{sp} are tabulated for many substances. Some examples are shown below. The K_{sp} values are related to ΔG^0 for the reaction by

$$K_{sp} = e^{-\Delta G^0/RT} \tag{7.111}$$

SOLUBILITY PRODUCTS AT 25°C

Compound	K_{sp}	*Compound*	K_{sp}
AgCl	1.7×10^{-10}	HgS	3×10^{-53}
AgBr	5×10^{-13}	CuS	4×10^{-38}
AgI	1.5×10^{-16}	Ag_2S	1×10^{-51}
$BaSO_4$	1.1×10^{-10}	CdS	1.4×10^{-28}
CaF_2	1.7×10^{-10}	PbS	7×10^{-29}
$CaCO_3$	1.0×10^{-8}	NiS	1.0×10^{-27}
$Cu(OH)_2$	1.6×10^{-19}	FeS	1×10^{-19}

EXAMPLE 7.13

Calculate K_{sp} for AgCl(s) at 25°C.

From Appendix E, the chemical potentials $\mu^0_{Ag^+(aq)}$, $\mu^0_{Cl^-(aq)}$, and $\mu^0_{AgCl(s)}$ are 18.43, −31.35, and −26.22 kcal/mole, respectively.

$$\Delta G^0 = \mu^0_{Ag^+(aq)} + \mu^0_{Cl^-(aq)} - \mu^0_{AgCl(s)}$$

$$\Delta G^0 = 18.43 - 31.35 + 26.22 \text{ kcal} = 13.30 \text{ kcal}$$

$$K_{sp} = 10^{-13{,}300/(2.30)(2.98)(1.987)} = 1.7 \times 10^{-10}$$

EXAMPLE 7.14

Calculate K_{sp} for $BaCl_2(s)$ if 10^{-2} mole of $BaCl_2$ dissolves in 1 liter of pure water.

For $BaCl_2(s)$ the solubility reaction is

$$BaCl_2(s) \leftrightarrows Ba^{2+}(aq) + 2Cl^-(aq)$$

so

$$K_{sp} = [Ba^{2+}][Cl^-]^2$$

Since

$$[Ba^{2+}] = 10^{-2}\ M$$

and

$$[Cl^-] = 2 \times 10^{-2}\ M$$

then

$$K_{sp} = (10^{-2})\ (2 \times 10^{-2})^2 = 4 \times 10^{-6}$$

EXAMPLE **7.15**

Calculate the Ag^+(aq) concentration when AgCl is dissolved in (a) pure water at 25°C and (b) a solution of 10^{-4} M NaCl. The solubility reaction is

$$AgCl(s) \leftrightarrows Ag^+(aq) + Cl^-(aq)$$

a. Let $x = [Ag^+] = [Cl^-]$. Then

$$K_{sp} = 1.7 \times 10^{-10} = x^2$$
$$x = 1.3 \times 10^{-5}\ M = [Ag^+]$$

b. The equilibrium concentrations are

$$[Ag^+] = x$$
$$[Cl^-] = 10^{-4} + x$$

Then

$$K_{sp} = 1.7 \times 10^{-10} = (x)(10^{-4} + x)$$
$$x = \frac{1.7 \times 10^{-10}}{10^{-4} + x}$$

First approximation (assume $x << 10^{-4}$):

$$x = \frac{1.7 \times 10^{-10}}{10^{-4}} = 1.7 \times 10^{-6}\ M$$

Second approximation:

$$x = \frac{1.7 \times 10^{-10}}{10^{-4} + 0.017 \times 10^{-4}} = \frac{1.7 \times 10^{-10}}{1.02 \times 10^{-4}} = 1.7 \times 10^{-6}\ M$$
$$[Ag^+] = 1.7 \times 10^{-6}\ M$$

This shows that the addition of NaCl reduces the Ag^+ concentration and therefore lowers the solubility of AgCl(s). This is sometimes termed the *common ion effect*.

PROBLEMS

1. Consider the following reaction at 25°C:

$$PbS(s) \rightarrow Pb^{2+}(aq) + S^{2-}(aq)$$

(a) Calculate ΔG^0.

(b) In which direction will this reaction proceed spontaneously under standard-state conditions?

(c) If the concentrations of $Pb^{2+}(aq)$ and $S^{2-}(aq)$ were decreased, how would their chemical potentials change? Show graphically, by representing the Gibbs Free energy of reactants and products, what the equilibrium condition is.

(d) Calculate the equilibrium concentrations of $Pb^{2+}(aq)$ and $S^{2-}(aq)$ when PbS(s) is added to water.

2. Consider the following reactions:
(a) $N_2(g) + O_2(g) \rightarrow 2NO(g)$
(b) $3H_2(g) + N_2(g) \rightarrow 2NH_3(g)$
(c) $CaCO_3(s) \rightarrow CaO(s) + CO_2(g)$
How many moles of each reactant and product are used or formed if $\xi = 3$? If $\xi = -2$?
3. Calculate ΔG^0 for the reactions in problem 2. Represent ΔG^0 graphically by drawing the free energy level of reactants and products. Indicate the direction of spontaneous reaction and whether the change in extent of reaction, $d\xi$, is positive or negative in that direction.
4. Write the equilibrium-constant expressions for the following reactions. Indicate the units of K.
(a) $2NOCl(g) \rightleftarrows 2NO(g) + Cl_2(g)$
(b) $Zn(s) + 2H_3O^+(aq) \rightleftarrows Zn^{2+}(aq) + H_2(g) + 2H_2O(l)$
(c) $COCl_2(g) \rightleftarrows CO(g) + Cl_2(g)$
5. Determine ΔG^0 and the equilibrium constant K for the following reactions by referring to the appropriate data in Appendix E. Give the units applicable to each K.
(a) $3H_2(g) + SO_2(g) \rightleftarrows H_2S(g) + 2H_2O(l)$
(b) $3H_2(g) + N_2(g) \rightleftarrows 2NH_3(g)$
(c) $4I^-(aq) + O_2(g) + 4H^+ \rightleftarrows 2H_2O(l) + 2I_2(g)$
(d) $CaCO_3(s) \rightleftarrows CaO(s) + CO_2(g)$
6. Calculate the fraction of PCl_5 dissociated for the following reaction at a total pressure of 5.0 atm at 200°C, where $K = 0.1719$ atm:

$$PCl_5 \rightleftarrows PCl_3 + Cl_2$$

7. Consider the following reaction at 375°K, where $K = 2.4$ atm:

$$SO_2Cl_2(g) \rightleftarrows SO_2(g) + Cl_2(g)$$

(a) Calculate the equilibrium partial pressure of all species if originally 8.5 g of SO_2Cl_2 was placed in an evacuated 2.0-liter flask, closed off, and the temperature raised to 375°K.

(b) What is the total pressure of the equilibrium mixture?

8. Calculate the value of K for the reaction

$$I_2(g) \rightleftarrows 2I(g)$$

at 800°C if the pressure due to $I_2(g)$ before it dissociates is calculated as $P_0 = 0.3153$ atm, and the total pressure after equilibrium is $P = 0.3429$ atm. Note that the pressure is proportional to the number of moles in the gas, or $P = P_0(1 + \alpha)$, where α is the fraction of I_2 dissociated.

9. Calculate the maximum pressure of $CO_2(g)$ that can develop at 800°C in the reaction

$$CaCO_3(s) \rightleftarrows CaO(s) + CO_2(g)$$

where $K = 0.24$ atm.

10. Consider the reaction

$$H_2O(l) \rightleftarrows H_2O(g)$$

(a) Calculate the vapor pressure of water at 25°C using the data in Appendix E.
(b) Determine ΔG^0, K, and the partial pressure of H_2O.

11. For the reaction

$$C_2N_2(g) \rightleftarrows 2CN(g)$$

it is found that K is 3.23×10^{-9} atm and 1.08×10^{-2} atm at 1500°K and 2500°K, respectively. Calculate ΔH^0, ΔG^0, and ΔS^0 at 1500°K and at 2500°K.

12. Calculate ΔH^0 for the reaction

$$H_2O(g) \rightleftarrows H_2(g) + \tfrac{1}{2}O_2(g)$$

from the knowledge that steam at a total pressure of 1 atm is 1.77% dissociated at 2257°K and 1.18% dissociated at 2155°K.

13. The preparation of nickel from NiO(s) involves the following reaction:

$$NiO(s) + CO(g) \rightleftarrows Ni(s) + CO_2(g)$$

The equilibrium constant at various temperatures is given as

T(°K)	936	1027	1125
K	4.54×10^3	2.55×10^3	1.58×10^3

Plot log K versus $1/T$ to find ΔH^0. Determine ΔG^0 and ΔS^0 at 1000°K.

14. Calculate ΔG for the following reactions at 25°C with the conditions shown in parentheses. Calculations of ΔG^0 for these reactions were made in problem 5.
(a) $3H_2$(g, 2 atm) + SO_2(g, 3 atm) $\rightarrow$ H_2S(g, 0.1 atm) + H_2O(l)
(b) $3H_2$(g, 10^{-6} atm) + SO_2(g, 3 atm) $\rightarrow$ H_2S(g, 0.1 atm) + H_2O(l)
(c) $4I^-$(aq, 0.01 M) + O_2(g, 2 atm) + $4H^+$(aq, 0.01 M) $\rightarrow$ $2H_2O$(l, 1 atm) + $2I_2$(g, 3 atm)
(d) $CaCO_3$(s) $\rightarrow$ CaO(s) + CO_2(g, 2 atm)

15. Predict the effect that an increase of temperature and pressure has on the equilibrium position for the following reactions:
(a) C(s, graphite) + $2H_2(g) \rightleftarrows CH_4(g)$ $\quad \Delta H^0 = -17.89$ kcal
(b) $LaCl_3(s) + H_2O(g) \rightleftarrows LaOCl(s) + HCl(g)$ $\quad \Delta H^0 = 26.7$ kcal
(c) $2NH_3(g) \rightleftarrows N_2(g) + 3H_2(g)$ $\quad \Delta H^0 = 22.08$ kcal

16. (a) Calculate the concentrations of H_3O^+, $HOAc^-$, OAc^-, and OH^- for a 5.0-liter solution made with 2.0 moles of acetic acid ($HOAc$) in water at 25°C.
(b) Calculate the same species concentrations if a similar solution is made with 0.00100 moles of acetic acid in 5 liters of water at 25°C.

17. Calculate the ionic species concentrations of a solution made with 1.0 moles of acetic acid and 0.75 moles of hydrochloric acid (HCl) in enough water to make 1.0 liter of solution.

18. Calculate the pH of the solutions with the following H_3O^+ or OH^- concentrations:

(a) $[OH^-] = 3 \times 10^{-5}$ M
(b) $[H_3O^+] = 4.8 \times 10^{-3}$ M
(c) $[H_3O^+] = 6.0$ M

19. Calculate the concentrations of H_3O^+ and OH^- in a solution with (a) pH = 7.0; (b) pH = 5.2; (c) pH = 14.1; (d) pH = 0; (e) pH = −0.30.
20. Calculate the pH and pOH of a solution at 25°C prepared from 0.010 mole of NH_3 and enough water to make 1.0 liter of solution Ammonia reacts with water according to

$$NH_3 + H_2O \rightleftarrows NH_4^+ + OH^-$$

21. Arrange the following solutions in order of increasing pH. Assume each solute concentration is 0.20 M.
    (a) NH_4Cl (c) HCl (e) NaOH
    (b) NH_3 (d) NaCl (f) HO*Ac* (acetic acid)
22. Calculate the pH of a 0.20 M aqueous solution of NH_4Cl at 25°C.
23. Calculate the pH of a 0.50 M aqueous solution of $NaNO_2$ at 25°C.
24. Calculate the pH of a 1.00 M aqueous solution of Na_2CO_3 at 25°C.
25. Calculate the pH of a solution at 25°C prepared by adding 50.00 ml of 0.100 M NaOH to 50.00 ml of 0.250 M HO*Ac*.
26. Using pure trichloroacetic acid (Cl_3CCO_2H) and its sodium salt, give instructions for preparing 1 liter of solution with a pH of 0.45.
27. What weak acids or bases could be used to prepare buffer solutions with the following pH values: (a) 1.0; (b) 3.0; (c) 4.0; (d) 5.0; (e) 9.0.
28. Write electron dot structures for all the acids in Table 7-1 that contain oxygen. In each case identify those hydrogens that ionize in water to yield H^+ ions.
29. From the information in Table 7-2, estimate the pK for the dissociation of the indicators methyl orange and litmus.
30. Calculate the concentration of the various species (H_3O^+, HCO_3^-, and CO_3^{2-}) of a solution saturated with CO_2 to give a solution whose carbonate concentration is 0.04 M at 25°C.
31. Calculate the pH and the H_2S concentration of a 0.1 M solution of Na_2S at 25°C.
32. Calculate the pH of a 0.1 M solution of $NaHCO_3$ at 25°C.
33. Write the reactions for the stepwise replacement of H_2O in $Cu(H_2O)_4^{2+}$ by NH_3.
34. Calculate the concentration of $Cu(H_2O)_4^{2+}$ in 1.0 liter of a solution made by dissolving 0.1 mole of $Cu(NO_3)_2$ in 1 liter of 1.0 M NH_3. Assume the overall formation reaction is appropriate for this calculation. See the list of formation constants on p. 190.
35. Set up equations, analogous to those used for polyprotic acids, for the concentrations of $HgCl_2$, $HgCl^+$, and Hg^{2+} in terms of Cl^- in the situation where

$$HgCl_2(aq) \rightleftarrows HgCl^+(aq) + Cl^-(aq) \qquad K_1 = 3.3 \times 10^{-7}$$
$$HgCl^+(aq) \rightleftarrows Hg^{2+}(aq) + Cl^-(aq) \qquad K_2 = 1.8 \times 10^{-7}$$

36. From the values of $\overline{G}_f^0$ in Appendix E calculate the acid dissociation constants, K_1 and K_2, for H_2CO_3.
37. Using data from Appendix E, calculate the solubility product, K_{sp}, for the following salts: (a) AgCl(s); (b) AgBr(s); (c) NaCl(s).
38. The solubility of BaF_2 in pure water at 25°C is 7.6×10^{-3} mole/liter.
    (a) Give the concentrations of Ba^{2+}(aq) and F^-(aq) in a saturated solution of BaF_2(s).
    (b) Calculate K_{sp} for BaF_2(s) in water at 25°C.

39. Calculate the solubility of CaF_2 in a solution initially with (a) 4×10^{-2} *M* $Ca^{2+}(aq)$; (b) 5.0 *M* $F^-(aq)$. The K_{sp} of CaF_2 is 1.7×10^{-10}.
40. Calculate the solubility of FeS in a solution of pH 3 that is saturated at 0.1 *M* H_2S. The dissociation of H_2S is given as

$$H_2S(aq) + 2H_2O \rightleftarrows 2H_3O^+(aq) + S^{2-}(aq)$$

with $K = 1.1 \times 10^{-21}$.

8 OXIDATION-REDUCTION REACTIONS: ELECTROCHEMISTRY

Oxidation-reduction (*redox*) reactions constitute a major class of chemical reactions. They are reactions in which electrons are transferred between species, with the result that the oxidation states of these species change during the course of the reaction. Oxidation is defined as the process in which electrons are lost and is characterized by an increase in the oxidation number of a species as a result of the reaction. Reduction is the process in which electrons are gained and the oxidation number of a species decreases.

An example of a solution oxidation-reduction reaction is

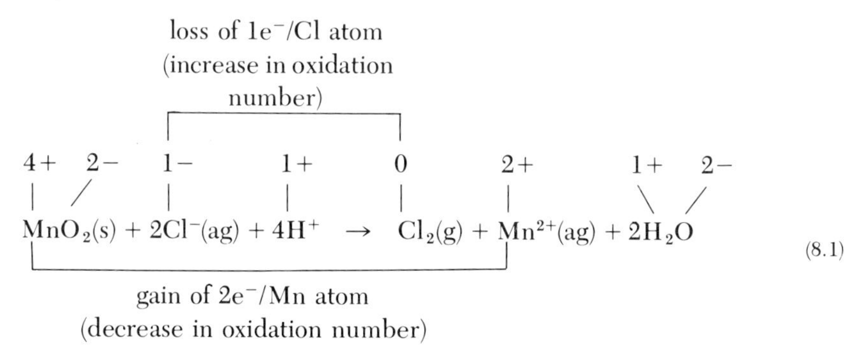

$$MnO_2(s) + 2Cl^-(ag) + 4H^+ \rightarrow Cl_2(g) + Mn^{2+}(ag) + 2H_2O \tag{8.1}$$

Manganese gains $2e^-$/Mn atom in going from MnO_2 to Mn^{2+}. This corresponds to a decrease in oxidation number; hence MnO_2 is reduced. Chlorine loses 1 electron/Cl atom in going from Cl^- to elemental chlorine; hence Cl^- is oxidized. In the balanced reaction, the number of electrons lost in the oxidation process must equal the number gained in the reduction process.

The burning of $CH_4(g)$ with $O_2(g)$ is another example of oxidation-reduction:

$$\overset{4-}{CH_4}(g) + 2\overset{0}{O_2}(g) \rightarrow \overset{4+}{C}\overset{2-}{O_2}(g) + 2H_2\overset{2-}{O}(g) \qquad (8.2)$$

(8e⁻ change from C in CH_4 to C in CO_2; 8e⁻ change from O in O_2 to O in CO_2 and H_2O)

The oxidation state of carbon changes from 4− in CH_4 to 4+ in CO_2; hence CH_4 is oxidized. The oxidation state of oxygen changes from 0 in O_2 to 2− in H_2O and CO_2; hence O_2 is reduced.

In the examples shown by equations 8.1 and 8.2, MnO_2 and O_2 are the *oxidizing agents,* and Cl^- and CH_4 are the *reducing agents.*

8.1 BALANCING OXIDATION-REDUCTION REACTIONS

To be dealt with quantitatively, oxidation-reduction reactions, like all reactions, must be balanced. Since oxidation-reduction reactions often are difficult to balance by inspection, we will present a systematic method for balancing them called the *ion-electron* (half-reaction) method.

Let us consider the following reaction in acid solution:

$$NO_3^-(aq) + Cu_2O(s) \rightarrow Cu^{2+}(aq) + NO(g) \qquad (8.3)$$

The equation shows the principle species involved in the oxidation-reduction reaction, but, since the reaction occurs in aqueous acid solution, we might expect H_2O and H_3O^+ to appear in the final balanced reaction.

Step 1 Establish oxidation numbers for all elements in the reaction.

$$\overset{5+}{N}\overset{2-}{O_3^-}(aq) + \overset{1+}{Cu_2}\overset{2-}{O}(s) \rightarrow \overset{2+}{Cu^{2+}}(aq) + \overset{2+}{N}\overset{2-}{O}(g) \qquad (8.4)$$

Step 2 Rewrite the reaction in terms of two separate half-reactions, the oxidation part and the reduction part of the equation.

$$\text{Oxidation half:} \quad Cu_2O(s) \rightarrow Cu^{2+}(aq) \qquad (8.5a)$$

$$\text{Reduction half:} \quad NO_3^-(aq) \rightarrow NO(g) \qquad (8.5b)$$

Step 3 If necessary, balance the principle atoms in the half-reactions (all atoms except O or H).

$$Cu_2O(s) \rightarrow 2Cu^{2+}(aq) \qquad (8.6a)$$

$$NO_3^-(aq) \rightarrow NO(g) \qquad (8.6b)$$

Step 4 To each half-reaction add the number of electrons involved in the oxidation or reduction process.

$$Cu_2O(s) \rightarrow 2Cu^{2+}(aq) + 2e^- \quad (8.7a)$$

$$3e^- + NO_3^-(aq) \rightarrow NO(g) \quad (8.7b)$$

Step 5 Balance the charge of each half-reaction. Since this reaction occurs in acid solution, we balance using H_3O^+; in a basic aqueous solution, we would use OH^- to balance charges.

$$2H_3O^+ + Cu_2O(s) \rightarrow 2Cu^{2+}(aq) + 2e^- \quad (8.8a)$$

$$4H_3O^+ + 3e^- + NO_3^-(aq) \rightarrow NO(g) \quad (8.8b)$$

Step 6 Balance the O and H atoms in the half-reactions, using H_2O.

$$2H_3O^+ + Cu_2O(s) \rightarrow 2Cu^{2+}(aq) + 2e^- + 3H_2O \quad (8.9a)$$

$$4H_3O^+ + 3e^- + NO_3^-(aq) \rightarrow NO(g) + 6H_2O \quad (8.9b)$$

Step 7 Before combining the half-reactions, we must make sure equal numbers of electrons are involved in each. Thus, in this instance we multiply equation 8.9a times 3 and equation 8.9b times 2. We then add the half-reactions to obtain the overall reaction.

$$6H_3O^+ + 3Cu_2O(s) \rightarrow 6Cu^{2+}(aq) + 6e^- + 9H_2O \quad (8.10a)$$

$$8H_3O^+ + 6e^- + 2NO_3^-(aq) \rightarrow 2NO(g) + 12H_2O \quad (8.10b)$$

$$14H_3O^+ + 3Cu_2O(s) + 2NO_3^-(aq) \rightarrow 6Cu^{2+}(aq) + 2NO(g) + 21H_2O$$

8.2 FARADAY'S LAW OF ELECTROLYSIS: ELECTROLYTIC CELLS

Electrical effects are associated with oxidation-reduction reactions in two general electrochemical situations: (1) when an electric current is passed through an ionic solution in a process called *electrolysis* and (2) when chemical reactions produce an electric potential difference between two electrodes in a device called a *galvanic cell.*

When an electric current is passed through an ionic mixture such as a salt dissolved in water or a molten salt, oxidation and reduction reactions occur at the electrodes. Electrons are transferred from the electrodes, which are electron conductors, to ions in the system. A characteristic minimum applied voltage is necessary to make the oxidation-reduction reactions occur.

For a system of copper electrodes immersed in a solution of $CuSO_4$ in water (Fig. 8-1), the following reactions occur when sufficient voltage is applied:

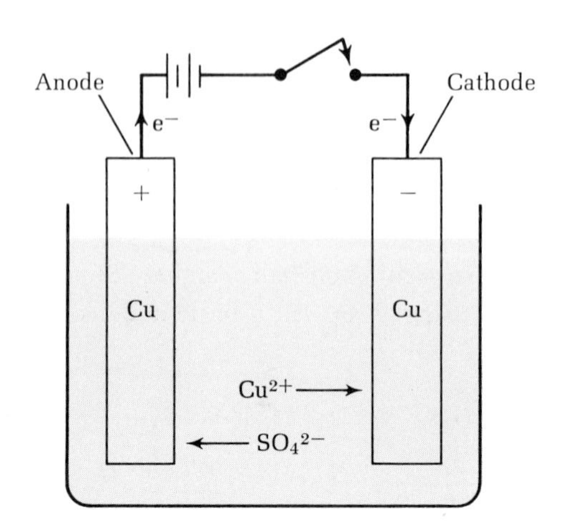

Fig. 8-1. Electrochemical cell for electrolysis of copper. Cu is oxidized at anode, and Cu^{2+} is reduced at cathode.

$$\text{Oxidation:} \qquad Cu(s) \rightarrow Cu^{2+} + 2e^- \qquad \text{anode} \tag{8.11}$$

$$\text{Reduction:} \qquad Cu^{2+} + 2e^- \rightarrow Cu(s) \qquad \text{cathode} \tag{8.12}$$

The electrode at which oxidation occurs is called the *anode*, and the electrode at which reduction occurs is called the *cathode*. In the solution, Cu^{2+} ions move from anode to cathode. As electricity is passed through the system, the copper anode is gradually eroded while the cathode increases in mass due to the electroplating of copper.

Faraday's law states that the amount of material change in an electrochemical reaction is proportional to the amount of electricity passed through the cell. The quantity of electricity that contains 1 mole of electrons is designated as the *Faraday*, F, and is equivalent to 96,500 coulombs of electric charge. One *coulomb* of charge is delivered when a current of 1 ampere flows for 1 second, that is, 1 coulomb = 1 amp-sec. The relation between charge, q, current, i, and time, t, is given by

$$q = \int i dt \tag{8.13}$$

For the reaction given in equation 8.12, two Faradays are needed to convert 1 mole of Cu^{2+} to Cu(s) at the cathode. We symbolize the stoichiometric number of electrons in an electrochemical reaction by n, so for

$$Cu(s) \rightarrow Cu^{2+} + 2e^- \qquad n = 2 \tag{8.14}$$

The extent of an electrochemical reaction, $\Delta\xi$, is determined by the number of Faradays, q/F, divided by the stoichiometric number of electrons, n:

$$\Delta\xi = \frac{q}{nF} \tag{8.15}$$

For a unit extent of reaction, $\Delta\xi = 1$ and $q = nF$.

EXAMPLE **8.1**

Calculate the amount of $H_2(g)$ evolved when water is electrolyzed for 1.0 hour at a current of 1.0 amp.

The electrode reactions are

$$\begin{aligned} 2H_2O + 2e^- &\rightarrow H_2(g) + 2OH^- \\ 2H_2O &\rightarrow O_2(g) + 4H^+ + 2e^- \end{aligned}$$

One mole of H_2 gas is evolved for every 2 moles of electrons. The number of moles of electrons will be

$$\frac{it}{F} = \frac{(1.0 \text{ amp})(3600 \text{ sec})}{96{,}500 \text{ coulombs/mole}} = 3.7 \times 10^{-2} \text{ moles of e}^-$$

Thus, 1.9×10^{-2} moles of H_2 are evolved.

Electrolytic preparation of metals: applications of electrolysis

Many metals, such as copper and aluminum, are prepared industrially using electrolytic processes. For some metals, such as Al, electrolysis is used to obtain the metal from the crude, natural ore. In other cases, such as with Cu, electrolysis is used only to obtain highly purified metal from a crude material obtained by smelting the metal-containing ore. In addition to providing interesting examples of the application of electrolysis, these industrial processes are often masterpieces of engineering technique.

The Hall process for aluminum preparation. A diagram of the electrochemical cell used to reduce aluminum ores to aluminum metal is shown in Fig. 8-2. The cell consists of a carbon-lined vat that serves as the cathode in the ore-reduction process. Aluminum oxide (Al_2O_3), obtained from bauxite by washing the ore with strong base, is mixed with Na_3AlF_6 (cryolite), placed in the cell, and heated to melting at about 1000°C. A series of carbon electrodes that serve as anodes are placed in the molten mixture. When an electrical current is applied to the cell, electrolysis takes place. The half-cell reactions at the electrodes can be represented as

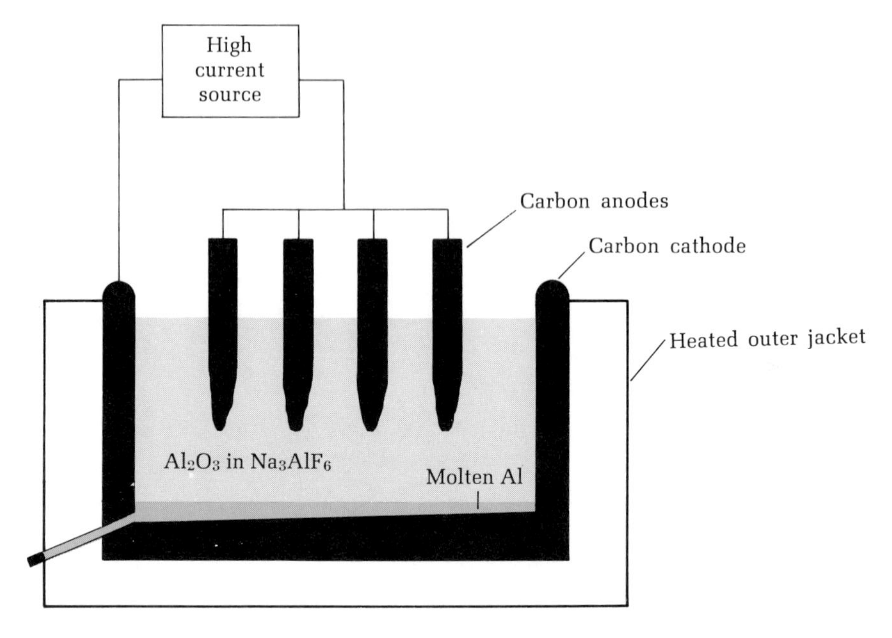

Fig. 8-2. Electrochemical cell for preparation of aluminum. Molten aluminum is formed at cathode and drained from bottom of cell.

$$2Al^{3+} + 6e^- \rightarrow 2Al(l) \qquad \text{cathode}$$
$$3O^{2-} \rightarrow \tfrac{3}{2}O_2(g) + 6e^- \qquad \text{anode}$$

The overall reaction is

$$2Al^{3+} + 3O^{2-} \rightarrow 2Al(l) + \tfrac{3}{2}O_2(g)$$

The molten aluminum formed at the cathode (the carbon cell walls) is deposited at the bottom of the cell, from where it can be drained off periodically. In the actual electrolysis reaction, the $O_2(g)$ formed at the carbon anodes slowly attacks the anodes to form CO_2 and CO. Consequently, the carbon anodes are slowly consumed and occasionally must be replaced.

Although the Hall process produces very pure aluminum (>99.9%), it requires a considerable expenditure of energy. Typically, the production of 1 pound of aluminum requires about 10 kilowatt hours of electrical energy.

Electrochemical purification of copper. To obtain pure copper from crudely refined metal, one generally uses an electrochemical apparatus of the type shown in Fig. 8-3. A large anode formed from the impure copper and a cathode made of a thin sheet of highly purified copper are immersed in an aqueous H_2SO_4-$CuSO_4$

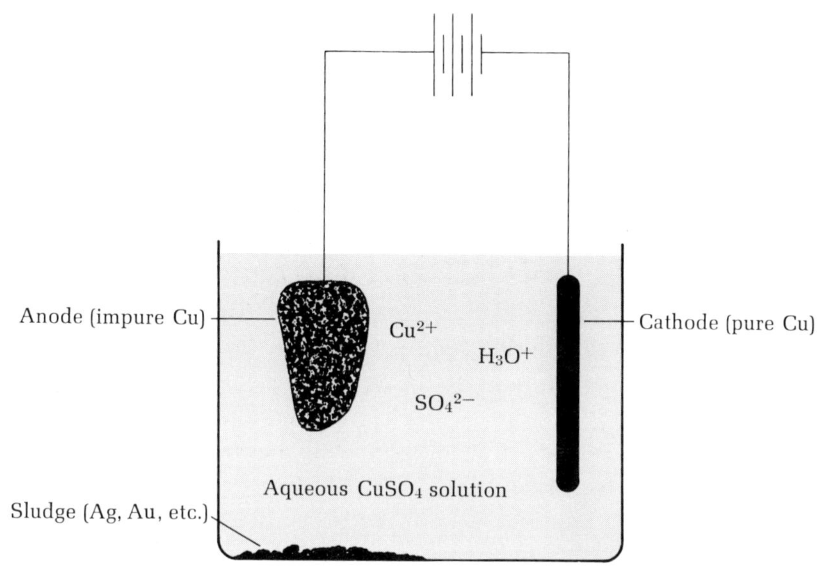

Fig. 8-3. Cell for electrochemical purification of copper. Highly pure copper (purity >99.99%) is formed at cathode.

solution. In the electrolysis, the potential is adjusted so that copper from the anode is oxidized to Cu^{2+} ions:

$$\mathrm{Cu(impure)} \rightarrow \mathrm{Cu^{2+}(aq)} + 2e^- \qquad \text{anode}$$

The Cu^{2+} ions in solution are then reduced at the cathode to Cu metal and deposited on the cathode surface:

$$\mathrm{Cu^{2+}(aq)} + 2e^- \rightarrow \mathrm{Cu(s)} \qquad \text{cathode}$$

The weight of the cathode continually increases due to the deposition of copper. During the electrolysis, impurities in the anode material that are more difficult to oxidize than copper, such as Ag and Au, settle as a sludge to the bottom of the electrolysis vat. Any metal that is more difficult to reduce, such as iron, remains in the solution. When this electrochemical refinement method is used, the purity of the copper obtained is greater than 99.99%.

An extremely important feature of this electrolytic purification method is that the sludge contains Au and Ag and is of such form that further processing will yield substantial quantities of these precious metals. These valuable by-product metals help make the electrolytic purification method economically feasible.

8.3 GALVANIC CELLS AND GIBBS FREE ENERGY

A galvanic cell, commonly called a battery, generates an electric-potential difference between two electrodes. The potential difference depends on the half-cell chemical reactions involved at the electrodes. The chemical reaction in the cell requires that electrons be transferred from one electrode to the other by means of an external electron conductor. The Gibbs free-energy change, ΔG, is equivalent to the electrical work involved in the charge transfer between electrodes.

For an electrochemical cell to generate a voltage difference between electrodes, the electrode reactions must differ in some respect. There are various ways to accomplish this; before considering specific examples, however, we shall consider the general thermodynamics of an electrochemical cell.

Fig. 8-4 is a schematic diagram of an electrochemical cell that consists of metal electrodes, A and B, immersed in a connecting electrolyte, Specific chemical reactions occur at each electrode:

$$\mathrm{A} \rightarrow \mathrm{A}^{+} + \mathrm{e}_{A}^{-} \tag{8.16}$$

$$B \rightarrow B^{+} + \mathrm{e}_{B}^{-} \tag{8.17}$$

where A and B are metals, e_A^- and e_B^- are electrons delivered to electrodes A and B, and A^+ and B^+ are ions in the interconnecting electrolyte.

Chemical equilibrium exists at both electrode surfaces. We write this in terms of the chemical potentials of the reaction species:

$$\text{At electrode } A: \quad \mu_A = \mu_{A^+} + \mu_{\mathrm{e}_A^-} \tag{8.18}$$

$$\text{At electrode } B: \quad \mu_B = \mu_{B^+} + \mu_{\mathrm{e}_B^-} \tag{8.19}$$

The chemical potentials of the electrons in electrodes A and B are $\mu_{\mathrm{e}_A^-}$ and $\mu_{\mathrm{e}_B^-}$.

The difference in electromotive force between electrodes, $\mathscr{E}$ volts, is directly

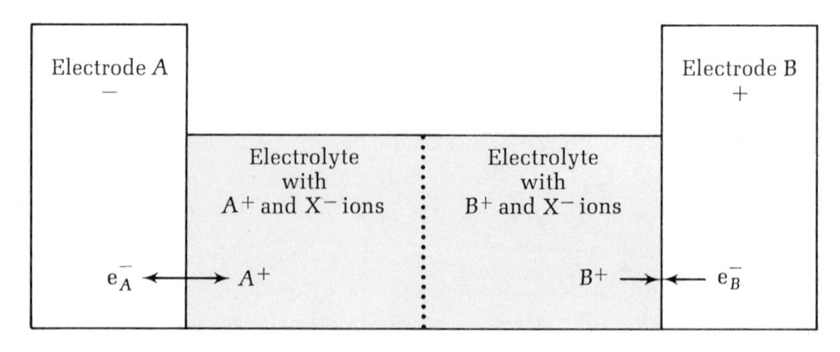

Fig. 8-4. Schematic representation of galvanic cell. By convention we write the electrode reaction at left electrode, A, as an oxidation reaction.

proportional through the Faraday constant (expressed as 23,030 cal/volt-mole)* to the difference in electron chemical potentials:

$$\mu_{e_A^-} - \mu_{e_B^-} = F\mathscr{E} \tag{8.20}$$

Substracting equation 8.18 from 8.19, and inserting equation 8.20, we obtain

$$\mu_{e_B^-} - \mu_{e_A^-} = \mu_B + \mu_{A^+} - \mu_A - \mu_{B^+} = -F\mathscr{E} \tag{8.21}$$

This equation gives the free-energy change for the chemical process

$$A + B^+ \rightarrow A^+ + B \tag{8.22}$$

The difference in the Gibbs free energy for the reaction can therefore be measured from the electromotive force, $\mathscr{E}$. When n electrons are involved in the stoichiometric electrochemical reaction, we obtain the general result

$$\Delta G = -nF\mathscr{E} \tag{8.23}$$

The sign convention for the potential $\mathscr{E}$ is defined as follows. If the electrode reactions for a shorted cell (or a spontaneous reaction), as shown in Fig. 8-4, are

$$\text{Left:} \quad A \rightarrow A^+ + e_A^- \tag{8.24}$$

$$\text{Right:} \quad B^+ + e_B^- \rightarrow B \tag{8.25}$$

the left electrode, A, is negative (has excess electrons), and the right electrode, B, is positive (is deficient in electrons). When this occurs, $\mathscr{E}$ is given a positive sign and ΔG is negative, as it must be for the spontaneous reaction given by equation 8.22. If the cell is reversed so that the B electrode is on the left, we have

$$\text{Left:} \quad B \rightarrow B^+ + e_B^- \tag{8.26}$$

$$\text{Right:} \quad A^+ + e_A^- \rightarrow A \tag{8.27}$$

Since these reactions are not spontaneous in the direction written, $\mathscr{E}$ is negative for such a cell.

A shorthand scheme for representing a cell is to write the essential cell components, with different regions shown separated by solid lines. For example

$$A \,|\, A^+(\text{aq}) \,|\, B^+(\text{aq}) \,|\, B \tag{8.28}$$

describes the cell in Fig. 8-4. By convention we write the electrode reactions as equations 8.24 and 8.25. The sign convention assumes oxidation occurs at the left electrode and reduction occurs at the right electrode. If the reactions as given by equations 8.24 and 8.25 occur spontaneously when the cell is shorted, $\mathscr{E}$ is positive. Otherwise, $\mathscr{E}$ is negative.

---

*Note that (1 mole e^-)(1 volt) = (1 Faraday)(1 volt) = (96,500 coulombs)(1 volt) = 96,500 joules = 23,030 calories.

8.4 TYPICAL GALVANIC CELLS

The *Weston cell* (Fig. 8-5), a galvanic cell often used as a voltage standard in scientific measurements, consists of one electrode of cadium dissolved in mercury and a second electrode of pure mercury. The connecting electrolyte solution is saturated $CdSO_4$ in water. A mixture of Hg_2SO_4(s) and $CdSO_4$(s) is added to assure saturation of the electrolyte solution. We represent this cell schematically as

$$Cd(14\% \text{ in Hg}) \mid CdSO_4(sat) \mid Hg_2SO_4(s) \mid Hg$$

The electrode reactions written in the spontaneous direction are

$$Cd(s) \rightarrow Cd^{2+}(aq) + 2e^-$$
$$Hg_2SO_4(s) + 2e^- \rightarrow 2Hg(l) + SO_4^{2-}(aq)$$

$\mathscr{E}$ is therefore positive and equals +1.018 volts. When the Weston cell generates an electric current, there are no concentration changes within the connecting $CdSO_4$ solution except at the electrode regions. Such cells are said to be without *liquid junctions*.

A *Daniell cell* (Fig. 8-6) has a liquid junction. Electrodes of copper and zinc are immersed in solutions of their respective ions. A porous plug allows electrical connection between the solutions and prevents their rapid mixing. However, within the porous-plug region there is a section of changing Zn^{2+} and Cu^{2+} concentrations. This is called the liquid-junction region. A potential arises in the liquid-junction

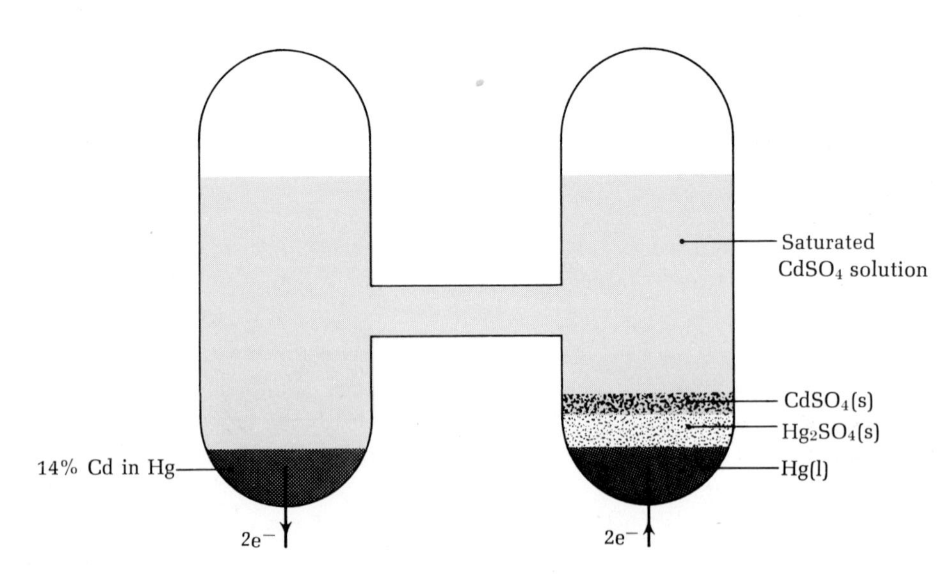

Fig. 8-5. Standard Weston cell.

region due to the concentration gradient that causes a difference in chemical potentials. This effect can be minimized by introducing another salt, such as KCl, into the connecting region so that relatively small amounts of Cu^{2+} and Zn^{2+} are transferred when electrical conduction occurs. The cell is represented by

$$Zn(s) \,|\, Zn^{2+}(aq) \,||\, Cu^{2+}(aq) \,|\, Cu(s)$$

where the || represents the liquid-junction connection.

The concentrations of Zn^{2+} and Cu^{2+} affect the cell potential, $\mathscr{E}$, as we would expect from previous considerations of the effect of reaction-species concentrations on ΔG. The cell as written would involve the electrode reactions

$$\begin{aligned} Zn(s) &\rightarrow Zn^{2+} + 2e^- \\ Cu^{2+}(aq) + 2e^- &\rightarrow Cu(s) \end{aligned}$$

The measured voltage is 1.100 volts when the concentrations of Zn^{2+} and Cu^{2+} are at unit activity.* The notation $\mathscr{E}^0$ is used to indicate the voltage of a cell whose components are at standard-state conditions. In such a cell, dissolved species are at unit activity, and the temperature is 298°K.

Gas-reaction electrodes are also possible. Particularly important is the hydrogen electrode, shown in Fig. 8-7. Gaseous hydrogen is bubbled over platinum metal, which serves as an electron carrier for the reaction

$$H_2(g) \rightarrow 2H^+(aq) + 2e^- \tag{8.29}$$

*The activity of a species was defined (sec. 6.5) as the corrected concentration of the species in solution. For practical purposes, unit activity is approximately equal to a concentration of 1 mole/liter.

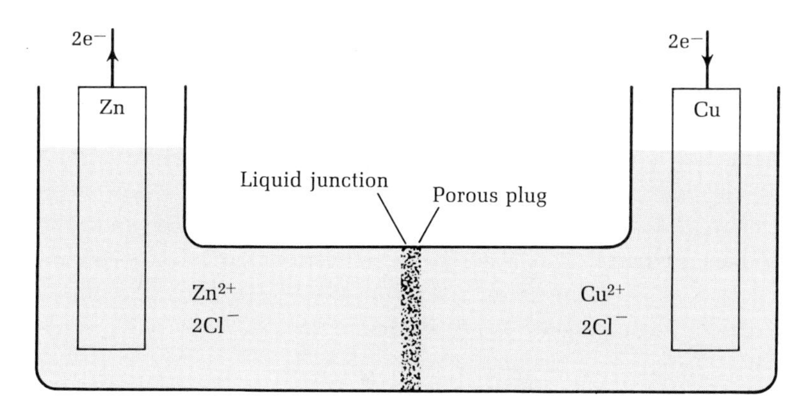

Fig. 8-6. Daniell cell.

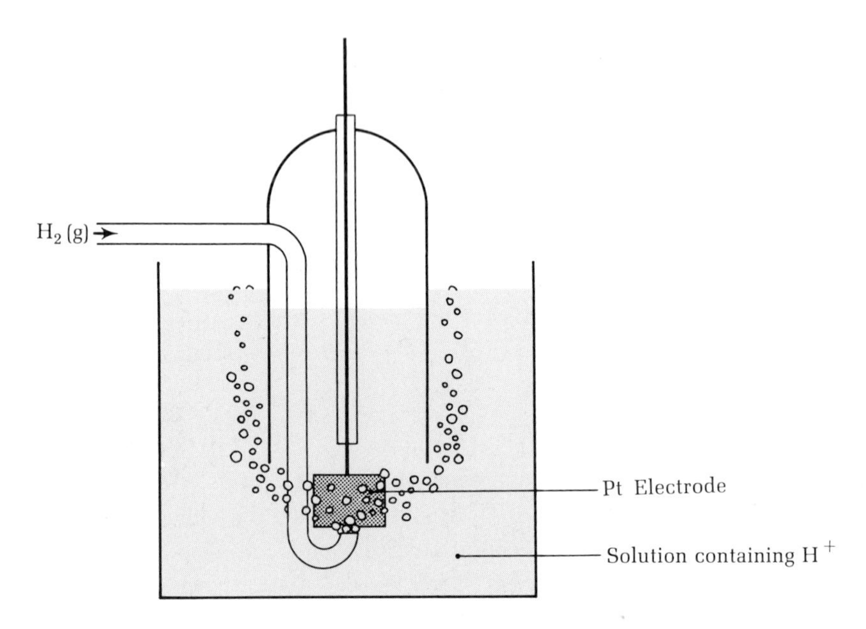

Fig. 8-7. Hydrogen gas electrode.

To measure a cell potential, we must have a second electrode reaction, such as

$$2e^- + Zn^{2+}(aq) \rightarrow Zn(s)$$

This cell is schematically represented by

$$Pt \mid H_2(g) \mid H^+(aq) \parallel Zn^{2+}(aq) \mid Zn(s)$$

and has an $\mathscr{E}^0$ of -0.76 volts.

An essential feature of all galvanic cells is physical separation of the overall chemical reaction into two electrode regions. Because of this separation, the transfer of electrons between electrodes is necessary for the chemical reaction to occur; the chemical reaction is coupled to the external transfer of electrons at the electrode surface. In this way we obtain the chemical energy of the reaction in the form of electrical energy. All galvanic cells eventually reach a state in which they can no longer produce a voltage. This occurs when all components in the cell are at equal chemical potentials. In some cases, such as in the Weston cell, the diffusion of the spatially separated components to all regions of the cell takes millions of years. In the case of a Daniell cell, the liquid connections between different regions allow the diffusion to proceed much faster; such cells are useful only for a few weeks or months.

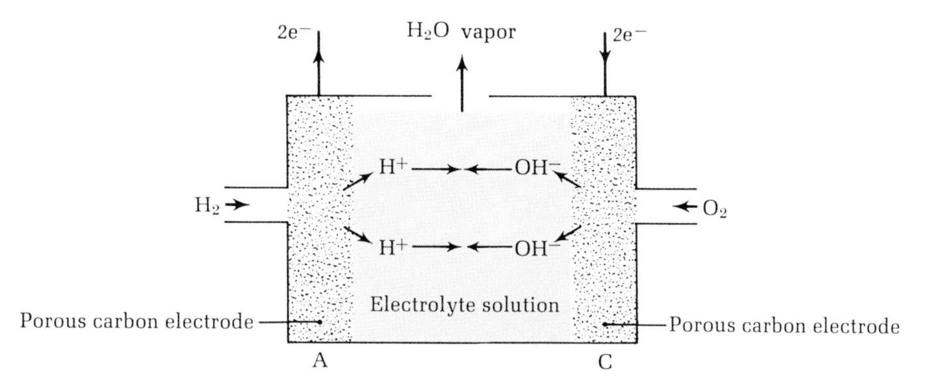

Fig. 8-8. Schematic diagram of simple hydrogen-oxygen fuel cell. Cell consists of container with electrolyte solution and two porous carbon electrodes. Gaseous H_2 is admitted at anode; gaseous O_2 is admitted at cathode. Cell reaction produces H_2O, which is removed by vaporization.

Fuel cells: an application of galvanic cells

Fuel cells offer a highly efficient way to convert the Gibbs free energy (ΔG^0 for standard states) of chemical reactions to electricity. Fuel cells make this conversion in a direct way at a fixed temperature. This is in contrast to what happens when a chemical reaction is used to generate heat. Heat can be converted only partially into work by means of a thermal engine. The most efficient thermal engine (steam engine) can convert only about one half this heat (ΔH^0) into useful work.

The heat of a spontaneous reaction is ΔH^0. For a thermal engine, the conversion of heat into work is about $\Delta H^0/2$. The work obtained from an ideal electrochemical cell under standard-state conditions is ΔG^0. The ratio of these two quantities, $2\Delta G^0/\Delta H^0$, provides a comparison of the efficiencies of a fuel cell and a thermal engine. For the reaction

$$CH_4(g) + 2O_2(g) \rightarrow CO_2(g) + 2H_2O(l) \qquad \begin{aligned} \Delta H^0 &= -212.8\text{ kcal} \\ \Delta G^0 &= -195.6\text{ kcal} \end{aligned}$$

From the values of ΔH^0 and ΔG^0, we can see that the reaction of methane with oxygen in an appropriate electrochemical cell produces about twice as much work as a conventional thermal-engine system.

A fuel cell currently in use that could be a major source of electrical energy in the future is the hydrogen-oxygen fuel cell. A schematic diagram of this cell is shown in Fig. 8-8. The anode and cathode reactions are

$$\begin{aligned} H_2(g) &\rightarrow 2H^+(aq) + 2e^- && \text{anode} \\ \tfrac{1}{2}O_2(g) + H_2O + 2e^- &\rightarrow 2OH^-(aq) && \text{cathode} \end{aligned}$$

The overall reaction is

$$2H_2(g) + O_2(g) = 2H_2O(g) \qquad \Delta H^0 = -115.6 \text{ kcal}$$
$$\Delta G^0 = -109.2 \text{ kcal}$$

The ratio, $2\Delta G^0/\Delta H^0 = 1.9$, shows that again the fuel cell is about twice as effective as a thermal engine.

The use of fuel cells in place of conventional thermal engines provides an important ecological advantage since fuel cells discharge very little heat to the surroundings. The maximum work at constant pressure is

$$W = -p\Delta V + \Delta G$$

The enthalpy change is

$$\Delta H = \Delta E + p\Delta V$$

where

$$\Delta E = Q_p + W = Q_p + \Delta G - p\Delta V$$

Thus

$$\Delta H = Q_p + \Delta G$$

The heat obtained from the fuel cell is

$$Q_p = \Delta H - \Delta G$$

When hydrogen reacts with oxygen in a fuel cell, $Q_p = -6$ kcal. If hydrogen is simply burned to produce heat, and half this heat is converted to work, 57 kcal still are expelled to the surroundings. Thus, the heat discharged to the surroundings is reduced tremendously by the use of a fuel cell.

8.5 STANDARD ELECTRODE POTENTIALS

The electromotive force of a cell is determined by the difference in potential between the two electrode reactions. It is convenient to use a *standard electrode reaction* and arbitrarily define its electrode potential as zero. The standard chosen is the hydrogen electrode with the conditions of $H_2(g)$ at 1 atm pressure and of H^+ concentration at unit activity:

$$2H^+(aq, a = 1\ M) + 2e^- \rightarrow H_2(g, 1 \text{ atm}) \qquad \mathscr{E}^0 = 0.0000 \text{ volts} \tag{8.30}$$

The electrode potential of any other half-cell reaction can be compared against this standard. For example, under standard-state concentration conditions

$$Ag^+(aq) + e^- \rightarrow Ag(s) \qquad \mathscr{E}^0 = 0.799 \text{ volts}$$
$$V^{3+}(aq) + e^- \rightarrow V^{2+}(aq) \qquad \mathscr{E}^0 = -0.255 \text{ volts}$$

The electromotive force of a combined reaction, also written as $\mathscr{E}^0$, is the difference between the appropriate standard electrode potentials. For example, the combination of the above reactions gives

$$Ag^+(aq) + V^{2+}(aq) \rightarrow Ag(s) + V^{3+}(aq)$$
$$\mathscr{E}^0 = 0.799 - (-0.255) \text{ volts} = 1.054 \text{ volts}$$
$$\Delta G^0 = -nF\mathscr{E}^0 = \left(-23{,}030 \frac{\text{cal}}{\text{volt-mole}}\right)(1 \text{ mole})(1.054 \text{ volt}) = -24{,}300 \text{ cal}$$

This reaction is spontaneous as written from left to right for standard-state conditions of reactants and products.

Selected values of standard electrode potentials measured in acid solution are shown in Table 8-1. From a table of this sort with ten electrode reactions, we can form 45 different chemical reactions. Using data from such tables, the change in

Table 8-1. SELECTED ELECTRODE POTENTIALS (ACID SOLUTION)

Half-reaction	$\mathscr{E}^0$ (volts)
$Li^+(aq) + e^- \rightarrow Li(s)$	−3.045
$Na^+(aq) + e^- \rightarrow Na(s)$	−2.714
$Zn^{2+}(aq) + 2e^- \rightarrow Zn(s)$	−0.763
$Fe^{2+}(aq) + 2e^- \rightarrow Fe(s)$	−0.440
$Cr^{3+}(aq) + e^- \rightarrow Cr^{2+}(aq)$	−0.41
$2H^+(aq) + 2e^- \rightarrow H_2(g)$	0.000
$S(s) + 2H^+(aq) + 2e^- \rightarrow H_2S(g)$	+0.141
$Cu^{2+}(aq) + e^- \rightarrow Cu^+(aq)$	+0.153
$AgCl(s) + e^- \rightarrow Ag(s) + Cl^-(aq)$	+0.222
$Cu^{2+}(aq) + 2e^- \rightarrow Cu(s)$	+0.337
$I_2(s) + 2e^- \rightarrow 2I^-(aq)$	+0.536
$MnO_4^-(aq) + e^- \rightarrow MnO_4^{2-}(aq)$	+0.564
$O_2(g) + 2H^+(aq) + 2e^- \rightarrow H_2O_2(aq)$	+0.682
$Fe^{3+}(aq) + e^- \rightarrow Fe^{2+}(aq)$	+0.771
$Hg_2^{2+}(aq) + 2e^- \rightarrow 2Hg(l)$	+0.789
$Ag^+(aq) + e^- \rightarrow Ag(s)$	+0.799
$Hg^{2+}(aq) + e^- \rightarrow \frac{1}{2}Hg_2^{2+}(aq)$	+0.920
$Br_2(l) + 2e^- \rightarrow 2Br^-(aq)$	+1.065
$MnO_2(s) + 4H^+(aq) + 2e^- \rightarrow Mn^{2+}(aq) + 2H_2O$	+1.23
$Cr_2O_7^{2-}(aq) + 14H^+(aq) + 6e^- \rightarrow 2Cr^{3+}(aq) + 7H_2O$	+1.33
$Cl_2(g) + 2e^- \rightarrow 2Cl^-(aq)$	+1.359
$Mn^{3+}(aq) + e^- \rightarrow Mn^{2+}(aq)$	+1.51
$MnO_4^-(aq) + 8H^+(aq) + 5e^- \rightarrow Mn^{2+}(aq) + 4H_2O$	+1.51
$H_2O_2(aq) + 2H^+(aq) + 2e^- \rightarrow 2H_2O$	+1.77
$F_2(g) + 2e^- \rightarrow 2F^-(aq)$	+2.65

Gibbs free energy for each of these reactions can be calculated. Thus, such tables represent a tremendous economy in the presentation of Gibbs free-energy data for chemical reactions.

To obtain the $\mathscr{E}^0$ value for the overall cell, we simply combine $\mathscr{E}^0$ values for the half-reactions involved. The stoichiometry of the electrode reaction does not affect the magnitude of $\mathscr{E}^0$; however, the direction in which the reaction is written does affect the sign:

$$Li^+(aq) + e^- \rightarrow Li(s) \qquad \mathscr{E}^0 = -3.045 \text{ volts}$$
$$2Li^+(aq) + 2e^- \rightarrow 2Li(s) \qquad \mathscr{E}^0 = -3.045 \text{ volts}$$
$$Li(s) \rightarrow Li^+(aq) + e^- \qquad \mathscr{E}^0 = 3.045 \text{ volts}$$

The rules for combining half-cell reaction potentials are based on the Gibbs free-energy relationship. Consider the following electrodes:

$$Cu^{2+}(aq) + 2e^- \rightarrow Cu(s) \qquad \mathscr{E}_1^0 = 0.337 \text{ volts}$$

and

$$2Li^+(aq) + 2e^- \rightarrow 2Li(s) \qquad \mathscr{E}_2^0 = -3.045 \text{ volts}$$

The overall reaction is

$$Cu^{2+}(aq) + 2Li(s) \rightarrow Cu(s) + 2Li^+(aq)$$

The free-energy change is

$$\Delta G^0 = \Delta G_1^0 - \Delta G_2^0$$
$$-2F\mathscr{E}^0 = -2F\mathscr{E}_1^0 + 2F\mathscr{E}_2^0$$

Thus

$$\mathscr{E}^0 = \mathscr{E}_1^0 - \mathscr{E}_2^0$$
$$= (0.337 + 3.045) = 3.382 \text{ volts}$$

Thus we see the basis for the simple rule that for a complete cell reaction the cell potential is obtained by algebraic addition of the half-cell potentials.

The combination of half-cell reactions can also be used to obtain another half-cell reaction. This can be important when a certain half-cell reaction is not tabulated. Again, the calculation of the $\mathscr{E}^0$ value is based on the combination of free-energy changes. For example, we find $\mathscr{E}_3^0$ for the half-cell reaction

$$Fe^{3+}(aq) + 3e^- \rightarrow Fe(s)$$

by combining

$$Fe^{3+}(aq) + e^- \rightarrow Fe^{2+}(aq) \qquad \mathscr{E}_1^0 = 0.771 \text{ volt}, \ \Delta G_1^0 = -F(0.771)$$
$$Fe^{2+}(aq) + 2e^- \rightarrow Fe(s) \qquad \mathscr{E}_2^0 = -0.440 \text{ volt}, \ \Delta G_2^0 = -2F(-0.440)$$

Addition of these two half-cell reactions gives the desired half-cell reaction; the Gibbs free energies are added:

$$Fe^{3+}(aq) + 3e^- \rightarrow Fe(s) \qquad \begin{aligned} \Delta G^0 &= \Delta G_1{}^0 + \Delta G_2{}^0 \\ &= -F(0.771) - 2F(-0.440) \\ &= F(0.109) \end{aligned}$$

Also

$$\Delta G^0 = -3F\mathscr{E}_3{}^0$$

Thus

$$\mathscr{E}_3{}^0 = \frac{F(0.109)}{-3F} = -0.036 \text{ volts}$$

8.6 EFFECT OF CONCENTRATION ON CELL VOLTAGE

Nernst equation

The change in free energy for a reaction whose components are not in standard-state concentrations is given by equation 7.17 as

$$\Delta G = \Delta G^0 + RT \ln Q \tag{8.31}$$

where Q is the quotient of non-equilibrium concentrations, in the same form as the equilibrium constant K. In terms of cell voltages as expressed in equation 8.23, equation 8.31 becomes

$$\mathscr{E} = \mathscr{E}^0 - \frac{RT}{nF} \ln Q \tag{8.32}$$

At 298 °K (25 °C)

$$\mathscr{E} = \mathscr{E}^0 - \frac{0.05915}{n} \log Q \tag{8.33}$$

Equation 8.33 is called the Nernst equation.

EXAMPLE **8.2**

Calculate $\mathscr{E}$ for the cell reaction

$$Zn(s) + Cu^{2+}(0.1\ M) \rightarrow Zn^{2+}(1\ M) + Cu(s)$$

where the concentrations (strictly speaking, the activities) of Cu^{2+} and Zn^{2+} are 0.1 and 1.0 molar, respectively.

The value of $\mathscr{E}^0$ at 25°C is found from half-cell reactions

$$Cu^{2+}(aq) + 2e^- \rightarrow Cu(s) \qquad \mathscr{E}_1^0 = 0.337 \text{ volts}$$
$$Zn^{2+}(aq) + 2e^- \rightarrow Zn(s) \qquad \mathscr{E}_2^0 = -0.763 \text{ volts}$$

and is 1.100 volts. The effect of the non-standard state concentration of the Cu^{2+} ion manifests itself in the quotient $Q = [Zn^{2+}]/[Cu^{2+}] = 10$. This gives

$$\mathscr{E} = 1.100 - \frac{0.0592}{2} \log 10 = 1.070 \text{ volts}$$

When equilibrium concentrations are present, the quotient Q is denoted by K. Since $\Delta G = 0$, $\mathscr{E} = 0$, so from equation 8.32

$$\mathscr{E}^0 = \frac{RT}{nF} \ln K \tag{8.34}$$

At 298°K

$$\log K = 16.9\, n\mathscr{E}^0 \tag{8.35}$$

For the zinc-copper cell

$$Zn(s) + Cu^{2+}(aq) \rightarrow Zn^{2+}(aq) + Cu(s) \qquad \mathscr{E}^0 = 1.100 \text{ volts}$$

From equation 8.35

$$\log K = 37.2$$

or

$$K = 1.5 \times 10^{37}$$

This large value of K signifies that the reaction goes to a state in which the ratio $[Zn^{2+}]/[Cu^{2+}]$ has an extremely large value. For all practical purposes, the reaction goes completely to the right.

Ion-selective electrodes: measurement of pH

An extremely important application of the Nernst equation, that is, of the concentration dependence of $\mathscr{E}$, arises in connection with the determination of the concentrations of ions in solutions. In equation 8.33 we saw that cell voltages can be calculated if concentrations are known. Conversely, we can measure the cell voltage and relate it back to the concentrations of a particular ion, if concentrations of all species but the one of interest are known. One ion whose concentration is frequently of interest is H_3O^+. The device used to measure H_3O^+ concentration, or pH, is called a pH meter.

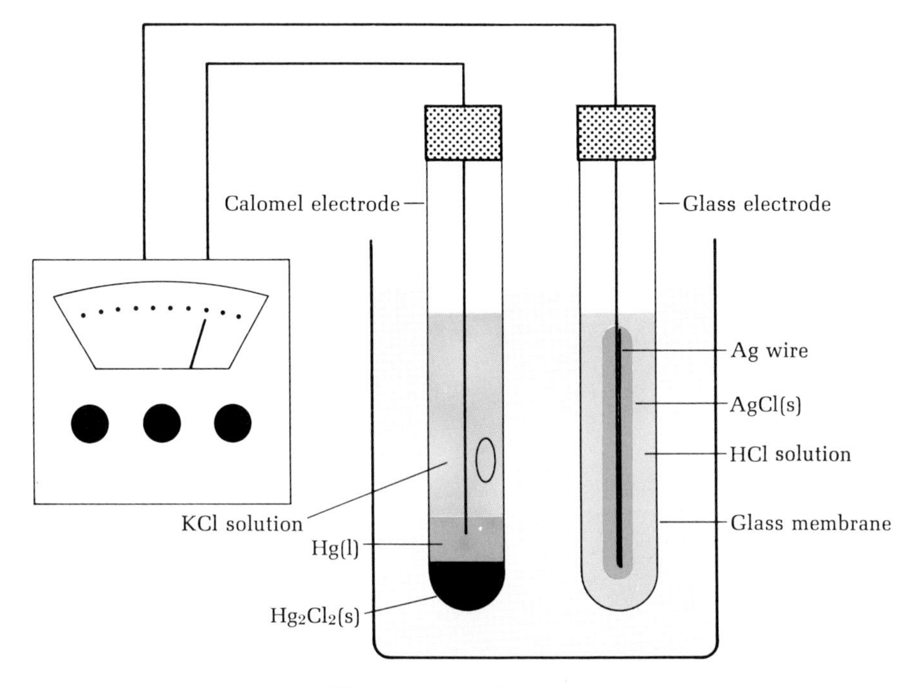

Fig. 8-9. Typical pH meter.

A diagram of a typical pH meter is shown in Fig. 8-9. The meter consists of three main parts: a vacuum-tube voltmeter or potentiometer capable of measuring voltage to ± 0.005 volts, a reference electrode, and a glass electrode. In general, the reference electrode is a *calomel* electrode, which consists of a saturated KCl solution in contact with liquid Hg and solid Hg_2Cl_2, contained in a glass electrode assembly. The electrode materials are separated from the unknown solution by a porous-plug barrier. The glass electrode consists of a thin-walled glass tube that contains solid silver chloride on a silver wire immersed in an HCl solution. The potential across this glass electrode, and thus the cell voltage, is a linear function of the pH ($-\log [H_3O^+]$) of the solution outside the glass membrane. The cell can be designated as

$$\underbrace{\mathrm{Ag(s)} \mid \mathrm{AgCl(s)} \mid \mathrm{HCl(aq)} \mid \mathrm{glass}}_{\text{glass electrode}} \mid \text{unknown solution} \parallel \underbrace{\mathrm{KCl(sat)} \mid \mathrm{Hg_2Cl_2(s)} \mid \mathrm{Hg(l)}}_{\text{reference electrode}}$$

The potential of the system, which is measured on the voltmeter, arises from five sources: (1) the Ag(s)-AgCl(s) couple, (2) the calomel reference electrode, (3) the potential between the glass and the HCl in the glass electrode, (4) the potential of the junction of the calomel electrode and the unknown solution, and (5) the glass electrode-unknown solution potential. In a given pH-meter cell system, the first three potentials are constant and fixed. The potential between the calomel electrode and the unknown solution is nullified by adjustment of the voltmeter. Thus, the observed potential depends only on the pH of the unknown solution, and the pH can be read directly from the voltmeter scale in terms of units of pH.

8.7 EFFECT OF T AND p ON $\mathcal{E}$

The effect of temperature and pressure on $\mathcal{E}$ of a cell is easily developed from these effects on ΔG as seen in section 7.4.

$$\Delta G = -nF\mathcal{E} \tag{8.36}$$

$$\left(\frac{d\Delta G}{dT}\right)_p = -\Delta S = -nF\left(\frac{d\mathcal{E}}{dT}\right)_p \tag{8.37}$$

$$\left(\frac{d\Delta G}{dp}\right)_T = \Delta V = -nF\left(\frac{d\mathcal{E}}{dp}\right)_T \tag{8.38}$$

$$\left(\frac{d\Delta G/T}{dT}\right)_p = -\frac{\Delta H}{T^2} = -nF\left(\frac{d\mathcal{E}/T}{dT}\right)_p \tag{8.39}$$

From these equations, we see that the study of $\mathcal{E}$ as a function of T and p enables us to determine the thermodynamic quantities ΔG, ΔS, ΔV, and ΔH.

EXAMPLE 8.3

Calculate ΔG^0, ΔH^0, and ΔS^0 for the cell reaction

$$Hg_2Cl_2(s) + Pb(s) \rightarrow 2Hg(l) + PbCl_2(s)$$

where

$$\mathcal{E}^0 = 0.5359 \text{ volts}$$

and

$$\left(\frac{d\mathcal{E}^0}{dT}\right)_p = 1.45 \times 10^{-4} \text{ volt/deg}$$

Thus

$$\Delta G^0 = -(2)(23.06)(0.5359) \text{ kcal} = -24.72 \text{ kcal}$$

$$\Delta S^0 = nF\left(\frac{d\mathcal{E}}{dT}\right)_p = (2)(23.06)(10^3)(1.45 \times 10^{-4}) \text{ cal/deg} = 6.69 \text{ cal/deg}$$

$$\Delta H^0 = \Delta G^0 + T\Delta S^0 = -22.73 \text{ kcal}$$

8.8 OXIDATION-REDUCTION BEHAVIOR OF THE ELEMENTS

In section 8.5 we indicated that half-cell electrode-potential data provide a highly efficient route for calculating free-energy changes of many chemical reactions. The $\mathscr{E}^0$ values indicate the direction of spontaneous reaction and the chemical behavior of the elements and their compounds.

Frost diagrams provide a convenient method for depicting the chemical behavior of various ionic and molecular species. By this method, the $\mathscr{E}^0$ values for an entire reaction system can be handled graphically. No information is contained in Frost diagrams that is not present in tables of $\mathscr{E}^0$ values; however, a Frost diagram offers the advantage of presenting the overall chemical behavior of an element at a glance. Using these diagrams (Figs. 8-10 to 8-16), we will summarize in a simple but thorough way the chemistry of several elements in acid solution.

The Gibbs free-energy change, ΔG, of a reaction determines whether the reaction will occur. ΔG^0 is related to $\mathscr{E}^0$ by equation 8.13:

$$\Delta G^0 = -nF\mathscr{E}^0 \tag{8.40}$$

where n is the number of electrons involved in the half-cell reaction. When we plot $\Delta G^0/F$ values (in terms of $-n\mathscr{E}^0$) as a function of oxidation state for a given element, we obtain a Frost diagram. The parameter $\Delta G^0/F$ is the free-energy change in units of electron-volts, relative to the element in its zero oxidation state.* The half-reactions that relate Mn(s) to its various oxidized species in acid solution along with their $\mathscr{E}^0$ values and their values of $\Delta G^0/F$ are shown in Table 8-2. The plot of $\Delta G^0/F$ data versus oxidation number for the manganese system is shown in Fig. 8-10, *A*. As we will see, several important features are displayed in a Frost diagram.

The reduction potential $\mathscr{E}^0$ for a half-reaction between any two species with oxidation numbers b and a is calculated from

$$\Delta G_b^0 - \Delta G_a^0 = (b - a)F\mathscr{E}^0 \tag{8.41}$$

*To convert electron-volts to kcal, remember that F is expressed as 23.05 kcal/electron-volt.

Table 8-2. MANGANESE HALF-REACTIONS IN ACID SOLUTION

Half-reaction	$\mathscr{E}^0$ *(volts)*	$\Delta G^0/F$ *(electron-volts)*
$Mn(s) \rightarrow Mn^{2+}(aq) + 2e^-$	1.05	−2.16
$Mn(s) \rightarrow Mn^{3+}(aq) + 3e^-$	0.20	−0.60
$Mn(s) + 2H_2O \rightarrow MnO_2(s) + 4H^+(aq) + 4e^-$	−0.115	0.46
$Mn(s) + 4H_2O \rightarrow MnO_4^{2-} + 8H^+ + 6e^-$	−0.82	4.92
$Mn(s) + 4H_2O \rightarrow MnO_4^- + 8H^+ + 7e^-$	−0.78	5.47

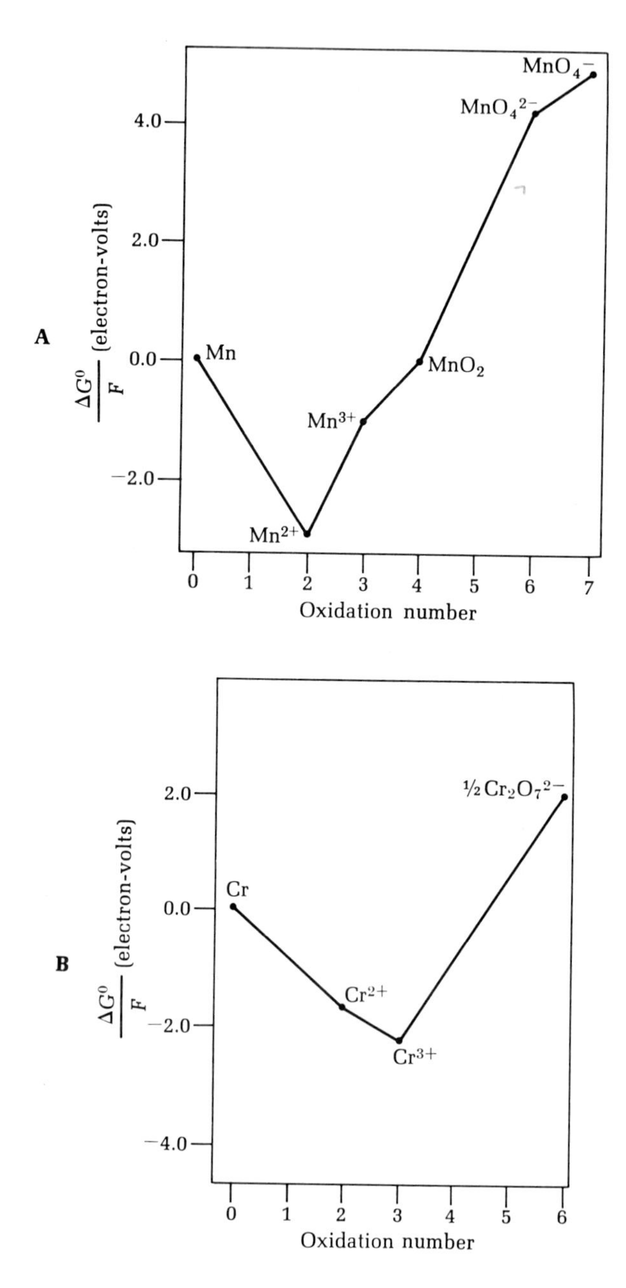

Fig. 8-10. Frost diagrams for species in aqueous acid solution. **A,** Manganese. **B,** Chromium.

as

$$\mathscr{E}^0 = \frac{(\Delta G_b{}^0/F) - (\Delta G_a{}^0/F)}{b - a} \tag{8.42}$$

This last expression gives the slope of the line between any two species on a Frost diagram. A positive slope determines the relative oxidizing ability of a given half-reaction. For example, $MnO_4^-(aq)$ is a stronger oxidizing agent in the MnO_4^--Mn^{2+} half-reaction than it is in the MnO_4^--MnO_4^{2-} half-reaction. A half-reaction with a negative slope indicates that the species with the lower oxidation number is a reducing agent. Thus, Mn(s) is a stronger reducing agent in the Mn(s)-Mn^{2+} half-reaction than it is in the Mn(s)-Mn^{3+}(aq) half-reaction.

A second use of Frost diagrams arises in the prediction of possible chemical reactions. The basis for such predictions is the overall free-energy change for the combination of two half-cell reactions. For example, to determine whether Li(s) will react with H^+(aq), we superimpose the Frost diagram for hydrogen species (Fig. 8-11, *A*) on that for lithium species (Fig. 8-11, *C*). The reactants are superimposed at the same point, as shown in Fig. 8-12, *A*. Each half-reaction involves a change of one electron, so the reaction is balanced. Since $\Delta G^0/F$ is zero for the $\frac{1}{2}H_2$-H^+ half-reaction, the overall $\Delta G^0/F$ is equal to that of the Li(s)-Li^+ half-reaction. $\Delta G^0/F$ is negative, so the reaction occurs.

A convenient way to diagrammatically determine the free-energy change for any reaction is to draw a tie-line between product species as shown. The vertical distance from the reactants' point to the tie-line gives $\frac{1}{2}(\Delta G^0/F)$.

When combining two half-reactions that involve different numbers of electrons, we must modify the diagrams to represent a balanced reaction if $\Delta G^0/F$ is to be obtained directly from the final diagram. Consider the reaction

$$H_2(g) + \tfrac{1}{2}O_2(g) \quad \rightarrow \quad H_2O(l)$$

Data from Fig. 8-11, *A* and *B*, are superimposed as shown in Fig. 8-12, *B*. Since the O_2-H_2O half-reaction involves $2e^-$, we must double the length of the $\frac{1}{2}H_2$-H^+ half-reaction line in order to balance the reaction. The distance from the reactants' point to the tie-line then gives $\frac{1}{2}(\Delta G^0/F)$. Since ΔG^0 is negative, the reaction occurs.

The tendency of a given species to disproportionate into forms of higher and lower oxidation numbers can be determined from these diagrams also. In the case of manganese (Fig. 8-13, *B*) the MnO_4^{2-} ion is above the tie-line between products MnO_4^- and MnO_2. The disproportionation

$$4H_3O^+ + 3MnO_4^{2-} \quad \rightarrow \quad 2MnO_4^- + MnO_2 + 6H_2O$$

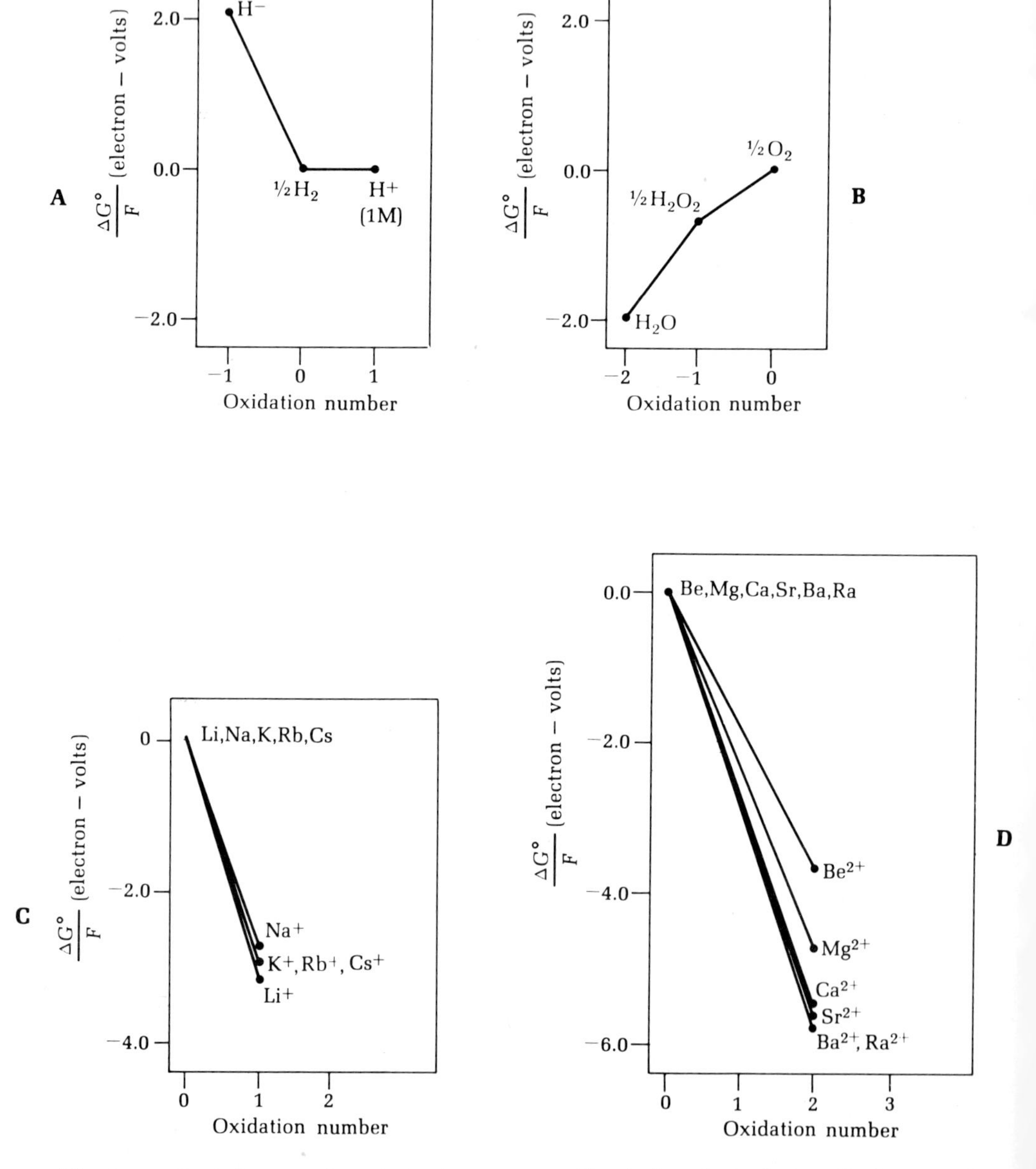

Fig. 8-11. Frost diagrams for species in aqueous acid solution. **A,** Hydrogen. **B,** Oxygen. **C,** Alkali metals (Li, Na, K, Rb, Cs). **D,** Alkaline earth metals (Be, Mg, Ca, Sr, Ba, Ra).

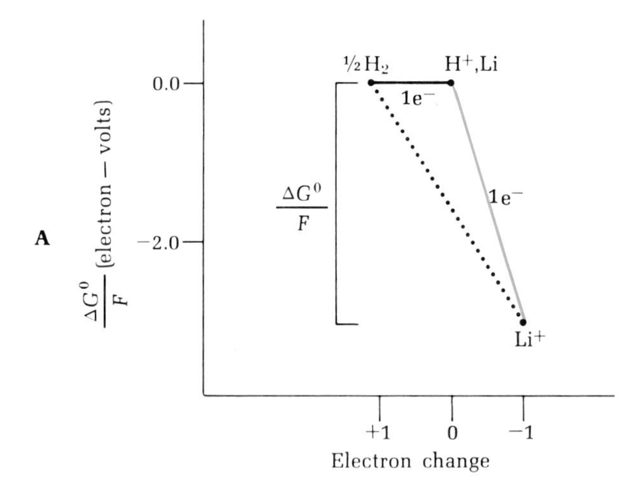

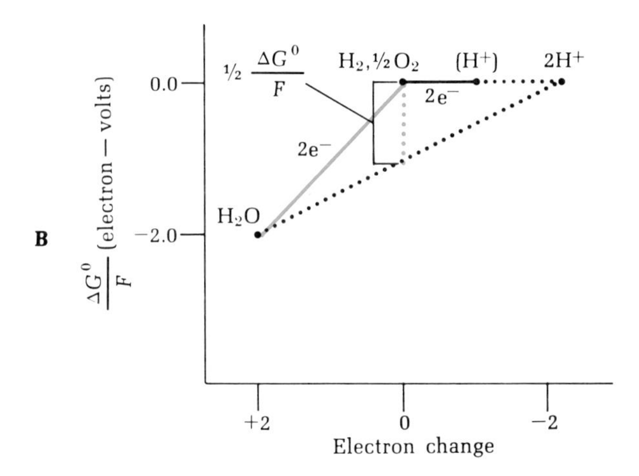

Fig. 8-12. Reactions described in terms of Frost diagrams. **A,** $H^+ + Li(s)$. **B,** $\frac{1}{2}H_2(g) + O_2(g)$.

results in a decrease in free energy as shown. Conversely, if the position of a given species (or pair of species in two half-reactions) lies below the tie-line between two species of higher and lower oxidation numbers, the reaction proceeds to give the species of intermediate oxidation number. For example, consider Mn^{2+} and MnO_4^- in acid solution, shown in Fig. 8-13, *A*. From the diagram, $\Delta G^0/F$ is negative for the reaction

$$6H_2O + 3Mn^{2+} + 2MnO_4^- \rightarrow 5MnO_2 + 4H_3O^+$$

so we conclude the reaction will occur.

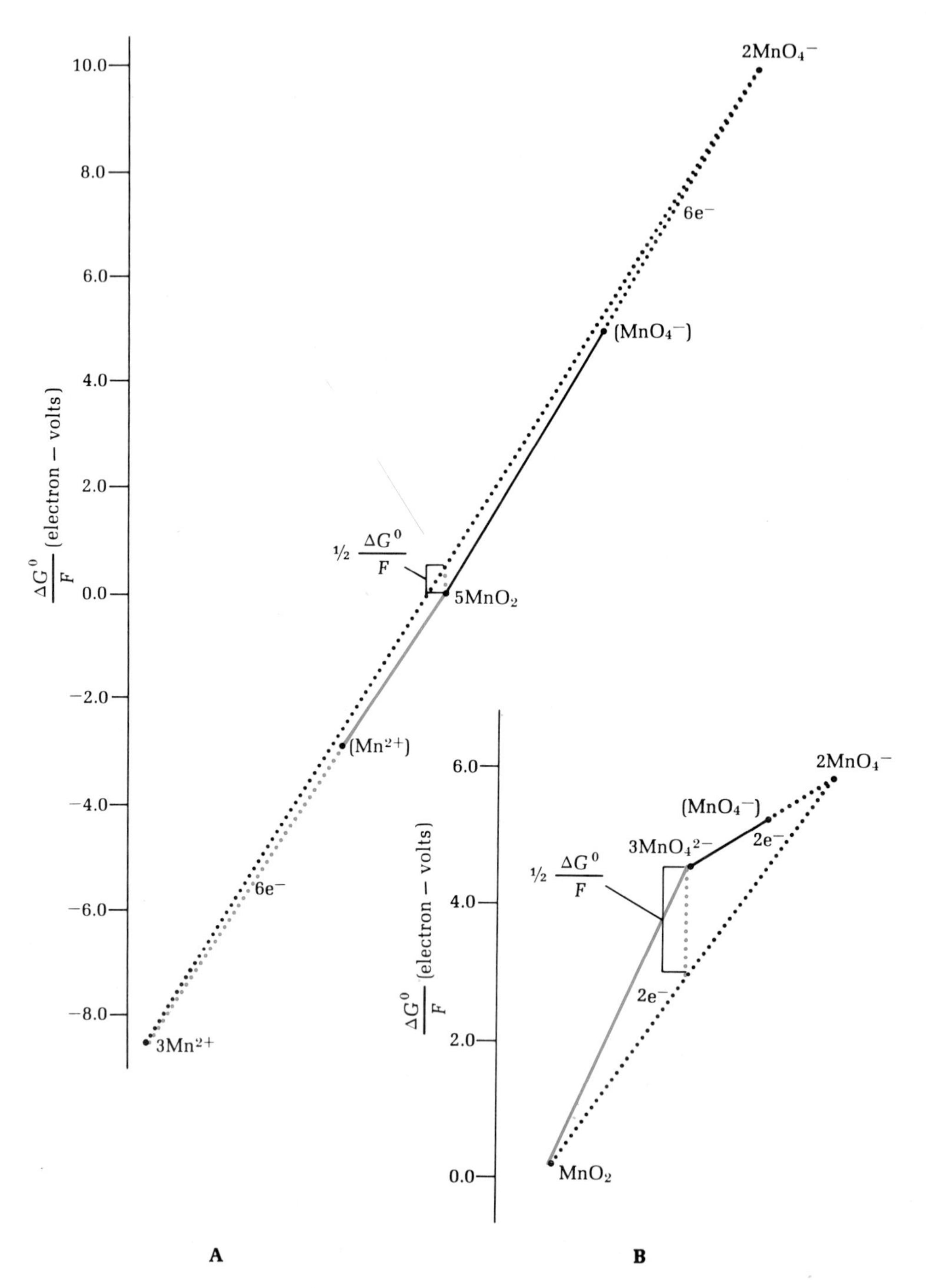

Fig. 8-13. Frost diagrams of manganese species in aqueous acid solution. **A,** Reaction of MnO_4^- and Mn^{2+} to form $MnO_2(s)$. **B,** Disporportionation of MnO_4^{2-} ion.

Several conclusions about the chemistry of the elements shown in Figs. 8-10 to 8-16 can be made:

1. Many metals function as reducing agents relative to their first stable oxidation state. The alkali metals (Li, Na, K, Rb, and Cs; Fig. 8-11, *C*) and the alkaline earth metals (Be, Mg, Ca, Sr, Ba, and Ra; Fig. 8-11, *D*) are the strongest

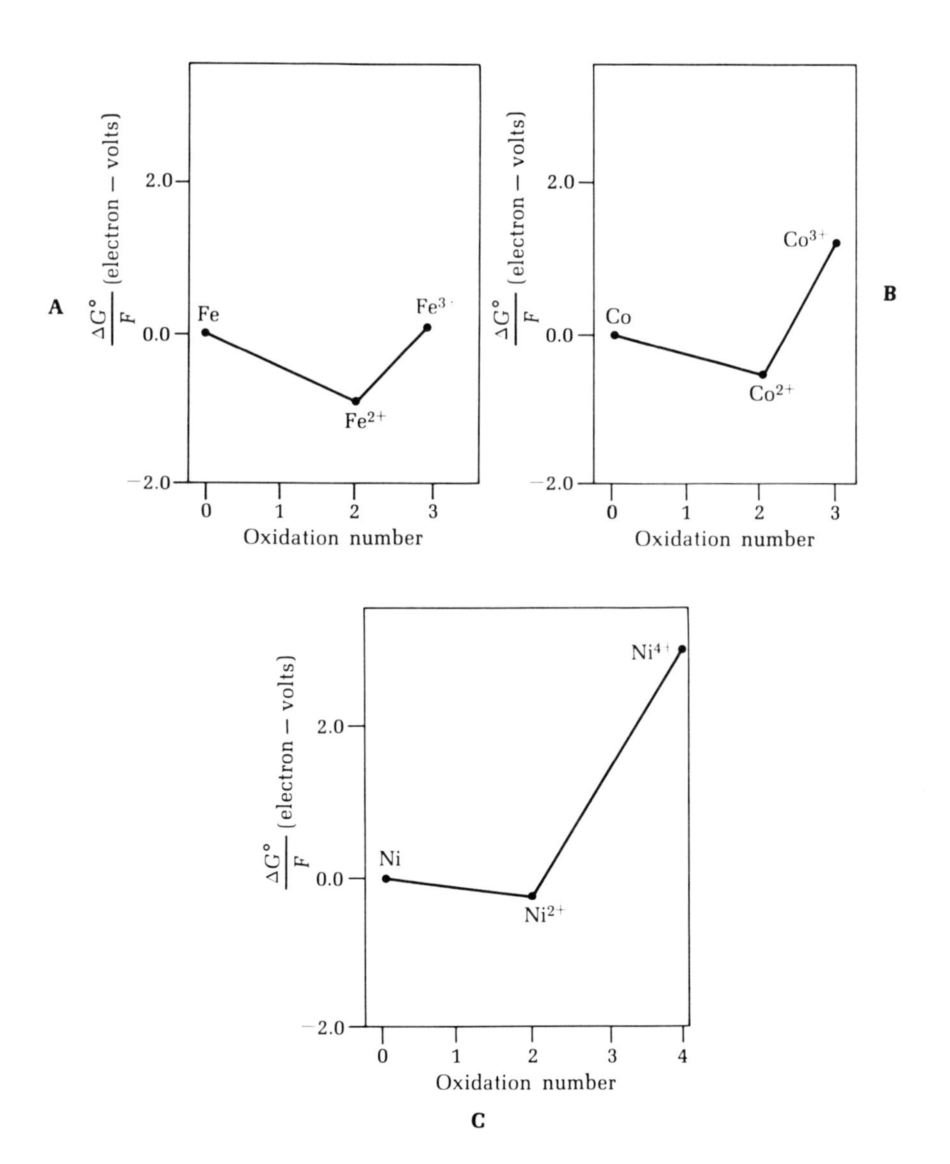

Fig. 8-14. Frost diagrams of species in aqueous acid solution. **A,** Iron. **B,** Cobalt. **C,** Nickel.

reducing agents and are notably similar in behavior. The first-row transition metals are weaker reducing agents; their reducing abilities decrease (for those metals shown in the diagrams) in the series Mn > Cr > Fe > Co > Ni (Figs. 8-10, *A* and *B*, and 8-14, *A* to *C*). However, second- and third-row transition metals generally do not show reducing behavior.

2. Half-reactions involving a transition-metal species in its highest oxidation state and a metal species in some lower oxidation state are oxidizing half-reactions relative to the standard $\frac{1}{2}H_2$-H^+ half-reaction. For example, the Ni^{4+}-Ni^{2+}, Ni^{4+}-Ni, Co^{3+}-Co^{2+}, Co^{3+}-Co, Fe^{3+}-Fe^{2+}, $\frac{1}{2}Cr_2O_7^{2-}$-Cr^{3+}, etc., half-reactions can all oxidize $\frac{1}{2}H_2$ gas to H^+ ion. Of the metals species shown, MnO_4^-, $Cr_2O_7^{2-}$ and Ni^{4+} are the strongest oxidizing agents. Metals species in high oxidation states are generally strong oxidizing agents.
3. The oxidation-reduction behavior of metal species in a given half-reaction is markedly affected if other complex ions can form in the reaction solution. Metal cations in water are present as $M(H_2O)_x^{y+}$ complex ions. Frost diagrams of silver (Ag-Ag^+) and mercury (Hg-Hg^{2+}) half-reactions are shown in Fig. 8-15, *A* and *B*. With the silver ion, replacement of water with NH_3 [$Ag(NH_3)_2^+$] and with CN^- [$Ag(CN)_2^-$] lowers the free energy of the complex ion. Thus we see that the Ag-Ag^+ half-reaction is oxidizing, whereas the Ag-$Ag(CN)_2^-$ half-reaction is reducing. Similar behavior is shown for the Hg-Hg^{2+} half-reaction system (Fig. 8-15, *B*).

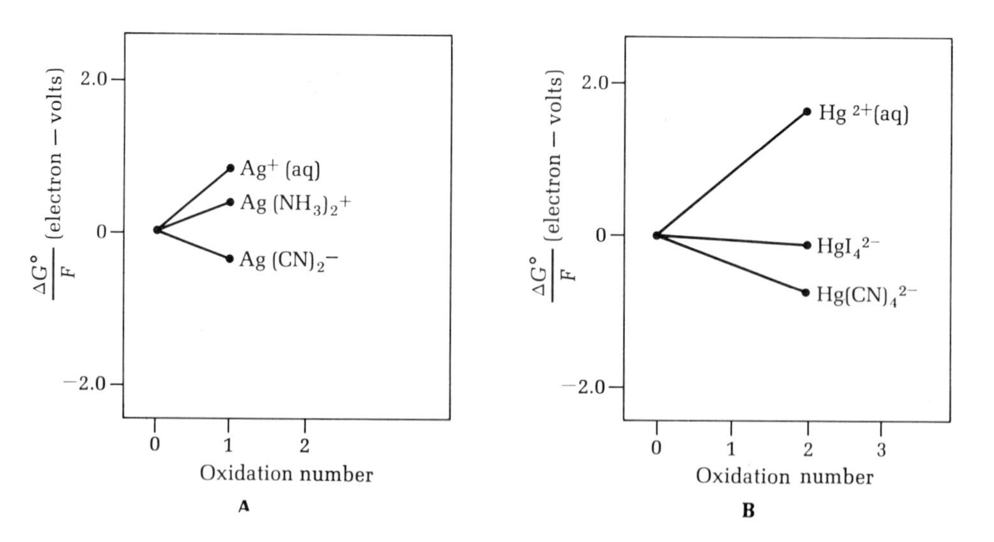

Fig. 8-15. Frost diagrams. **A,** Silver complexes. **B,** Mercury complexes.

4. The halogens show oxidizing behavior in elemental forms (F_2, Cl_2, Br_2, and I_2) and in all forms with positive oxidation states. (Fig. 8-16). The elemental forms differ in oxidizing ability, decreasing in the order $F_2 > Cl_2 > Br_2 > I_2$. Thus a given halogen in its elemental form can oxidize the (1−)-oxidation-state form of any other halogen below it on the diagram. The halogen species with the higher oxidation states are notably similar in their oxidizing ability, as shown by the chlorine and bromine species in Fig. 8-16.

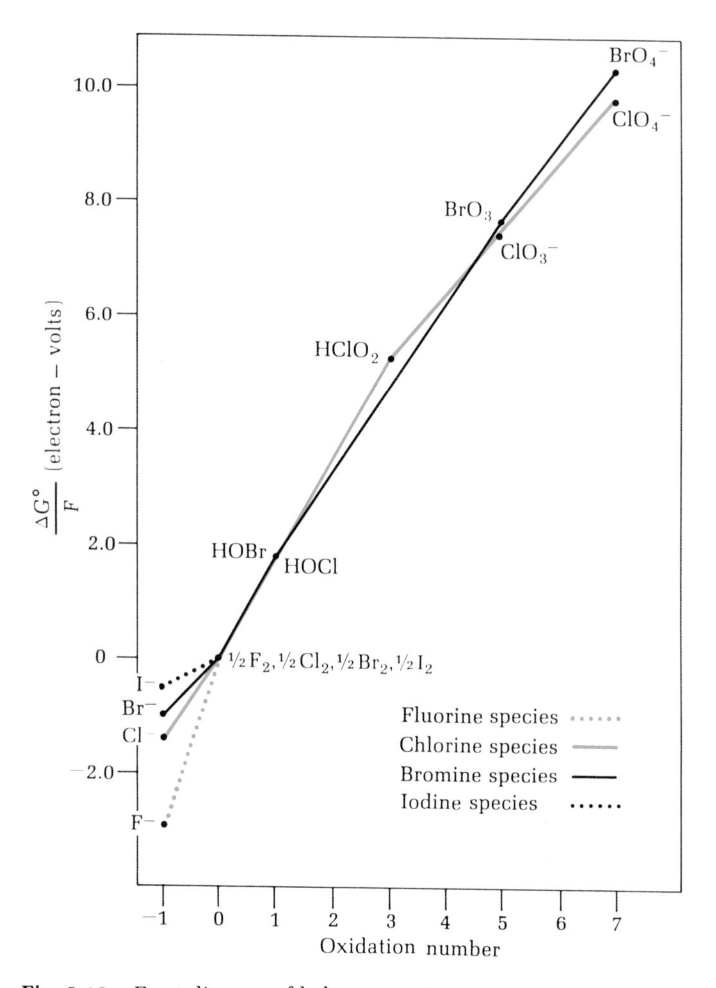

Fig. 8-16. Frost diagram of halogen species in aqueous acid solution.

PROBLEMS

1. Balance the following reactions:
   (a) $Cu(s) + NO_3^-(aq) \rightarrow NO_2(g) + Cu^{2+}(aq)$ (in acid)
   (b) $Bi(OH)_3(s) + MnO_4^-(aq) \rightarrow MnO_2(s) + BiO_3^-(aq)$ (in base)
   (c) $I_2(s) + H_2S(g) \rightarrow I^-(aq) + S(s)$ (in acid)
   (d) $Ag(s) + NO_3^-(aq) \rightarrow Ag^+(aq) + NO(g)$ (in acid)
   (e) $Al(s) + NO_3^-(aq) \rightarrow Al(OH)_4^-(aq) + NH_3(g)$ (in base)
   (f) $ClO^-(aq) + Fe(OH)_3 \rightarrow Cl^-(aq) + FeO_4^{2-}(aq)$ (in base)
   (g) $ClO_3^-(aq) + As_2S_3(s) \rightarrow Cl^-(aq) + H_2AsO_4^-(aq) + SO_4^{2-}$ (in acid)
   (h) $MnO_4^{2-}(aq) \rightarrow MnO_2(s) + MnO_4^-(aq)$ (in acid)
   (i) $Cl_2(g) \rightarrow ClO_3^-(aq) + 5Cl^-(aq)$ (in base)
2. A current of 10.0 amps flows for 10.0 hours. How many coulombs and moles of electric charge does this represent?
3. How much time would it take for a current of 1.3 amps to electroplate
   (a) 10.0 g of Ag from a large $AgNO_3$ solution
   (b) 3.0 g of Cu from a large $CuSO_4$ solution
   (c) 1.2 g of Fe from a large $FeCl_3$ solution
4. What is the oxidation state of a molten tin salt if a current of 1.50 amps deposits 13.3 g of tin in 4.0 hours?
5. Calculate the number of kilowatt-hours required to produce 1000 kg of aluminum for a Hall-process cell operating at 10.0 volts. See Fig. 8-2.
6. When sodium sulfate is electrolyzed, the anode reaction is

$$6H_2O \rightarrow 4H_3O^+ + O_2(g) + 4e^-$$

   How many liters of $O_2(g)$ are evolved at 25°C and 1 atm if a current of 2.00 amps is passed for three hours?
7. Calculate ΔG for the following reactions at 25°C. Note concentrations and pressures are unspecified.
   (a) $2H_2(g) + O_2(g) \rightarrow 2H_2O(l)$ $\mathscr{E} = 1.03$ volts
   (b) $Co(s) + Ni^{2+}(aq) \rightarrow Co^{2+}(aq) + Ni(s)$ $\mathscr{E} = -0.03$ volts
   (c) $2Fe^{3+}(aq) + 3I^-(aq) \rightarrow 2Fe^{2+}(aq) + I_3^-(aq)$ $\mathscr{E} = 0.24$ volts
   In which direction will these reactions occur spontaneously?
8. Write reactions for the following galvanic cells:
   (a) Pt, $Cl_2(g)|Cl^-(aq)||Fe^{2+}(aq), Fe^{3+}(aq)|$Pt
   (b) Pb(s), $PbSO_4(s)|H_2SO_4(aq)|PbSO_4(s), PbO_2(s)$, Pb(s)
   (c) Ag(s), AgCl(s)|HCl(aq)|$Cl_2(g)$, Pt
   (d) $Zn(s)|Zn^{2+}(aq, 0.01\ M)||Zn^{2+}(aq, 0.10\ M)|Zn$
   (e) Hg(l), $Hg_2Cl_2(s)|HCl(aq)|H_2(g)$, Pt
   Remember the convention that oxidation occurs at the left electrode. Draw a workable cell of types (a) and (e).
9. Calculate $\mathscr{E}^0$ for the following reactions at 25°C:
   (a) $Hg^{2+}(aq) + Hg \rightarrow Hg_2^{2+}(aq)$
   (b) $Fe^{3+}(aq) + I^-(aq) \rightarrow Fe^{2+}(aq) + \frac{1}{2}I_2(s)$
10. Calculate the equilibrium constant at 25°C for the reaction

$$Al^{3+}(aq) + 4OH^-(aq) \rightarrow Al(OH)_4^-(aq)$$

from

$$Al^{3+}(aq) + 3e^- \rightarrow Al(s) \qquad \mathscr{E}^0 = -1.66 \text{ volts}$$
$$Al(OH)_4^-(aq) + 3e^- \rightarrow Al(s) + 4OH^- \qquad \mathscr{E}^0 = -2.35 \text{ volts}$$

11. From data in Table 8-1, calculate the $\mathscr{E}^0$ value for the following reactions:
    (a) $MnO_4^-(aq) + 4H_3O^+(aq) + 3e^- \rightarrow MnO_2(s) + 6H_2O(l)$
    (b) $Hg^{2+}(aq) + 2e^- \rightarrow Hg(l)$
12. Calculate $\mathscr{E}$ for the following half-cell reactions at 25°C:
    (a) $Zn^{2+}(aq, 0.0100\ M) \rightarrow Zn(s) + e^-$
    (b) $Cr_2O_7^{2-}(aq, 2.0\ M) + 14H_3O^+(aq, 0.100\ M) + 6e^- \rightarrow 2Cr^{3+}(aq, 3.0\ M) + 21H_2O(l)$
    (c) $MnO_2(s) + 4H_3O^+(aq, 2.0\ M) + 2e^- \rightarrow Mn^{2+}(aq, 0.100\ M) + 6H_2O(l)$
13. Calculate the pH needed to obtain an $\mathscr{E}$ value of 0.800 volts for the following half-cell reaction at 25°C:

$$O_2(g, 1 \text{ atm}) + 2H_3O^+(aq) + 2e^- \rightarrow H_2O_2(aq, 1.0\ M) + 2H_2O(l)$$

14. Calculate $\mathscr{E}$ for the Daniell cell given by Fig. 8-6 if $[Zn^{2+}(aq)] = 0.100\ M$ and $[Cu^{2+}(aq)] = 2.00\ M$. In which direction does this reaction occur spontaneously?
15. (a) Calculate $\mathscr{E}$ at 25°C for the concentration cell given by

$$Zn\,|\,Zn^{2+}(aq, 1.0\ M)\,||\,Zn^{2+}(aq, 0.50\ M)\,|\,Zn$$

    (b) As the cell discharges, what happens to the concentration of $Zn^{2+}(aq)$?
16. Calculate the maximum work obtainable at 25°C from a Daniel cell that initially has a 65.38-gram zinc electrode immersed in 1.00 liter of 1.00 M $Zn^{2+}(aq)$ and a 63.54-gram copper electrode immersed in 1.00 liter of 2.00 M $Cu^{2+}(aq)$.
17. Calculate ΔG^0, ΔH^0, and ΔS^0 for the cell reaction at 25°C described by

$$Ag(s),\ AgCl(s)\,|\,KCl(aq)\,|\,Hg_2Cl_2(s),\ Hg(l)$$

    where $\mathscr{E}^0 = 0.0455$ volt and $d\mathscr{E}^0/dT = 3.38 \times 10^{-4}$ volt/deg.
18. Prepare a Frost diagram for mercury in acid solutions using data from Table 8-1.
19. From the appropriate Frost diagram, predict the products for the following species in aqueous acid: (a) MnO_4^{2-}; (b) Mn^{3+}; (c) $Mn + MnO_4^-$; (d) $Fe^{2+} + MnO_2(s)$; (e) $Mn + HCl(1\ M)$; (f) $Fe^{2+}(1\ M) + Co^{3+}(1\ M)$; (g) $Ni^{2+}(1\ M) + Co^{3+}(1\ M)$; (h) $Br_2(l) + I^-(1\ M)$; (i) $MnO_4^-(1\ M) + Fe^{2+}(1\ M)$; (j) $MnO_2(s) + I^-(1\ M)$.

9 THE STRUCTURE OF SMALL MOLECULES

Molecular structure involves consideration of the three-dimensional relationships among the atoms in a molecule. In this chapter we examine the structural properties of small molecules. The principles that apply to them also apply to large molecules, synthetic and biological polymers, as we will see in the next chapter.

The structural properties of a molecule are studied by a variety of physical and chemical techniques. Commonly used physical methods are x-ray crystallography and mass, infrared, microwave, and nuclear magnetic resonance (NMR) spectroscopy. Several of these techniques are discussed in Chapter 14.

9.1 BOND LENGTHS AND ANGLES

Except at 0 °K the atoms of a molecule are always in vibrational motion. There is thus no single fixed distance or angle between them. However, there are average distances or angles, which represent the values about which the atoms vibrate relative to one another.

Covalent bond lengths

The average distance between atoms in a covalent bond is defined as the bond length. Bond lengths for a series of single-bonded diatomic molecules are shown below. Notice that in the halogen (F_2 to I_2) and hydrogen halide (HF to HBr) series, the bond lengths increase down the group. This is to be expected since the atoms themselves increase in size within a group as the number of electrons increase. In general, in a series of bonds of the same type, that is, in a series of all single or all double bonds, as the atoms become larger, the bond lengths increase.

The length of a given type of bond is surprisingly independent of the molecule in which it occurs. In Table 9-1, C—C and C—H bond distances for a series of organic molecules are given. Like bond enthalpies (sec. 4.4), the property of bond

DIATOMIC-MOLECULE BOND LENGTHS

Molecule	*Bond length (Å)*	*Molecule*	*Bond length (Å)*	*Molecule*	*Bond length (Å)*
F—F	1.42	Cl—F	1.63	H—H	0.74
Cl—Cl	1.99	Br—F	1.76	H—F	0.92
Br—Br	2.28	Br—Cl	2.14	H—Cl	1.27
I—I	2.67	I—Cl	2.32	H—Br	1.41

length is primarily a function of the atoms that form the bond and not the overall molecular system.

Distances of double and triple bonds (multiple bonds) are shown below. The bond length decreases as the bond multiplicity increases. As bonds of higher order are formed, bond enthalpies increase, as seen in section 4.4.

MULTIPLE-BOND LENGTHS

Bond	*Bond length (Å)*	*Bond*	*Bond length (Å)*
C=C	1.33	C≡O	1.10
C≡C	1.20	C=N	1.27
C=O	1.22	C≡N	1.15

Bond angles

A bond angle is the internal angle formed by the intersection of lines drawn through the nucleus of the central atom and the nuclei of two atoms bonded to it. Structures of water (H_2O) and phosgene ($COCl_2$) are shown in Fig. 9-1. Both are planar molecules. In H_2O (*A*) there is only one bond angle. In $COCl_2$ (*B*) there are three bond angles. These angles are designated by ∠H—O—H in *A* and ∠Cl—C—O, ∠Cl′—C—O, and ∠Cl—C—Cl′ in *B*.

Table 9-1. TYPICAL C—C AND C—H BOND LENGTHS

Bond	*Molecule*	*Bond length (Å)*
C—H	CH_4, methane	1.096
C—H	C_2H_6, ethane	1.095
C—H	C_2H_4, ethylene	1.087
C—C	C_2H_6, ethane	1.54
C—C	C_3H_8, propane	1.54
C—C	C_2H_5OH, ethanol	1.55

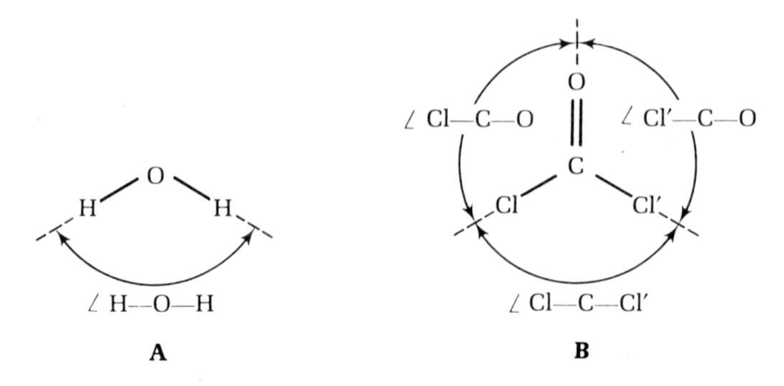

Fig. 9-1. Bond angles in **A**, H_2O and **B**, $COCl_2$.

Bond angles for molecules with identical central atoms and different adjacent atoms show variations as demonstrated by the oxygen-containing molecules below. However, bond angles between a common central atom and similar adjacent atoms are relatively constant, as shown below for H—C—H angles as they occur in organic molecules. In the alkanes, ∠H—C—H is always close to the tetrahedral angle, 109.5°. The trigonal angle, 120°, is observed in alkenes.

∠*X*—O—*X* IN SOME REPRESENTATIVE MOLECULES (°)

Molecule	Structure	Angle	Molecule	Structure	Angle
H_2O	H—O—H	104.5	F_2O	F—O—F	106
Cl_2O	Cl—O—Cl	111	CH_3OH	CH_3—O—H	110

SOME REPRESENTATIVE H—C—H ANGLES

Alkanes	*Angle (°)*	*Alkenes*	*Angle (°)*
CH_4	109.5	C_2H_4	120
CH_3Cl	110.5	C_3H_6	120
CH_3CH_3	109.3	C_4H_8	120
CH_3OH	109.3		

9.2 VAN DER WAAL'S RADII

It is useful to know how much space a molecule occupies or how close the molecules or atoms in a molecule can come to one another. The distance of closest

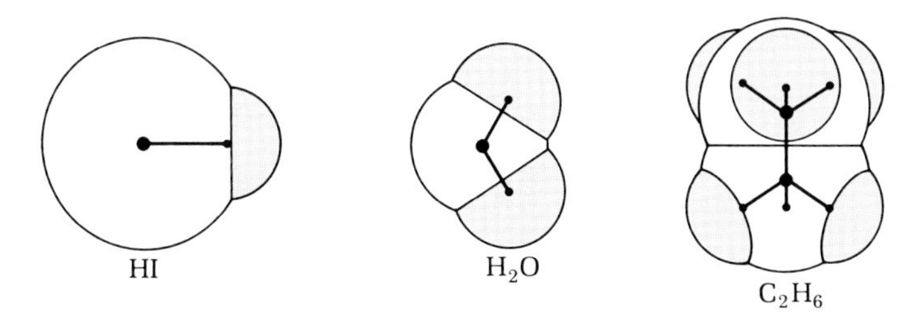

Fig. 9-2. Van der Waal's sizes of HI, H_2O, and C_2H_6.

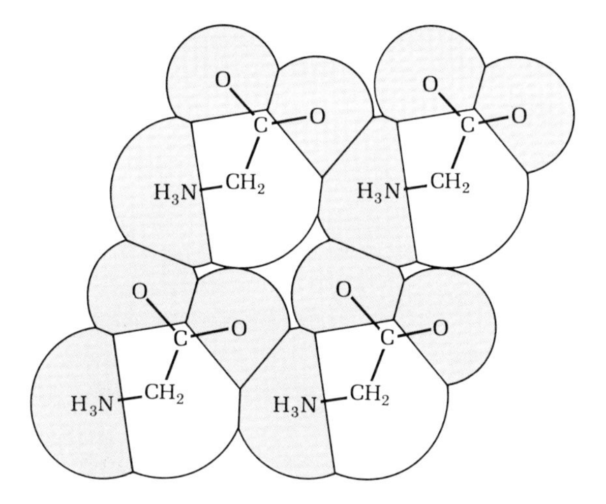

Fig. 9-3. Molecules in molecular crystal of glycine. Packing of glycine molecules is determined largely by their van der Waal sizes.

approach of non-bonded atoms or groups of atoms is called the van der Waal's distance.

Van der Waal's distances can be measured directly in molecular crystals. They can also be found from liquid molecular volumes. From the volume of 1 mole of liquid, such as CH_4, we can estimate the volume occupied by a single molecule. One mole of CH_4(l) occupies 32 ml. One molecule occupies 53×10^{-24} ml. Since the volume, V, of a sphere of radius r is $4\pi r^3/3$, the van der Waal's radius of the CH_4 molecule is

$$\left(\frac{3V}{4\pi}\right)^{1/3} = 2.3 \times 10^{-8} \text{ cm} = 2.3 \text{ Å}$$

Some van der Waal's radii are shown below for several representative elements. From these values we can represent the effective sizes of molecules. HI, H_2O, and

VAN DER WAAL'S RADII			
Element	*Radius* (Å)	*Element*	*Radius* (Å)
H	1.0	F	1.4
C	1.7	Cl	1.8
N	1.5	Br	2.0
O	1.4	I	2.2

C_2H_6 are shown in Fig. 9-2. In a crystal, the intermolecular contacts are largely determined by the van der Waal size of the molecule. This is shown for a layer of glycine in Fig. 9-3.

9.3 STRUCTURAL DESCRIPTIONS

Small molecules show a variety of basic geometric structures. The simplest types, the *single-center* structures, occur in molecules where a group of atoms is clustered around a central atom or point. They are classified by AX_n, where A represents the central atom; X, the surrounding atoms; and n, the number of groups around A. In Table 9-2 the structural types for AX_1 to AX_6, with an example of each, are shown. The black lines between A and X groups represent the bonds; the green lines help outline the geometry of the molecule.

Structural formulas that show the three-dimensional features of a molecule are called *perspective formulas*. A perspective line, ◄, indicates a group or atom in front of the plane of the paper; a broken line, ---, indicates a group or atom behind the plane of the paper; a single solid line refers to an atom or group in the plane of the paper. Formulas that show the structure flattened out into two dimensions are called *projection formulas*.

The AX structure can only be linear. An AX_2 structure can be linear or bent. The trigonal planar AX_3 structure has all the atoms in the same plane; the X groups are symmetrically located at the corners of a triangle around A. The non-planar, trigonal AX_3 structure is called trigonal pyramidal because it resembles a triangular-based pyramid. An AX_4 structure can be tetrahedral or square planar, or distorted forms of these. As pointed out in Chapter 2, a tetrahedron is a symmetrical polyhedron with four triangular sides. In a tetrahedral AX_4 structure, all the X-A-X angles are equal, as are all the A-X distances. In a square planar AX_4 structure, all atoms lie in a plane with the four X atoms in a square arrangement around A; all X-X distances are equal, and all X-A-X angles are 90°. An AX_5 structure can be trigonal bipyramidal or square pyramidal. In the trigonal bipyramid the two X groups above and below the trigonal plane are different from those in the plane. Those above and below are called *axial*

Table 9-2. SINGLE-CENTER STRUCTURES

AX_n	General structure	Structure name	Example
AX	A—X	Linear	H—Cl
AX_2	X—A—X	Linear	O=C=O
	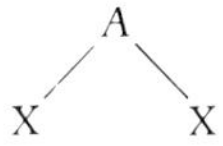	V-shaped	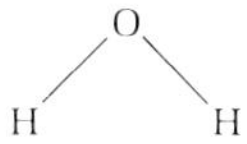
AX_3	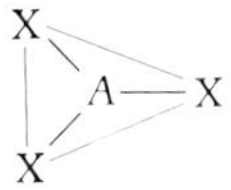	Trigonal planar	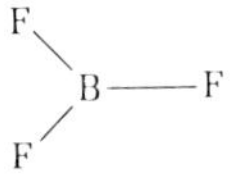
	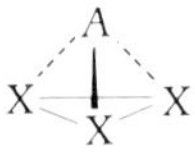	Trigonal pyramidal	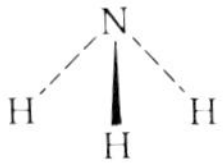
AX_4	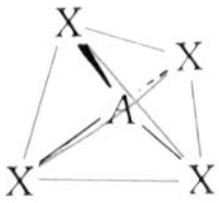	Tetrahedral	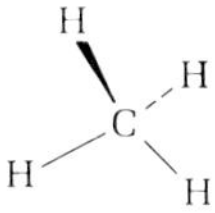
	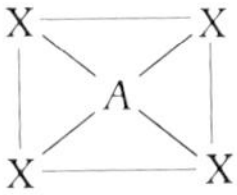	Square planar	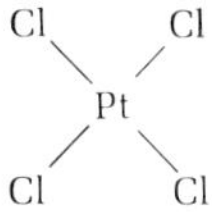
AX_5	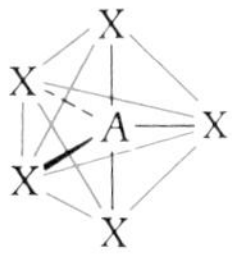	Trigonal bipyramidal	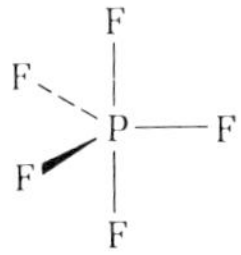
	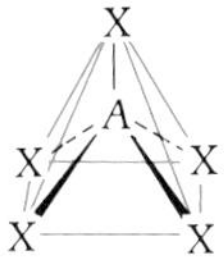	Square pyramidal	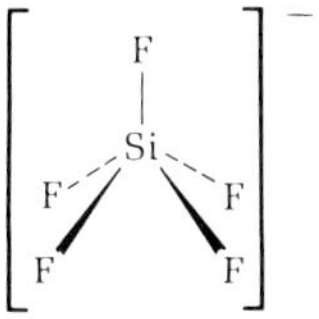 $[SiF_5]^-$
AX_6	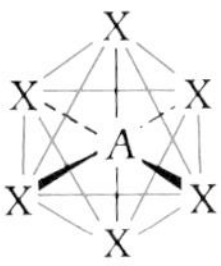	Octahedral	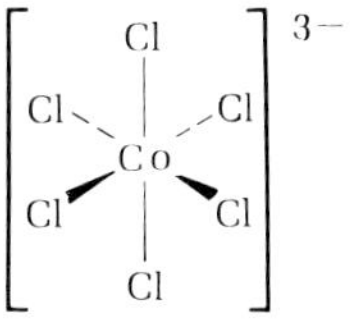 $[CoCl_6]^{3-}$

Table 9-3. CHAIN AND RING STRUCTURES

Example structure	*Example name*	*General designation of structure*
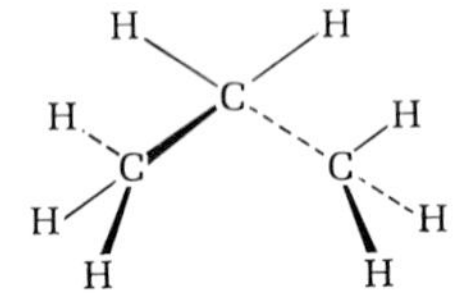	C_3H_8 propane	Chain
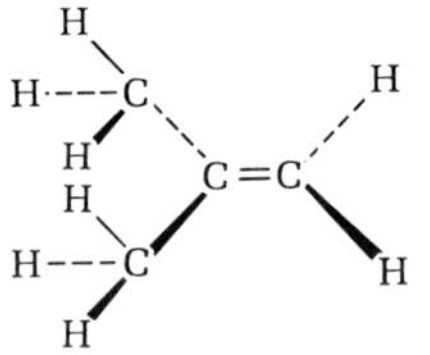	C_4H_8 2-methylpropylene	Chain
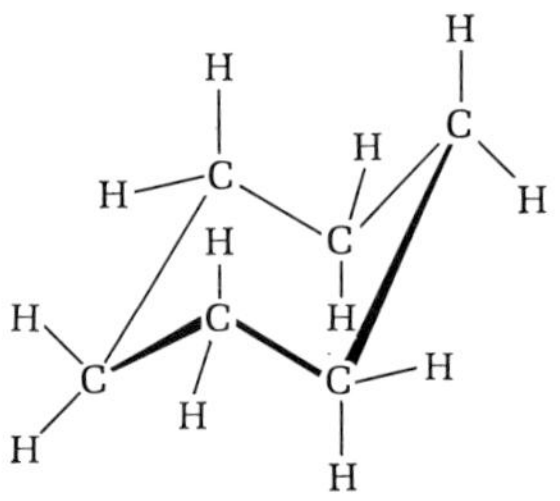	C_6H_{12} cyclohexane	Ring (6-membered)
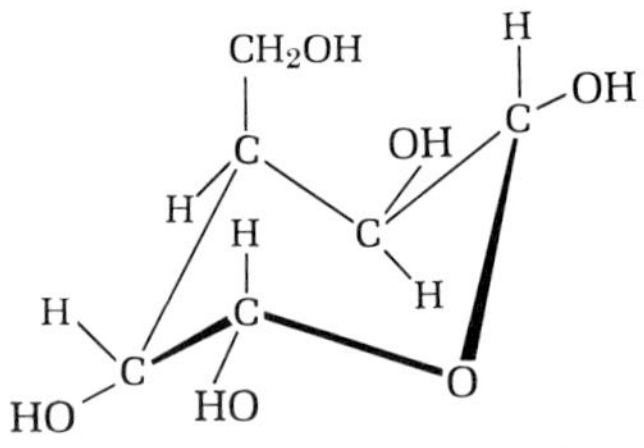	$C_6H_{12}O_6$ glucose	Ring (6-membered)
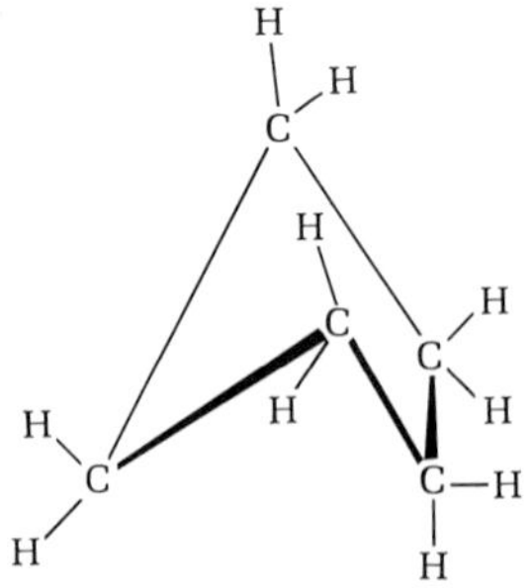	C_5H_{10} cyclopentane	Ring (5-membered)

groups (X_a), and those in the plane are called *equatorial groups* (X_e). The X_a-A-X_e angles are 90°, and the X_e-A-X_e angles are 120°. The square pyramid has four atoms in a square plane that forms the base, below A; the one X group directly above A is different than the four in the base. The AX_6 structure takes the form of a regular octahedron or one of its distorted forms. In the regular structure, all X groups are equidistant from the center, and the X-A-X angles are all 90°.

Another general class of simple molecules are those that have *multi-center* structures. A few examples of organic and biological molecules of this type are shown in Table 9-3. In each case the relationship between the general structural name and the structure can be readily seen.

9.4 THEORY FOR STRUCTURE OF SMALL MOLECULES

Single-centered molecules

The structures of many non-transition-metal single-centered molecules can be explained by the Valence Shell Electron Pair Repulsion (VSEPR) theory,* which states that the structure of a single-centered molecule depends on the number and arrangement of bonding and non-bonding (lone-pair) electron pairs in the valence shell of the central atom.

The basic assumption of this theory is that the geometry of the molecule depends on the number of electron pairs in the valence shell around the central atom (A). Each electron pair occupies a well-defined region of space called an orbital. The electron pairs around A will distribute themselves spacially so as to minimize the overall inter-electron-pair repulsions. The molecule achieves a state of minimum potential energy when all electron-pair repulsions are minimized. The most energetically favorable ways for two to six electron pairs to distribute themselves are shown in Fig. 9-4. The most favorable arrangement for two electron pairs is linear (A). Three electron pairs form a triangular (trigonal planar) arrangement (B). Four electron pairs are tetrahedrally distributed (C). Five electron pairs are at the corners of a trigonal bipyramid (D). Six electron pairs are octahedrally distributed (E).

*The structures of some transition-metal compounds can be rationalized by the VSEPR method, but the method generally is not applied to such compounds.

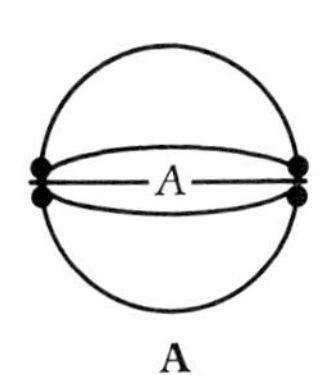

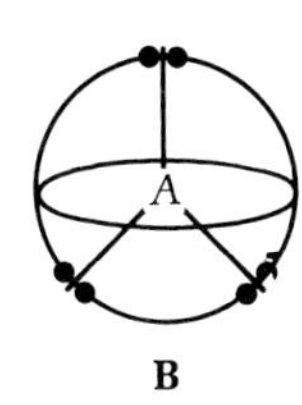

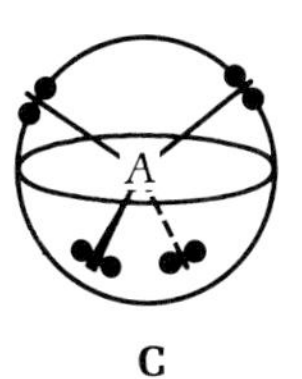

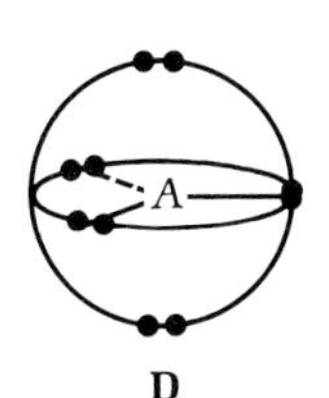

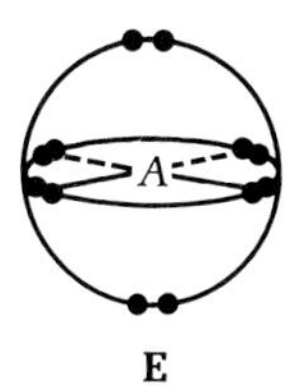

Fig. 9-4. Expected spatial distributions of two to six electron pairs in valence shell around A.

Table 9-4. STRUCTURES OF EXAMPLE MOLECULES

Molecule	*Valence shell electrons*	*Bonding electron pairs*	*Structure (Common name)*
BeH_2	H:Be:H	2	 (Linear)
BF_3	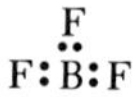 F:B:F with F above B	3	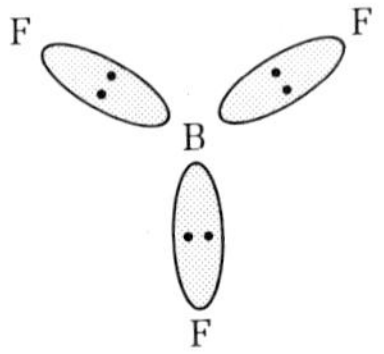 (Trigonal planar)
CH_4	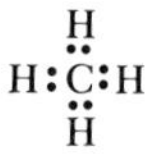 H:C:H with H above and below C	4	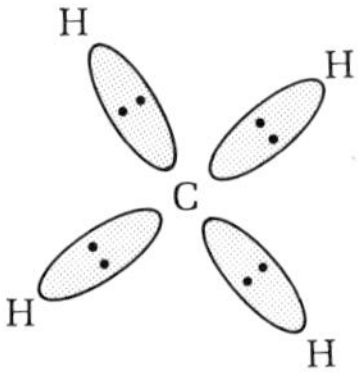 (Tetrahedral)
PF_5	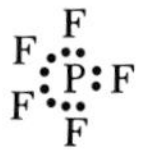 five F around P	5	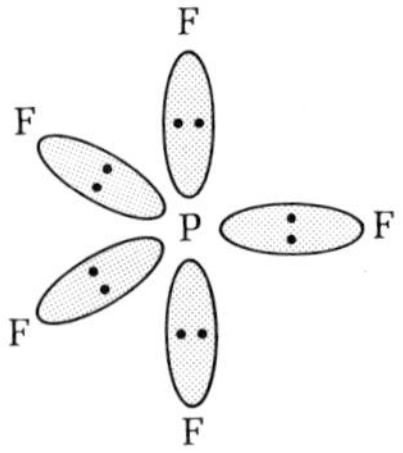 (Trigonal bipyramidal)
SF_6	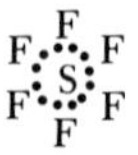 six F around S	6	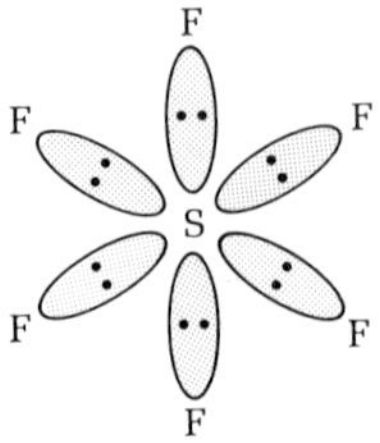 (Octahedral)

The application of basic VSEPR principles to molecules of BeH_2, BF_3, CH_4, PF_5, and SF_6 is shown in Table 9-4. The regions of space occupied by the electron pairs around the central atoms are shown in green. If the counting of the number of valence electrons is unclear, section 1.3 should be reviewed.

Various refinements to this theory can be made. We shall consider two of these: the effects of lone-pair size and the effect of multiple bonds on structure.

1. Non-bonding electron pairs occupy more space than bonding pairs. A bonding pair is under the influence of two nuclei and is confined to a region of space between them (Fig. 9-5). A lone pair is under the influence of only one nucleus and occupies a larger region of space. For inter-electron-pair repulsions at equal angular separations, the order of increasing repulsion is bonding-bonding $<$ bonding–lone pair $<$ lone pair–lone pair. Because lone pairs require more space than bonding pairs, their presence distorts the bonded pairs to positions closer to each other than predicted for the regular structure. This is seen in Table 9-5 for $SnCl_2$, NH_3, H_2O, SF_4, and ClF_3. Another effect arises in SF_4, ClF_3, ICl_2^-, and ICl_4^-, in which the lone pairs go into the positions of minimum repulsions. For SF_4, the lone pair goes into the trigonal plane. There are two 90° repulsions and two 120° repulsions. Similarly, ClF_3 and ICl_2^- have two and three lone pairs, respectively, in the trigonal plane. In ICl_4^-, the electron pairs distribute themselves as far from one another as possible, resulting in a square planar structure for the molecule.
2. Multiple bonds (double or triple bonds) require more space around a central atom, A, than single bonds. As we will see in Chapter 10, the four electrons (two pairs) of a double bond or six electrons (three pairs) of a triple bond are symmetrically arranged around the bond axis. However, multiple bonds are much "fatter" than single bonds (Fig. 9-6). The resulting order of sizes is triple bond $>$ double bond $>$ single bond.

For example, consider H_2CO and POF_3, which contain double bonds, shown in Table 9-6. A double or triple bond is treated as a single bonding unit. The direction of bond distortion from the pure trigonal or pure tetrahedral bond angle of 120° or 109.5°, respectively, is shown by the green arrows.

Fig. 9-5. Schematic representations of spatial distribution of electron pair. **A,** Bonding electron pair. **B,** Nonbonding electron pair.

Table 9-5. REPRESENTATIVE STRUCTURES

Molecule	B_xE_y*	*Structure*	*Name*	*Observed bond angles (Predicted for regular structure)*
$SnCl_2$	2 1	Sn, Cl, Cl	V-shaped	$\angle$Cl—Sn—Cl = 115° (120°)
NH_3	3 1	N, H, H, H	Pyramidal	$\angle$H—N—H = 107.3° (109.5°)
H_2O	2 2	O, H, H	V-shaped	$\angle$H—O—H = 104.5° (109.5°)
SF_4	4 1	F_a, F_e, S, F_e, F_a	Distorted tetrahedral	$\angle F_a$—S—F_e = 88° (90°) $\angle F_e$—S—F_e = 119.3° (120°)
ClF_3	3 2	F_a, Cl, F_e, F_a	T-shaped	$\angle F_a$—Cl—F_e = 87.5° (90°)

*B_x represents the number of bonding electron pairs, and E_y, the number of lone pairs.

Table 9-5. REPRESENTATIVE STRUCTURES—cont'd.

Molecule	B_xE_y*	*Structure*	*Name*	*Observed bond angles (Predicted for regular structure)*
ICl_2^-	2 3	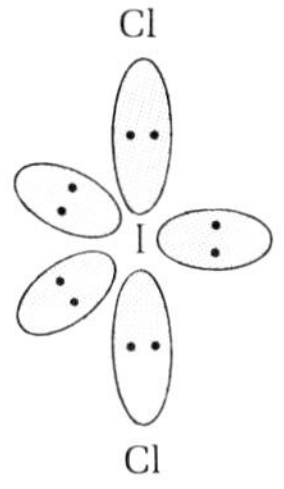	Linear	∠Cl—I—Cl = 180° (180°)
ICl_4^-	4 2	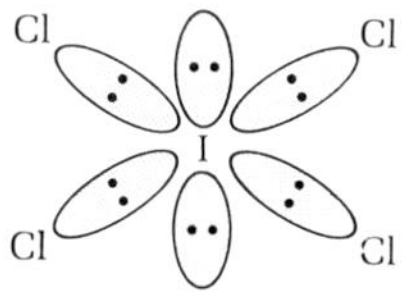	Square planar	∠Cl—I—Cl = 90° (90°)

Table 9-6. MOLECULES CONTAINING MULTIPLE BONDS

Molecule	*Valence shell electrons*	*Geometric structure*	*Bond angles*
H_2CO		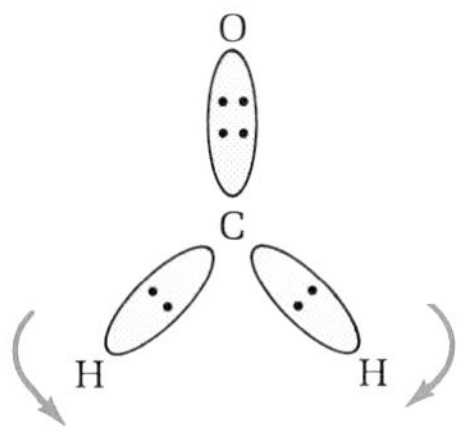	∠H—C—H = 118° ∠H—C—O = 121°
POF_3		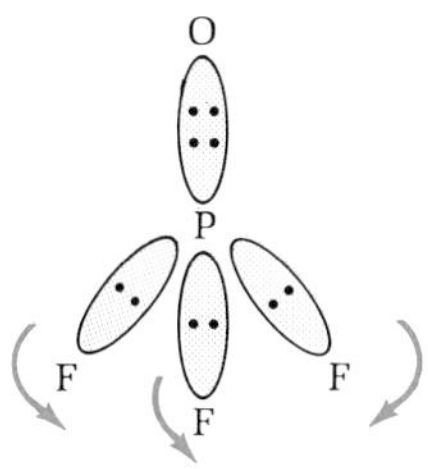	∠F—P—F = 102.5°

Fig. 9-6. Schematic representations of relative bond size. **A,** Single bond. **B,** Double bond.

Multicentered molecules

The basic concept of electron-pair distribution around central atoms in single-centered molecules can be extended to multicentered molecules. For example, consider the two organic molecules, propane (*A*) and 2-propanone (acetone) (*B*), shown in Fig. 9-7. In *A*, we see that each carbon and its surrounding bonds constitute an AX_4 unit. We would expect the bonds around each carbon of propane to be tetrahedrally arranged. Because of this, the molecule assumes the staggered chain structure shown in *C*. Acetone, *B*, contains two types of carbons. The terminal (end) carbons have four bonding units. The central carbon has three bonding units, one of which is a double bond. We expect the geometry around the terminal carbons to be tetrahedral and around the central carbon to be trigonal planar. The basic pattern around each carbon in the structures is shown in green.

9.5 ISOMERISM

Isomers are compounds that have identical molecular formulas but different structural formulas. They can be physically separated and studied individually. They show different physical and chemical properties. There are four main types of isomeric compounds: functional, structural, geometric, and optical.

Functional isomers

Isomers that contain different bond types or different functional groups are called functional isomers. Dimethyl ether and ethanol (Fig. 9-8) are examples of two such isomers. Both have the formula C_2H_6O. Dimethyl ether, *A*, contains six C—H bonds and two C—O bonds, whereas ethanol, *B*, has five C—H bonds, one C—O bond, and one O—H bond.

Examples of functional isomers of inorganic compounds are shown by the complex coordination cation, $Co(NH_3)_5NO_2^{2+}$, which has two functionally different isomers (Fig. 9-9, *A* and *B*). Each type of bond linkage for the NO_2 group is named differently; a nitrogen-bonded NO_2 is called a *nitro* group, and an oxygen-bonded NO_2 is called a *nitrito* group.

```
    H  H  H                 H  O  H
    |  |  |                 |  ‖  |
A H—C—C—C—H               H—C—C—C—H  B
    |  |  |                 |     |
    H  H  H                 H     H
```

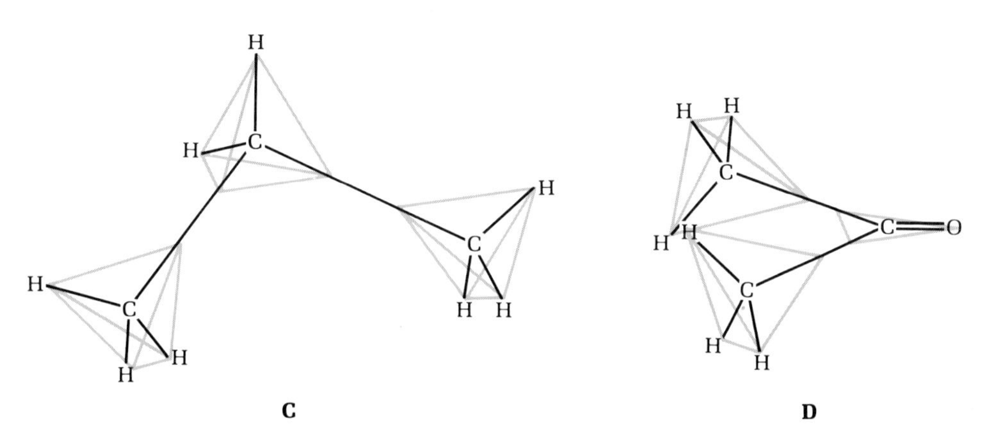

Fig. 9-7. Projection structures of propane, **A**, and acetone, **B**. Perspective formulas of propane, **C**, and acetone, **D**.

```
  H     H            H  H
  |     |            |  |
H—C—O—C—H          H—C—C—O—H
  |     |            |  |
  H     H            H  H

     A                 B
```

Fig. 9-8. Functional isomers of C_2H_6O. **A,** Dimethyl ether. **B,** Ethanol.

```
        NH3                      NH3
 H3N.   |  .NH3           H3N .  |  .NH3
      Co                       Co
 H3N    |   N—O           H3N    |   O
        NH3  \                  NH3   \N
              O                          \O

        A                        B
```

Fig. 9-9. Functional isomers of the $Co(NH_3)_5NO_2^{2+}$ cation. **A,** *Nitro* isomer. **B,** *Nitrito* isomer.

Structural isomers

Structural isomers are isomers that have different arrangements of equivalent bonds of different bonding patterns. The possible bond-equivalent arrangements for C_5H_{12} are shown in Fig. 9-10, *A* to *C*. There are five C—C bonds and 12 C—H bonds in each structure. Dichlorobenzene, shown in Fig. 9-11, has three bond-equivalent structures, *A* to *C*. The preferred, systematic names for the pentane and dichlorobenzene isomers are derived by assigning consecutive numbers to the C atoms of the chain or ring in such a way that the positional numbers are as small as possible. See Appendix D for systematic naming of simple organic molecules.

Geometric *(cis-trans)* isomers

Geometric isomers differ from one another with respect to the positioning of atoms around a central point or rigid bonding unit, such as a double bond or a ring. For example, the possible structures for 1,2-dichloroethylene (*A* and *B*) and 1,2-dichlorocyclopropane (*C* and *D*), are shown in Fig. 9-12. The structures in *A* and *B* differ in the positioning of Cl atoms around the C═C double bond. When the chlorine atoms are on the same side of the double bond, the molecule is called the *cis* isomer. When the chlorine atoms are on opposite sides, it is the *trans* isomer. The compounds in *C* and *D* differ in the positioning of Cl atoms relative to the plane of the ring.

Cis-trans isomers of alkenes are relatively stable but they can be interconverted by an internal rotation around the C═C bond (Fig. 9-13). If the CHCl group of *cis*-1,2-dichloroethylene is rotated 180° around the double bond, the *trans* isomer arises. This rotation requires 15 to 20 kcal/mole of energy in order to cross an energy barrier met upon rotation (Fig. 9-14). At room temperature, this energy barrier is much greater than the energy possessed by most molecules, and the rate of conversion of one form to the other is effectively zero.

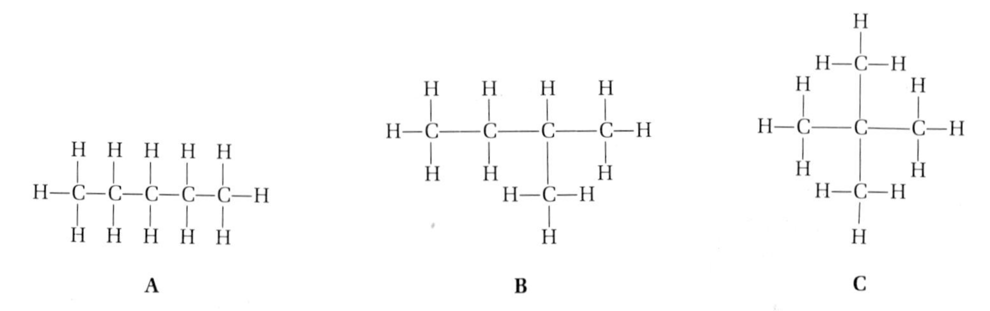

Fig. 9-10. The three possible structural isomers of C_5H_{12}. **A,** Normal pentane. **B,** 2-methylbutane. **C,** 2,2-dimethylpropane.

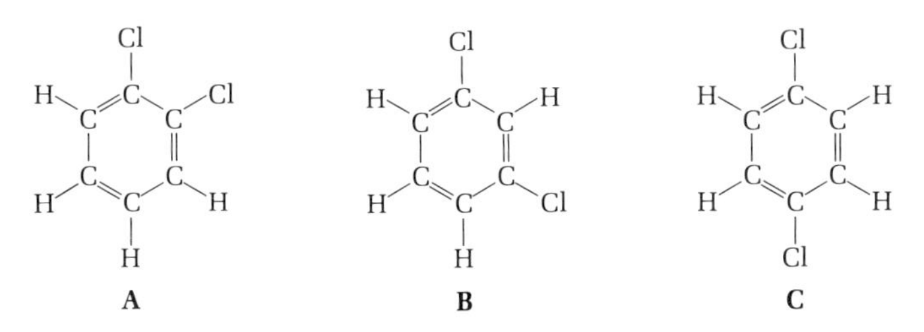

Fig. 9-11. The three possible structural isomers of $C_6H_4Cl_2$. **A,** 1,2-dichlorobenzene. **B,** 1,3-dichlorobenzene. **C,** 1,4-dichlorobenzene.

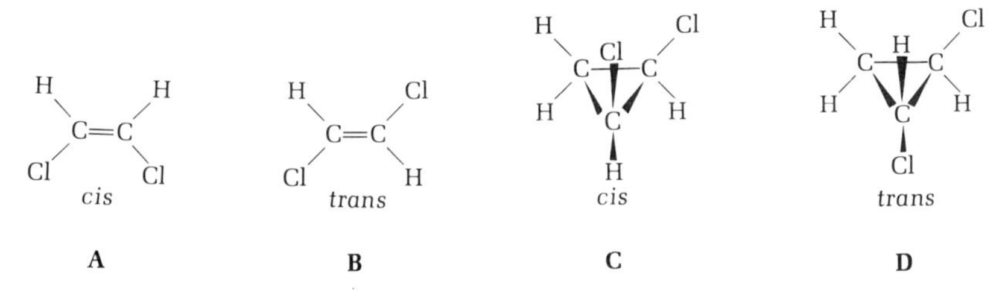

Fig. 9-12. *Cis* and *trans* isomers. **A** and **B,** 1,2-dichloroethylene. **C** and **D,** 1,2-dichlorocyclopropane.

Fig. 9-13. Conversion of *cis*-1,2-dichloroethylene to *trans*-1,2-dichloroethylene by rotating C′HCl group 180° around double bond.

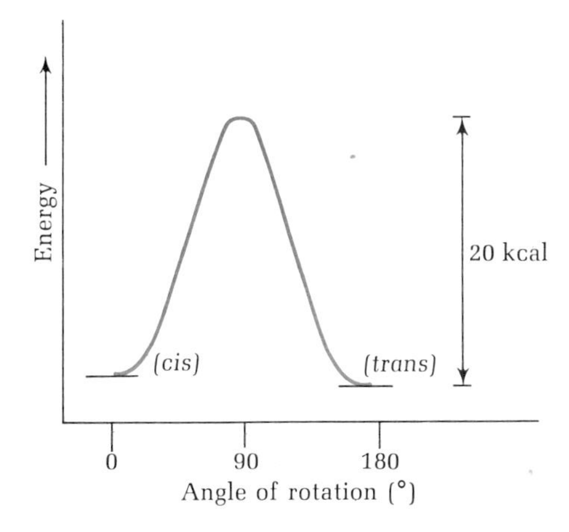

Fig. 9-14. Energy barrier to rotation between *cis* and *trans* 1,2-dichloroethylene.

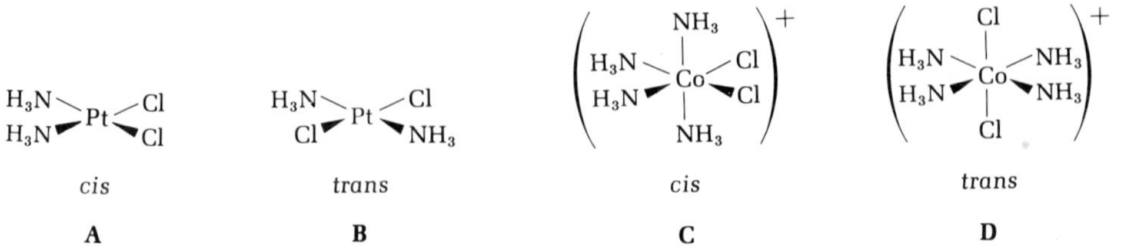

cis A | *trans* B | *cis* C | *trans* D

Fig. 9-15. *Cis*, **A**, and *trans*, **B**, forms of $Pt(NH_3)_2Cl_2$. *Cis*, **C**, and *trans*, **D**, forms of $Co(NH_3)_4Cl_2^+$.

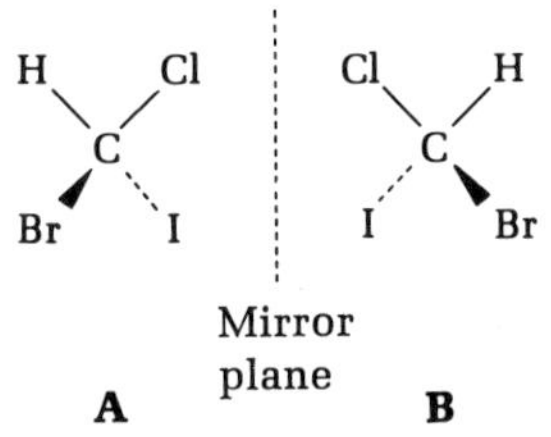

Mirror plane

A | B

Fig. 9-16. Mirror-image forms of CHClBrI. **A** and **B** are not superimposable.

Cis-trans isomerism occurs frequently in metal complex ions. The square planar compound, $Pt(NH_3)_2Cl_2$, and the octahedral complex cation $Co(NH_3)_4Cl_2^+$, have *cis* and *trans* forms as shown in Fig. 9-15.

Optical isomers: chirality

Optical isomers are isomers that bear a non-superimposable mirror image structural relationship to one another. Consider the molecule CHClBrI (Fig. 9-16). Examination of the mirror images, *A* and *B*, shows that no matter how they are rotated or translated, they are not superimposable. We conclude that CHClBrI can exist in two non-identical isomeric forms, which are related to each other just as the right and left hand are related. This property of symmetry is sometimes referred to as chirality.

Physical property differences in isomers

Functional, structural, and geometric isomers show differences in properties such as melting point, boiling point, entropy, enthalpy, and free energy. Boiling point and melting point data for a group of representative isomeric compounds are shown in Table 9-7. Some thermodynamic data are shown in Table 9-8.

We see that the more compact isomers have lower entropies, as shown by the functional and structural isomers. The enthalpies differ greatly between functional isomers due to the differences in bonding. The enthalpies of structural and geometric

Table 9-7. BOILING AND MELTING POINTS OF ISOMERS (°C)

Isomer	*m.p.*	*b.p.*
Functional		
Dimethyl ether	−139	−24
Ethyl alcohol	−117	79
Structural		
Pentane	−132	36
1-methylbutane	−161	28
Geometric		
Cis-1,2-dichloroethylene	−81	60
Trans-1,2-dichloroethylene	−50	48

Table 9-8. THERMODYNAMIC DATA OF ISOMERS

Isomer	$\bar{H}_f^0$ (*kcal/mole*)	$\bar{S}_f^0$ (*cal/mole-deg*)	$\bar{G}_f^0$ (*kcal/mole*)
Functional			
$CH_3-C(=O)-CH_3$	−52.0	70.49	26.81
$H_2C=CH-CH_2OH$	−31.55	73.51	12.48
CH_2-O / CH_2-CH_2 (ring)	−19.25	65.46	1.71
Structural			
$CH_3-CH_2-CH_2-CH_2-CH_3$	−35.0	83.4	−2.0
$CH_3-CH(CH_3)-CH_2-CH_3$	−36.92	82.12	−3.5
$CH_3-C(CH_3)_2-CH_3$	−39.7	73.2	−3.6
Geometric			
$(CH_3)HC=CH(CH_3)$ (cis: CH_3, CH_3 on same side; H, H)	−1.67	71.9	15.74
$(CH_3)HC=CH(CH_3)$ (trans: CH_3 opposite CH_3)	−2.67	70.86	15.05

isomers are generally quite similar due to identical bond types. The $\overline{G}_f^0$ values reflect the difference between the enthalpy and entropy effects. In the case of the geometric isomers in Table 9-8, the *trans* isomer is more stable than the *cis* isomer.

Since optical isomers differ from one another as non-superimposable mirror images, they do not differ in most of their physical properties. However, one important difference occurs in the manner in which they interact with plane-polarized light. Plane-polarized light results when light is passed through a polarizing medium, such as Polaroid glass, in such a way that the resultant light has an electric-field component in one direction only. This plane wave can be viewed as the resultant of two component waves, one circularly polarized to the left and one circularly polarized to the right (Fig. 9-17).

When plane-polarized light is passed through an optically active medium such as a solution containing an optical isomer, either the right or the left circular wave component is retarded with respect to the other, as shown in Fig. 9-18 for the case of rotation of the plane of polarization to the right.

The degree of rotation, α, depends on the type of optically active compound as

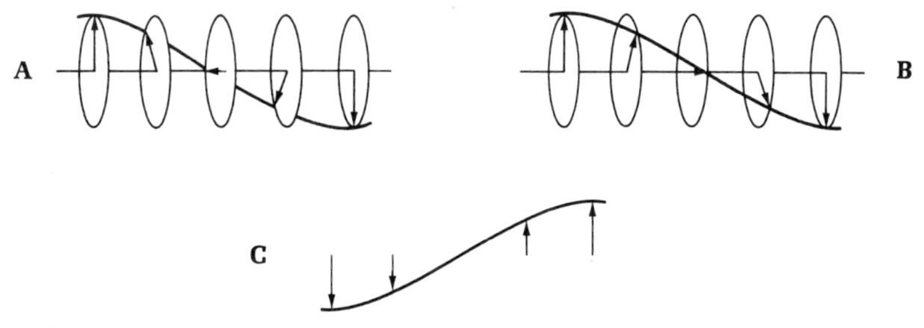

Fig. 9-17. **A,** Light circularly polarized to left. **B,** Light circularly polarized to right. **C,** Plane-polarized light, resultant of **A** plus **B.**

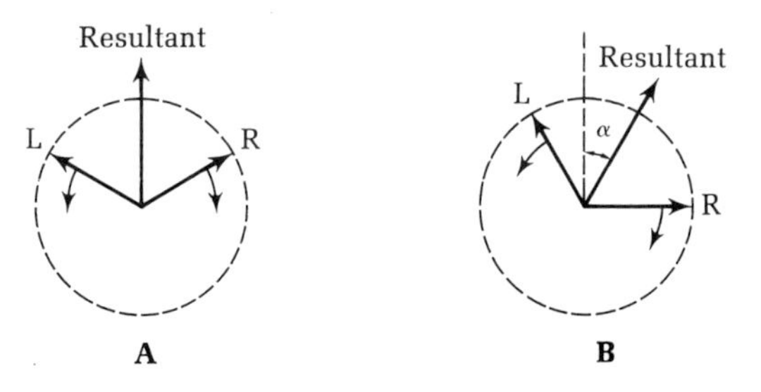

Fig. 9-18. Light circularly polarized to left and right and resultant plane of polarized light before, **A,** and after, **B,** passing through a sample of dextrorotary material. Plane of polarization is rotated in degrees α.

well as the frequency of the light. When we use light from a sodium lamp and examine optical rotation of different isomers, isomers that rotate the plane-polarized light to the right are called D-*isomers* (dextrorotatory) and those that rotate it to the left are called L-*isomers* (levorotatory). A mixture of equal amounts of both isomers has no optical rotation effect and is called a *racemic* mixture.

Optical isomerism plays an important role in many biological systems. Often a molecule can participate in a biological reaction only if it is in one optical isomeric form. For example, amino acids, the important constituent acids in proteins, are nearly always in the levorotatory form.

EXAMPLE **9.1**

Let us determine the number and types of isomers possible for a compound of molecular formula C_3H_5Cl.

The analysis is best approached by determining what general types of compounds are possible. The C_3H_5Cl formula rules out substituted alkanes, but substituted alkenes and cycloalkanes are possible. Thus, all the isomers will be based on a propylene or cyclopropane skeleton system. The possible isomers in these systems are shown in Fig. 9-19. With the propylenes, we see that when the chlorine is on C_1, a pair of *cis-trans* isomers arises (*A* and *B*). When the chlorine is on C_2 and C_3, there are two additional structural isomers, *C* and *D*. In the cyclopropane system, there is only one form, *E*. Since all the isomers are superimposable on their mirror images, none are optically active.

9.6 DYNAMIC ASPECTS OF MOLECULAR STRUCTURE

Molecular vibrations

At any temperature except 0°K, the atoms of a molecule are in rotational or vibrational motion relative to one another. Vibrational motions involve bond bending and stretching, as shown for the H_2O molecule in Fig. 9-20. At any given time

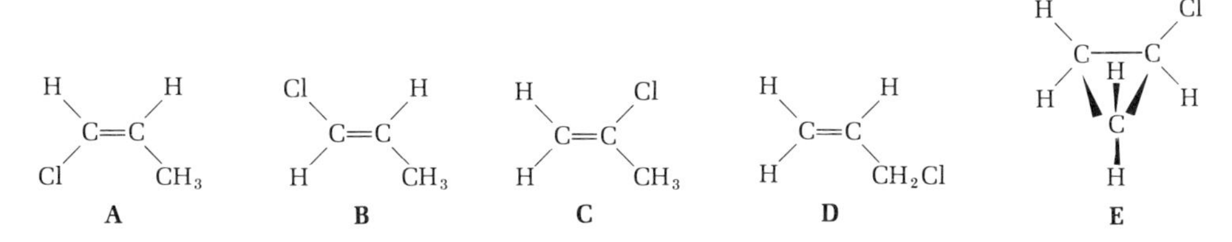

Fig. 9-19. Possible isomers of C_3H_5Cl.

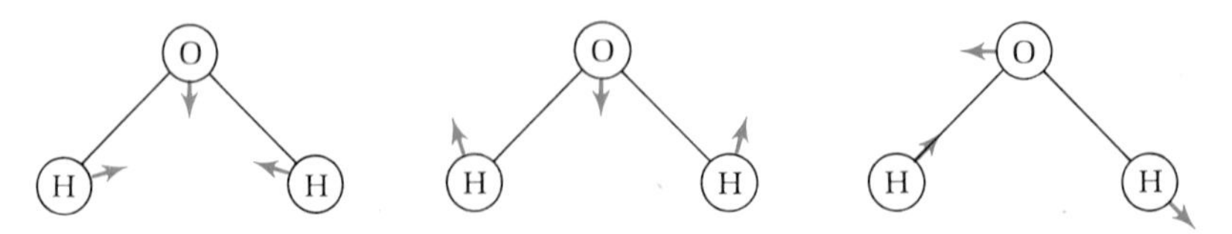

Fig. 9-20. The three vibrational modes of water molecule.

the actual vibrational activity of a molecule will be a mixture of all the possible stretching and bending vibrations.

Vibrational motions occur about the average positions of atoms relative to one another and as a result do not influence the general structure of a molecule. Vibrational motion often can be detected and studied by techniques such as infrared and Raman spectroscopy.

Molecular rotation: molecular conformations

Multicentered molecules can rotate around a single bond axis and exhibit structural variations. Consider the ethane (C_2H_6) molecule shown in Fig. 9-21. In structure *A*, hydrogens 1, 2, and 3 are aligned with hydrogens 4, 5, and 6. The methyl groups are said to be *eclipsed*. In *B*, the upper methyl group is rotated by an angle of 60° so that its hydrogens lie between those of the lower methyl group. These methyl groups are *staggered*. Structures *A* and *B* represent limiting situations of rotation for C_2H_6; however, an infinite number of structures that differ by only slight rotations are possible. These structural configurations, called *conformers*, are readily interconverted by rotational processes.

The various conformations of a molecule have different energies. The eclipsed conformer, where repulsive interactions are strongest, has the highest energy. The transition from the eclipsed to the staggered conformation occurs with a rotation of 60°. The staggered form has minimum energy. In general, the energy depends on the angle of rotation, as shown in Fig. 9-22 for ethane. The difference in energy between staggered and eclipsed forms is the energy barrier to free rotation. Typical values for some ethanes are shown in Table 9-9.

Although barrier heights vary somewhat, for C—C bonds they are generally between 3 and 4 kcal/mole. Other single bonds show similar values. Because these energy barriers are comparable to the thermal energy possessed by a large fraction of molecules at room temperature, the rotation between staggered conformations occurs frequently, and the different conformers cannot be physically isolated.

Certain ring structures can twist or rotate and give rise to a variety of conformational forms. An important example, because of its wide occurrence in nature, is

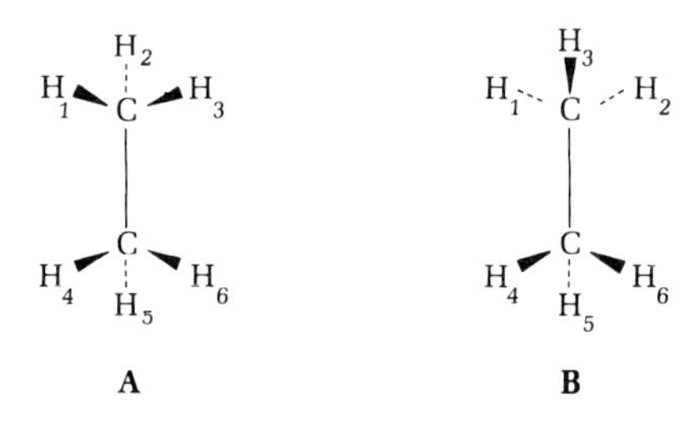

Fig. 9-21. Conformations of ethane. **A,** Eclipsed. **B,** Staggered.

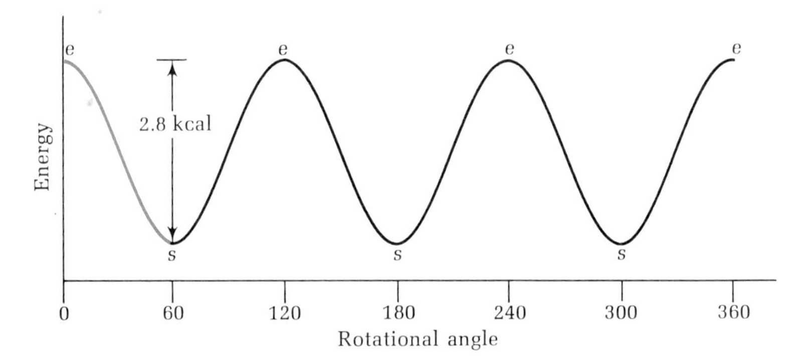

Fig. 9-22. Potential energy of ethane as function of rotational angle between methyl groups. Points e correspond to energy maxima (eclipsed conformations), and points s, to energy minima (staggered conformations).

Table 9-9. BARRIERS TO ROTATION

Ethane	*Barrier height (kcal/mole)*
CH_3—CH_3	2.80
CH_3—CH_2F	3.30
CH_3—CH_2Cl	3.56
CH_3—CH_2Br	3.57

the six-membered ring. Cyclohexane (C_6H_{12}), whose two extreme conformations are shown in Fig. 9-23, is such a ring. Conformation *A* is called the *chair* form. Conformation *B* is called the *boat* form. In the chair conformation, the six hydrogens that point approximately above and below the ring are called axial hydrogens (green in *A*). Those pointing out from the ring are called equatorial hydrogens (green in *C*). In the chair conformation all the C—H bonds of adjacent CH_2 units and all

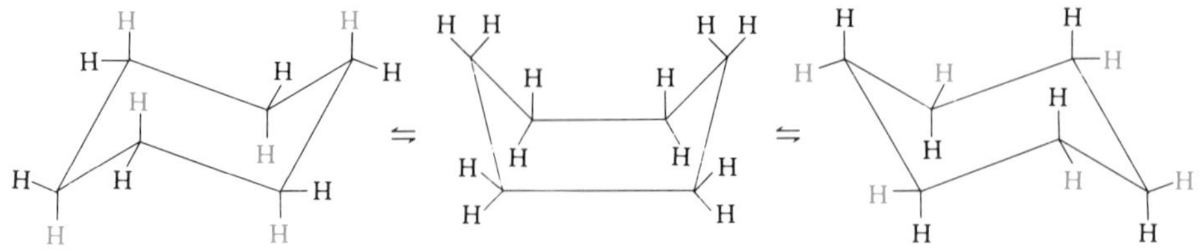

A B C

Fig. 9-23. Conformations of cyclohexane. **A** and **C,** Chair forms. **B,** Boat form. In **A,** axial hydrogens are shown in green. In **C,** equatorial hydrogens are in green.

C—C bonds are staggered; also, all the bond angles around the carbons are 109.5°. Thus, this conformation is free of strain and as such is the most stable conformation of cyclohexane, that is, the one with the lowest energy. The boat form is less stable because of eclipsing of C—H and C—C bonds and direct interatomic repulsion between the hydrogens at the top of the molecule. The energy difference between boat and chair forms is about 10 kcal/mole. Since the energy barrier between forms is low, rapid interconversion occurs.

Cis-trans isomers in the chemistry of vision: an application of isomer properties

Rhodopsin is an essential molecular species in the vision process. It consists of a large protein molecule called opsin and a smaller molecule called retinal ($C_{18}H_{28}O$):

$$\text{rhodopsin} = \text{opsin} + \text{retinal}$$

The *cis-trans* isomerism properties of retinal are essential to vision.

Retinal has the structural formula

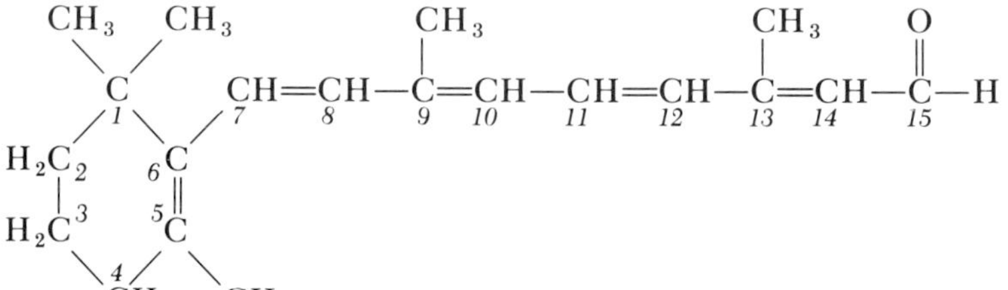

```
 CH3   CH3              CH3                    CH3      O
   \   /                 |                      |       ||
     C        CH=CH—C=CH—CH=CH—C=CH—C—H
    /1\      /7    8    9  10   11   12   13  14   15
H2C2    6C
 |3      5||
H2C      C
   \4  /   \
   CH2      CH3
```

The system contains five C=C double bonds, four of which are in the chain attached to the ring; that is, $C_7{=}C_8$, $C_9{=}C_{10}$, $C_{11}{=}C_{12}$, and $C_{13}{=}C_{14}$. The terminal

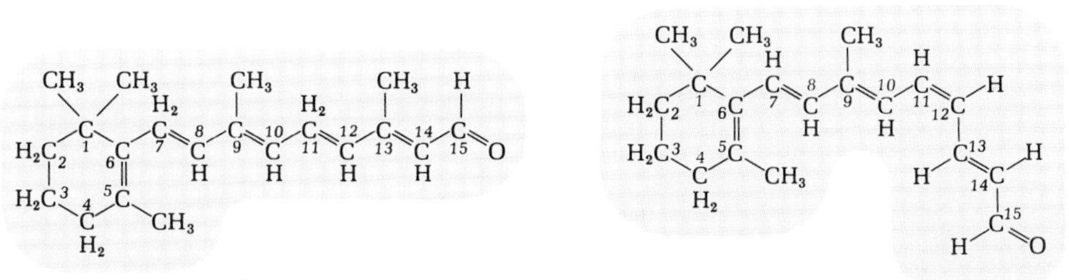

all-*trans*
A

11-*cis*
B

Fig. 9-24. Forms of retinal. **A,** All-*trans*. **B,** 11-*cis*.

group, C_{15}, is an aldehyde group, $-\mathrm{C}\begin{array}{l}{/\!\!/}\mathrm{O}\\ \backslash\,\mathrm{H}\end{array}$. The C=C double bonds alternate and as a result form what is called a *conjugated* system. In a conjugated system, all carbons lie in one plane since the barrier to rotation about any of the bonds is greater than the energy available at room temperature.

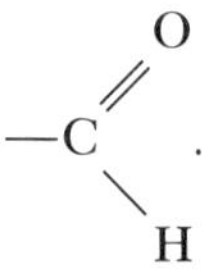

The presence of the four external double bonds in retinal allows for many *cis-trans* isomer combinations. The two that are important in the vision process are shown in Fig. 9-24. The all-*trans* form, *A*, has *trans* arrangements around each double bond. The 11-*cis* form, *B*, has a *cis* arrangement around the double bond between C_{11} and C_{12}. The approximate spatial requirements of the isomers are shown by the green outlines. The all-*trans* form is thermodynamically more stable than the 11-*cis* form, the latter being unstable due to repulsion effects between the ends of the molecule, which cause a tendency to twist.

Rhodopsin is attached to the cone and rod cells of the retina of the eye. When struck by light, *cis*-retinal is converted to the *trans* isomer:

$$\begin{array}{ccc} \text{(Rhodopsin)} & \text{light} & \\ 11\text{-}cis\text{-retinal} + \text{opsin} & \leftrightarrows & trans\text{-retinal} \quad + \text{opsin} \\ \upharpoonleft\!\downharpoonright & & \upharpoonleft\!\downharpoonright \\ 11\text{-}cis\text{-vitamin A} + \text{opsin} & \leftrightarrows & trans\text{-vitamin A} + \text{opsin} \end{array}$$

The shape of the retinal changes and thus its geometric relationship to opsin is altered. The straight *trans* isomer is bound to opsin less strongly than the *cis* form, so that retinal is released upon the conversion of the *cis* form to the *trans* form (Fig. 9-25). The exact nature of the resulting changes in opsin structure and the nerve excitation that results is not known.

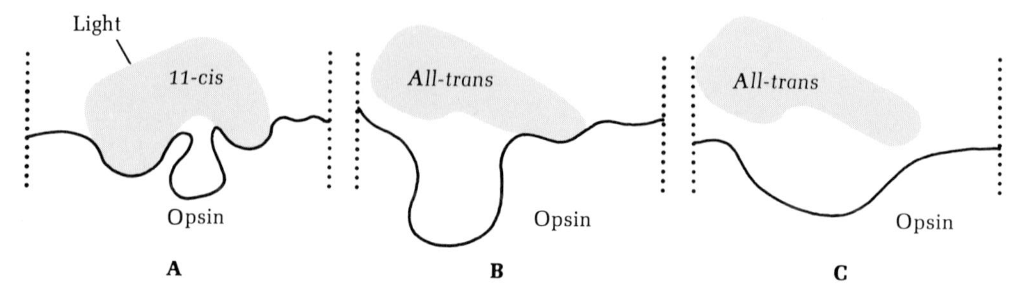

Fig. 9-25. Schematic representations of **A,** light-activated conversion of *cis*-retinal to *trans*-retinal, **B,** release of *trans*-retinal from opsin, and **C,** alteration of opsin.

The process of reforming rhodopsin is complex, as is shown above. In a series of reactions, two hydrogens are added to *trans*-retinal, converting it to all-*trans*-vitamin A. This isomer is then apparently converted to 11-*cis*-vitamin A and finally back to 11-*cis*-retinal. The reformed 11-*cis*-retinal combines with opsin to reform the rhodopsin molecule.

PROBLEMS

1. Without referring to Table 9-1 or the box on p. 229, arrange the following bonds in order of decreasing length: (a) C=O, C—O, C≡O; (b) C≡N, C—N, C=N.
2. Calculate the distance between H atoms in ethylene.
3. Which has the smallest bond angles, NH_3, CH_4, or BH_3?
4. What is the diameter of a sphere just large enough to enclose a molecule of BrCl? [Hint: Use data from the boxes on pp. 232 and 229.]
5. Which atom would you expect to have the largest van der Waal's radius? (a) H or C; (b) O or S; (c) N or P; (d) P or S.
6. Draw perspective structural formulas for (a) C_2H_6; (b) CH_2Cl_2; (c) $CoCl_6^{3-}$; (d) $Ni(CO)_4$ (tetrahedral structure); (e) glycine (refer to Fig. 9-3).
7. Draw the following: (a) square pyramid; (b) tetrahedron; (c) octahedron; (d) trigonal bipyramid.
8. Draw perspective structural formulas for (a) cyclobutane; (b) chloroethane; (c) propylene.
9. Why does a lone pair of electrons occupy more space around a central atom than a pair of bonding electrons?
10. Draw structures for the following molecules (the central atom is in boldface): (a)$\mathbf{B}F_3$; (b) $\mathbf{Sn}Cl_2$; (c) $H_2\mathbf{S}$; (d) $\mathbf{P}Cl_3$; (e) $\mathbf{P}OCl_3$; (f) $\mathbf{I}Cl_3$; (g) $\mathbf{S}F_6$. Indicate those cases in which distortions from the simple geometric forms are expected.
11. Show the structure of formaldehyde, H_2CO. Estimate the bond angles and bond distances.
12. Without referring to the box on p. 229, arrange the molecules in the following groups in order of increasing bond length: (a) HBr, HCl, HI; (b) Cl_2, Br_2, I_2; (c) BrCl, BrF, BrI.

13. Show the functional isomers for compounds with the following formulas: (a) C_2H_6O; (b) C_3H_6; (c) C_2H_7N; (d) C_3H_6O.
14. Draw all structural isomers of (a) C_5H_{12}; (b) C_4H_{10}; (c) trichlorobenzene.
15. Write structural formulas for all possible isomers of the coordination compounds: (a) $Co(NH_3)_2Cl_4^-$; (b) $Cr(H_2O)_3Cl_3$; (c) $NiCl_2(NH_3)_4^{2+}$; (d) $Co(H_2O)(NO_2)^{2+}$. Indicate the type of isomerism exhibited.
16. Which of the molecules below are chiral?

(a)

H H H Cl Cl H

(b)

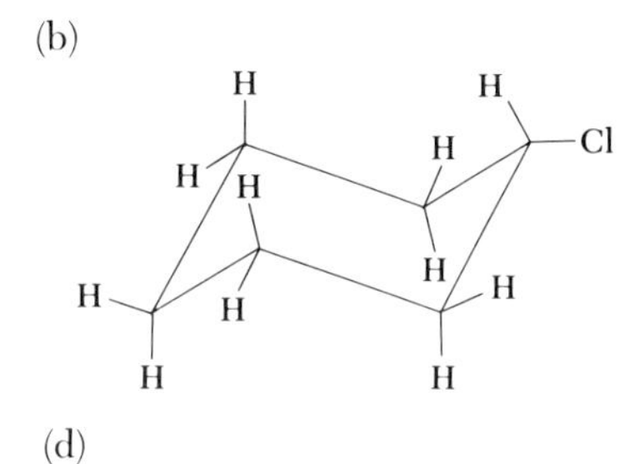

(c)

Cl Cl H Cl H H

(d)

CCl_2Br_2

17. Which of the molecules in problem 15 would you expect to be optically active? Justify your answers.
18. Which of the inorganic molecules shown below would exhibit optical activity?

(a)

OC CO Ni OC CO

(b)

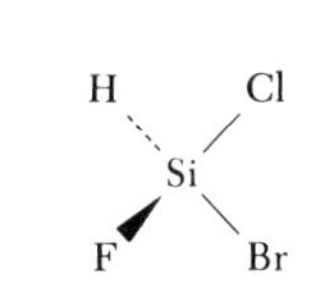

(c)

$(H_2C$—CH_2—H_2N, H_2N—CH_2—H_2C, NH_2, NH_2, Cr, Cl, Cl$)^+$

(d)

$(Cl\ Cl\ Cu\ Br\ Cl)^{2+}$

19. Show all structural isomers of $C_3H_6Cl_2$.
20. Will any of the isomeric forms in problem 19 be optically active? Defend your answer.
21. Show all possible *cis-trans* isomers for the molecule

$$H_3C-\underset{H}{\underset{|}{C}}=\underset{H}{\underset{|}{C}}-\underset{H}{\underset{|}{C}}=\underset{H}{\underset{|}{C}}-\underset{H}{\underset{|}{C}}=\underset{H}{\underset{|}{C}}-CH_3$$

22. Which of the following complex ions can exhibit *cis-trans* isomerism? Use drawings to help determine your answer.
(a) $Co(NH_3)_4Cl_2^+$
(b) $PtCl_2(NH_3)_2$ (assume a square planar arrangement around Pt)
(c) $Cr(H_2O)_5Cl^{2+}$
(d) $NiCl_2Br_2$ (assume a tetrahedral arrangement around Ni)

23. Suggest a reason why the *cis* isomer of 2-butene,

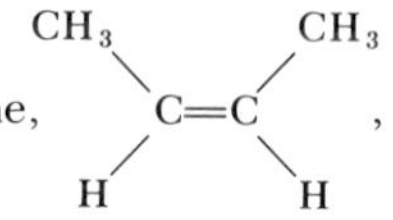

$$\begin{array}{ccc} CH_3 & & CH_3 \\ & \diagdown\;\diagup & \\ & C{=}C & \\ & \diagup\;\diagdown & \\ H & & H \end{array}$$

, is thermodynamically less stable than the *trans* isomer,

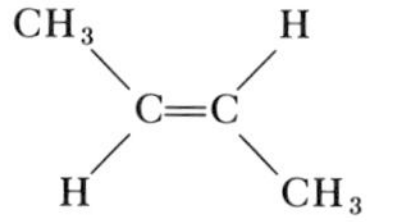

$$\begin{array}{ccc} CH_3 & & H \\ & \diagdown\;\diagup & \\ & C{=}C & \\ & \diagup\;\diagdown & \\ H & & CH_3 \end{array}$$

24. Draw structures for the most stable conformations of (a) hydrazine ($H_2\ddot{N}{-}\ddot{N}H_2$); (b) methylcyclohexane; (c) bromoethane; (d) 1,2-dichloroethane.

25. Predict the order of increasing entropy ($\bar{S}_f^0$) for the structural isomers of C_4H_{10}. Defend your answer.

26. Using data from Table 9-8, determine the ratio of

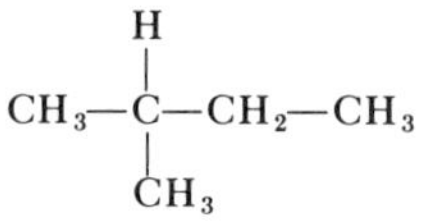

$$CH_3{-}\underset{\large CH_3}{\overset{\large H}{\underset{|}{\overset{|}{C}}}}{-}CH_2{-}CH_3 \text{ to } CH_3{-}\underset{\large CH_3}{\overset{\large CH_3}{\underset{|}{\overset{|}{C}}}}{-}CH_3$$

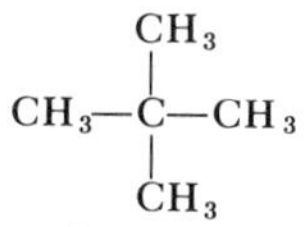

at 298°K in an equilibrium mixture.

10 THE STRUCTURES AND PROPERTIES OF LARGE MOLECULES

Polymers are large molecules with high molecular weights. The more important naturally occurring polymers are the natural rubbers, and the biopolymers: carbohydrates, proteins, and nucleic acids. Carbohydrates are the major energy source for animals and the principal building material for plants. Proteins are the major building material for muscles and tendons and also make up the enzymes critical to life processes. Nucleic acids (RNA and DNA) are polymers whose role is the transmission and determination of hereditary traits. Examples of synthetic polymers include polyethylene, Nylon, and Teflon.

Polymers vary markedly in size, molecular weight, structure, and composition. Molecular weights vary from a few hundred to an extreme of two billion, seen in nucleic acids. In spite of their large sizes and high molecular weights, polymers generally are represented simply as some number of basic repeating units called *monomers*. The formulas of a variety of synthetic and naturally occurring polymers are shown in Tables 10-1, 10-2, and 10-3. The classification of polymers as "addition" or "condensation" types depends on the mode of formation.

10.1 STRUCTURE OF POLYMERS

The structure of a polymer can be described at several different levels, primary, secondary, tertiary, and so on, depending on the type of structural information we wish to specify.

Primary structure

The primary structure of a polymer is simply the rudimentary description of how the atoms or monomer units are bonded together. The simplest form of a polymer is a linear chain:

Table 10-1. SYNTHETIC ADDITION POLYMERS

Name	*Formula**
Polyethylene	$-\!\!(CH_2-CH_2)_n-$
Teflon (polyperfluoroethylene)	$-\!\!(CF_2-CF_2)_n-$
Polystyrene	$-\!\!(CH_2-CH(C_6H_5))_n-$ (benzene ring attached to CH)
Orlon (polyacrylonitrile)	$-\!\!(CH(CN)-CH_2)_n-$
Polypropylene	$-\!\!(CH(CH_3)-CH_2)_n-$
Polyisobutylene	$-\!\!(C(CH_3)_2-CH_2)_n-$
Polyvinyl chloride	$-\!\!(CH(Cl)-CH_2)_n-$
Lucite (polymethyl methacrylate)	$-\!\!(CH_2-C(CH_3)(CO_2CH_3))_n-$

*The subscript n refers to the number of repeating units in the polymer.

$$-M-M-M-M-M-M-M-M-$$

Nylon is an example of such a polymer:

$$-\underset{}{\overset{H}{\overset{|}{N}}}-(CH_2)_6-\overset{H}{\overset{|}{N}}-\overset{O}{\overset{\|}{C}}-(CH_2)_6-\overset{O}{\overset{\|}{C}}-\overset{H}{\overset{|}{N}}-(CH_2)_6-\overset{H}{\overset{|}{N}}-\overset{O}{\overset{\|}{C}}-(CH_2)_6-\overset{O}{\overset{\|}{C}}-$$

If the chain branches periodically, a branched chain arises:

Table 10-2. SYNTHETIC CONDENSATION POLYMERS

Name	*Formula**
Dacron	$-\!\!\left(O-\underset{\underset{O}{\|}}{C}-C_6H_4-\underset{\underset{O}{\|}}{C}-O-CH_2-CH_2\right)\!\!_n-$
Nylon 6-6	$-\!\!\left(\underset{\underset{O}{\|}}{C}-(CH_2)_4-\underset{\underset{O}{\|}}{C}-\underset{\underset{H}{\mid}}{N}-(CH_2)_6-\underset{\underset{H}{\mid}}{N}\right)\!\!_n-$
Bakelite	$\left(-CH_2-C_6H_2(OH)(CH_2-)(CH_2)-\right)_n$
Silicone oil	$\left(-O-\underset{\underset{CH_3}{\mid}}{\overset{\overset{CH_3}{\mid}}{Si}}-\right)_n$

*The subscript n refers to the number of repeating units in the polymer.

$$
\begin{array}{l}
-M-M-M-M-M-M-M-M-M-M- \\
\qquad\qquad\qquad\qquad \diagdown \\
\qquad\qquad\qquad\qquad\quad M \\
\qquad\qquad\qquad\qquad\qquad \diagdown \\
\qquad\qquad\qquad\qquad\qquad\quad M-M-M-M-
\end{array}
$$

Some forms of polyethylene show branching:

$$
\begin{array}{l}
-CH_2-CH_2-CH_2-\underset{|}{CH}-CH_2-CH_2-CH_2-CH_2- \\
\qquad\qquad\qquad\quad \underset{|}{CH_2} \\
\qquad\qquad\qquad\quad CH \\
-CH_2-CH_2-CH_2 \diagup \quad \diagdown CH_2-CH_2-CH_2-CH_2-
\end{array}
$$

If polymer chains are linked together periodically, a cross-linked polymer arises:

$$
\begin{array}{cccccccccc}
-M- & M- & M- & M- & M- & M- & M- & M- & M- & M- \\
| & & | & & & | & & & | & \\
X & & X & & & X & & & X & \\
| & & | & & & | & & & | & \\
-M- & M- & M- & M- & M- & M- & M- & M- & M- & M-
\end{array}
$$

Table 10-3. NATURALLY OCCURRING POLYMERS

Name	*Formula* *
Natural rubber	$\left(-\overset{\overset{\large CH_3}{\vert}}{C}=CH-CH_2-CH_2-\right)_n$ (all *cis*)
Cellulose	H OH CH$_2$OH; –O–; OH H H H H; O; H OH H H; H; O; CH$_2$OH H OH; n
Silk	$-\overset{\overset{O}{\Vert}}{C}-\underset{\underset{R}{\vert}}{\overset{\overset{H}{\vert}}{C}}-\overset{\overset{H}{\vert}}{N}-\overset{\overset{O}{\Vert}}{C}-\underset{\underset{R'}{\vert}}{\overset{\overset{H}{\vert}}{C}}-\overset{\overset{H}{\vert}}{N}-\overset{\overset{O}{\Vert}}{C}-\underset{\underset{R''}{\vert}}{\overset{\overset{H}{\vert}}{C}}-$ (where R = substituent group)
DNA (deoxyribonucleic acid)	B; C; H; CH$_2$; O; C; H; C; O; O; CH$_2$; H; P; HO; O; B; C; H; CH$_2$; O; C; H; C; CH$_2$; H; O; O; P; HO; O— (where B = "base group")

*The subscript n refers to the number of repeating units in the polymer.

where X is the cross-linking species. Vulcanized natural rubber consists of linear chains cross-linked with sulfur atoms:

```
         +                              +
   CH3   S                       CH3    S                  CH3
    |   /                         |    /                    |
 +C—CH—CH2—CH2—CH2—C—CH—CH2—CH2—C+
    \                              \                          \
     S                              S                          S
     |                              |                          |
CH3  S                      CH3     S                  CH3     S
   \ /                          \  /                       \  /
 +C—CH—CH2—CH2—CH2—C—CH—CH2—CH2—C+
      |                              |
      S                              S
      |                              |
      S                              S
      +                              +
```

A basic feature of primary polymer structure is the order or sequence of occurrence of monomer units in the polymer chain. If a polymer contains only one type of monomer, as many synthetic polymers do, its repeat sequence can take only one form. However, proteins, nucleic acids, and some synthetic polymers consist of more than one monomer type. In general terms, the problem can be illustrated by examining two possible ways three types of monomers, (R, S, and T), might be arranged in a chain:

$$—R—S—T—R—S—T—R—S—T—R—S—T—$$
$$—R—R—S—S—T—T—R—R—S—S—T—T—$$

Proteins are comprised of some combination of 20 monomers called amino acids, shown in Table 10-4. Except for proline, these amino acids differ only in their R groups (shown shaded). Each repeat unit of a protein is bonded by a peptide (amide) bond, as shown by the shaded area below:

```
     R     O       R'
     |     ||      |
  --CH—C—NH—CH—
```

In a protein there is a specific sequence of amino acids. Insulin is shown in Fig. 10-1.

Nucleic-acid polymers also depend on a specific monomer sequence. The monomer units are sugar-phosphate groups to which organic base groups are attached. The two sugars that function as monomers in nucleic acids are ribose and deoxyribose. Their structures differ only in the presence of an H or OH at C_2:

Table 10-4. COMMON AMINO ACIDS

Amino acid	*Symbol*	*Structure*
Glycine	Gly	$H-CH(NH_2)-COOH$
Alanine	Ala	$CH_3-CH(NH_2)-COOH$
Valine	Val	$(CH_3)_2CH-CH(NH_2)-COOH$
Leucine	Leu	$(CH_3)_2CH-CH_2-CH(NH_2)-COOH$
Isoleucine	Ile	$CH_3CH_2CH(CH_3)-CH(NH_2)-COOH$
Serine	Ser	$HO-CH_2-CH(NH_2)-COOH$
Threonine	Thr	$CH_3-CH(OH)-CH(NH_2)-COOH$
Tyrosine	Tyr	$HO-C_6H_4-CH_2-CH(NH_2)-COOH$
Phenylalanine	Phe	$C_6H_5-CH_2-CH(NH_2)-COOH$

Table 10-4. COMMON AMINO ACIDS—cont'd

Amino acid	*Symbol*	*Structure*
Tryptophan	Trp	(benzene ring fused)—C(=CH—N(H)—)—CH_2—C(H)(NH_2)—C(=O)OH
Aspartic acid	Asp	HO—C(=O)—CH_2—C(H)(NH_2)—C(=O)OH
Glutamic acid	Glu	HO—C(=O)—CH_2—CH_2—C(H)(NH_2)—C(=O)OH
Lysine	Lys	H_2N—CH_2—CH_2—CH_2—CH_2—C(H)(NH_2)—C(=O)OH
Arginine	Arg	H_2N—C(=NH)—NH—CH_2—CH_2—CH_2—C(H)(NH_2)—C(=O)OH
Histidine	His	HC=C—CH_2—C(H)(NH_2)—C(=O)OH, with HC—N=C(H)—NH—C ring
Cysteine	Cys	HS—CH_2—C(H)(NH_2)—C(=O)OH
Methionine	Met	CH_3—S—CH_2—CH_2—C(H)(NH_2)—C(=O)OH

Continued.

Table 10-4. COMMON AMINO ACIDS—cont'd

Amino acid	*Symbol*	*Structure*
Asparagine	Asn	$H_2N-C(=O)-CH_2-CH(NH_2)-C(=O)OH$
Glutamine	Gln	$H_2N-C(=O)-CH_2-CH_2-CH(NH_2)-C(=O)OH$
Proline	Pro	CH_2-CH_2 / CH_2 $CH-C(=O)OH$ / N–H (ring)

HOCH₂ O OH C4 1C H H H H 3 2 C C HO OH

Ribose

HOCH₂ O OH C4 1C H H H H 3 2 C C HO H

Deoxyribose

There are two types of base units attached to the sugars: *purines* and *pyrimidines*. There are two purines, adenine and guanine; there are three pyrimidines, cytosine, uracil, and thymine.

Purines

Adenine (A)

Guanine (G)

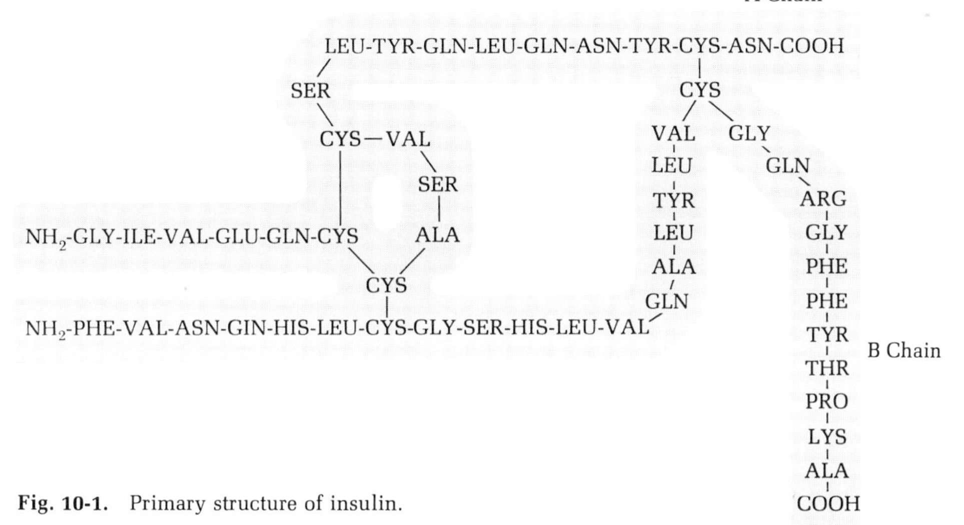

Fig. 10-1. Primary structure of insulin.

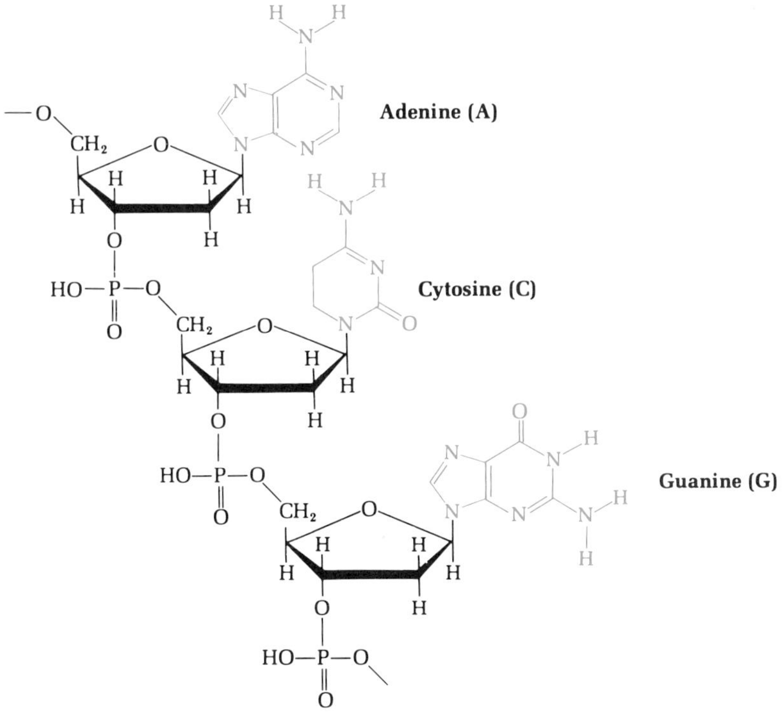

Adenine (A)

Cytosine (C)

Guanine (G)

Fig. 10-2. Primary structure of segment of DNA (deoxyribonucleic acid). "Base" groups are shown in green. Same C and H atoms have been omitted from the drawing for clarity.

Pyrimidines

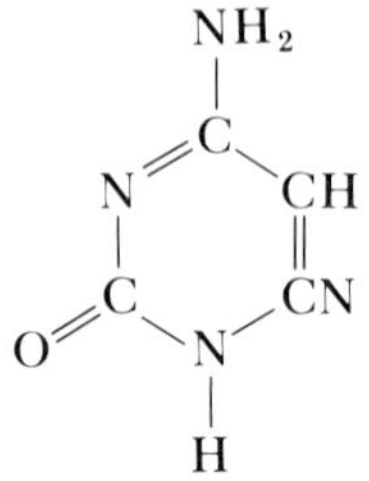

Cytosine (C) 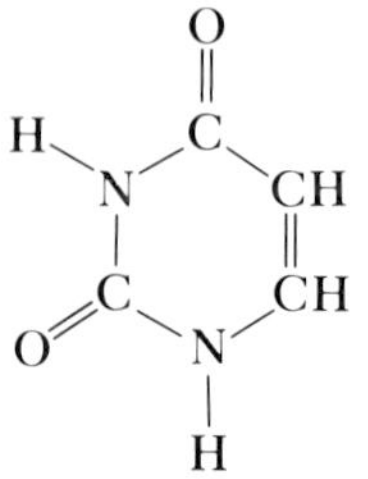 Uracil (U) 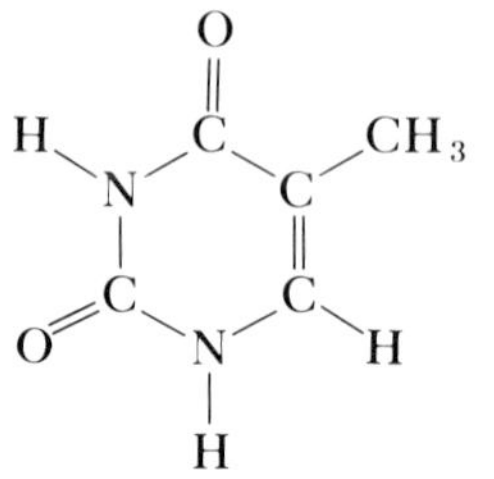 Thymine (T)

The sugar-phosphate units and the base units are shown for a short segment of DNA in Fig. 10-2.

Secondary structure

Secondary polymer structure is concerned with the local twisting and side-group arrangement of polymer chains. The effects result from the conformer and isomer properties of the monomer units. Polyethylene and polyisobutylene, the synthetic polymers shown in Fig. 10-3, assume structures in which the polymer backbone has a zigzag arrangement. The bond angles around each carbon are about 109°, the angle expected for alkanes. The C—C and C—H bond distances are also normal for alkane compounds.

The predominant conformational form of polyethylene (Fig. 10-3, *A*) is an extended *trans* arrangement. The reason for such an arrangement can be seen by examining Fig. 10-4, in which the three lowest-energy conformations around each C—C bond are shown. The ⌖ and ⅄ units represent carbon atoms behind and in front of the page, respectively. In conformations *A* and *C*, the $—CH_2$ units are close to one another, whereas in *B*, they are far apart (*trans*) as possible. Repulsions between the $—CH_2$ units are greatest in *A* and *C* and least in *B*. Thus, for polyethylene, the preferred conformation is *trans*.

The three main conformational forms of polyisobutylene are shown in Fig. 10-5. The portion of the polymer chain attached to the rear C can be between the $CH_3—$ groups on the front carbon, *B*, or between a $CH_3—$ group and the polymer chain,

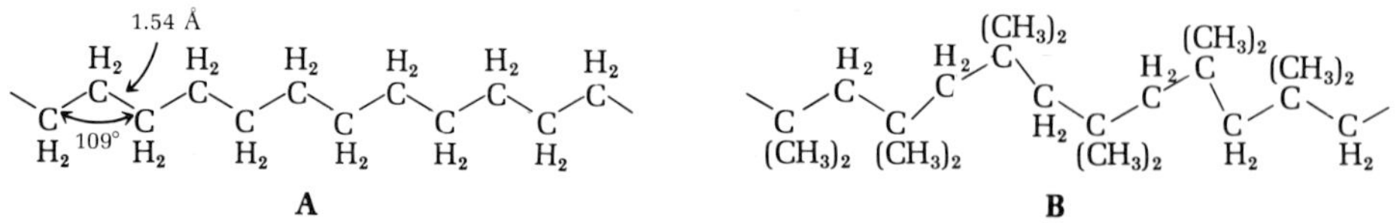

1.54 Å 109°

A **B**

Fig. 10-3. Secondary structures. **A,** Polyethylene. **B,** Polyisobutylene.

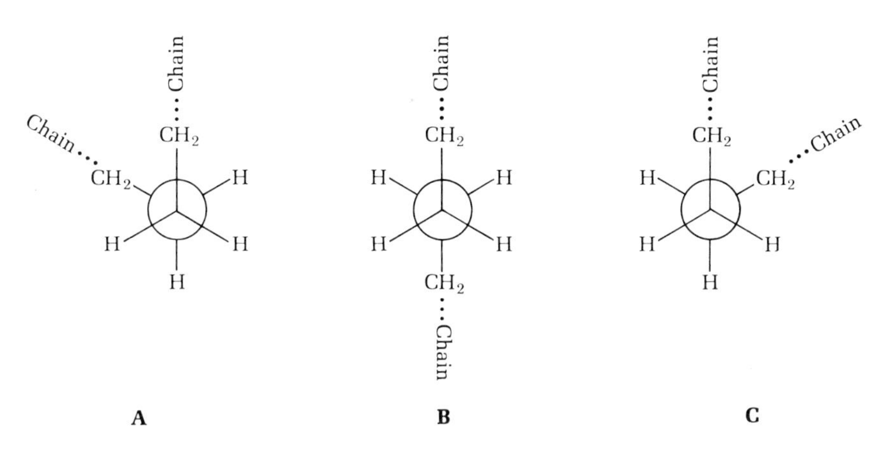

Fig. 10-4. Three lowest-energy conformations around C—C bond in polyethylene.

Fig. 10-5. Three lowest-energy conformations around C—C bond in polymer chain of polyisobutylene.

A and *C*. Conformer *B* is *trans*, conformers *A* and *C* are *skew* forms. The CH_3— groups and the CH_2— units have similar spacial requirements, so the energy difference between conformers *A* (or *C*) and *B* are slight. Thus all conformations are equally preferred, and polyisobutylene is a randomly oriented chain.

The conformational differences between polyethylene and polyisobutylene cause differences in their physical properties. Polyethylene is hard, tough, and stretch resistant, whereas polyisobutylene is soft, rubbery, and easily stretched.

In polyethylene, three conformations around each C—C bond are most stable (Fig. 10-4). Around two C—C bonds, each with three stable conformations, there is a total of 3^2 different stable conformations. A polymer containing 1000 C—C bonds would then have 3^{1000}, or about 10^{500}, different stable conformational states.

The number of conformations available for any molecule determines its *conformational entropy*. From the Boltzmann equation, the conformational entropy, S_c, would be

$$S_c = k \ln \Omega \tag{10.1}$$

where Ω is the number of possible conformations. The number of possible conformations decreases as the polymer is elongated. Thus, S_c decreases upon stretching. Conversely, the entropy increases upon contraction. Since entropy always increases for spontaneous events, we have the molecular explanation for why a stretched flexible polymer snaps back to its unstretched state.

Stereoregular polymers

When the monomer units of a polymer are optically active (or asymmetric), the polymer can show stereoregularity. For example, the primary structure of polypropylene is

```
  CH3         CH3         CH3
  |           |           |
+C*—CH2—C*—CH2—C*—
  |           |           |
  H           H           H
```

Each of the starred carbons atoms is asymmetric, that is, bonded to four different groups. In Fig. 10-6 we see that the placement of CH_3— groups could be all on one side of the polymer, *A*, alternating, *B*, or completely random, *C*. Each of these forms is unique and cannot be interconverted by simple rotation. In *A*, the polymer is said to be *isotactic*. If the CH_3— groups alternate, the polymer is called *syndiotactic*, *B*. If, as in *C*, they are random, the polymer is *atactic*. Isotactic and syndiotactic polypropylene can be obtained by the polymerization of propylene in the presence of stereoselective catalysts.

Stereoregular properties play an important role in determining the overall secondary structural features of a polymer. The energetically favored structures of isotactic, syndiotactic, and atactic polypropylene are shown in Fig. 10-7. In the isotactic form, *A*, the chain twists into a helix due to the steric repulsions that arise from all CH_3— groups being on one side. In syndiotactic polypropylene, *B*, where the side groups alternate, a regular zigzag structure occurs. Atactic polypropylene, *C*, because the side groups are randomly placed, exists as an irregular chain.

Stereoregularity occurs frequently in naturally occurring polymers because

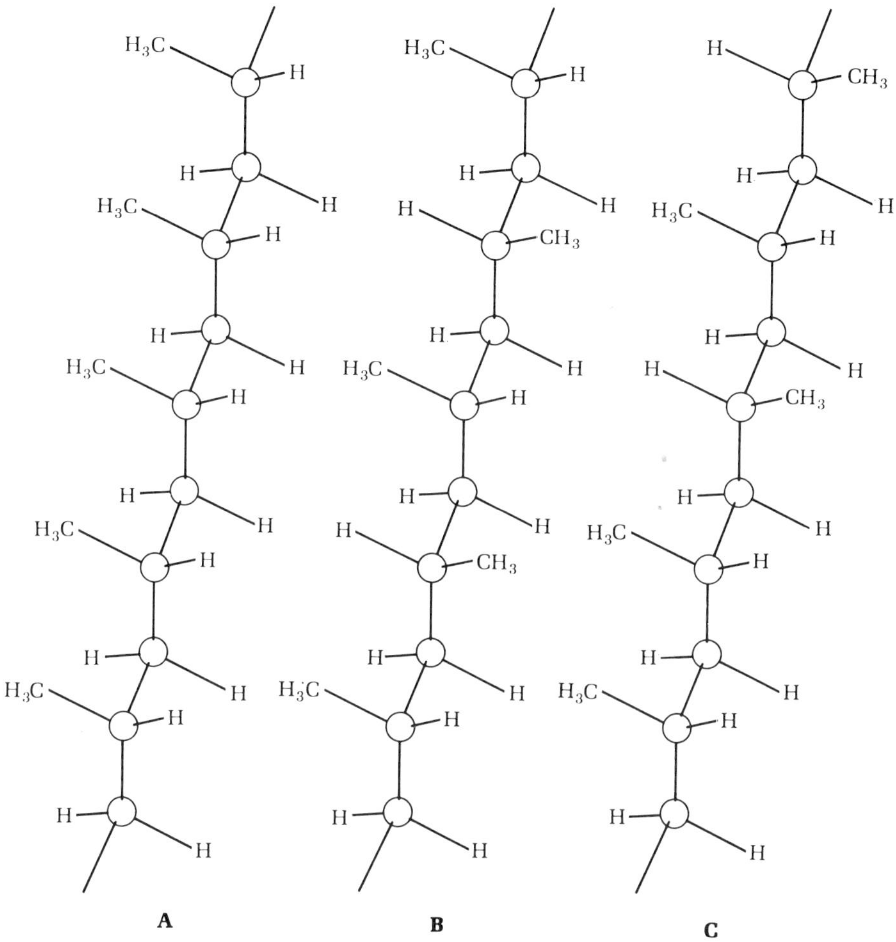

Fig. 10-6. Stereochemical relationships of $—CH_3$ groups in polypropylene: isotactic, **A**, syndiotactic, **B**, and atactic, **C**, forms.

the monomer units of most natural polymers are asymmetric. For example, in a protein each monomer unit is an amino acid

$$H_2N—\overset{*}{C}H(R)—C(=O)—OH$$

in which the starred carbon is asymmetric. All natural amino acids are L-optical isomers, which means that in the protein polymer all *R*-side groups will be on one side. Like isotactic polypropylene, proteins can form helical structures. A

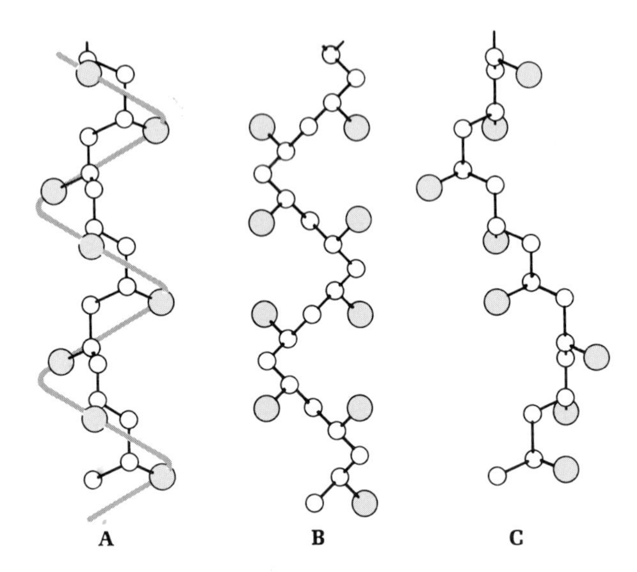

Fig. 10-7. Secondary structures of forms of polypropylene. **A,** Isotactic. **B,** Syndiotactic. **C,** Atactic.

helical structure known as the α-helix is shown in Fig. 10-8, *B*. The α-helix is stabilized by hydrogen bonds as well as conformational effects. *Hydrogen bonds* are weak bonds that arise when a hydrogen atom is located between two highly electronegative atoms such as O, N, or F. These bonds are shown by dotted lines in Fig. 10-8, *B*.

Tertiary structure

Tertiary structure deals with the long-range twisting and arrangement of polymer chains. For example, a protein entirely in the α-helical form would have the tertiary structure of a long rod. However, many proteins are globular, tightly packed structures consisting of folded chains. Fig. 10-9 shows a diagram of the myoglobin molecule. The shaded area represents the volume occupied by the polypeptide chain. Through complex intramolecular hydrogen and Van der Waals bonding, the basic α-helix is folded into the structure with minimum energy.

Quaternary structure

The spacial relationship between two or more polymer molecules is known as quaternary structure. For example, the hemoglobin molecule consists of four protein molecules, each similar to myoglobin, packed together into a unique spacial arrangement to form a globular tetramer (Fig. 10-10).

Solid polymers that show a great degree of interchain ordering exhibit crystal-

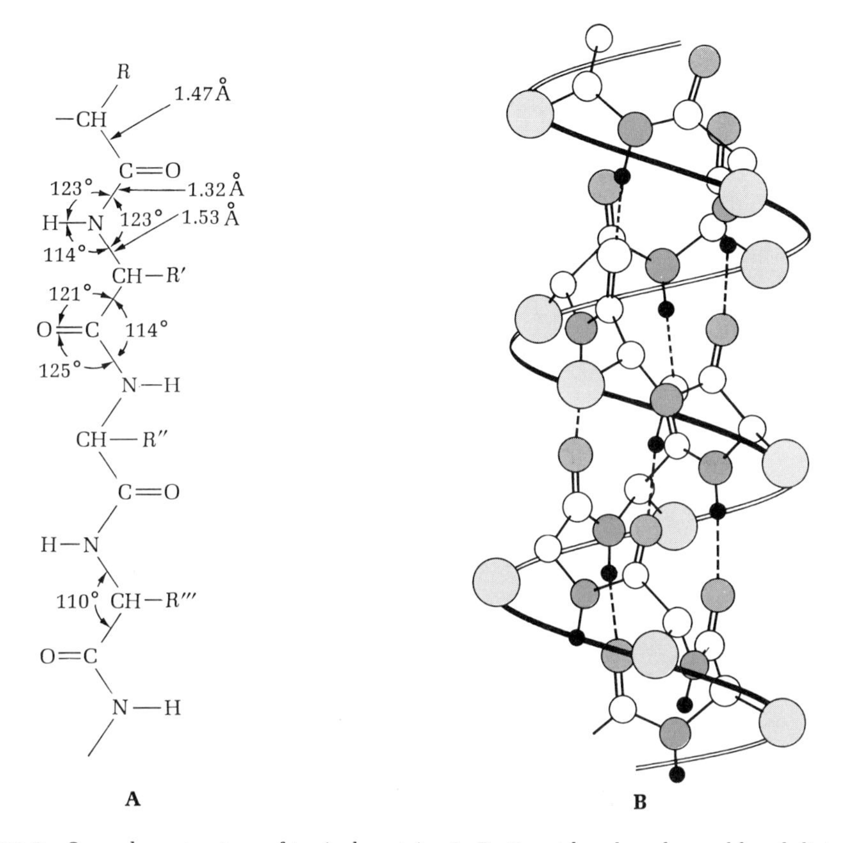

Fig. 10-8. Secondary structure of typical protein. **A,** Pertinent bond angles and bond distances. **B,** Structure showing α-helix form and its hydrogen-bonding details. Small black spheres represent H atoms; shaded spheres, O atoms; light green spheres, *R* groups; dark green spheres, N atoms; open spheres, C atoms.

linity. Although linear-chain polymers resist long-range ordering because of their long, flexible chains, domains of ordered chains can arise within them. These ordered domains are called *crystallites* (Fig. 10-11). Nylon 6-6 shows a high degree of crystallinity because of interchain hydrogen bonding (Fig. 10-12).

The degree of crystallinity in a polymer is of fundamental importance to its physical properties and is critically affected by molecular weight, polymer composition, and temperature. An *amorphous* polymer has virtually no crystallinity. Such materials are rubbery or viscous liquid polymers. On the other hand, the properties of highly crystalline polymers resemble those of simple crystalline solids. Such materials have sharp melting points and tend to be brittle and hard.

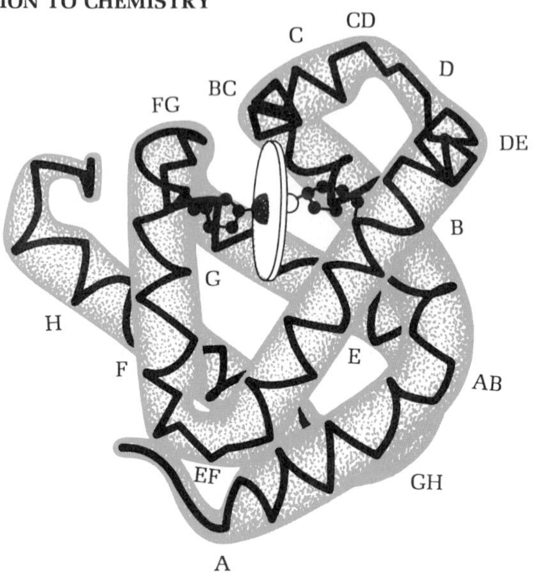

Fig. 10-9. Schematic diagram of myoglobin molecule showing tertiary structure. Shaded tube represents volume occupied by polypeptide chain. The eight sections of α-helix are labeled *A* to *H*. Transition regions are labeled *AB*, *BC*, and so on.

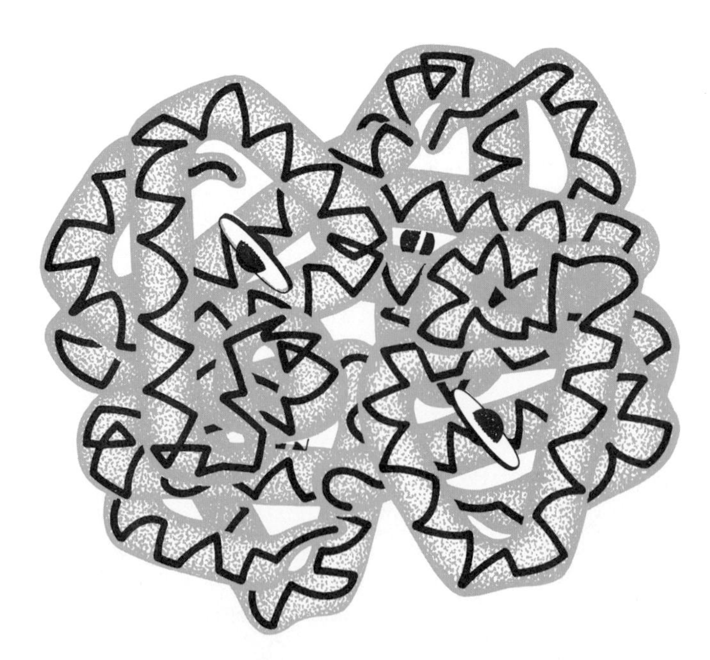

Fig. 10-10. Schematic representation of quaternary structure of hemoglobin, showing four myoglobinlike units known as α and β chains. Disk-shaped units indicate regions where oxygen binds to molecule. These binding centers are called "heme" groups.

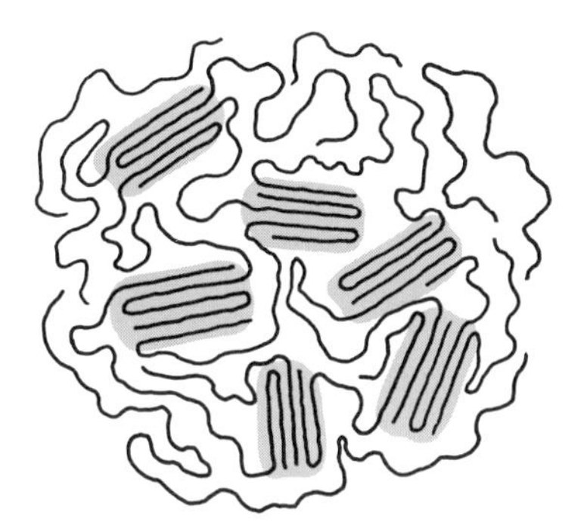

Fig. 10-11. Schematic representation of crystallite regions (shown in green) in polyethylene.

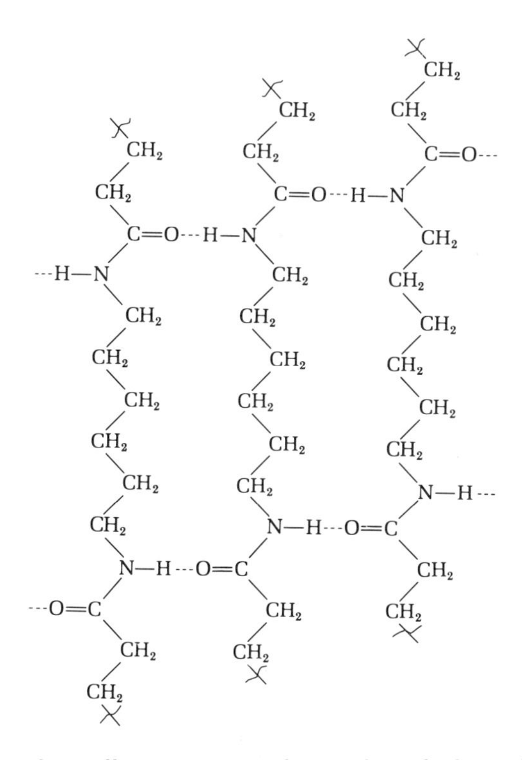

Fig. 10-12. Formation of crystalline regions in Nylon 6-6 due to hydrogen bonding (dotted lines) between polymer chains.

10.2 THE THERMODYNAMICS OF ELASTIC MATERIALS

When a material is stretched, work is done on the system. The work increment depends on the tensile force, f, and the change in length, dl:

$$dW = +fdl \tag{10.2}$$

Since there is essentially no volume change, this is the only work we need to consider. If the system changes are considered along reversible paths, from the first and second laws we obtain

$$dE = TdS + fdl \tag{10.3}$$

as the basic expression for the thermodynamics of elastic materials. The dependence of energy on length at a fixed temperature is found from equation 10.3 by dividing dE by dl to give

$$\left(\frac{dE}{dl}\right)_T = T\left(\frac{dS}{dl}\right)_T + f \tag{10.4}$$

The term $(dS/dl)_T$ is difficult to obtain experimentally, but is related to a more easily accessible derivative, $(df/dT)_l$, by

$$\left(\frac{dS}{dl}\right)_T = -\left(\frac{df}{dT}\right)_l \tag{10.5}$$

We combine equations 10.5 and 10.4 to obtain

$$\left(\frac{dE}{dl}\right)_T = -T\left(\frac{df}{dT}\right)_l + f \tag{10.6}$$

which gives

$$f = \left(\frac{dE}{dl}\right)_T + T\left(\frac{df}{dT}\right)_l \tag{10.7}$$

Thus, if the force is determined as a function of temperature at constant l, we can interpret the plot of such results (equation 10.7). A typical plot of this type for a rubberlike material is shown in Fig. 10-13. The slope of this plot at a particular temperature T_0 when multiplied by T_0 gives the term $T_0(df/dT)_l$. The force f consists of this term plus $(dE/dl)_T$. We see from the graph that $(dE/dl)_T$ is the intercept at $T = 0$.

These thermodynamic relations are applicable to any extensible material: a steel spring, a rubber band, and so on. However, the results obtained depend on the nature of the material. For a rubber band, the force is determined primarily by the term $T_0(df/dT)_l$ and secondarily by $(dE/dl)_T$. Since $(df/dT)_l$ is positive, by equation 10.5 the entropy of a rubber band decreases upon stretching. This decrease in entropy causes an increase in the tensile force of the material. The entropy term is the dom-

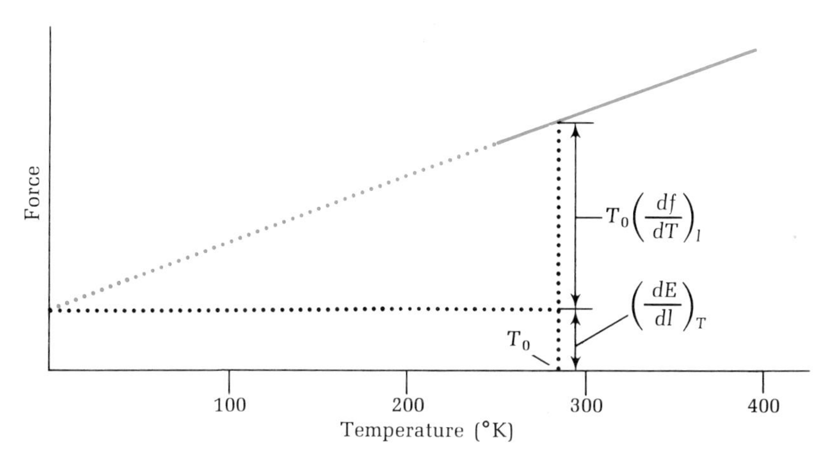

Fig. 10-13. Plot of force, f, versus temperature, T, for a stretched rubber band. Values of $(dE/dl)_T$ and $T_0\,(df/dT)_l$ are obtained from equation 10.7.

inant contributor to f for a rubber polymer, whereas the energy term is the dominant contributor to f for a steel spring.

10.3 POLYMERIZATION REACTIONS

General modes of polymerization

Linear polymerization results from the reaction of simple bifunctional monomer units, that is, monomers with two reactive ends. The polymerization of bifunctional monomers $-M-$ can be represented as

$$\begin{array}{rcl} -M- \;+\; -M- & \rightarrow & -M-M- \\ -M-M- \;+\; -M- & \rightarrow & -M-M-M- \\ -M-M-M- \;+\; -M- & \rightarrow & -M-M-M-M- \end{array} \qquad (10.8)$$

and so on. Cross-linking or branching occurs if some of the monomers are trifunctional. A mixture of mostly $-M-$ and a few $\underset{|}{-M-}$ units could yield

$$\begin{array}{rcl} -M- \;+\; -M- & \rightarrow & -M-M- \\ -M-M- \;+\; -M- & \rightarrow & -M-M-M- \\ -M-M-M- \;+\; \underset{|}{-M-} & \rightarrow & -M-M-M-\underset{|}{M}- \\ \cdots\cdots\cdots\cdots\cdots\cdots & & \\ & & -M-M-M-\underset{|}{M}-M-M- \\ & \rightarrow & \qquad\quad\;\; \begin{array}{c} M \\ | \\ M \\ | \\ M \\ | \end{array} \end{array} \qquad (10.9)$$

and so on. The greater the amount of $-\underset{|}{M}-$ present, the greater the degree of cross-linking in the chain. The $-M-/-\underset{|}{M}-$ ratio can be controlled in order to build desirable properties into a polymer system. If monofunctional units ($M-$) are present or introduced into the system, polymerization stops each time an $M-$ unit reacts. This is called polymerization termination.

Condensation polymerization

A condensation reaction is one in which two molecules react to eliminate a small molecule (H_2O, HCl, etc.) and thereby bond to form a condensed molecule. The types of condensation reactions important in polymer formation are typified by the examples shown below, in which amides, esters, and ethers are formed.

1. An *amide* results from the reaction of a carboxylic acid with an amine:

$$\underset{\text{Carboxylic acid}}{R-\overset{\overset{\displaystyle O}{\|}}{C}-O-H} + \underset{\text{Amine}}{R'-NH_2} \rightarrow \underset{\text{Amide}}{R-\overset{\overset{\displaystyle O}{\|}}{C}-NHR'} + H_2O \tag{10.10}$$

An amine is characterized by the $-NH_2$ *functional* group. An amide is characterized by the $-\overset{\overset{\displaystyle O}{\|}}{C}-NH-$ group.

2. An *ester* results from the reaction of a carboxylic acid with an alcohol:

$$\underset{\text{Carboxylic acid}}{R-\overset{\overset{\displaystyle O}{\|}}{C}-O-H} + \underset{\text{Alcohol}}{R'-OH} \rightarrow \underset{\text{Ester}}{R-\overset{\overset{\displaystyle O}{\|}}{C}-O-R'} + H_2O \tag{10.11}$$

An ester is characterized by the $-\overset{\overset{\displaystyle O}{\|}}{C}-O-$ group bonded at each end to a carbon-containing group.

3. An *ether* can form as a result of alcohol condensation:

$$R-OH + R'-OH \rightarrow R-O-R' + H_2O \tag{10.12}$$

An ether is characterized by the $-O-$ group between two $R-$ groups.

All three reactions yield a small molecule, H_2O, as a reaction product. They are the basis for the formation of many different condensation polymers.

The reaction of a diacid with a diamine results in the formation of a polymer chain as

Step 1

$$NH_2\text{—}(CH_2)_6\text{—}NH_2 + HO\text{—}\overset{\overset{\displaystyle O}{\|}}{C}\text{—}(CH_2)_6\text{—}\overset{\overset{\displaystyle O}{\|}}{C}\text{—}OH \rightarrow \tag{10.13}$$

$$NH_2\text{—}(CH_2)_6\text{—}NH\text{—}\overset{\overset{\displaystyle O}{\|}}{C}\text{—}(CH_2)_6\text{—}\overset{\overset{\displaystyle O}{\|}}{C}\text{—}OH + H_2O$$

Step 2

$$NH_2\text{—}(CH_2)_6\text{—}NH\overset{\overset{\displaystyle O}{\|}}{C}\text{—}(CH_2)_6\text{—}\overset{\overset{\displaystyle O}{\|}}{C}\text{—}OH + NH_2\text{—}(CH_2)_6\text{—}NH_2 \rightarrow \tag{10.14}$$

$$NH_2\text{—}(CH_2)_6\text{—}NH\text{—}\overset{\overset{\displaystyle O}{\|}}{C}\text{—}(CH_2)_6\text{—}\overset{\overset{\displaystyle O}{\|}}{C}\text{—}NH\text{—}(CH_2)_6\text{—}NH_2 + H_2O$$

and so on. The polymer is a polyamide because it has $\text{—}\overset{\overset{\displaystyle O}{\|}}{C}\text{—}NH\text{—}$ links. These linkages are called peptide links when they occur in proteins. The polymer shown is called Nylon 6-6 because there are six carbon atoms between each —NH— group in the chain.

Polyester formation is analogous to polyamide formation except that the characteristic chain linkages are ester linkages, $\text{—}\overset{\overset{\displaystyle O}{\|}}{C}\text{—}O\text{—}$, formed by the reaction of a diacid and a dialcohol. For example, the reaction of $HOCH_2CH_2OH$ with $HO_2C\text{—}C_6H_4\text{—}CO_2H$ proceeds as

$$HOCH_2CH_2OH + HO_2C\text{—}C_6H_4\text{—}CO_2H \rightarrow \tag{10.15}$$

$$HOCH_2CH_2O_2C\text{—}C_6H_4\text{—}CO_2H + H_2O$$

Virtually all biopolymers are the condensation type. They form in reactions analogous to those shown above. For example, the condensation of 1,4-α-glucose monomers occurs according to

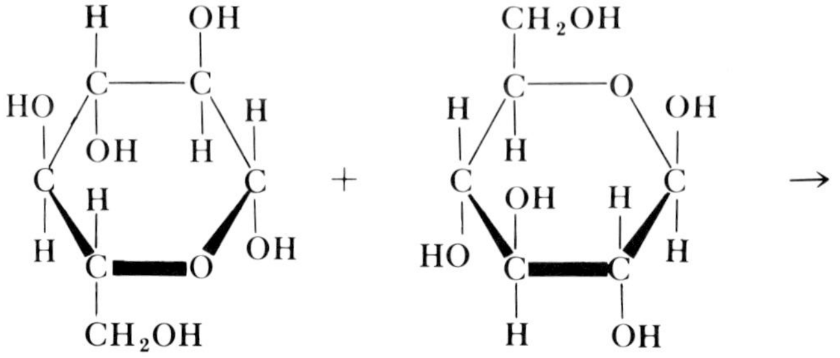

(glucose ring structure) + (glucose ring structure) $\rightarrow$ (10.16)

(linked glucose ring structures, —O— linkage) $+ \; H_2O$

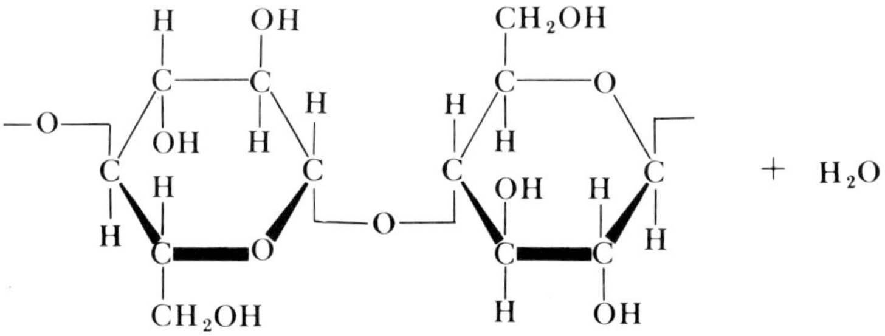

and so on, to yield cellulose polymer in which the characteristic linkages are ether linkages.

Addition polymerization

An addition polymer is a polymer whose composition is the same as that of the reactant monomers. No small molecules are eliminated in the polymerization; the monomer units simply add together.

Addition polymers form by three different types of reactions: (1) free-radical, (2) anionic, and (3) cationic polymerization. A *free-radical* polymerization reaction involves the formation of species with unpaired electrons called free radicals. These unpaired-electron species are highly reactive and serve as the reactive sites during polymerization. H_2O_2 and Cl_2 are examples of molecules that form free radicals upon decomposition, and in so doing initiate the polymerization of the monomer molecules. They can, in light or if heated, dissociate as

$$\text{H—O—O—H} \rightarrow 2\text{HO}\cdot \qquad (10.17)$$

$$\text{Cl—Cl} \rightarrow 2\text{Cl}\cdot \qquad (10.18)$$

The Cl$\cdot$-initiated polymerization of CH_2—CH_2 occurs as

Initiation

$$\begin{aligned} Cl{-}Cl &\rightarrow 2Cl\cdot \\ Cl\cdot + CH_2{=}CH_2 &\rightarrow Cl{-}CH_2{-}CH_2\cdot \end{aligned} \tag{10.19}$$

Propagation

$$\begin{aligned} Cl{-}CH_2CH_2\cdot + CH_2{=}CH_2 &\rightarrow Cl{-}CH_2CH_2CH_2CH_2\cdot \\ Cl{-}CH_2CH_2CH_2CH_2\cdot + CH_2{=}CH_2 &\rightarrow Cl{-}CH_2CH_2CH_2CH_2CH_2CH_2\cdot \end{aligned} \tag{10.20}$$

Termination

$$\begin{aligned} &Cl{-}(CH_2CH_2)_yCH_2CH_2\cdot + Cl{-}(CH_2CH_2)_xCH_2CH_2\cdot \rightarrow \\ &\qquad Cl{-}(CH_2CH_2)_xCH_2CH_2CH_2CH_2(CH_2CH_2)_y{-}Cl \end{aligned} \tag{10.21}$$

Polymerization terminates when the chains, with their reactive unpaired-electron ends, react to form a covalent bond.

Anionic and cationic polymerizations involve analogous steps with ionic species instead of free radicals.

Molecular-weight distribution

Polymers are built up in a series of chemical reactions. Millions of polymer molecules are formed in a typical polymerization reaction. Their molecular weights depend on the number of monomers they contain. Some polymer molecules contain only a few monomers, others contain many. Thus, in a typical polymerization reaction, the molecular weights are distributed over a range of values. In general this distribution depends on how the polymer is made. For example, consider what happens in a condensation polymerization. Originally only monomers are present. As the reactions proceed, dimers, trimers, and so on form randomly until an equilibrium state is

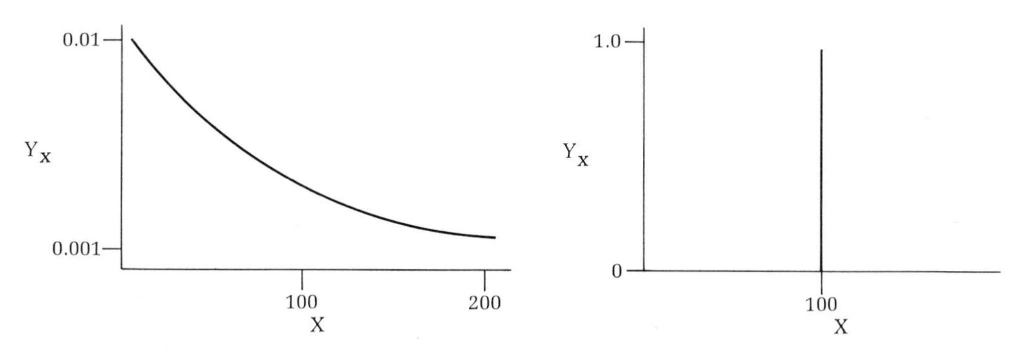

Fig. 10-14. Plots of fraction of molecules with X units, Y_X, as a function of X. **A,** "Most probable" distribution, where average of X is 100 units. **B,** Distribution of pure polymer, where X = 100 units.

achieved, resulting in a wide range of molecular weights. This type of distribution of molecular weights is called the "most probable" distribution (Fig. 10-14, *A*).

The "most probable" distribution is found approximately in addition polymerizations. It also occurs when a very long polymer is randomly broken into smaller polymer units by mechanical or radiation effects. Certain biological polymers, such as cellulose, show the "most probable" distribution. The implication is that these materials are synthesized in a more or less random manner. Other biological polymers, such as proteins and nucleic acids, are found to have very specific molecular weights. Such a distribution of molecular weights typically is shown as a straight line (Fig. 10-14, *B*).

10.4 THERMODYNAMIC STABILITY OF POLYMERS

Although polymers have vastly different structures and properties, the thermodynamics of polymerization reactions are surprisingly similar. From a thermodynamic point of view, most polymers are unstable ($\overline{G}_f^0$ is positive) with respect to their constituent elements. Why then do polymers form? Why are they fundamental building materials?

Thermodynamic data for a series of alkanes are shown in Table 10-5. We see that the value of $\overline{G}_f^0$ increases with chain length. The large positive value of $\overline{G}_f^0$ for alkanes with high molecular weights means that these alkanes are unstable relative to the elements, C(s, graph) and H_2(g). Furthermore, if we consider the example reaction

$$
\begin{aligned}
H_2(g) + C_{18}H_{38}(g) \;&\rightarrow\; C_8H_{18}(g) + C_{10}H_{22}(g) \qquad (10.22)\\
\Delta G^0 &= 7.94 + 3.92 - 24.02\\
&= -12.16 \text{ kcal}
\end{aligned}
$$

the negative value of ΔG^0 tells us that $C_{18}H_{38}$(g) is unstable with respect to being

Table 10-5. THERMODYNAMIC PROPERTIES OF SOME NORMAL ALKANES AT 25°C

Material	$\overline{S}^0$ *(cal/mole-deg)*	$\overline{H}_f^0$ *(kcal/mole)*	$\overline{G}_f^0$ *(kcal/mole)*
C_2H_6(g)	54.85	−20.24	−7.87
C_4H_{10}(g)	74.12	−30.15	−4.10
C_6H_{14}(g)	92.83	−39.96	−0.06
C_8H_{18}(g)	111.55	−49.82	3.92
$C_{10}H_{22}$(g)	130.17	−59.67	7.94
$C_{14}H_{30}$(g)	167.40	−79.38	15.97
$C_{18}H_{38}$(g)	204.64	−99.08	24.02

split into smaller molecules. In spite of this instability, the material can be used under normal conditions because the rate of the decomposition is so slow.

Polymers form from small molecules called monomers. From free-energy data, we see that the free energies of the monomers are higher than that of the combined polymer. The balanced polymerization reaction of nine ethylene monomers to form $C_{18}H_{38}(g)$ is

$$9\,C_2H_4(g) + H_2(g) \rightarrow C_{18}H_{38}(g) \qquad \Delta G^0 = -122.5 \text{ kcal} \tag{10.23}$$

The large negative ΔG^0 value shows that the reaction proceeds far to the right. Thus, we can form polymer molecules by using high-energy reactants.

PROBLEMS

1. Define (a) condensation polymer; (b) addition polymer; (c) monomer; (d) protein.
2. Identify the monomer unit from which the addition polymer was derived:

   (a) 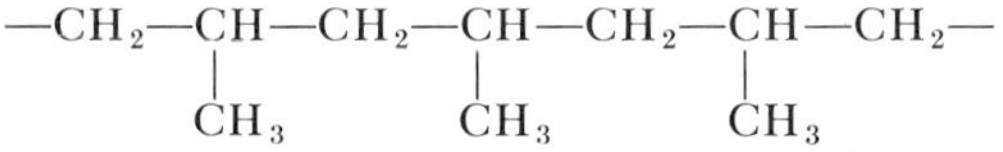 $-CH_2-CH(CH_3)-CH_2-CH(CH_3)-CH_2-CH(CH_3)-CH_2-$

   (b) $-O-CH_2-CH_2-O-CH_2-CH_2-O-CH_2-CH_2-O-CH_2-CH_2-O-$

   (c) 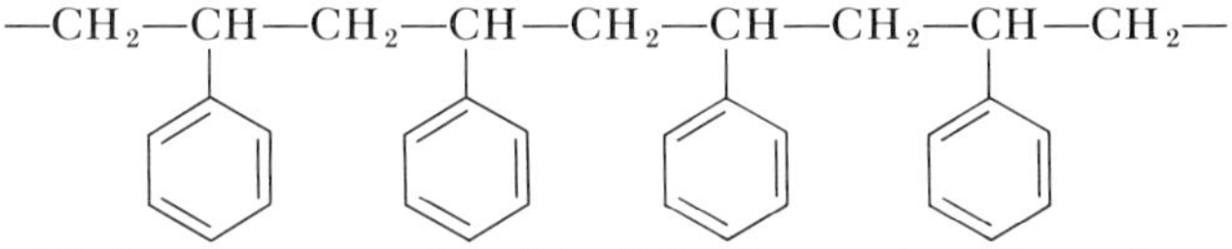 $-CH_2-CH(C_6H_5)-CH_2-CH(C_6H_5)-CH_2-CH(C_6H_5)-CH_2-CH(C_6H_5)-CH_2-$ (each CH bearing a benzene ring)

3. Identify the monomer units of the following condensation polymers:

   (a) 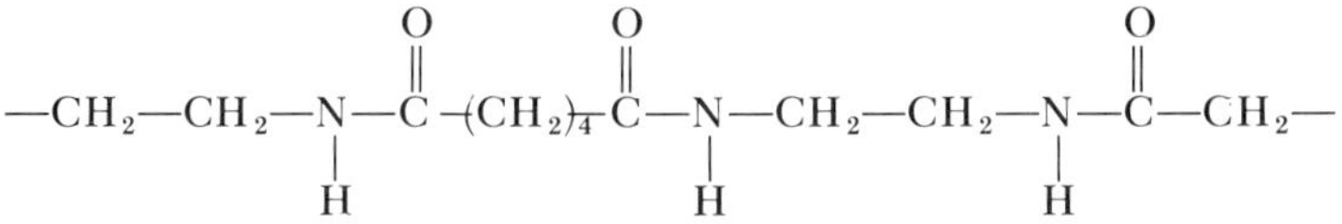 $-CH_2-CH_2-NH-C(=O)-(CH_2)_4-C(=O)-NH-CH_2-CH_2-NH-C(=O)-CH_2-$

   (b) $-C(=O)-C_6H_4-C(=O)-O-CH_2-CH_2-O-C(=O)-C_6H_4-C(=O)-O-CH_2-CH_2-$ (benzene rings)

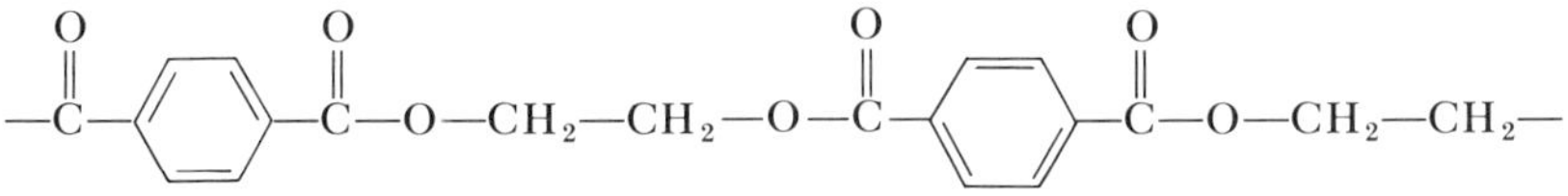

   (c) $-O-Si(CH_3)_2-O-Si(CH_3)_2-O-Si(CH_3)_2-O-Si(CH_3)_2-O-$

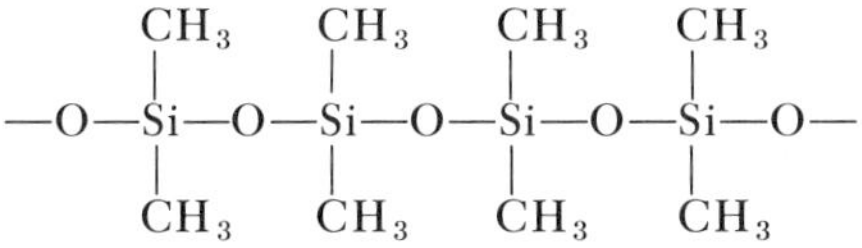

4. Write structural formulas for syndiotactic, atactic, and isotactic poly(propylene oxide), which has the form

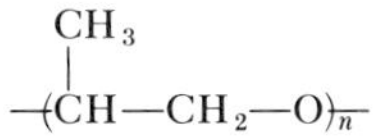

   $$-\!\!\left(CH(CH_3)-CH_2-O\right)_{n}\!\!-$$

5. The overlap of methyl groups on alternate carbons in isotactic polypropylene is large, causing the chain to "twist" into a coil structure. However, isotactic poly(propylene oxide) (see problem 4) can assume the all-*trans* configuration. Give a reason for the difference.
6. Polyethylene, when subjected to intense ionizing radiation such as from high-energy

X rays, becomes stronger and more difficult to melt. What effect could the X rays have on the polymer structure that could account for the change in properties?

7. Dipeptides are molecules composed of two amino-acid molecules.
   (a) How many dipeptides can be obtained from the twenty amino acids in Table 10-4?
   (b) Write structural formulas for the dipeptides in part (a) composed of glycine, alanine, or tyrosine.
8. Nitrocellulose, a type of gunpowder, is made by replacing the free —OH groups of cellulose with $—ONO_2$ groups. Write the structure for a segment of the nitrocellulose polymer.
9. (a) How many different protein molecules consisting of 100 amino acid monomers can be made from the 20 basic amino acids?
   (b) How does this number of molecules compare with the total number of atoms contained in the earth? (Assume there is 1 atom/cubic Å in the earth and that the earth's diameter is 8000 miles.)
10. (a) If each of the basic 20 amino acids has three conformations in the peptide chain, calculate the number of different conformations possible in a 100-unit peptide chain.
    (b) Calculate the entropy change in going from perfectly ordered peptide (for example an α-helix) to a randomly ordered peptide.
    (c) Calculate the enthalpy change for the process in part (b), assuming that 100 hydrogen bonds of 0.8 kcal each are broken.
    (d) Using ΔS and ΔH data from parts (b) and (c), calculate the temperature at which the process in part (b) would occur.
11. The biological polymer DNA (deoxyribonucleic acid) plays an essential role in heredity. The molecular weight of DNA is about 2.0×10^9, and its density is 1.4 g/cm^3. What is the volume occupied by one molecule?
12. Calculate the number of optical isomers of a polypeptide consisting of 10 monomer units of either D- or L-alanine.
13. For a rubber band stretched to a fixed length, experimental data of force versus temperature were found to fit the following equation:

$$f = 99.0 + 3.25T \text{ dynes}$$

    Calculate $(dE/dl)_T$ and $(dS/dl)_T$ for this material.
14. Using data from Table 10-5, determine which products, C_4H_{10} plus $C_{14}H_{30}$ or C_8H_{18} plus $C_{10}H_{22}$ (as shown by equation 10.22), would be more likely to result from the reaction of $C_{18}H_{38}$ with H_2.

11 THE ELECTRONIC STRUCTURE OF ATOMS

The theory of quantum mechanics gives a detailed picture of the nature of atoms and molecules. It was developed in the early part of this century to explain the results of a variety of experiments.

The combination of theory and experiment has led to the principle that atoms exist in discrete energy states; their energies are said to be quantized. These discrete states are studied through the interaction of light (electromagnetic radiation) with matter. It is found that a change in the energy state of an atom can take place by emission or absorption of electromagnetic radiation.

The experimental study of the energy states of atoms uses light, or photons, whose energy is given by

$$E = h\nu = hc/\lambda \tag{11.1}$$

where h is Planck's constant; c, the speed of light; v, the frequency; and λ, the wavelength. A photon can promote a transition from one energy state to another. By measuring the energy of the absorbed or emitted photon, we obtain information about the energy states of an atom.

Fig. 11-1, *A*, shows the absorption of a photon of energy equal to $E_2 - E_1$. The absorption from the lower state, E_1, to the higher state, E_2, causes a transition to occur. A photon is emitted when the atom undergoes a transition from a higher to a lower energy state (Fig. 11-1, *B*).

11.1 THE SCHRÖDINGER EQUATION

The basic equation of quantum theory is the Schrödinger equation:

$$\mathscr{H}\psi_n = E_n\psi_n \tag{11.2}$$

The $\mathscr{H}$ is called the *Hamiltonian operator*, and ψ_n is called the *wave function*. The energy of the wave function is given by E_n. The Hamiltonian operator is the sum

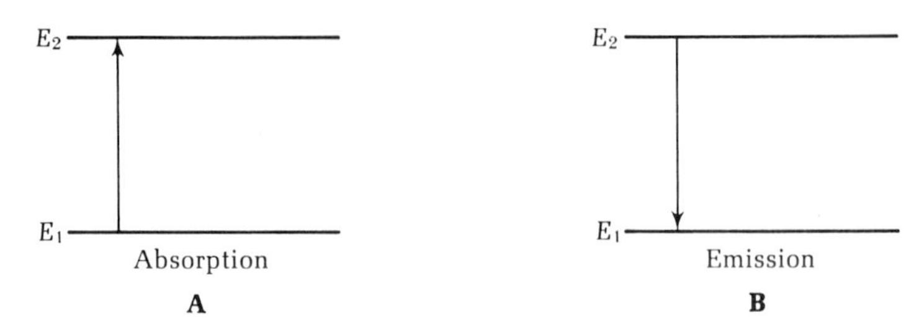

Fig. 11-1. **A,** Transition from state E_1 to state E_2 as result of absorption of energy. **B,** Transition from state E_2 to state E_1 as result of emission of energy.

of two terms, the kinetic-energy operator, T, and the potential-energy operator, V:

$$\mathcal{H} = T + V \tag{11.3}$$

The kinetic energy term is

$$T = \sum_i \left(-\frac{\hbar^2}{2m_i}\right) \nabla_i^2 \tag{11.4}$$

where the summation includes all particles (electrons or nuclei) in the atom under consideration. The term ∇_i^2 is a sum of second partial derivatives of the coordinates (x_i, y_i, z_i) for the ith particle in the atom:

$$\nabla_i^2 = \frac{\partial^2}{\partial x_i^2} + \frac{\partial^2}{\partial y_i^2} + \frac{\partial^2}{\partial z_i^2} \tag{11.5}$$

The symbol $\hbar$ represents $h/2\pi$, and m_i is the mass of the ith particle in the atom.

The potential energy, V, for two charged particles, $+e$ and $-e$, separated a distance r is given by

$$V = -\frac{e^2}{r} \tag{11.6}$$

For like charges ($+e$ and $+e$, or $-e$ and $-e$) the potential energy is given by

$$V = \frac{e^2}{r} \tag{11.7}$$

Our major goal at this point is to understand how the above equations can be applied to a simple system. For example, let us examine the formulation of the Schrödinger equation for a two-electron system. We label one electron 1 and the other electron 2. The kinetic-energy operator, T, is given from equation 11.4 by two terms

$$T = -\frac{\hbar^2}{2m}\nabla_1^2 - \frac{\hbar^2}{2m}\nabla_2^2 \tag{11.8}$$

The potential energy operator, V, is

$$V = +\frac{e^2}{r} \tag{11.9}$$

The Hamiltonian is then

$$\mathcal{H} = -\frac{\hbar^2}{2m}\nabla_1^2 - \frac{\hbar^2}{2m}\nabla_1^2 + \frac{e^2}{r} \tag{11.10}$$

The Schrödinger equation is given as

$$-\frac{\hbar^2}{2m}\nabla_1^2\psi_n - \frac{\hbar^2}{2m}\nabla_1^2\psi_n + \frac{e^2}{r}\psi_n = E_n\psi_n \tag{11.11}$$

While we do not expect the reader to comprehend the significance of equation 11.11 in its detailed mathematical form, we do want to emphasize that a Schrödinger equation can be written for any specific problem. The solution of the Schrödinger equation generally involves a knowledge of advanced mathematics. However, as we shall see in the next section, it is possible for us to solve a particularly simple problem, that of a particle in a box. In so doing we shall gain some feeling for the wave function ψ_n and the idea of discrete energy states E_n.

The wave function ψ_n represents the solution of the Schrödinger equation. The ψ_n has no physical significance. The value of ψ_n^2 represents the probability of finding the system with a particular set of coordinates. The sum of ψ_n^2 taken over all positions available to the system represents the total probability of the system and must equal 1.

11.2 PARTICLE IN ONE-DIMENSIONAL BOX

Let us consider a problem that illustrates how quantum mechanics works. A particle of mass m is confined to move in one dimension, x, between two barriers separated by a distance L. The potential energy for the particle becomes infinite outside the box and is zero inside the box. The problem is relatively simple because the potential energy has a very simple form. These conditions are stated as boundary conditions, as shown in Fig. 11-2. Since the problem is one dimensional (x), the kinetic-energy operator T is

$$T = -\frac{\hbar^2}{2m}\frac{d^2}{dx^2} \tag{11.12}$$

and the Schrödinger equation for the particle inside the box is

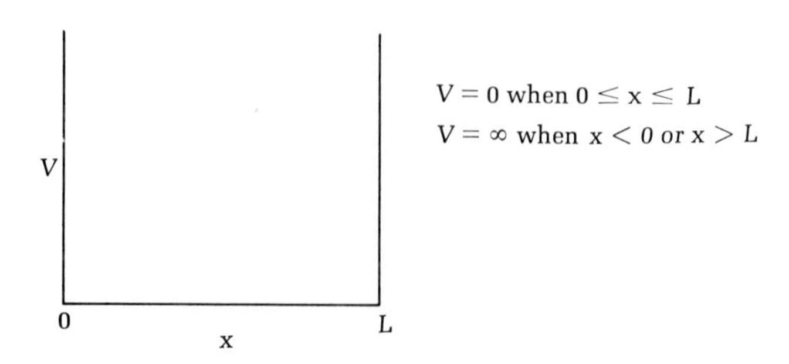

Fig. 11-2. Potential-energy diagram of one-dimensional box of length L.

$$-\frac{\hbar^2}{2m}\frac{d^2\psi_n}{dx^2} = E_n\psi_n \tag{11.13}$$

To solve this equation, we examine trial functions of ψ_n. Only a few satisfy the equation. One such function is

$$\psi_n = A \sin \alpha x \tag{11.14}$$

where A and α are constants. To show that equation 11.14 satisfies equation 11.13, we take the first derivative, which gives

$$\frac{d\psi_n}{dx} = A\alpha \cos \alpha x \tag{11.15}$$

and then the second derivative:

$$\frac{d^2\psi_n}{dx^2} = -A\alpha^2 \sin \alpha x \tag{11.16}$$

We substitute this into equation 11.13 and obtain

$$-\frac{\hbar^2}{2m}(-A\alpha^2 \sin \alpha x) = E_n(A \sin \alpha x) \tag{11.17}$$

which upon cancellation of like terms gives

$$\frac{\hbar^2}{2m}\alpha^2 = E_n \tag{11.18}$$

Equation 11.18 shows that for this problem the constant, E_n, is determined by the values of α and m. Most functions of x would not be eliminated upon substitution into equation 11.13. For example, if

$$\psi_n = \beta x^2 \tag{11.19}$$

then

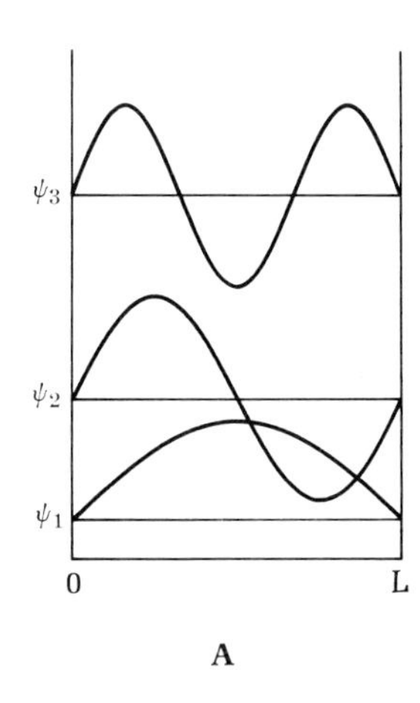

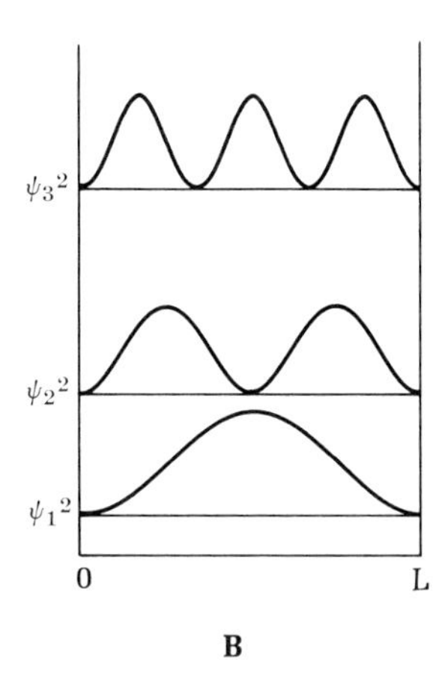

Fig. 11-3. Wave functions, ψ_n, **A**, and wave functions squared, ψ_n^2, **B**, n = 1, 2, 3, for particle in one-dimensional box.

$$\frac{d^2\psi}{dx^2} = 2\beta \tag{11.20}$$

and substitution into equation 11.13 would give

$$-\frac{\hbar^2}{2m}(2\beta) = E_n(\beta x^2) \tag{11.21}$$

The coordinate x is not eliminated, so equation 11.19 is not a satisfactory solution.

Because we require the particle to be in the box, the probability of finding the particle at and beyond the edges of the box must be zero. The wave function ψ_n must then have zero values at $x = 0$ and $x = L$. These conditions are satisfied by letting

$$\alpha = \frac{n\pi}{L},\ n = 1, 2, 3, \ldots \tag{11.22}$$

The wave function becomes

$$\psi_n = A \sin\left(\frac{n\pi x}{L}\right),\ n = 1, 2, 3, \ldots \tag{11.23}$$

The first three wave functions for $n = 1, 2, 3, \ldots$ are shown in Fig. 11-3, *A*. The end conditions are met in each case.

We can now solve for the energy E_n that is associated with each wave function ψ_n. From equation 11.13 we find

$$-\frac{\hbar^2}{2m}\left[-A\left(\frac{n\pi}{L}\right)^2 \sin\frac{n\pi x}{L}\right] = E_n\left(A \sin\frac{n\pi x}{L}\right) \tag{11.24}$$

or

$$E_n = \frac{\hbar^2 n^2 \pi^2}{2mL^2} = \frac{n^2 h^2}{8mL^2} \tag{11.25}$$

Thus each wave function has a discrete energy state determined by m, L, and the integer value of n. The integer n is called a *quantum number*.

The only unsolved aspect of this problem is the specification of A in equation 11.23. In order to solve for A, we impose the condition that the probability of finding the particle in the box is unity. The precise probability of finding a particle between x and $x + dx$ is $\psi_n^2 dx$. The sum of these terms over the whole box must be 1. This is given by the integral

$$\int_0^L \psi_n^2 dx = 1 \tag{11.26}$$

or with equation 11.23

$$\int_0^L A^2 \sin^2\left(\frac{n\pi x}{L}\right) dx = 1 \tag{11.27}$$

This process is called *normalization*. Integration of equation 11.27 gives

$$\frac{A^2 L}{2} = 1 \tag{11.28}$$

for any value of n. Thus, the normalized wave function is

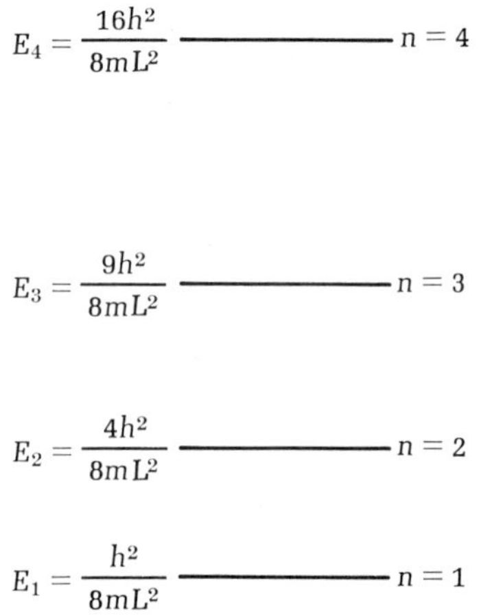

$E_4 = \dfrac{16h^2}{8mL^2}$ ———— $n = 4$

$E_3 = \dfrac{9h^2}{8mL^2}$ ———— $n = 3$

$E_2 = \dfrac{4h^2}{8mL^2}$ ———— $n = 2$

$E_1 = \dfrac{h^2}{8mL^2}$ ———— $n = 1$

Fig. 11-4. Energy levels for first four quantum states of particle in box.

$$\psi_n = \sqrt{\frac{2}{L}} \sin \frac{n\pi x}{L} \tag{11.29}$$

The term ψ_n^2 is proportional to the probability of finding the particle at a particular point, x:

$$\psi_n^2 = \frac{2}{L} \sin^2 \frac{n\pi x}{L} \tag{11.30}$$

Plots of ψ_n^2 for various values of n are shown in Fig. 11-3, B. In any particular n state, characterized by a specific energy E_n, the probability of finding the particle along the line varies with its position. This is a surprising result. The spacing of the energy states is directly proportional to n^2 and inversely proportional to mL^2. The heavier the particle, the more closely spaced the energy levels will be. The smaller the value of L, the more widely spaced the energy levels will be. The spacing for the first few levels is depicted in Fig. 11-4.

11.3 THE HYDROGEN ATOM

The H atom is the simplest atomic system because it has only one proton and one electron. However, the quantum mechanical solution of this problem provides the basis for understanding much more complicated atomic and molecular systems. We therefore examine the solution of this system in considerable detail.

Solutions of H-atom problem

The system of a nucleus and one electron is shown in Fig. 11-5, A. The nucleus of mass M with charge $+e$ is located at coordinates labeled by (2), and the electron of mass m with charge $-e$ is located at coordinates labeled by (1). The distance of separation between the nucleus and the electron is r. The potential energy of electrostatic attraction is given by

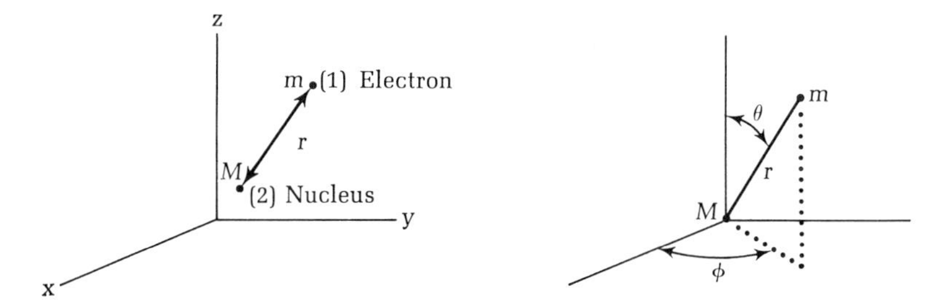

Fig. 11-5. Coordinate systems for the H-atom system. **A,** Cartesian coordinates. **B,** Spherical coordinates.

$$V = -\frac{e^2}{r} \tag{11.31}$$

There are two kinetic energy terms, one for the nuclear mass M, the other for the electron mass m. These are expressed as

$$T = -\frac{\hbar^2}{2M}\nabla_2^2 - \frac{\hbar^2}{2m}\nabla_1^2 \tag{11.32}$$

The Hamiltonian, $\mathcal{H}$, is

$$\mathcal{H} = -\frac{\hbar^2}{2M}\nabla_2^2 - \frac{\hbar^2}{2m}\nabla_1^2 - \frac{e^2}{r} \tag{11.33}$$

The Schrödinger equation can then be written as

$$-\frac{\hbar^2}{2M}\nabla_2^2\psi_n - \frac{\hbar^2}{2m}\nabla_1^2\psi_n - \frac{e^2}{r}\psi_n = E_n\psi_n \tag{11.34}$$

where the wave function is ψ_n, and the energy associated with ψ_n is E_n.

The problem posed by equation 11.34 is solved in terms of spherical coordinates, as shown in Fig. 11-5, *B*. The solution of this equation is not a trivial matter.

The solution has the following general characteristics. The wave function ψ depends upon two functions, $R(r)$ and $\chi(\theta, \phi)$, which are determined by the radial distance and angular coordinates of the system. The radial and angular functions are uniquely quantized with quantum numbers n, ℓ, and m_ℓ. The dependence of these functions on coordinates and quantum numbers is

$$\psi(r, \theta, \phi) = R(r)\,\chi(\theta, \phi) \tag{11.35}$$

and

$$\psi(n, \ell, m_\ell) = R(n, \ell)\,\chi(\ell, m) \tag{11.36}$$

The wave function of the system is determined by the set of three quantum numbers, n, ℓ, and m_ℓ. They are called the *principal* (n), *angular momentum* (ℓ), and *magnetic* (m_ℓ) *quantum numbers*. The wave function for a particular set of quantum numbers, n, ℓ, and m_ℓ is called an *orbital*. The n quantum number primarily determines the energy of the electron and the volume around the nucleus in which the electron can be found. The ℓ quantum number determines the angular momentum of the electron and the shape of the volume in which the electron is found. The m_ℓ quantum number determines the orientation relative to one another of a set of orbitals of given ℓ value. The square of the wave function gives the probability of locating the electron at each location in a given orbital. As we saw in detail for the particle in the box, only certain wave functions formally related by particular quantum numbers can satisfy the Schrödinger equation. Because the H-atom problem has a more complicated potential energy term, and because it is a three-dimensional problem, it is not surprising that a more complex set of quantum numbers arises from its solution than from the solution of the problem of the particle in the box.

The rules that govern the rules of the quantum numbers are

$$\begin{aligned} n &= 1, 2, 3, 4, \ldots \\ \ell &= n-1, n-2, \ldots, 0 \\ m_\ell &= -\ell, \ldots, 0, \ldots, +\ell \end{aligned} \tag{11.37}$$

The value of n determines the discrete energy state, E_n, of the system:

$$E_n = -\frac{\mu e^2}{2\hbar^2 n^2} \tag{11.38}$$

where μ is called the *reduced mass* and is given in terms of the mass of the nucleus, M, and the mass of the electron, m:

$$\mu = \frac{mM}{m + M} \tag{11.39}$$

The hydrogen-atom orbitals arise from the solution of the Schrödinger equation. The angular and radial parts of the wave function are shown in Tables 11-1 and 11-2.

Table 11-1. RADIAL PARTS OF HYDROGEN-ATOM WAVE FUNCTIONS, $R(n, \ell) = R(r)$

R	n	ℓ
$R(1s) = 2\left(\frac{Z}{a_0}\right)^{3/2} e^{\sigma/2}$	1	0
$R(2s) = \frac{1}{2\sqrt{2}}\left(\frac{Z}{2a_0}\right)^{3/2}(2-\sigma)e^{-\sigma/2}$	2	0
$R(2p) = \frac{1}{2\sqrt{6}}\left(\frac{Z}{a_0}\right)^{3/2}\sigma e^{-\sigma/2}$	2	1
$R(3s) = \frac{1}{9\sqrt{3}}\left(\frac{Z}{a_0}\right)^{3/2}(6-6\sigma+\sigma^2)e^{-\sigma/2}$	3	0
$R(3p) = \frac{1}{9\sqrt{6}}\left(\frac{Z}{a_0}\right)^{3/2}(4-\sigma)\sigma e^{-\sigma/2}$	3	1
$R(3d) = \frac{1}{9\sqrt{30}}\left(\frac{Z}{a_0}\right)^{3/2}\sigma^2 e^{-\sigma/2}$	3	2

$\sigma = \frac{2Zr}{na_0}$

$a_0 = \frac{h^2}{4\pi^2 me^2} = 0.529$ Å

Table 11-2. ANGULAR PARTS OF HYDROGEN-ATOM WAVE FUNCTIONS, $\chi(\ell, m_\ell) = \chi(\theta, \phi)$

χ	ℓ	m_ℓ
$\chi(s) = \left(\frac{1}{4\pi}\right)^{1/2}$	0	0
$\chi(p_x) = \left(\frac{3}{4\pi}\right)^{1/2} \sin\theta \cos\phi$	0	−1
$\chi(p_y) = \left(\frac{3}{4\pi}\right)^{1/2} \sin\theta \sin\phi$	1	0
$\chi(p_z) = \left(\frac{3}{4\pi}\right)^{1/2} \cos\theta$	1	+1
$\chi(d_{x^2-y^2}) = \left(\frac{15}{16\pi}\right)^{1/2} \sin^2\theta \cos 2\phi$	2	−2
$\chi(d_{xz}) = \left(\frac{15}{4\pi}\right)^{1/2} \sin\theta \cos\theta \cos\phi$	2	−1
$\chi(d_{z^2}) = \left(\frac{5}{16\pi}\right)^{1/2} (3\cos^2\theta - 1)$	2	0
$\chi(d_{yz}) = \left(\frac{15}{4\pi}\right)^{1/2} \sin\theta \cos\theta \sin\phi$	2	1
$\chi(d_{xy}) = \left(\frac{15}{16\pi}\right)^{1/2} \sin^2\theta \sin 2\phi$	2	2

The radial parts depend on both the principal (n) and angular (ℓ) quantum number. However, the angular parts depend only on ℓ; hence all wave functions of a given type (that is, *s*, *p*, *d*, or *f*) show the same angular dependence. Also, we note that the angular part of the wave function for an *s* orbital is always the same, $(1/4\pi)^{1/2}$. For any given orbital, the overall wave function is found by combining the appropriate radial and angular parts.

Let us first examine the *s* orbitals in detail. The 1*s*-orbital wave function, $\psi(1s)$, is given by $\chi(s)$ times $R(1s)$:

$$\psi(1s) = \frac{1}{\sqrt{\pi}}\left(\frac{Z}{a_0}\right)^{3/2} e^{-Zr/a_0} \tag{11.40}$$

This wave function decreases exponentially with increasing r from a maximum value at $r = 0$. Since wave functions for *s* orbitals show no angular dependence, they are always spherical in shape. The square of the $\psi(1s)$ function

$$\psi^2(1s) = \frac{1}{\pi}\left(\frac{Z}{a_0}\right)^{3} e^{-2Zr/a_0} \tag{11.41}$$

gives the probability of finding an electron within a small cubical element of space at a distance r from the origin. This plot also decreases exponentially. Plots of

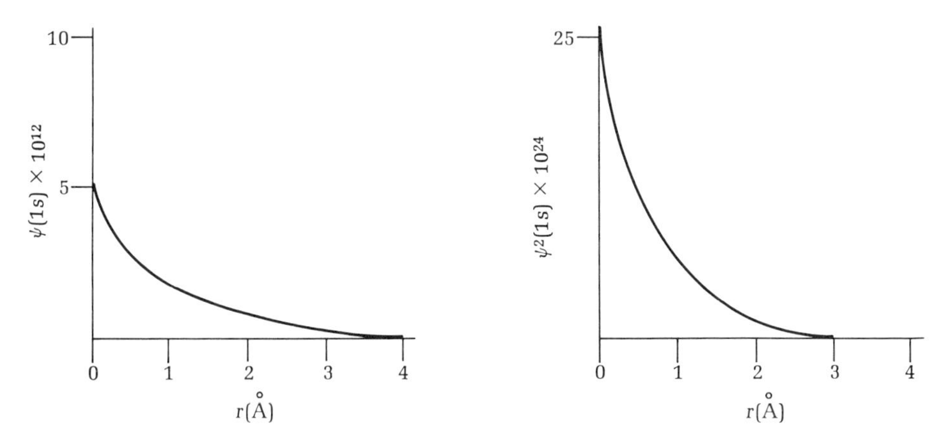

Fig. 11-6. Plots of $\psi(1s)$ and $\psi^2(1s)$ versus r.

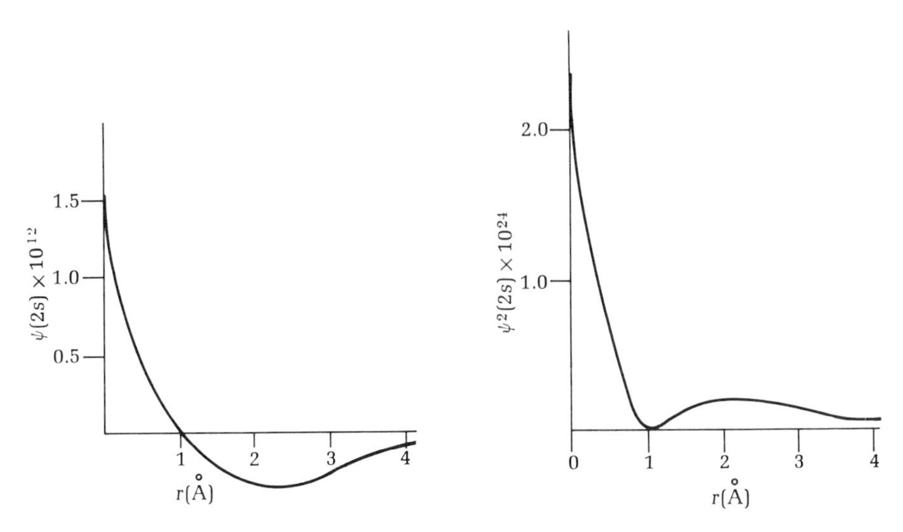

Fig. 11-7. Plots of $\psi(2s)$ and $\psi^2(2s)$ versus r.

$\psi(1s)$ and $\psi^2(1s)$ versus r for $1s$ orbital are shown in Fig. 11-6. The plots of ψ and ψ^2 for a $2s$ orbital are shown in Fig. 11-7. The wave function $\psi(2s)$ changes sign at about $r = 1$ Å. The point at which the sign change occurs is called a *node*. The plot of $\psi^2(2s)$ shows that it is more probable to find the electron farther from the nucleus in a 2s orbital than in a 1s orbital. However, as with the $1s$ orbital, the $2s$ orbital has no angular dependence and consequently is spherical.

Two alternate ways of representing orbitals are often used in connection with

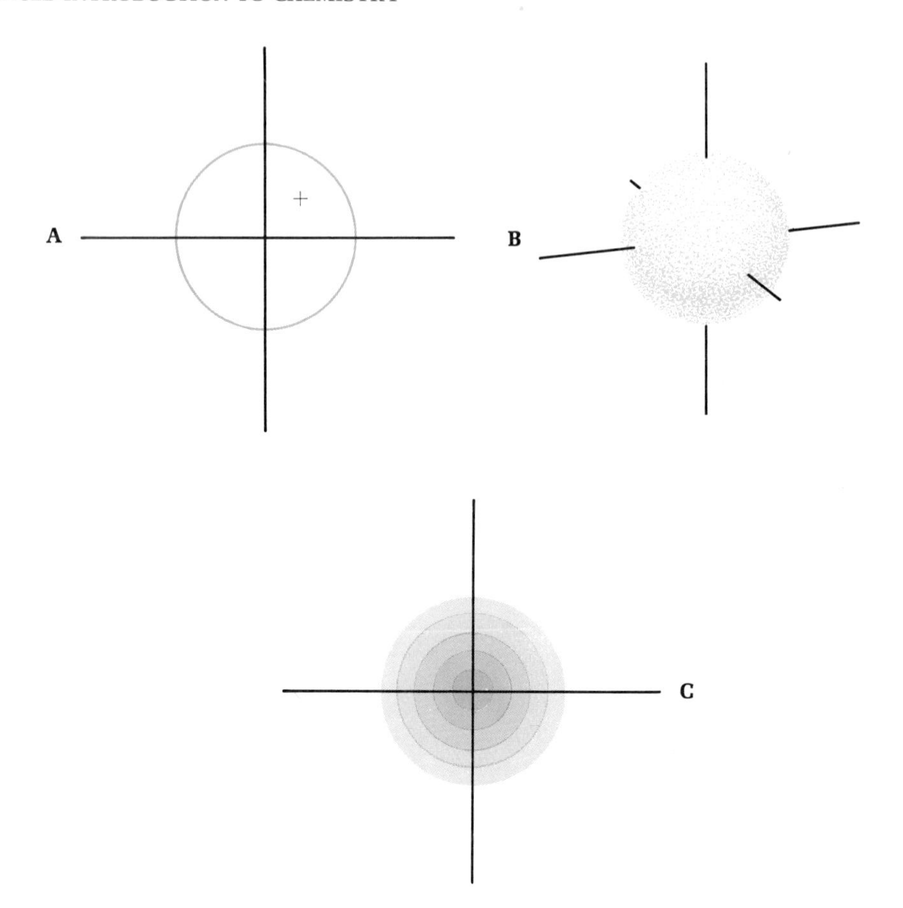

Fig. 11-8. **A,** "Cross-sectional" representation of $\psi(1s)$. **B,** Three-dimensional representation of $\psi^2(1s)$. **C,** "Cross section" of $\psi^2(1s)$ on the *x-y* plane.

discussions of covalent bonding (see Chapter 12). These are shown in Fig. 11-8 for the $1s$ orbital. In *A*, a "cross section" of the $\psi(1s)$ wave function is shown. The boundary line represents a cross section of a sphere within whose volume there is a 90% probability of locating the electron. The "+" sign indicates that the sign of the wave function is positive in all regions. A three-dimensional representation of ψ^2 is shown in *B*. The spherical boundary surface includes 90% of the electron probability. In *C*, a "cross section" of the $1s$ orbital is depicted. The value of ψ^2 is proportional to the color density in the figure.

The p orbitals show both an angular and a radial dependence. The radial part of the wave function for the $2p$ orbital equals zero at $r = 0$, increases to a maximum

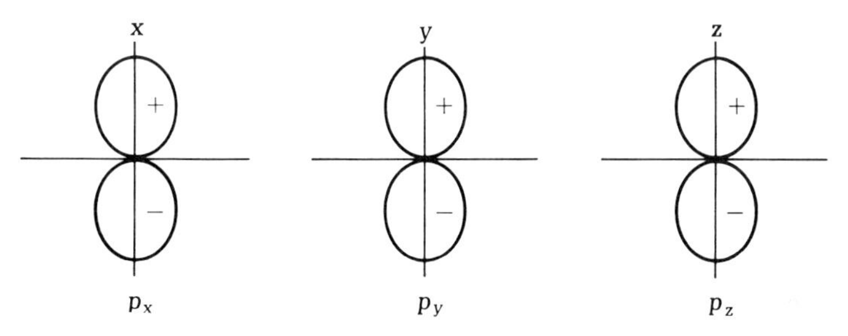

Fig. 11-9. Angular parts χ of $2p$ wave functions.

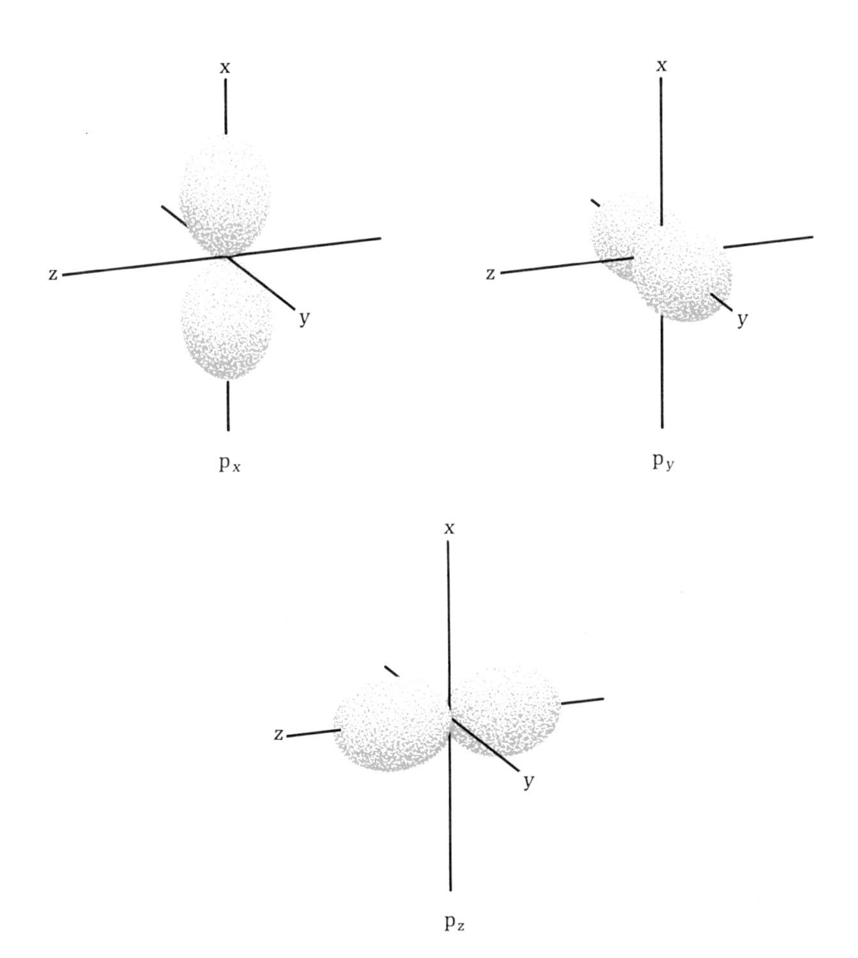

Fig. 11-10. Three-dimensional representations of ψ^2 for the three $2p$ orbitals.

value as r increases, and finally decreases exponentially to zero at large values of r. The angular parts of the $2p$ wave functions, $\chi(p_x)$, $\chi(p_y)$, and $\chi(p_z)$, are shown in Fig. 11-9. They are not spherically symmetric like an s wave function, but instead are symmetric about the three coordinate axes (x, y, and z). For this reason they are called the p_x, p_y, and p_z orbitals. The sign of χ changes between the lobes of the wave function. A plot of ψ^2 for the $2p$ orbitals yields orbitals directed along the x, y, and z axes as shown in Fig. 11-10. Again, the boundary surface defines the minimum volume that includes 90% of the electron probability.

The radial parts (R) of the wave functions give an indication of the relative sizes of the various orbitals. Consider the probability of finding the electron within a shell of thickness dr at radius r. The volume of the shell is $4\pi r^2 dr$. The probability of finding the electron in this shell is $4\pi r^2 R^2 dr$. The plot of $4\pi r^2 R^2$ versus r then becomes a *radial probability distribution*. Radial probability distribution curves for the $1s$, $2s$, $3s$, $2p$, $3p$, and $3d$ orbitals are shown in Fig. 11-11. Note that these

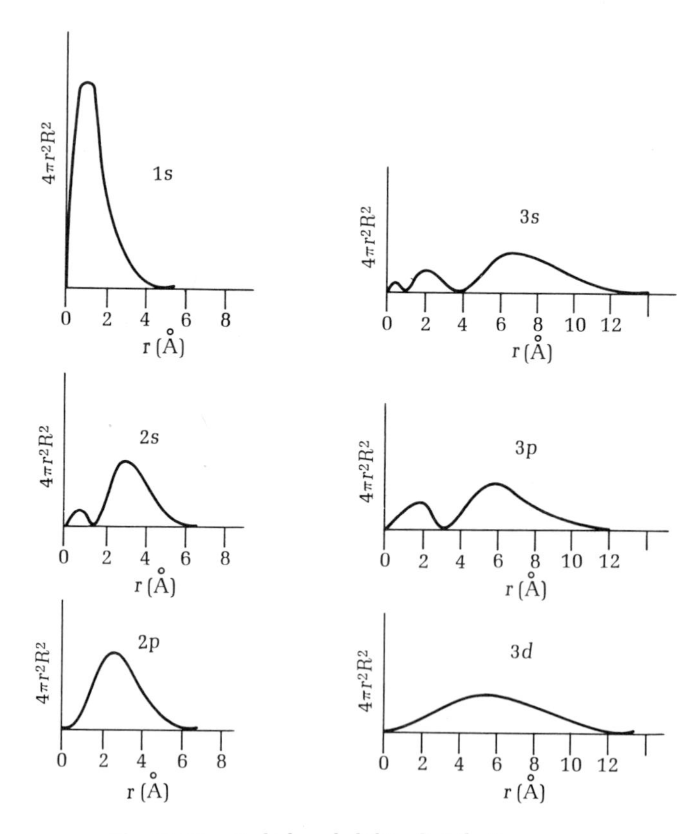

Fig. 11-11. Radial probability distribution curves.

curves are different from plots of ψ^2 or R^2 versus r. The probability represented by ψ^2 or R^2 is the probability of locating the electron in a small cubical element in space at distance r from the nucleus, whereas $4\pi r^2 R^2$ represents the probability of locating the electron in a spherical shell composed of all small cubical elements at distance r. The radial probability distribution curves give us the best indication of the effective size of a given orbital. The location of maximum probability increases from $1s$ to $2s$ to $3s$, and so on. The effective size decreases from $2s$ to $2p$ and from $3s$ to $3p$ to $3d$. The five d orbitals exhibit more complex angular dependence than the s and p orbitals. Diagrams of the boundary surfaces, again containing 90% of the electron probability, are shown in Fig. 11-12.

Energy-level diagrams

A diagram showing the relative energies of the various hydrogen-atom orbitals is shown in Fig. 11-13. The energies can be calculated using equation 11.38. The orbital with lowest energy is the $1s$ orbital. Each successive orbital represents a higher energy state. At quantum levels of $n = 2$, there are sublevels corresponding to the $2s$ and $2p$ orbitals. At $n = 3$, there are $3s$, $3p$, and $3d$ orbitals, and so on. For

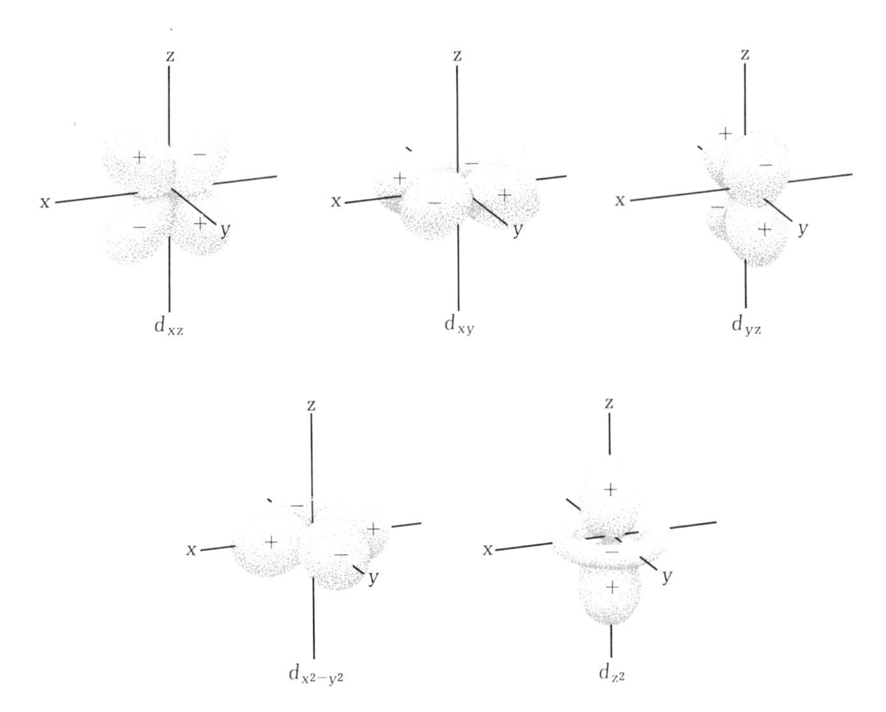

Fig. 11-12. The five d orbitals.

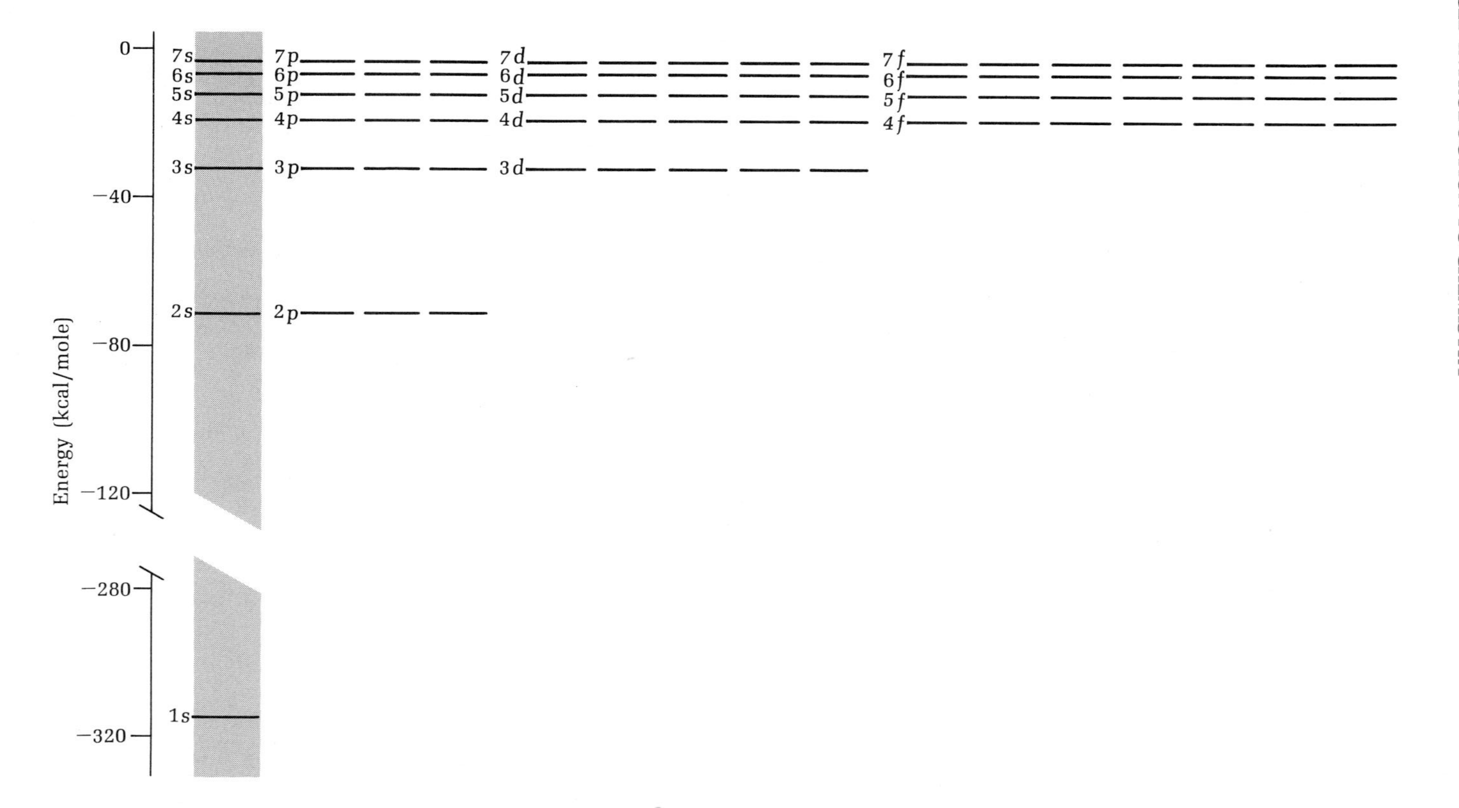

Fig. 11-13. Energy levels for hydrogen-atom orbitals.

the hydrogen-atom system, which has only one electron, the sublevels for a given n value have the same energy and are called *degenerate*. However, for atoms with more than one electron, the sublevels are not at equal energy, as we will see later in this chapter.

11.4 MULTIELECTRON ATOMS

The helium atom

We shall now examine what happens when the nucleus is surrounded by more than one electron. The helium atom has a doubly charged nucleus ($Z = 2$) and two electrons. In Fig. 11-14, the nucleus, N, and electrons, e_1 and e_2, are shown in a coordinate system in which the nucleus is fixed at the origin. The distances from nucleus to electrons e_1 and e_2 are r_{N-1} and r_{N-2}. The interelectron distance is r_{1-2}. The kinetic energy term is expressed for the two electrons and the nucleus as

$$T = -\frac{\hbar^2}{2m}\nabla_1^2 - \frac{\hbar^2}{2m}\nabla_2^2 - \frac{\hbar^2}{2M_N}\nabla_N^2 \qquad (11.42)$$

where m is the mass of the electron; M_N, the mass of the nucleus; and the different ∇^2 terms apply to the coordinates of electrons 1 and 2 and nucleus N. The potential energy term for this system is the sum of three pairs of coulombic interactions:

$$V = -\frac{2e^2}{r_{N-1}} - \frac{2e^2}{r_{N-2}} + \frac{e^2}{r_{1-2}} \qquad (11.43)$$

The sum of the kinetic and potential energy terms gives the Hamiltonian, $\mathcal{H}$. The Schrödinger equation for the He atom is

$$\left(-\frac{\hbar^2}{2m}\nabla_1^2 - \frac{\hbar^2}{2m}\nabla_2^2 - \frac{\hbar^2}{2M_N}\nabla_N^2 - \frac{2e^2}{r_{N-1}} - \frac{2e^2}{r_{N-2}} + \frac{e^2}{r_{1-2}}\right)\psi_n = E_n\psi_n \qquad (11.44)$$

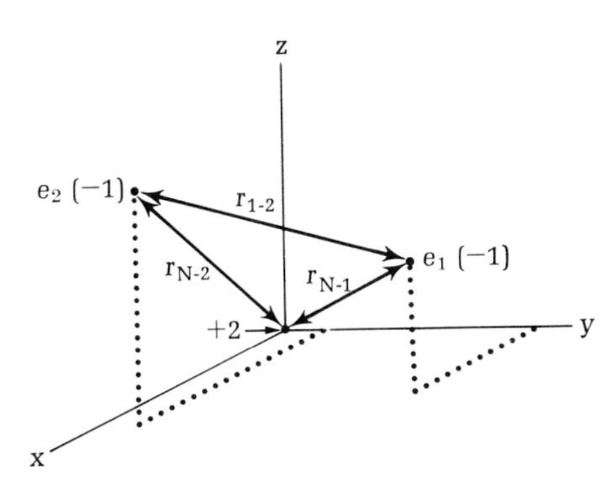

Fig. 11-14. Coordinate system for He-atom problem.

Unfortunately, this problem cannot be solved as easily as the H-atom problem because the addition of the second electron introduces an interaction effect between the electrons that markedly increases the mathematical complexity of the problem. To solve the equation, we must use approximation techniques. It is possible to prove that the exact solution, though impossible to express mathematically in simple form, can be approached by a combination of approximate solutions.

To solve equation 11.44, we first neglect the terms for the kinetic energy of the nucleus and the interaction between electrons. Neglecting the kinetic energy of the nucleus is a fairly minor approximation; however, neglecting the inter-electron interaction is quantitatively much more serious. Examination of the terms in equation 11.44 reveals that they can be separated into two terms, one for electron 1 and one for electron 2:

$$\left[\left(-\frac{\hbar^2}{2m}\nabla_1^2 - \frac{2e^2}{r_{N-1}}\right) + \left(-\frac{\hbar^2}{2m}\nabla_2^2 - \frac{2e^2}{r_{N-2}}\right)\right]\psi_n \cong E_n\psi_n \tag{11.45}$$

We substitute the one-electron wave function solutions found in the H-atom problem for each part of equation 11.45 and combine the parts to give the total approximate solution. In the lowest energy state *(ground state)*, the $1s$ orbital is used. Both electrons would be in the $1s$ orbital. Based on this independent-electron approximation, the wave function for He in the ground state would be

$$\psi = \phi_1(1s)\phi_2(1s) \tag{11.46}$$

We now have a wave function for He with two electrons in the same orbital. Both electrons have the same quantum numbers (n, ℓ, m_ℓ). Pauli proposed, based on experimental observation, that no two electrons can have the same set of quantum numbers in the same atom or molecule. It was suggested that an additional quantum number called the *spin quantum number* is needed to further specify the quantum state of an electron. The spin quantum number, m_s, is $+\frac{1}{2}$ or $-\frac{1}{2}$ and determines the angular momentum that arises due to the spinning of the electron (like a spinning top) around its own axis. Since there are two possible spin states (in opposite directions, that is, clockwise or counterclockwise), there are two values of m_s. Two electrons can occupy the same orbital if their spin quantum numbers are different. The quantum numbers for the two $1s$ electrons in He would be

Electron	n	ℓ	m_ℓ	m_s
1	1	0	0	$+\frac{1}{2}$
2	1	0	0	$-\frac{1}{2}$

The ground state electronic configuration of He is written as $1s^2$.

Elements beyond helium

The reasoning applied to the helium atom can now be applied to subsequent elements. The lithium atom consists of a nucleus and three electrons. We could write the Schrödinger equation for the Li atom, make the same approximations as we did for the He-atom problem, and solve for ψ as a combination of hydrogen-atom wave function solutions. In the lowest energy state, two electrons are accomodated in the $1s$ orbital and the third electron is in the $2s$ orbital. The independent-electron description for Li would be $1s^2 2s^1$. Application of these ideas to beryllium yields a configuration of $1s^2 2s^2$.

Before discussing the multielectron atoms further, we need to summarize again how many electrons can be placed in the various types of orbitals and the quantum number designations for these electrons. These are shown in Table 11-3 for the $n = 1$ to $n = 4$ levels. At quantum level 2, there are eight possibilities (2 in s and 6 in p), so eight electrons can be accommodated. At $n = 3$, there are 18 possibilities (2 in s, 6 in p, and 10 in d), allowing a total occupancy of 18 electrons. At $n = 4$, there is room for 32 electrons.

The procedures used for the qualitative description of multielectron atoms are extensions of those used above to describe H, He, Li, and Be. In multielectron atoms the electrons are associated with orbitals qualitatively similar to the hydrogen-atom orbitals.

Energy levels in multielectron atoms

Fig. 11-13 gave the energy-level diagram for the H atom. Similar diagrams arise for multielectron systems, but since the ℓ levels are no longer degenerate, more

Table 11-3. QUANTUM NUMBER COMBINATIONS

n	ℓ	*Orbital*	m_ℓ	m_s	*Number of combinations*	
1	0	$1s$	0	$+\frac{1}{2}, -\frac{1}{2}$	2	
2	0	$2s$	0	$+\frac{1}{2}, -\frac{1}{2}$	2	8
	1	$2p$	$+1, 0, -1$	$+\frac{1}{2}, -\frac{1}{2}$	6	
3	0	$3s$	0	$+\frac{1}{2}, -\frac{1}{2}$	2	18
	1	$3p$	$+1, 0, -1$	$+\frac{1}{2}, -\frac{1}{2}$	6	
	2	$3d$	$+2, +1, 0, -1, -2$	$+\frac{1}{2}, -\frac{1}{2}$	10	
4	0	$4s$	0	$+\frac{1}{2}, -\frac{1}{2}$	2	32
	1	$4p$	$+1, 0, -1$	$+\frac{1}{2}, -\frac{1}{2}$	6	
	2	$4d$	$+2, +1, 0, -1, -2$	$+\frac{1}{2}, -\frac{1}{2}$	10	
	3	$4f$	$+3, +2, +1, 0, -1, -2, -3$	$+\frac{1}{2}, -\frac{1}{2}$	14	

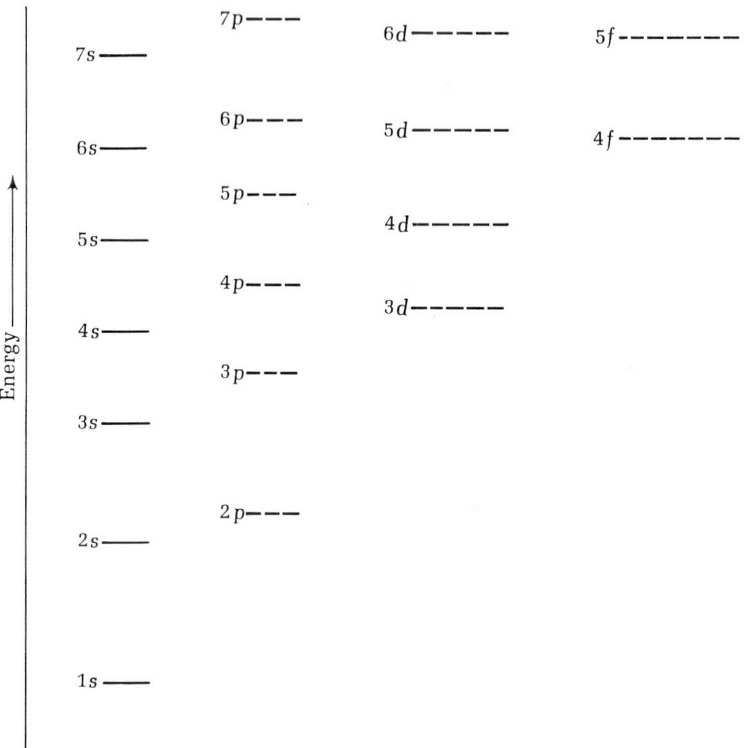

Fig. 11-15. Relative energy levels of valence-shell electrons in multielectron atoms.

complex patterns arise. The relative energy levels of the valence-shell orbitals in multielectron atoms are shown schematically in Fig. 11-15. The order of electron filling for ground state configurations can generally be determined using this diagram. The order of orbital filling is

$$1s,\ 2s,\ 2p,\ 3s,\ 3p,\ 4s,\ 3d,\ 4p,\ 5s,\ 4d,\ 5p,\ 6s,\ 4f,\ 5d,\ 6p,\ 7s,\ 5f,\ 6d,\ 7p$$

and so on. In general, for a given n level the order of ℓ levels is

$$s < p < d < f$$

This order arises due to differences in the wave-function properties of the s, p, d, and f orbitals. An electron in an s orbital has a relatively high probability of being near the nucleus as compared to a p, d, or f electron. An s electron experiences a strong attraction to the nucleus and thus has low energy. An electron in a p orbital is partially shielded from the nucleus by the s electrons, and its energy is somewhat higher. Similar effects influence electrons in the d and f orbitals.

The ground-state electronic configurations of the elements are shown in Table

Table 11-4. GROUND-STATE ELECTRONIC CONFIGURATIONS OF ELEMENTS

Atomic no.	*Element*	*Configuration*	*Atomic No.*	*Element*	*Configuration*
1	H	$1s^{1}$	53	I	$[-]4d^{10}5s^{2}5p^{5}$
2	He	$1s^{2}$	54	Xe	$[-]4d^{10}5s^{2}5p^{6}$
3	Li	$[\mathrm{He}]2s^{1}$	55	Cs	$[\mathrm{Xe}]6s^{1}$
4	Be	$[-]2s^{2}$	56	Ba	$[-]6s^{2}$
5	B	$[-]2s^{2}2p^{1}$	57	La	$[-]5d^{1}6s^{2}$
6	C	$[-]2s^{2}2p^{2}$	58	Ce	$[-]4f^{2}6s^{2}$
7	N	$[-]2s^{2}2p^{3}$	59	Pr	$[-]4f^{3}6s^{2}$
8	O	$[-]2s^{2}2p^{4}$	60	Nd	$[-]4f^{4}6s^{2}$
9	F	$[-]2s^{2}2p^{5}$	61	Pm	$[-]4f^{5}6s^{2}$
10	Ne	$[-]2s^{2}2p^{6}$	62	Sm	$[-]4f^{6}6s^{2}$
11	Na	$[\mathrm{Ne}]3s^{1}$	63	Eu	$[-]4f^{7}6s^{2}$
12	Mg	$[-]3s^{2}$	64	Gd	$[-]4f^{7}5d^{1}6s^{2}$
13	Al	$[-]3s^{2}3p^{1}$	65	Tb	$[-]4f^{9}6s^{2}$
14	Si	$[-]3s^{2}3p^{2}$	66	Dy	$[-]4f^{10}6s^{2}$
15	P	$[-]3s^{2}3p^{3}$	67	Ho	$[-]4f^{11}6s^{2}$
16	S	$[-]3s^{2}3p^{4}$	68	Er	$[-]4f^{12}6s^{2}$
17	Cl	$[-]3s^{2}3p^{5}$	69	Tm	$[-]4f^{13}6s^{2}$
18	Ar	$[-]3s^{2}3p^{6}$	70	Yb	$[-]4f^{14}6s^{2}$
19	K	$[\mathrm{Ar}]4s^{1}$	71	Lu	$[-]4f^{14}5d^{1}6s^{2}$
20	Ca	$[-]4s^{2}$	72	Hf	$[-]4f^{14}5d^{2}6s^{2}$
21	Sc	$[-]3d^{1}4s^{2}$	73	Ta	$[-]4f^{14}5d^{3}6s^{2}$
22	Ti	$[-]3d^{2}4s^{2}$	74	W	$[-]4f^{14}5d^{4}6s^{2}$
23	V	$[-]3d^{3}4s^{2}$	75	Re	$[-]4f^{14}5d^{5}6s^{2}$
24	Cr	$[-]3d^{5}4s^{1}$	76	Os	$[-]4f^{14}5d^{6}6s^{2}$
25	Mn	$[-]3d^{5}4s^{2}$	77	Ir	$[-]4f^{14}5d^{7}6s^{2}$
26	Fe	$[-]3d^{6}4s^{2}$	78	Pt	$[-]4f^{14}5d^{9}6s^{1}$
27	Co	$[-]3d^{7}4s^{2}$	79	Au	$[-]4f^{14}5d^{10}6s^{1}$
28	Ni	$[-]3d^{8}4s^{2}$	80	Hg	$[-]4f^{14}5d^{10}6s^{2}$
29	Cu	$[-]3d^{10}4s^{1}$	81	Tl	$[-]4f^{14}5d^{10}6s^{2}6p^{1}$
30	Zn	$[-]3d^{10}4s^{2}$	82	Pb	$[-]4f^{14}5d^{10}6s^{2}6p^{2}$
31	Ga	$[-]3d^{10}4s^{2}4p^{1}$	83	Bi	$[-]4f^{14}5d^{10}6s^{2}6p^{3}$
32	Ge	$[-]3d^{10}4s^{2}4p^{2}$	84	Po	$[-]4f^{14}5d^{10}6s^{2}6p^{4}$
33	As	$[-]3d^{10}4s^{2}4p^{3}$	85	At	$[-]4f^{14}5d^{10}6s^{2}6p^{5}$
34	Se	$[-]3d^{10}4s^{2}4p^{4}$	86	Rn	$[-]4f^{14}5d^{10}6s^{2}6p^{6}$
35	Br	$[-]3d^{10}4s^{2}4p^{5}$	87	Fr	$[\mathrm{Rn}]7s^{1}$
36	Kr	$[-]3d^{10}4s^{2}4p^{6}$	88	Ra	$[-]7s^{2}$
37	Rb	$[\mathrm{Kr}]5s^{1}$	89	Ac	$[-]6d^{1}7s^{2}$
38	Sr	$[-]5s^{2}$	90	Th	$[-]6d^{2}7s^{2}$
39	Y	$[-]4d^{1}5s^{2}$	91	Pa	$[-]5f^{2}6d^{1}7s^{2}$
40	Zr	$[-]4d^{2}5s^{2}$	92	U	$[-]5f^{3}6d^{1}7s^{2}$
41	Nb	$[-]4d^{4}5s^{1}$	93	Np	$[-]5f^{5}7s^{2}$
42	Mo	$[-]4d^{5}5s^{1}$	94	Pu	$[-]5f^{6}7s^{2}$
43	Tc	$[-]4d^{5}5s^{2}$	95	Am	$[-]5f^{7}7s^{2}$
44	Ru	$[-]4d^{7}5s^{1}$	96	Cm	$[-]5f^{7}6d^{1}7s^{2}$
45	Rh	$[-]4d^{8}5s^{1}$	97	Bk	$[-]5f^{8}6d^{1}7s^{2}$
46	Pd	$[-]4d^{10}$	98	Cf	$[-]5f^{9}6d^{1}7s^{2}$
47	Ag	$[-]4d^{10}5s^{1}$	99	Es	$[-]5f^{10}6d^{1}7s^{2}$
48	Cd	$[-]4d^{10}5s^{2}$	100	Fm	$[-]5f^{11}6d^{1}7s^{2}$
49	In	$[-]4d^{10}5s^{2}5p^{1}$	101	Md	$[-]5f^{12}6d^{1}7s^{2}$
50	Sn	$[-]4d^{10}5s^{2}5p^{2}$	102	No	$[-]5f^{13}6d^{1}7s^{2}$
51	Sb	$[-]4d^{10}5s^{2}5p^{3}$	103	Lw	$[-]5f^{14}6d^{1}7s^{2}$
52	Te	$[-]4d^{10}5s^{2}5p^{4}$			

11-4. Only the outer electrons, that is, those electrons beyond the preceding rare-gas configuration, are indicated. In general, those electrons that make up the preceding rare-gas configuration are called *core electrons.*

When *p, d,* and *f* orbitals are partially filled, another detail of electronic configuration arises. For example, with C ($1s^22s^22p^2$) there are two electrons in the $2p$ orbitals. In the ground state, both electrons do not occupy the same *p* orbital; rather the configuration is $1s^22s^22p_x{}^12p_y{}^1$. The spins of the two $2p$ electrons are in the same direction, indicated as

$$\text{C } (2p \text{ levels}) \qquad \underline{\uparrow}\ \underline{\uparrow}\ \underline{\ \ }$$

The electrons occupy different *p* orbitals in order to avoid the interelectron repulsion that arises if they are in the same orbital. When there are four electrons in a *p* level, as with oxygen, electron pairing in one *p* orbital must occur:

$$\text{O } (2p \text{ levels}) \qquad \underline{\uparrow\downarrow}\ \underline{\uparrow}\ \underline{\uparrow}$$

Similar effects occur in the configurations of other atoms with partially filled *d* and *f* orbitals.

Fig. 11-16 shows the relationship of the periodic table to the electronic configuration of the elements. Each horizontal row *(period)* starts with an element that has an ns^1 configuration. The first three periods, H to He, Li to Ne, and Na to Ar, contain two, eight, and eight elements, respectively. The fourth period (beginning with K) and the fifth period (beginning with Rb) each contain 18 elements. The last two periods (beginning with Cs and Fr) are long periods that can contain 32 elements each. The period beginning with Fr is incomplete to date. The elements whose outer configurations are of the *ns* or *nsnp* types are called *representative* elements. Those elements that arise through the filling of *d* orbitals are called *outer transition* metals, and those characterized by the filling of *f* orbitals are called *inner transition* metals (that is, the *lanthanide* and *actinide* series).

In general, the elements in a given vertical row *(group)* have the same valence-shell electron configurations, which is why they have strongly similar chemistries.

GROUP ELECTRONIC CONFIGURATIONS

Group I		*Group VII*	
Li	$[He]2s^1$	F	$[He]2s^22p^5$
Na	$[Ne]3s^1$	Cl	$[Ne]3s^23p^5$
K	$[Ar]4s^1$	Br	$[Ar]3d^{10}4s^24p^5$
Rb	$[Kr]5s^1$	I	$[Kr]4d^{10}5s^25p^5$
Cs	$[Xe]6s^1$	At	$[Xe]4f^{14}5d^{10}6s^26p^5$
Fr	$[Rn]7s^1$		

	IA	IIA													IIIA	IVA	VA	VIA	VIIA	0
1s	1 H																			2 He
2s	3 Li	4 Be												2p	5 B	6 C	7 N	8 O	9 F	10 Ne
3s	11 Na	12 Mg												3p	13 Al	14 Si	15 P	16 S	17 Cl	18 Ar
4s	19 K	20 Ca	3d	21 Sc	22 Ti	23 V	24 Cr	25 Mn	26 Fe	27 Co	28 Ni	29 Cu	30 Zn	4p	31 Ga	32 Ge	33 As	34 Se	35 Br	36 Kr
5s	37 Rb	38 Sr	4d	39 Y	40 Zr	41 Nb	42 Mo	43 Tc	44 Ru	45 Rh	46 Pd	47 Ag	48 Cd	5p	49 In	50 Sn	51 Sb	52 Te	53 I	54 Xe
6s	55 Cs	56 Ba	5d	57 La	72 Hf	73 Ta	74 W	75 Re	76 Os	77 Ir	78 Pt	79 Au	80 Hg	6p	81 Tl	82 Pb	83 Bi	84 Po	85 At	86 Rn
7s	87 Fr	88 Ra	6d	89 Ac	104									7p						

4f	58 Ce	59 Pr	60 Nd	61 Pm	62 Sm	63 Eu	64 Gd	65 Tb	66 Dy	67 Ho	68 Er	69 Tm	70 Yb	71 Lu
5f	90 Th	91 Pa	92 U	93 Np	94 Pu	95 Am	96 Cm	97 Bk	98 Cf	99 Es	100 Fm	101 Md	102 No	103 Lw

Fig. 11-16. Grouping of elements in periodic table based on similarities in valence-shell-electron configurations.

The variation of the relative energies of orbitals is responsible for the detailed electronic structural features shown in Table 11-4. Several important features of the electronic configurations should be noted. For potassium, the electronic configuration is $1s^2 2s^2 2p^6 3s^2 3p^6 4s^1$. The $4s$ level is highest in energy, but still lower than the $3d$ level. When two more electrons are added, to yield Sc(Z = 21), the levels rearrange and the $3d$ level becomes lower than the $4s$ level, as shown in Table 11-4. Another irregularity is seen in the electronic configuration of Cr. Instead of the expected $[Ne]3d^4 4s^2$ configuration, the $[Ne]3d^5 4s^1$ configuration is found. The observed configuration has a maximum number of unpaired electrons in the valence shell. This demonstrates the important general principle that half-filled and completely filled shells have enhanced stability.

11.5 PERIODIC PROPERTIES

An examination of the properties of the elements reveals trends related to the positions of the elements in the periodic table. Those properties that show periodic behavior are called periodic properties. Some examples are atomic radii, ionic radii, densities, ionization potentials, electron affinities, oxidation states, melting points, boiling points, and magnetic behavior.

Atomic size

We cannot measure the size of individual isolated atoms, but we can determine their size in the solid state by x-ray crystallographic analysis of single crystals of the elements. Ideally, we consider the van der Waals radius as the true size of an atom, but there are problems in so doing. Many elements form metallic crystals, some occur only in molecular crystals (for example, I_2), and some occur as covalent network systems (for example, carbon). These differences in bond types affect interatomic distances, making it difficult to establish a comparable scale for all elements. It is necessary to determine the size that is most representative of the true atom size. Thus, bond order, bond type (single or multiple), degree of ionic bonding, covalent or metallic character, oxidation number, crystal structure, and so on are all pertinent variables that affect the measured radii of atoms. In Fig. 11-17, values of atomic radii corrected for these effects are shown.

Trends in atomic size (Fig. 11-17) that parallel the positioning of the atoms in the periodic table are apparent. In a given group, for example group I, the size increases in moving down the group. Each member is larger than the one above it because as we go down the group, electrons go into successively higher n levels. For Li, the valence electrons are in the small, low energy, $2s$ orbital; for Fr, the outer electrons are in the large, diffuse, higher energy, $7s$ orbital. In general, as we go from left to right across a period, the atomic size decreases. The nuclear

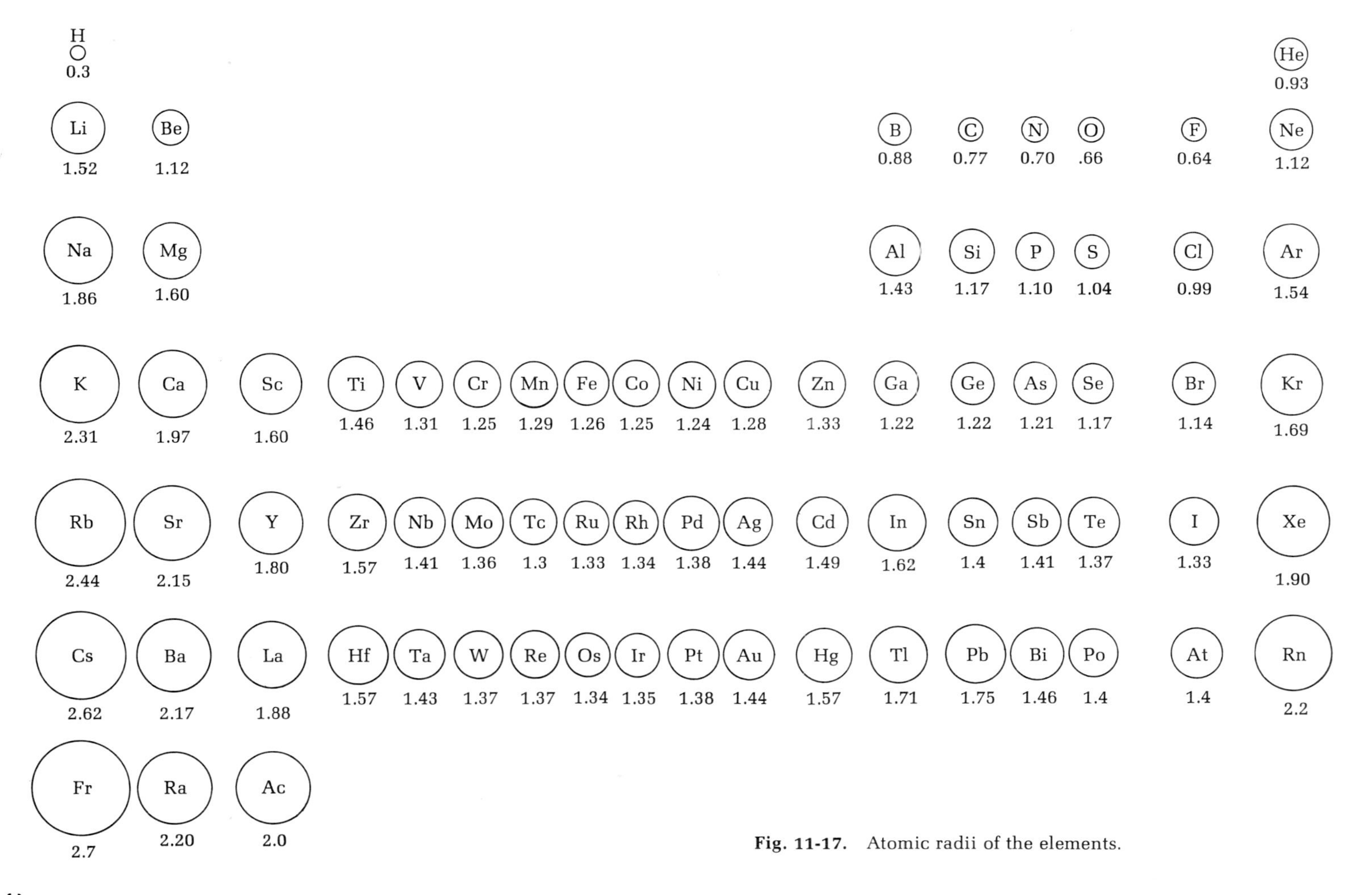

Fig. 11-17. Atomic radii of the elements.

charge increases by one at each step. The valence-shell electrons, subject to this increasing nuclear charge, are drawn progressively closer to the nucleus, and hence the atomic size decreases.

Ionization energies

The ionization energy is the quantity of energy required to remove to infinity an electron from an isolated gaseous atom. The first electron to be removed is described by

$$M(\mathrm{g}) \rightarrow M^{+}(\mathrm{g}) + \mathrm{e}^{-} \tag{11.47}$$

where M(g) represents a gaseous atom of element M. Equation 11.47 describes the first ionization step, with energy I_1. If a second electron is removed

$$M^{+}(\mathrm{g}) \rightarrow M^{2+}(\mathrm{g}) + \mathrm{e}^{-} \tag{11.48}$$

Table 11-5. IONIZATION ENERGIES (kcal/mole)

Atomic no.	*Element*	I_1	I_2	*Atomic no.*	*Element*	I_1	I_2
1	H	313.5		28	Ni	176.0	418.6
2	He	566.9	1254	29	Cu	178.1	467.9
3	Li	124.3	1744	30	Zn	216.6	414.2
4	Be	214.9	419.9	31	Ga	138.4	473.0
5	B	191.3	580.0	32	Ge	181.7	367
6	C	259.6	562	33	As	226.2	466
7	N	335.1	682	34	Se	224.8	496
8	O	314.0	810.6	35	Br	273.0	498
9	F	401.8	807	36	Kr	322.7	566.4
10	Ne	497.2	947.2	37	Rb	96.3	634
11	Na	118.5	1091	38	Sr	131.3	254.3
12	Mg	176.3	347	39	Y	147	282.1
13	Al	138.0	434	40	Zr	158	302.8
14	Si	187.9	376.8	41	Nb	158.7	320.4
15	P	243.3	453.2	42	Mo	164	362.5
16	S	238.9	540	43	Tc	168	342.9
17	Cl	300.0	548.9	44	Ru	169.8	382.7
18	Ar	363.4	637	45	Rh	172	367.1
19	K	100.1	733.6	46	Pd	192	447.9
20	Ca	140.9	273.8	47	Ag	174.7	495.4
21	Sc	151.3	297.3	48	Cd	207.4	389.9
22	Ti	158	314.3	49	In	133.4	435.0
23	U	155	337.8	50	Sn	169.3	337.4
24	Cr	156.0	380.3	51	Sb	199.2	438.1
25	Mn	171.4	360.7	52	Te	208	495.8
26	Fe	182	373.2	53	I	241.1	438.1
27	Co	181	393.2	54	Xe	279.7	489

we obtain a second ionization energy, I_2. First and second ionization energies for the first 54 elements are shown in Table 11-5. A plot of the first ionization potential as a function of Z is shown in Fig. 11-18. Since we are dealing with gaseous atoms, the I_1 values represent the minimum energy necessary to remove an electron from an atom.

Examination of Fig. 11-18 reveals that there are general periodic relationships among the I_1 values that parallel the electronic configurations of the atoms. The I_1 values for the rare gases are highest for any given period. The high I_1 values arise because the rare gases are the last members of their periods; they have the highest effective nuclear charge acting on their valence electrons. The alkali metals have the lowest I_1 values in a given period because they have only one electron in the outermost shell; they have the lowest effective nuclear charge acting on their valence electron since the core electrons effectively shield the nuclear charge.

In addition to general trends, we see details known as "fine structure." As an example, let us examine the elements in the Li to Ne period.

Lithium has the lowest I_1 value. Beryllium is slightly higher, a feature we can attribute to increased effective nuclear charge. Unexpectedly, Boron lies a little lower than Be. The electronic configuration of B is $1s^2 2s^2 2p$. Its surprisingly low I_1 indicates that the $2p$ electron is easier to remove (higher in energy) than the $2s$ electron. This can be explained in terms of relative screening effects. Because

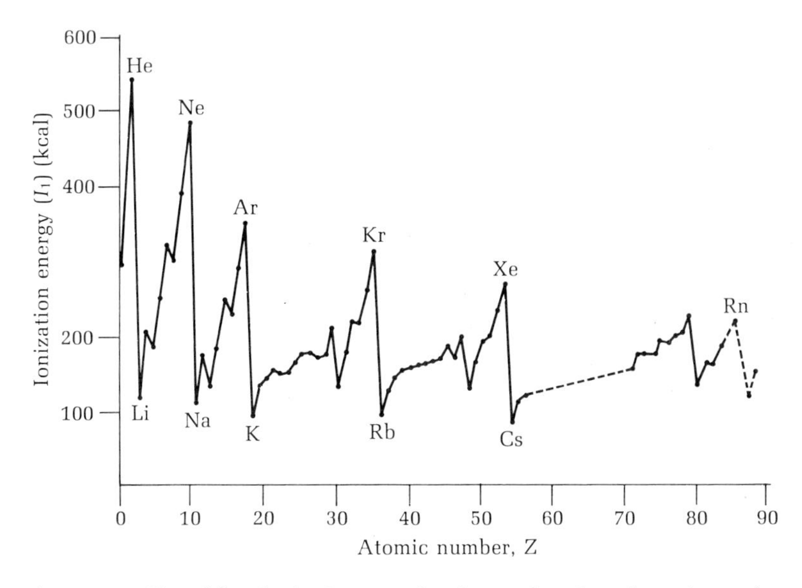

Fig. 11-18. Plot of first ionization energies, I_1, as a function of atomic number.

the $2s$ electron penetrates the $1s$ core more than the $2p$ electron does, it is subject to a higher effective nuclear charge.

Addition of the second and third electrons at carbon and nitrogen is accompanied by increased I values due to increased nuclear charge. I_1 decreases at oxygen. Since two electrons are in one p orbital (configuration = [He]$2s^22p^4$), they repel each other and lower the ionization potential.

Oxidation states

The common oxidation states of the representative and transition elements are shown in Fig. 11-19. A high correlation between the oxidation states of an element and its position in the periodic table may be recognized. For the representative elements, the oxidation states are related to electronic configuration by two rules:

1. In forming ions or compounds, the representative elements of the first, second, and third periods always gain or lose electrons so as to reach the rare-gas electronic configuration of He[$1s^2$], Ne[$1s^22s^22p^6$], or Ar[$1s^22s^22p^63s^23p^6$].
2. When several oxidation states occur for a given element, they generally differ by two units because electrons tend to be gained or lost in pairs.

The group IA elements have outer electronic configurations of ns^1. Because of their low ionization energies, they readily lose the ns^1 electron, yielding the 1+ oxidation state. Group IIA elements have ns^2 configurations and ionize to form 2+ states. Group IIIA elements, with ns^2np^1 configurations, most readily lose or share all three electrons to form 3+ states. However, in some cases only one electron (the np^1) is involved, and the 1+ state arises. Group IVA elements, with ns^2np^2 configurations, achieve stable configurations by losing two or four electrons to achieve 2+ or 4+ oxidation states, respectively. However, with carbon, which can bond to less electronegative atoms such as hydrogen, negative formal oxidation states such as 4− are possible. The group VA elements, with ns^2np^3 configurations, exist in 5+ and 3+ states, and can add three electrons to give the 3− state. Group VIA elements, with ns^2np^4 configurations, yield, except for O, a series of oxidation states, 6+, 4+, 2+, and 2−. With O, the 2− state predominates. However, when bonded to F, oxygen can be in positive oxidation states. Group VIIA elements, with ns^2np^5 configurations, are only 1 electron from rare-gas configurations and commonly form the 1− state. The only oxidation state of importance for F is the 1− state because no element is more electronegative. For the other halogens, with lower electronegativities, formal positive oxidation states of 7+, 5+, 3+, and 1+ can be attained.

The common oxidation states of the transition metal elements are shown in Fig. 11-19, *B*. The periodic nature of the oxidation states is less apparent for these elements than for the representative elements. For the first transition metal series,

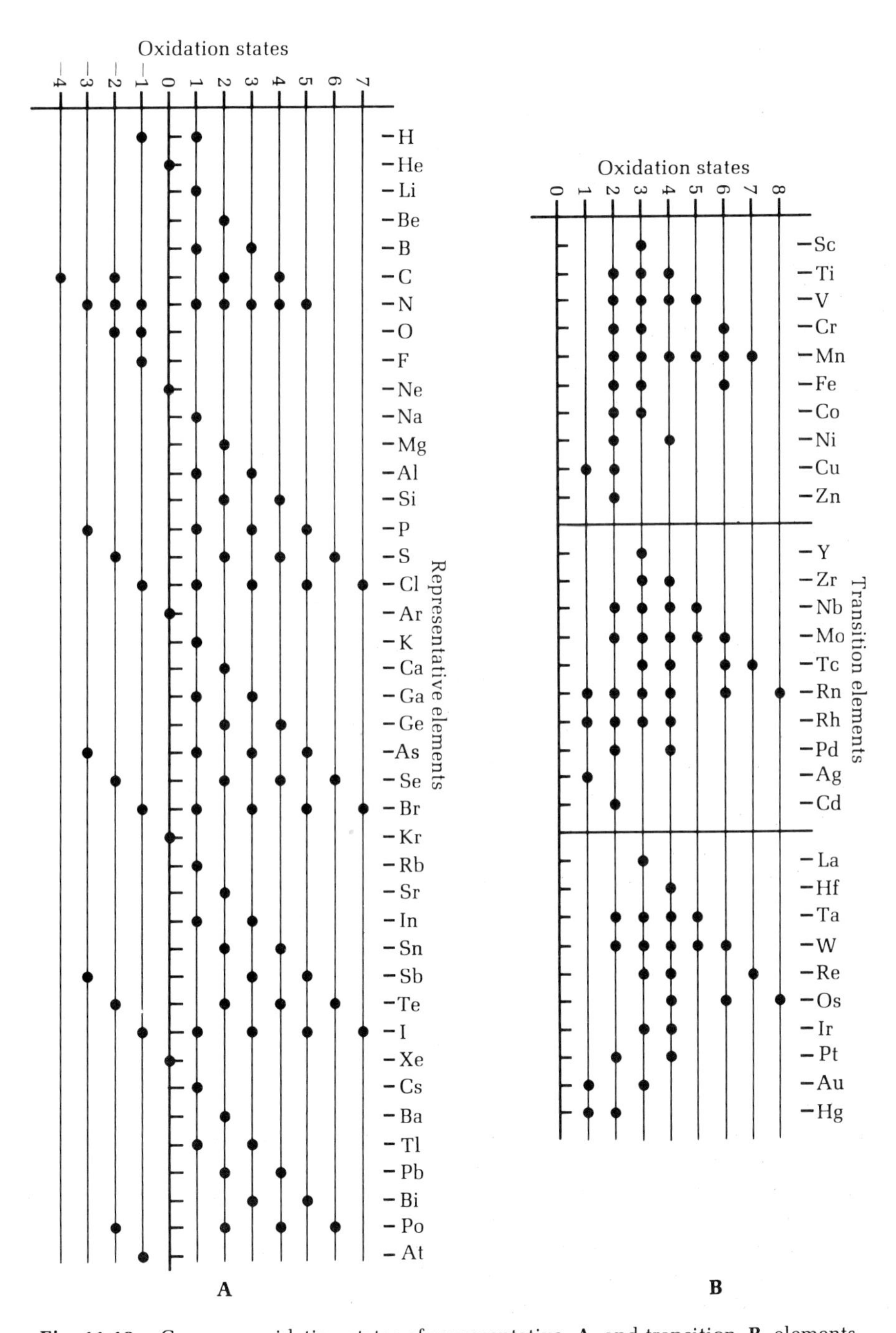

Fig. 11-19. Common oxidation states of representative, **A**, and transition, **B**, elements.

all except scandium show and 2+ state. This occurs because the $4s^2$ electrons are readily lost as a pair. The highest oxidation state that any of these elements can exhibit entails the loss of all its valence electrons, that is: Sc^{3+}, Ti^{4+}, V^{5+}, Cr^{2+}, Mn^{2+}. Elements in the later half of each period rarely reach this maximum oxidation number. A more complete explanation of the trends requires a more detailed look at bonding in transition-metal complexes and goes beyond our interest here.

PROBLEMS

1. What is the minimum wavelength of light that will ionize sodium atoms if the energy of ionization is 118.5 kcal/mole?
2. Write the expression for the Hamiltonian operator for the He^+ ion.
3. Write the Schrödinger equation for the H^- ion.
4. Calculate the energy in ergs of the first two energy levels of a particle in a box for (a) an electron in a box 1.0 Å long; (b) a billiard ball of mass 100 g in a box 1 m long.
5. Which of the following wave functions are satisfactory solutions to the problem of the particle in the box?
   (a) $\psi = A \cos \alpha x$
   (b) $\psi = A \cos \alpha x + B \sin \alpha x$
   (c) $\psi = Ae^{i\alpha x}$ $(i = \sqrt{-1})$
   (d) $\psi = Ae^{\alpha x}$
6. Using equation 11.30, find the values of x where the probability of finding an electron in a box of length L will be a maximum for $n = 1$, 2, and 3.
7. From tables of integrals, solve equation 11.27.
8. From equation 11.38, calculate the first two energy levels of the H_2 molecule. What wave length of light corresponds to the energy difference between these first two levels?
9. For the $2s$ state of the H atom, calculate the value of σ where the radial part of the wave function is at a maximum. Does this value of σ correspond to the position of highest probability of locating the electron?
10. Find the normalization constant, A, for the H-atom wave function

$$\psi_1 = Ae^{-\sigma/2}, \quad \sigma = \frac{2r}{a_0}$$

using

$$\int_0^\infty \psi_1^2\, 4\pi r^2\, dr = 1$$

11. Making use of Table 11-2, show that the linear combination of a $2p_x$ orbital and a $2p_y$ orbital gives an orbital with an electronic distribution $[\psi^2(p_x) + \psi^2(p_y)]$ that is cylindrically symmetric about the z axis.
12. Show that the linear combination of $2p_x$, $2p_y$, and $2p_z$ orbitals gives an orbital of spherical electron distribution. [See problem 11.]
13. Calculate the nodal distances from the nucleus for the $3s$ orbital. Refer to Table 11-1.
14. What is the degeneracy of $3s$, $3p$, and $3d$ orbitals?
15. Write ground-state electronic configurations for (a) Mg; (b) Na^+; (c) Sb; (d) V^+; (e) Se^{2-}.
16. Which of the following atoms or ions in the ground state would be expected to have

spherical electron distributions? (a) Rb^+; (b) C^+; (c) C^-; (d) Cr^{3+}; (e) Mn^{2+}; (f) Gd; (g) Pb^{2+}.

17. From Fig. 11-17, cite evidence that half-filled shells of *p* or *d* orbitals have extra stability.
18. From the periodic properties of the elements, predict which species in the following groups is largest. (a) O, O^{2-}, F^-; (b) C, N, O; (c) Cu, Ag, Au; (d) Ne, Na, Mg; (e) Tl, Tl^+, Tl^{3+}; (f) La, Eu, Lu.
19. Explain why the difference between the first and second ionization energies of Na is so much larger than the corresponding difference for Mg.

12 THE CHEMICAL BOND

In Chapter 2 we examined bonding in ionic solids. We saw that the basis for ionic bonding lies in simple coulombic forces among the ions. We now turn to an examination of covalent and metallic bonding, which arise when electrons are shared among a group of atoms. To examine the theory of these bonds, we again use the ideas of quantum mechanics. We will discuss how the Schrödinger equation can be written for simple molecules. The solutions of these problems provide the basis for the discussion of more complex systems.

12.1 THE H_2^+ MOLECULE ION

The simplest covalently bonded molecule ion is H_2^+. It is simple because it has only one electron and two proton nuclei. To describe it we use the coordinate positions of the two nuclei and the electron as shown in Fig. 12-1. Nuclei A and B are positioned on the z axis at a distance R_{A-B} apart. The position of the electron is r_A from A and r_B from B. The Hamiltonian $\mathscr{H}$ for this system, following the procedures shown in Chapter 11, includes the kinetic energy and potential energy terms as

$$\mathscr{H} = -\frac{\hbar^2}{2m}\nabla^2 - \frac{\hbar^2}{2M_A}\nabla_A{}^2 - \frac{\hbar^2}{2M_B}\nabla_B{}^2 - \frac{e^2}{r_A} - \frac{e^2}{r_B} + \frac{e^2}{R_{A-B}} \tag{12.1}$$

where ∇^2 applies to the coordinates of the electron. Again we face the task of solving the Schrödinger equation with this Hamiltonian. We seek the set of wave functions ψ_n for the energy states E_n of the molecule.

We assume the nuclei are fixed, thereby eliminating the two kinetic energy terms with masses M_A and M_B. This is a reasonable approximation since the mass of the electron is much smaller than the masses of the nuclei. With this approximation the problem can be mathematically solved. We find that the electron can occupy a set of wave-function states called *molecular orbitals.* These orbitals are analogous to the atomic orbitals that arise as solutions to the H-atom problem.

The energies of the two lowest-energy orbitals are found to depend on the dis-

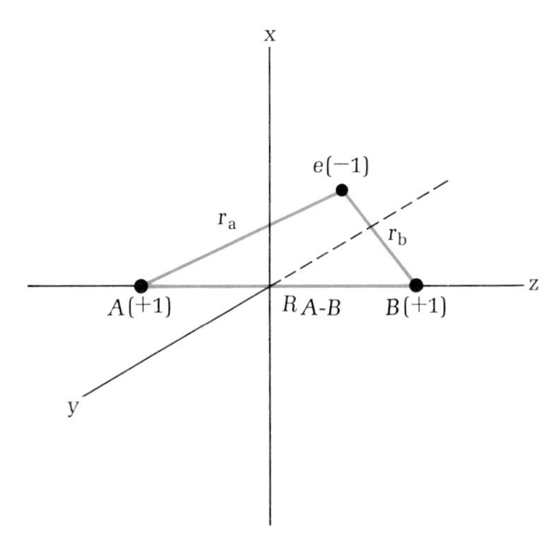

Fig. 12-1. Coordinate system for electron and two nuclei of H_2^+ molecule ion.

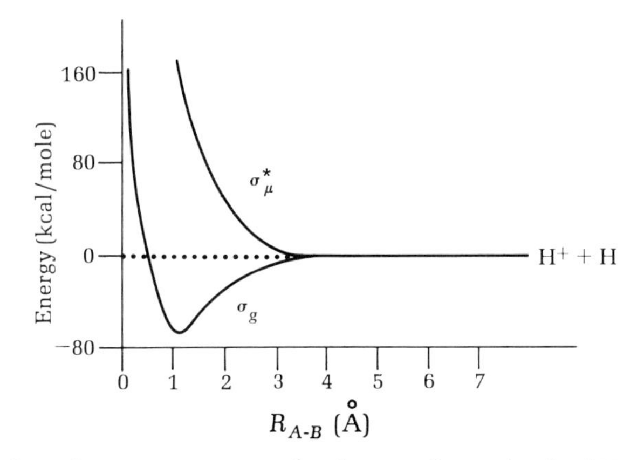

Fig. 12-2. Plots of energy versus R_{A-B} for the σ_g and $\sigma_\mu{}^*$ orbitals of H_2^+ molecule ion.

tance of nuclear separation R_{A-B} (Fig. 12-2). The lowest-energy orbital is termed the σ_g orbital. It reaches a minimum energy at an internuclear distance of about 1 Å. An H_2^+ molecule whose electron is in the σ_g state will be a stable molecule with an internuclear distance of 1 Å. The σ_g orbital is called a *bonding orbital.* Since it is the lowest-energy orbital, it is also called the *ground-state orbital.* The next orbital is designated $\sigma_\mu{}^*$. The energy of this orbital only increases with decreasing R_{A-B}. An H_2^+ molecule whose electron is in the $\sigma_\mu{}^*$ orbital is unstable and dissociates. Therefore, the $\sigma_\mu{}^*$ is an *antibonding* orbital, as designated by the asterisk (*).

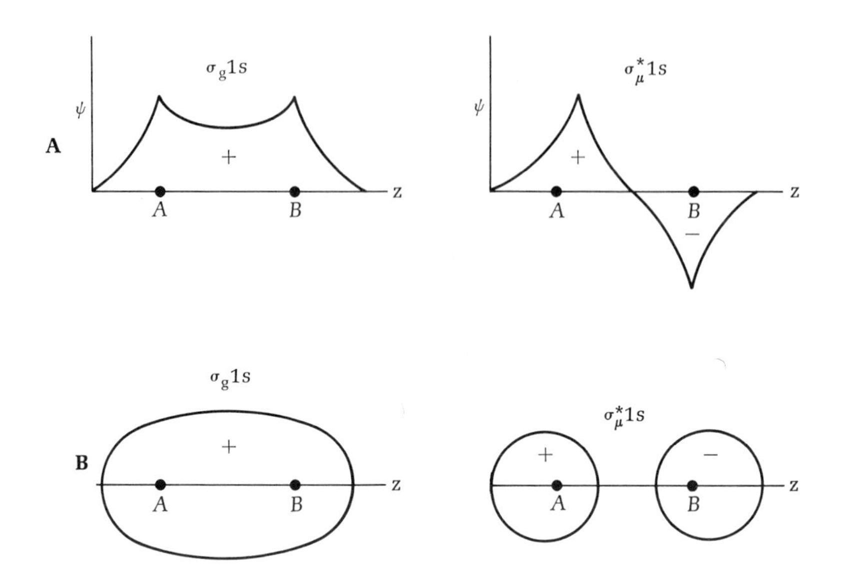

Fig. 12-3. **A,** Values of wave functions of σ_g and $\sigma_\mu{}^*$ orbital states along z (internuclear) axis. **B,** Cross-sectional representation in two-dimensions (x-z plane) of 90% contour for σ_g and $\sigma_\mu{}^*$ orbital states.

The notation used for molecular orbitals requires some explanation. The orbitals are designated by Greek letters. Analogous to the notation used for atomic orbitals, *s*, *p*, and *d*, molecular orbitals are denoted by σ, π, and δ. All σ orbitals have *cylindrical* symmetry about the internuclear axis, which means that rotation about this axis has no effect on the wave function of the orbital. The wave functions of the σ_g and $\sigma_\mu{}^*$ orbitals are shown in Fig. 12-3. The subscripts g and μ refer to a symmetry property of the orbital called *inversion*. Inversion is the process of taking all points of a system through its center to opposite distant positions (Fig. 12-4). The molecular orbital wave functions are characterized by positive and negative regions. Upon inversion, the σ_g orbital remains unchanged, whereas the $\sigma_\mu{}^*$ orbital changes sign.

The probability ψ^2 of locating the electron in space depends on which molecular orbital the electron is in. The electron-density contours for the σ_g and $\sigma_\mu{}^*$ orbitals are shown in Fig. 12-5. The bonding orbital shows a higher electron density between the two nuclei than the antibonding orbital does. In fact, ψ^2 for the antibonding orbital goes to zero midway between the nuclei.

Solution of the Schrödinger equation for $H_2{}^+$ also include molecular orbitals with higher energies. In the next section, we shall see that the most convenient way to describe their properties is by approximately representing them with atomic orbitals.

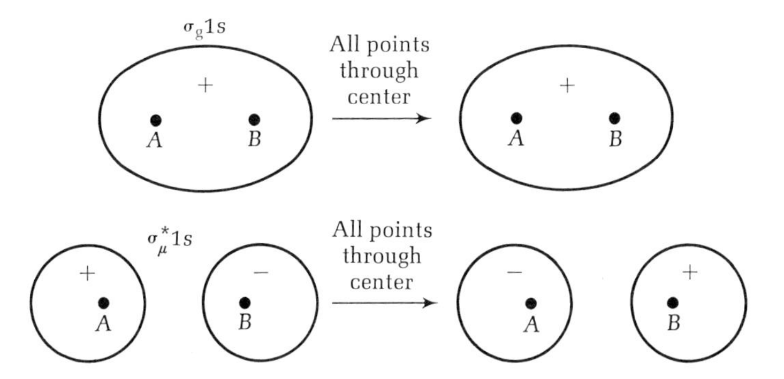

Fig. 12-4. Effect of inversion on σ_g and $\sigma_\mu{}^*$ orbitals.

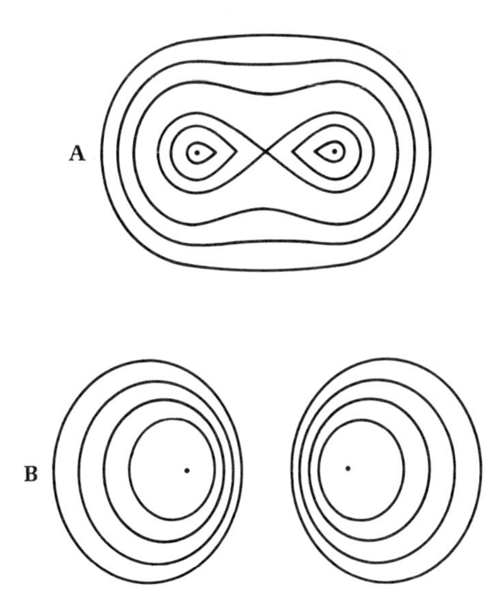

Fig. 12-5. Contour diagrams of ψ^2 for $\sigma_g 1s$, **A**, and $\sigma_\mu{}^* 1s$, **B**, orbitals. Contour line represents given electron density. Electron density highest at nuclei.

12.2 MOLECULAR ORBITALS FROM LINEAR COMBINATION OF ATOMIC ORBITALS

The equations for molecular orbitals are precise but complex mathematical functions. An extremely useful method for approximating molecular orbitals is known as the Linear Combination of Atomic Orbitals (LCAO). Using this method, we represent molecular orbitals by the sum of appropriate atomic orbitals.

A combination of two atomic orbitals will provide a reasonable representation of a particular molecular orbital. For example, the lowest-energy molecular orbital of H_2^+, σ_g, can be approximated by the sum of atomic orbitals $1s_A + 1s_B$, where $1s_A$ is the $1s$ atomic orbital on atom A and $1s_B$ is the $1s$ atomic orbital on atom B. The combination of these atomic orbitals is shown in Fig. 12-6, A. This combination compares favorably with the σ_g molecular orbital shown in Figure 12-4 and is therefore designated the $\sigma_g 1s$ molecular orbital. The combination obtained by subtraction, $1s_A - 1s_B$, gives a result approximating the $\sigma_\mu{}^*$ molecular orbital, as shown in Fig. 12-6, B. The orbital is designated $\sigma_\mu{}^*1s$.

Additional combinations of pairs of atomic orbitals yield approximate representations of higher-energy molecular orbitals. Some of these combinations are shown below and in Fig. 12-7. The sum of two $2p_z$ orbitals, $2p_{zA} + 2p_{zB}$, gives a σ orbital called the $\sigma_\mu{}^*2p_z$ molecular orbital. As seen in Fig. 12-7, this combination causes a cancellation of the value of the wave function between the two nuclei. This gives a less stable orbital than if these atomic wave functions reinforced each other in

MOLECULAR ORBITALS FROM LINEAR COMBINATION OF ATOMIC ORBITALS

LCAO function	*MO designation*	*LCAO function*	*MO designation*
$1s_A + 1s_B$	$\sigma_g 1s$	$2p_{zA} + 2p_{zB}$	$\sigma_\mu{}^*2p_z$
$1s_A - 1s_B$	$\sigma_\mu{}^*1s$	$2p_{xA} + 2p_{xB}$	$\pi_\mu 2p_x$
$2s_A + 2s_B$	$\sigma_g 2s$	$2p_{xA} - 2p_{xB}$	$\pi_g^* 2p_x$
$2s_A - 2s_B$	$\sigma_\mu{}^*2s$	$2p_{yA} + 2p_{yB}$	$\pi_\mu 2p_y$
$2p_{zA} - 2p_{zB}$	$\sigma_g 2p_z$	$2p_{yA} - 2p_{yB}$	$\pi_g^* 2p_y$

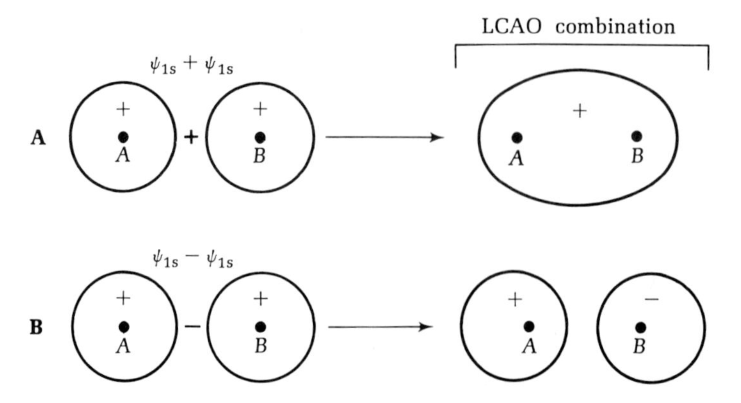

Fig. 12-6. Representation of molecular orbitals by combinations of atomic orbitals. **A,** $\psi_{1s} + \psi_{1s}$ gives $\sigma_g 1s$ orbital. **B,** $\psi_{1s} - \psi_{1s}$ gives $\sigma_\mu{}^*1s$ orbital.

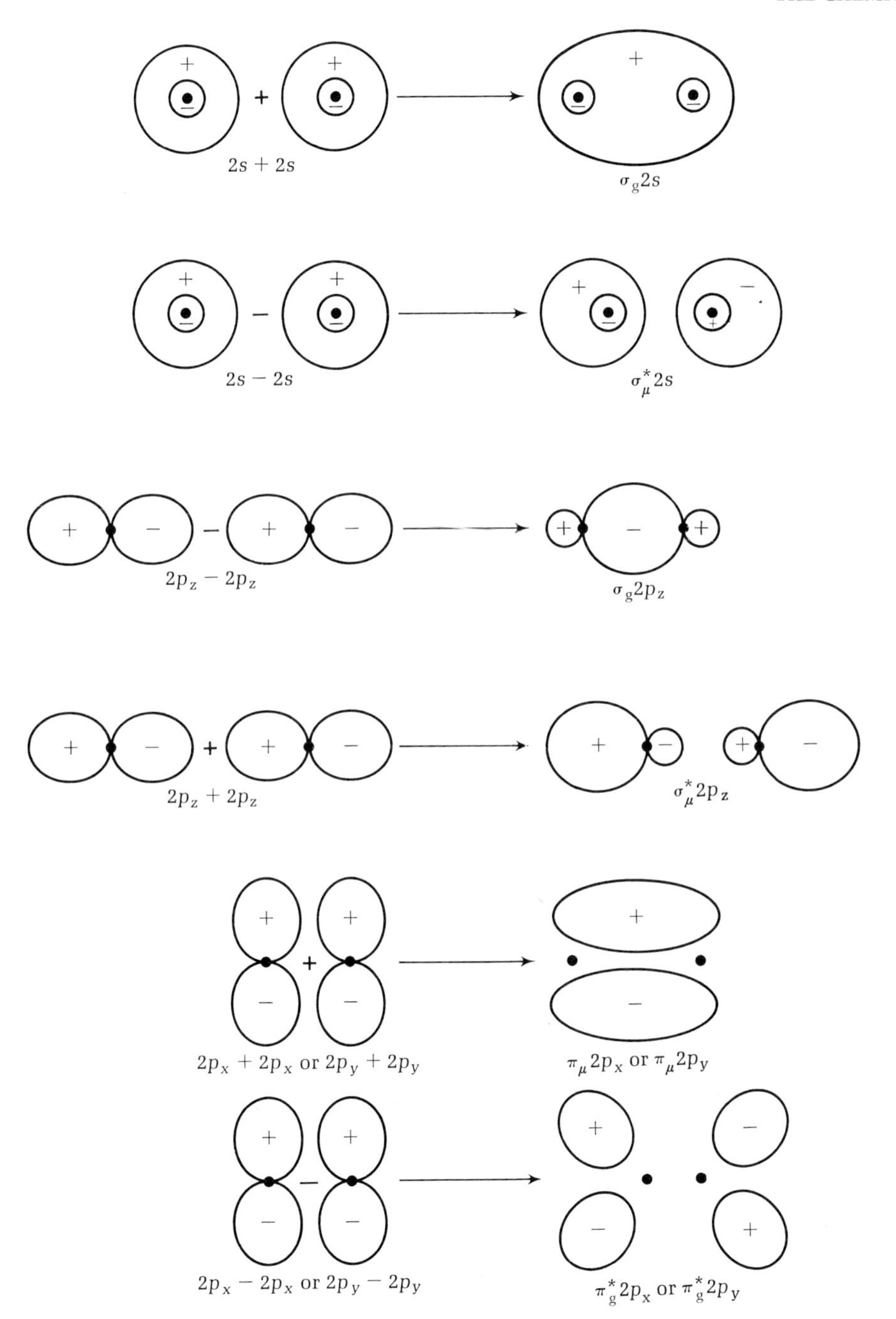

Fig. 12-7. Representation of molecular orbitals by combination of atomic orbitals. 2s + 2s gives $\sigma_g 2s$; 2s − 2s gives $\sigma_\mu{}^* 2s$. $2p_z - 2p_z$ gives $\sigma_g 2p_z$; $2p_z + 2p_z$ gives $\sigma_\mu{}^* 2p_z$; $2p_x + 2p_x$ or $2p_y + 2p_y$ gives $\pi_\mu 2p_x$ or $\pi_\mu 2p_y$; $2p_x - 2p_x$ or $2p_y - 2p_y$ gives $\pi_g{}^* 2p_x$ or $\pi_g{}^* 2p_y$.

the region between nuclei. The subtracted case, $2p_{zA} - 2p_{zB}$, gives an approximation for what is called the $\sigma_g 2p_z$ molecular orbital. In this case, the atomic wave functions reinforce in the region between the nuclei and give a more stable, or lower-energy, molecular orbital. The symmetry properties of the orbital relative to inversion are labeled appropriately with subscripts μ and g. It should be noted that combinations of $2p_z$ atomic orbitals result in molecular orbitals with cylindrical symmetry about the internuclear axis, z. This is the characteristic feature of a σ orbital.

The sum of two $2p_x$ orbitals, $2p_{xA} + 2p_{xB}$, gives a molecular orbital denoted by $\pi_\mu 2p_x$, and the difference, $2p_{xA} - 2p_{xB}$, gives the molecular orbital $\pi_g{}^* 2p_x$. These two orbitals do not have cylindrical symmetry about the internuclear axis. They are called π orbitals. The orbital with lower energy, $\pi_\mu 2p_x$, has a larger wave-function value in the region between the nuclei than the $\pi_g 2p_x$, orbital does. The $\pi_\mu 2p_x$ orbital is the bonding orbital. An analogous pair of π orbitals, oriented in the y direction and obtained by $2p_{yA} + 2p_{yB}$ and $2p_{yA} - 2p_{yB}$, are denoted $\pi_\mu 2p_y$ and $\pi_g{}^* 2p_x$.

This LCAO process can be used to represent higher-energy orbitals of an increasingly complex form. However, for our purposes in discussing chemical bonds, the above molecular orbitals will suffice.

12.3 BONDING IN DIATOMIC MOLECULES

We will now apply the results obtained from the description of the H_2^+ ion to a group of more complicated molecules, such as H_2, N_2, O_2, CO, and their ions, which have two nuclei but more than one electron.

The hydrogen molecule

The hydrogen molecule consists of two electrons and two nuclei (Fig. 12-8). The Hamiltonian can be written much as it was for the H_2^+ ion, with the addition of terms for the second electron. If we assume the nuclear positions are fixed, then the Hamiltonian is

$$\mathscr{H} = -\frac{\hbar^2}{2m}(\nabla_1{}^2 + \nabla_2{}^2) - \frac{e^2}{r_{A-1}} - \frac{e^2}{r_{A-2}} - \frac{e^2}{r_{B-1}} - \frac{e^2}{r_{B-2}} + \frac{e^2}{r_{1-2}} + \frac{e^2}{r_{A-B}} \qquad (12.2)$$

The Schrödinger equation is

$$\left[-\frac{\hbar^2}{2m}(\nabla_1{}^2 + \nabla_2{}^2) - \frac{e^2}{r_{A-1}} - \frac{e^2}{r_{A-2}} - \frac{e^2}{r_{B-1}} - \frac{e^2}{r_{B-2}} + \frac{e^2}{r_{1-2}} + \frac{e^2}{r_{A-B}}\right]\psi_n = E_n\psi_n \qquad (12.3)$$

The solution of the Schrödinger equation with this Hamiltonian is difficult due to the presence of the interelectron potential-energy term, e^2/r_{1-2}. This term also caused difficulty in the He-atom problem and again we must resort to approximation methods.

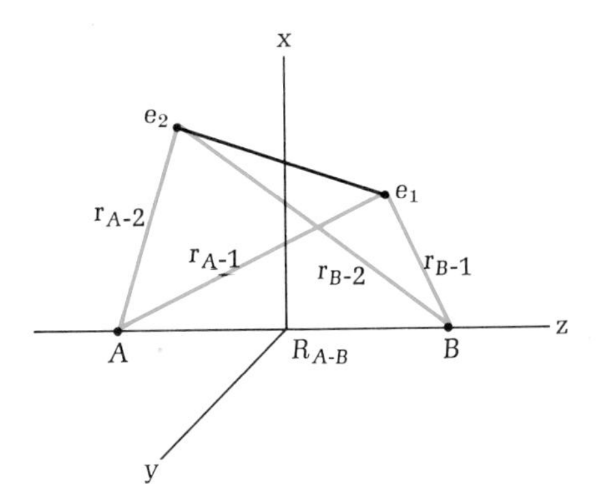

Fig. 12-8. Coordinate system used to describe H_2 molecule. Two nuclei are positioned at A and B, a distance R_{A-B} apart. Two electrons are denoted by e_1 and e_2.

The first approximation is to neglect the term. The remaining terms of equation 12.3 can be separated into two parts, one pertaining to electron 1 and the other part pertaining to electron 2:

$$\left[\left(-\frac{\hbar^2\nabla_1^2}{2m} - \frac{e^2}{r_{A-1}} - \frac{e^2}{r_{B-1}} + \frac{e^2}{R_{A-B}}\right) + \left(-\frac{\hbar^2\nabla_2^2}{2m} - \frac{e^2}{r_{A-2}} - \frac{e^2}{r_{B-2}} + \frac{e^2}{R_{A-B}}\right) - \frac{e^2}{R_{A-B}}\right]\psi_n = E_n\psi_n \tag{12.4}$$

The terms in the parentheses are the same as the Hamiltonian for the H_2^+ ion, equation 12.1. They can be solved separately and combined to give the approximate wave-function and energy solutions for the H_2 molecule. In this approximation each electron is in a state given by H_2^+ molecular orbitals. By the Pauli exclusion principle, two electrons of opposite spin can reside in the same molecular orbital. When the two electrons are in the lowest-energy molecular orbital, the energy minimum of the molecule is −67 kcal at a nuclear separation of 0.850 Å. Experiments have shown that the equilibrium internuclear distance is 0.74 Å and the energy is −110 kcal. Thus, neglecting the r_{1-2} term has a considerable effect. More sophisticated methods are needed to produce better quantitative agreement, but the general qualitative features of bond stability are found with this first approximation.

From precise molecular-orbital calculations one obtains a complete description of the energy levels in H_2^+ and H_2. The two lowest-energy orbitals of H_2^+ and H_2 are shown in Fig. 12-9. The energy levels depend on internuclear distance. The levels shown are for the molecules at the internuclear distance of greatest stability.

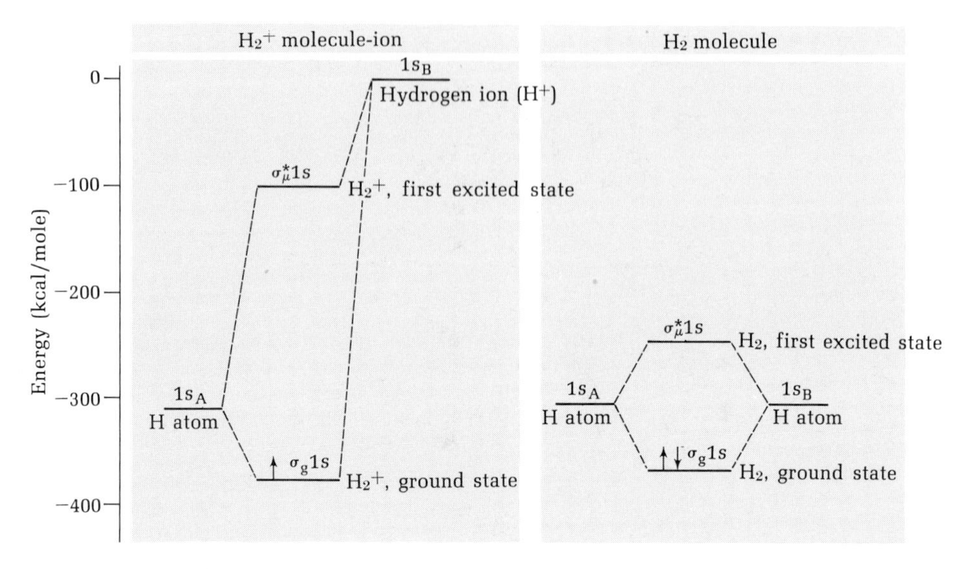

Fig. 12-9. Energy-level diagrams for formation of H_2^+ from H atom plus H^+ ion and of H_2 from H atom plus H atom.

The H_2^+ ion can be formed from an H atom and a proton, which in their separated states have a total energy of −314 kcal. The ground-state ($\sigma_g 1s$) energy of the H_2^+ ion is −381 kcal. Therefore, the bond energy is 67 kcal. The first excited state ($\sigma_\mu{}^* 1s$) of H_2^+ is 284 kcal above the ground state.

The H_2 molecule is formed from two separated H atoms with a total energy of 2×-314 kcal $= -628$ kcal. The ground state $(\sigma_g 1s)^2$ has two electrons with a total energy of 2×-370 kcal $= -740$ kcal. The bond energy is then 112 kcal. The energy level of the first excited state is also 112 kcal above the ground state.

Second-period diatomic molecules

We can now undertake a molecular orbital description of the bonding in the diatomic molecules Li_2, Be_2, B_2, C_2, N_2, O_2, and F_2. The energy-level diagrams for the molecular orbitals of these species are shown in Figs. 12-10 and 12-11. The diagrams in Fig. 12-10 differ from those of Fig. 12-11 in the order of the $\sigma_g 2p_z$ and $\pi_\mu 2p_x$ (or $\pi_\mu 2p_y$) levels. This situation is analogous to the change in order of energy levels in multielectron atoms as compared to the energy-level order for the H atom. There we recognized the effect of different degrees of shielding of nuclear charge on the energy levels. In addition to this charge effect, the energy levels in molecules are sensitive to the internuclear separation.

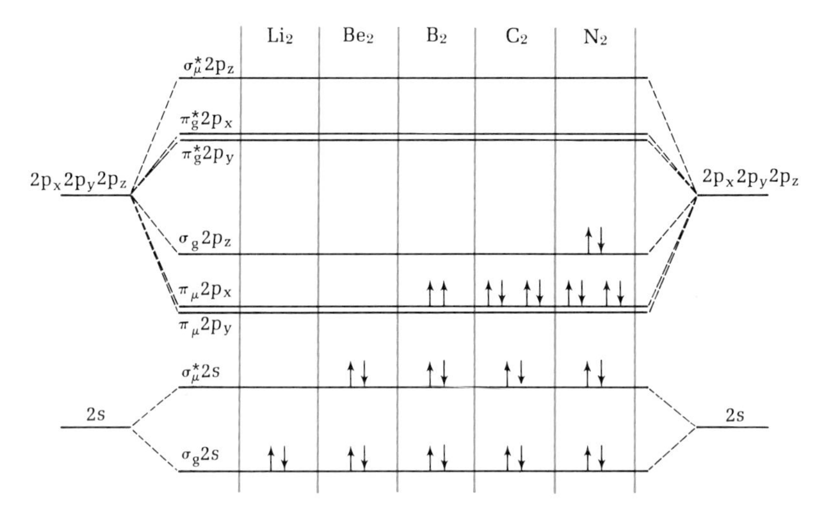

Fig. 12-10. Relative energy-level diagrams for diatomic molecules Li_2, Be_2, B_2, C_2, and N_2. Arrows indicate ground-state electronic configurations of bonding and antibonding orbitals.

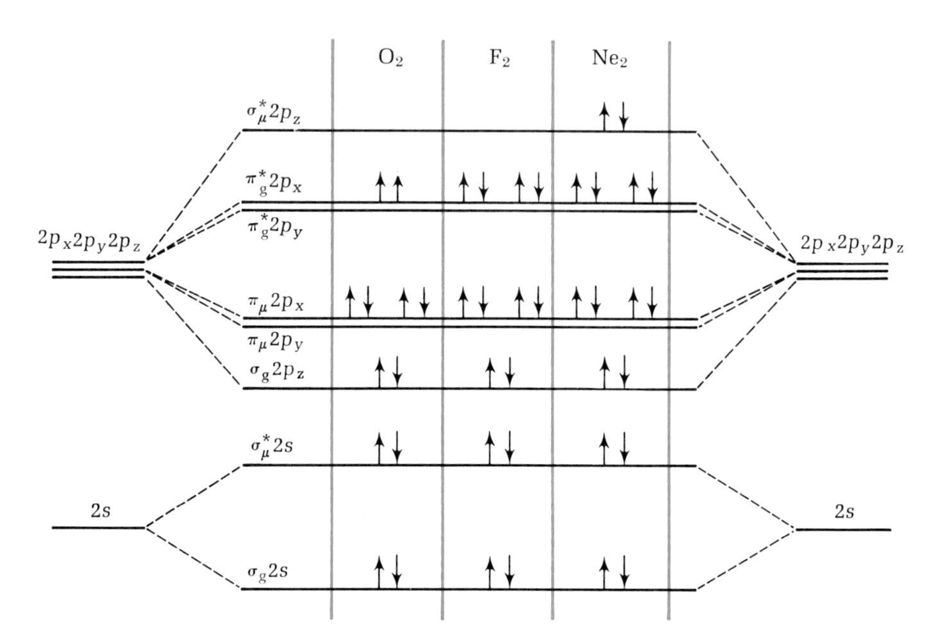

Fig. 12-11. Relative energy-level diagrams for diatomic molecules O_2, F_2, and Ne_2.

For Li_2 to N_2, Fig. 12-10 applies; for O_2 to Ne_2, Fig. 12-11 applies. Note that there are two π and two π^* orbitals with the same energy. These orbitals arose in similar fashion when we considered the LCAO combinations of p ($2p_x$ and $2p_y$) atomic orbitals.

The stability of a given molecule with respect to the separated atoms depends on how the levels are filled. For a molecule to be stable, there must be more electrons in bonding orbitals than in antibonding (*) orbitals. A single covalent bond arises when there are two more electrons in bonding orbitals than in antibonding orbitals. Four excess electrons in bonding orbitals gives a double bond.

With Li_2, there is a total of $2 \times 1 = 2$ valence electrons in molecular orbitals. The orbital of lowest energy is the $\sigma_g 1s$, in which two electrons are located. Each lithium atom has two core electrons in addition to the valence electron. The core electrons are only slightly involved in chemical bond formation and for our purposes will be ignored. Since Li_2 has one excess pair of bonding electrons, it is expected to be stable. This is found to be true experimentally. The bonding in Li_2 is described as a single covalent bond. For Be_2 through N_2, similar patterns arise.

Be_2 has four valence electrons, which would occupy the $\sigma_g 2s$ and $\sigma_\mu{}^* 2s$ orbitals. Since there are no excess bonding electrons, the molecule is predicted to be unstable.

For B_2, with six electrons, the outermost electrons are in $\pi_\mu 2p_x$ and $\pi_\mu 2p_y$ bonding orbitals. Because these two orbitals have equivalent energies, one electron goes into each orbital. Furthermore, the electrons in these two orbitals have the same spin. This is indicated in the diagram by drawing the arrows in the same direction. The B_2 molecule has one excess pair of bonding electrons and, as predicted, is stable.

For C_2, with a total of eight valence electrons, there are four electrons in the $\pi_\mu 2p_x$ and $\pi_\mu 2p_y$ bonding orbitals to give a predicted stable structure with two covalent bonds.

With N_2, there are six electrons in the upper bonding orbitals, $\pi_\mu 2p_x$, $\pi_\mu 2p_y$, and $\sigma_g 2p_z$. Thus, we would expect N_2 to be a stable molecule with three covalent bonds.

For O_2, the effect of the upper six bonding electrons in $\sigma_g 2p_z$, $\pi_\mu 2p_x$ and $\pi_\mu 2p_y$ is in part offset by the two unpaired electrons in $\pi_g{}^* 2p_x$ and $\pi_g{}^* 2p_y$. Thus, there are four excess bonding electrons, giving a stable molecule with a double bond. The unpaired electron spins in the $\pi_g{}^* 2p_x$ and $\pi_g{}^* 2p_y$ orbitals are an important feature in explaining the magnetic properties of oxygen.

The F_2 molecule has two excess bonding electrons, giving a stable molecule with a single covalent bond.

Ne_2, with twelve valence electrons, would have no excess bonding electrons and is thus predicted to be unstable. It has not been observed experimentally. The

Table 12.1. ELECTRONIC CONFIGURATIONS OF SIMPLE DIATOMIC MOLECULES

Molecule	*Configuration*
H_2^+	$(\sigma_g 1s)^1$
H_2	$(\sigma_g 1s)^2$
*He_2	$(\sigma_g 1s)^2(\sigma_\mu^* 1s)^2$
Li_2	$(\sigma_g 1s)^2(\sigma_\mu^* 1s)^2(\sigma_g 2s)^2$
*Be_2	$(\sigma_g 1s)^2(\sigma_\mu^* 1s)^2(\sigma_g 2s)^2(\sigma_\mu^* 2s)^2$
B_2	$(\sigma_g 1s)^2(\sigma_\mu^* 1s)^2(\sigma_g 2s)^2(\sigma_\mu^* 2s)^2(\pi_\mu 2p_x)^1(\pi_\mu 2p_y)^1$
C_2	$(\sigma_g 1s)^2(\sigma_\mu^* 1s)^2(\sigma_g 2s)^2(\sigma_\mu^* 2s)^2(\pi_\mu 2p_x)^2(\pi_\mu 2p_y)^2$
N_2	$(\sigma_g 1s)^2(\sigma_\mu^* 1s)^2(\sigma_g 2s)^2(\sigma_\mu^* 2s)^2(\pi_\mu 2p_x)^2(\pi_\mu 2p_y)^2(\sigma_g 2p_z)^2$
O_2	$(\sigma_g 1s)^2(\sigma_\mu^* 1s)^2(\sigma_g 2s)^2(\sigma_\mu^* 2s)^2(\sigma_g 2p_z)^2(\pi_\mu 2p_x)^2(\pi_\mu 2p_y)^2(\pi_g^* 2p_x)^1(\pi_g^* 2p_y)^1$
F_2	$(\sigma_g 1s)^2(\sigma_\mu^* 1s)^2(\sigma_g 2s)^2(\sigma_\mu^* 2s)^2(\sigma_g 2p_z)^2(\pi_\mu 2p_x)^2(\pi_\mu 2p_y)^2(\pi_g^* 2p_x)^2(\pi_g^* 2p_y)^2$
*Ne_2	$(\sigma_g 1s)^2(\sigma_\mu^* 1s)^2(\sigma_g 2s)^2(\sigma_\mu^* 2s)^2(\sigma_g 2p_z)^2(\pi_\mu 2p_x)^2(\pi_\mu 2p_y)^2(\pi_g^* 2p_x)^2(\pi_g^* 2p_y)^2(\sigma_\mu^* 2p_z)^2$

*These molecules have not been experimentally observed.

Table 12-2. DIATOMIC MOLECULES

Molecule	*Bond energy (kcal/mole)*	*Internuclear distance (Å)*	*Predicted number of covalent bonds*
Li_2	24	2.672	1
Be_2	Not observed		0
B_2	69	1.589	1
C_2	136	1.2422	2
N_2	222	1.09	3
O_2	117	1.207	2
F_2	37	1.435	1
Ne_2	Not observed		0

detailed electronic configurations of the above diatomic molecules are summarized in Table 12-1.

Some experimental data for simple diatomic molecules is shown in Table 12-2. The predicted number of covalent bonds (bond order) is shown also. We observe a correlation between the bond energy and the predicted number of covalent bonds. Also, the bond distance decreases from single to triple bonds.

These types of molecular-orbital descriptions can be extended to ions of the above molecules, for example, O_2^+ and O_2^-, and to heteronuclear diatomic molecules, such as CO, NO, and HF. As we have seen, the precise order and specific location of the energy states of molecular orbitals depends on the electronic and nuclear properties of the molecule in question. Some caution is thus needed in any application of these general energy diagrams.

12.4 DIRECTED VALENCY AND BOND DESCRIPTIONS OF MORE COMPLEX MOLECULES

We could set up Schrödinger equations for multiatomic molecules as we did for diatomic molecules, but because of the complexity of the equations, we would lose the simple idea of representing chemical bonds as localized effects between atoms. The idea of localized bonds is helpful in understanding chemical phenomena, such as reactivity and molecular geometry.

In this section we show how atomic orbitals can be combined to form a set of new orbitals called *hybrid orbitals*. Hybrid orbitals are oriented in directions that coincide with the known bond directions in complex molecules; they provide a basis for the description of bonding in these molecules. In Chapter 9 we examined five basic structural arrangements found in single-centered molecules: linear, trigonal, tetrahedral, trigonal bipyramidal, and octahedral. The directional features of these five structures are found in the hybridization of atomic orbitals.

The simplest hybridization arises from the combination of an *s* and a *p* atomic orbital on the same atom to give two *sp* hybrid atomic orbitals. By addition and subtraction, $s + p$ and $s - p$, we obtain two hybrid atomic orbitals as shown in Fig. 12-12, *A*. These hybrid orbitals have one-half *s*-orbital character and one-

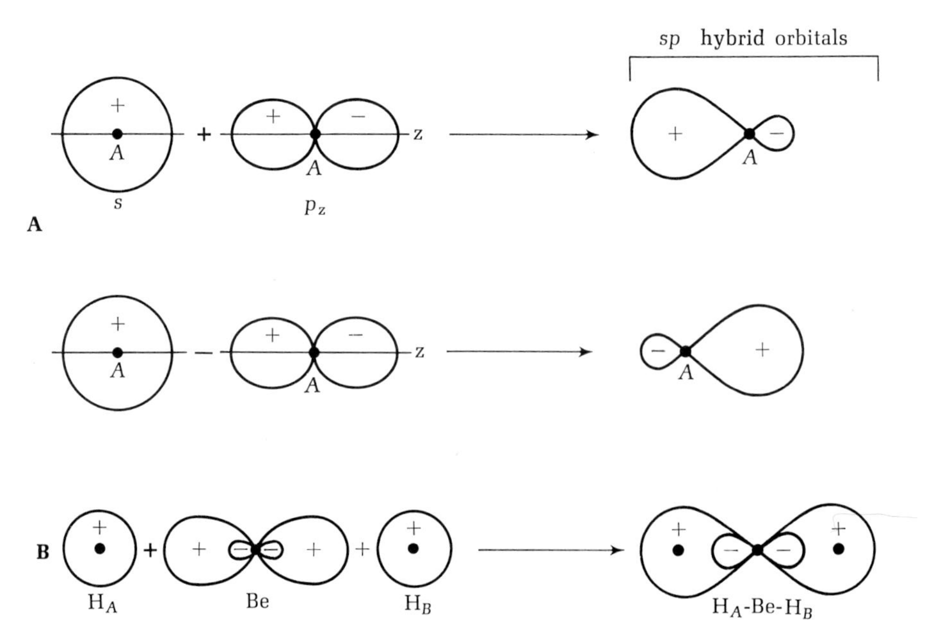

Fig. 12-12. **A,** Formation of *sp* hybrid orbitals from s and *p* orbitals. **B,** Use of *sp* hybrid orbitals on Be and 1s orbitals on H_A and H_B to form bonding molecular orbitals.

half *p*-orbital character. The *s* and *p* orbitals can each accommodate two electrons. Likewise, an *sp* hybrid orbital can contain two electrons. From Figure 12-12, *A*, we see that *sp* hybridization results in the two orbitals being directed 180° from each other.

The molecule BeH_2 has a linear H—Be—H structure. In the ground state, Be has the electronic configuration $1s^22s^2$, which can be promoted easily to $1s^22s^12p^1$. This promotion requires relatively little energy because the 2*s* and 2*p* energy levels are similar. The 2*s* and 2*p* atomic orbitals can then combine to form two *sp* hybrid orbitals, each of which contains one electron and can combine with a 1*s* atomic orbital on a H atom to form a bonding molecular orbital. Each of the two bonding orbitals arising in this fashion contains two electrons (one from Be and one from H) and constitutes a single covalent bond. The formation of these bonds is shown in Fig. 12-12, *B*. The bonding molecular orbitals have cylindrical symmetry and are therefore σ orbitals. The bonds are called σ bonds.

Trigonal hybridization arises by combining one *s* and two *p* atomic orbitals of similar energy to give three sp^2 hybrid atomic orbitals (Fig. 12-13). The orbitals have one-third *s*-orbital and two-thirds *p*-orbital character, lie in a plane, and are directed 120° from each other.

The BH_3 molecule is trigonal planar. The electronic configuration of B is $1s^22s^22p_x^1$, which can be promoted to $1s^22s^12p_x^12p_y^1$. The hybrid combination of the 2*s*, $2p_x$, and $2p_y$ orbitals yields three sp^2 hybrid orbitals of the required orientation. The combination of the sp^2 hybrid orbitals with 1*s* atomic orbitals on H atoms gives three σ bonding molecular orbitals. Two electrons go into each bonding molecular orbital to give a total of three covalent σ bonds, as shown in Fig. 12-14, *A*.

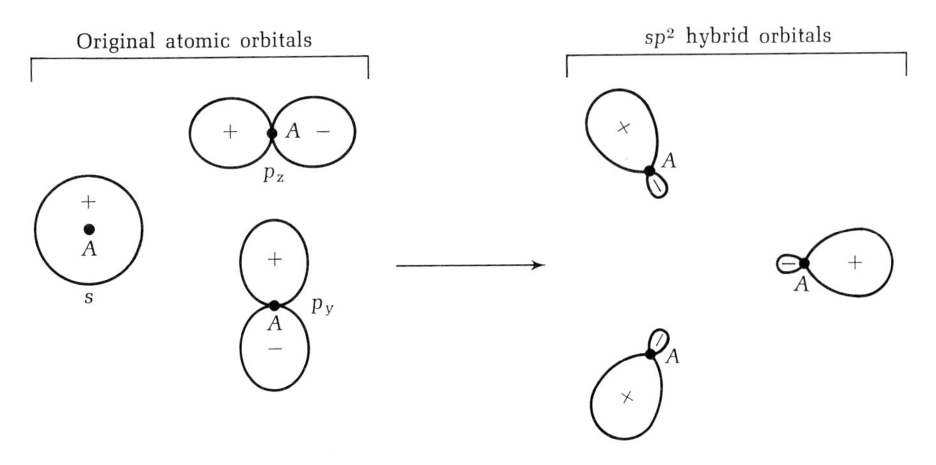

Fig. 12-13. Formation of sp^2 hybrid orbitals from one s and two p orbitals.

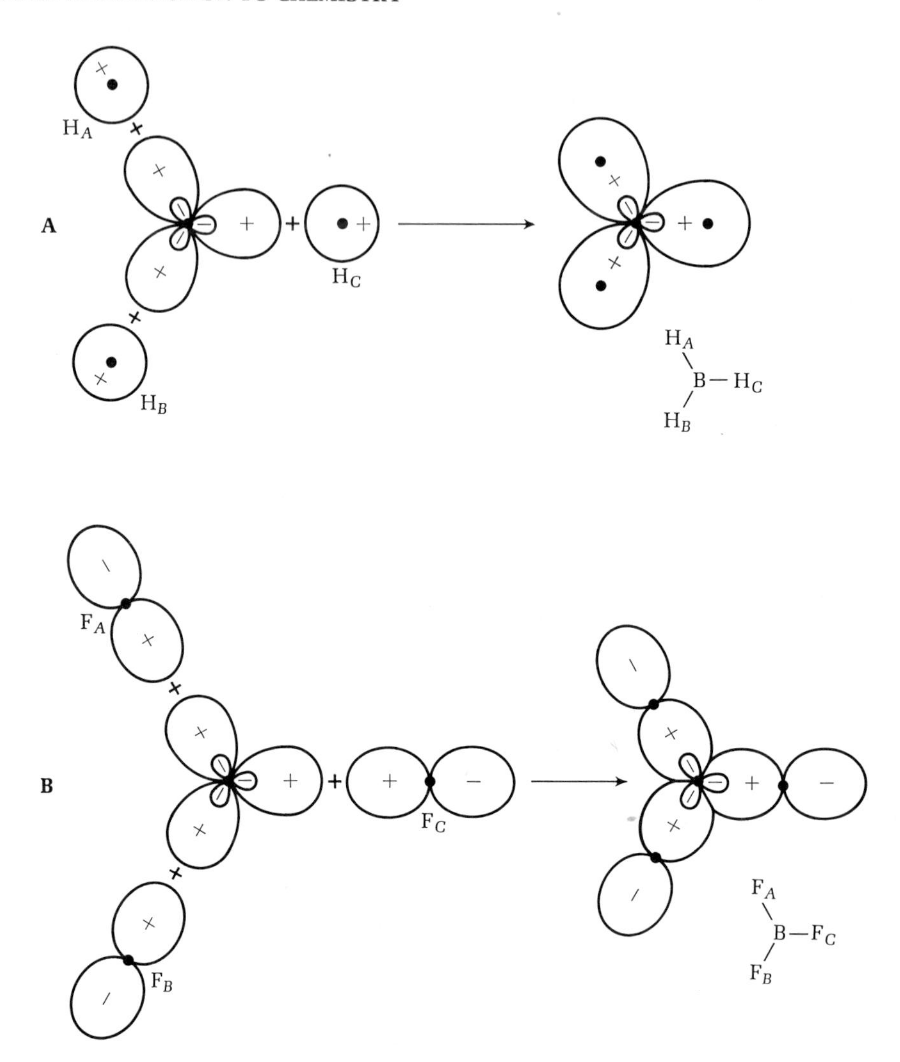

Fig. 12-14. Use of sp² hybrid orbitals to form molecular bonding orbitals. **A,** BH_3. **B,** BF_3.

Covalent σ bonds can also arise from the combination of hybrid atomic orbitals and p atomic orbitals. For example, consider BF_3. Here, the B is sp^2 hybridized. Each hybrid orbital can combine with a $2p_z$ atomic orbital from an F atom to give three bonding molecular orbitals as shown in Fig. 12-14, *B*. These molecular orbitals are cylindrically symmetric and thus are σ bonds. Again there are two electrons in each bonding molecular orbital, giving a total of three single covalent bonds.

Other types of hybrid orbitals, sp^3, dsp^2, dsp^3, and d^2sp^3, have the directional properties required for tetrahedral, square planar, trigonal bipyramidal, and octa-

Table 12-3. PRINCIPLE TYPES OF HYBRIDIZATION

Hybrid orbital type	*Number of orbitals*	*Orbitals used*	*Type of coordination*
sp	2	s, p_x	Linear
sp_2	3	s, p_x, p_y	Trigonal
sp^3	4	s, p_x, p_y, p_z	Tetrahedral
dsp^2	4	$s, p_x, p_y, d_{x^2-y^2}$	Square planar
dsp^3	5	$s, p_x, p_y, p_z, d_{z^2}$	Trigonal bipyramidal
d^2sp^3	6	$s, p_x, p_y, p_z, d_{z^2}, d_{x^2-y^2}$	Octahedral

hedral structures, respectively, as noted in Table 12-3. In dsp^2, dsp^3, and d^2sp^3 hybridization, d atomic orbitals are involved. In each case the number of hybrid orbitals is equivalent to the number of original atomic orbitals that go into their formation. Thus, there are four sp^3, four dsp^2, five dsp^3, and six d^2sp^3 hybrid orbitals (Fig. 12-15, *A* to *C*).

Methane, CH_4, is a tetrahedral molecule. The C atom is promoted to a $1s^22s^12p_x^{\,1}2p_y^{\,1}2p_z^{\,1}$ configuration, and the s and p orbitals hybridize to form four sp^3 orbitals. Each hybrid orbital combines with a $1s$ atomic orbital from a H atom to form a σ C—H bond.

The PF_5 molecule is trigonal bipyramidal. The P atom is promoted from $[\mathrm{Ne}]3s^23p_x^{\,1}3p_y^{\,1}3p_z^{\,1}$ to $[\mathrm{Ne}]3s^13p_x^{\,1}3p_y^{\,1}3p_z^{\,1}3d_{z^2}^{\,1}$ and hybridized to form five dsp^3 hybrid atomic orbitals, each of which forms a σ bond with a $2p_z$ atomic orbital from an F atom.

The SF_6 molecule has an octahedral structure. The S atom is promoted from $[\mathrm{Ne}]3s^23p_x^{\,2}3p_y^{\,1}3p_z^{\,1}$ to $[\mathrm{Ne}]3s^13p_x^{\,1}3p_y^{\,1}3p_z^{\,1}3d_{z^2}^{\,1}3d_{x^2-y^2}^{\,1}$ and hybridized to form six d^2sp^3 hybrid atomic orbitals. Six σ bonds are formed from the combination of $2p_z$ atomic orbitals from the F atoms with the octahedrally hybridized orbitals on the S atom.

These molecules are shown in Fig. 12-15, *D* to *F*.

The bonding in transition-metal complex ions can be described through the use of hybridized atomic orbitals. We recall that complex ions arise when ligands (electron-pair donors) coordinate to the metal ion. Each ligand donates two electrons to an empty metal orbital to form a coordinate covalent bond. The orbitals of the metal ion that participate in bond formation are the orbitals of the valence shell. First-row transition metals use some combination of $4s$, $3d$, $4p$, and sometimes $4d$ orbitals to construct the hybrid atomic orbitals that accommodate the ligand electrons. How the valence-shell electrons of the metal are accommodated in the atomic orbitals of the metal depends on the nature of the ligands.

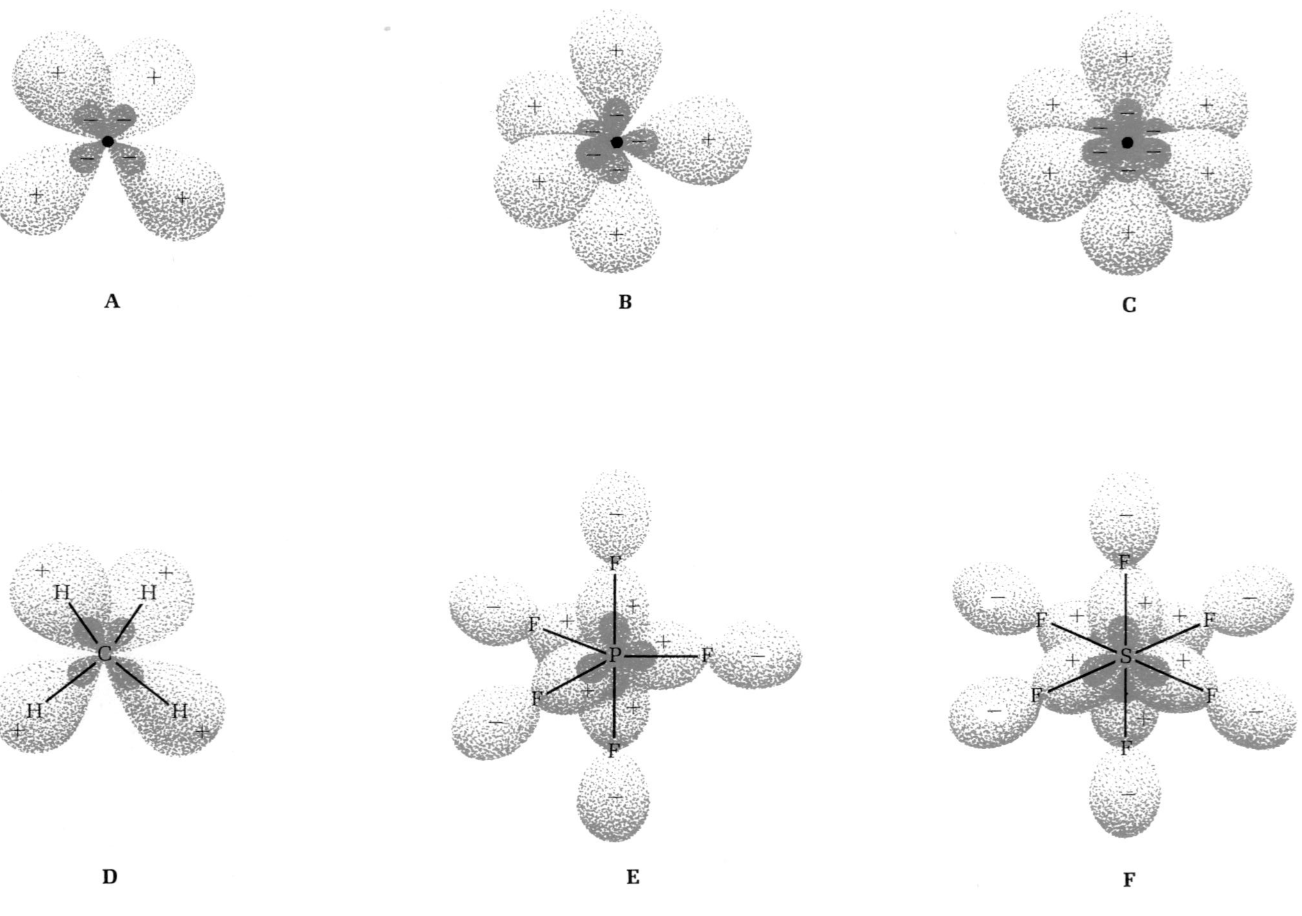

Fig. 12-15. Three-dimensional representation of hybrid orbitals. **A,** sp^3. **B,** dsp^3. **C,** d^2sp^3. Examples of the use of these hybrid orbitals. **D,** CH_4. **E,** PF_5. **F,** SF_6.

For example, the bonding description of $Cr(H_2O)_6^{3+}$ would begin with the electronic configuration of Cr, $1s^22s^22p^63s^23p^63d^54s^1$. Chromium(III) has the outer electronic configuration $3d^3$, which may be represented as

	3d	4s	4p
Cr^{3+}	↑ ↑ ↑ _ _	_	_ _ _

The diagram shows that the electrons in Cr^{3+} are unpaired using three $3d$ atomic orbitals. The remaining $3d$, $4s$, and $4p$ orbitals can combine into six d^2sp^3 hybrid atomic orbitals that can accommodate six pairs of electrons from ligands. This is shown as

	3d	4s	4p
		d^2sp^3	
$Cr(H_2O)_6^{3+}$	↑ ↑ ↑ oo oo	oo	oo oo oo

where the arrows represent the electrons from the metal and the circles represent the electrons from the ligands. We would predict the complex to have an octahedral structure (Fig. 12-16, *A*) and magnetic properties that reflect the presence of three unpaired electrons.*

The nature of the ligand affects the nature of the pairing of electrons in the metal ion. This is seen in the case of the Ni(II) complexes, $NiCl_4^{2-}$ and $Ni(CN)_4^{2-}$, which use sp^3 and dsp^2 hybrid atomic orbitals, respectively:

	3d	4s	4p
Ni^{2+}	⇅ ⇅ ⇅ ↑ ↑	_	_ _ _
		sp^3	
$Ni(Cl)_4^{2-}$	⇅ ⇅ ⇅ ↑ ↑	oo	oo oo oo
		dsp^2	
$Ni(CN)_4^{2-}$	⇅ ⇅ ⇅ ⇅ oo	oo	oo oo _

The $NiCl_4^{2-}$ complex has two unpaired electrons and a tetrahedral structure (Fig.

*For many simple transition-metal ions, the number of unpaired electrons, n, is related to the magnetic moment, μ_B, of the substance by

$$\mu_B = [n(n + 1)]^{1/2}$$

The magnetic moment can be measured experimentally. For $Cr(H_2O)_6^{3+}$, the magnetic moment μ_B is predicted to be $[3(3 + 1)]^{1/2} = 12^{1/2} = 3.46$, in close agreement with the experimentally determined value.

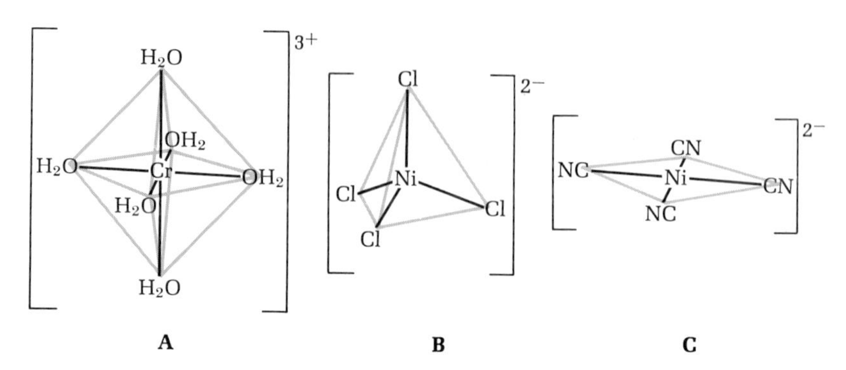

Fig. 12-16. Structures of transition-metal complex ions. **A,** $Cr(H_2O)_6^{3+}$, octahedral. **B,** $NiCl_4^{2-}$, tetrahedral. **C,** $Ni(CN)_4^{2-}$, square planar.

12-16, *B*). The $Ni(CN)_4^{2-}$ complex has no unpaired electrons and a square planar structure (Fig. 12-16, *C*).

Another example of the way a ligand affects the pairing of electrons is shown in the Co(III) complexes, $Co(NH_3)_6^{3+}$ and CoF_6^{3-}:

	3*d*	4*s*	4*p*	4*d*
Co^{3+}	⇅ ↑ ↑ ↑ ↑	—	— — —	— — — — —
	(last two 3*d*, 4*s*, 4*p*: d^2sp^3)			
$Co(NH_3)_6^{3+}$	⇅ ⇅ ⇅ ○○ ○○	○○	○○ ○○ ○○	— — — — —
		(4*s*, 4*p*, two 4*d*: sp^3d^2)		
CoF_6^{3-}	⇅ ↑ ↑ ↑ ↑	○○	○○ ○○ ○○	○○ ○○ — — —

In the case of CoF_6^{3-}, two 4*d* orbitals are involved in the formation of the hybrid orbitals. Complexes formed with sp^3d^2 hybrid orbitals are called *outer orbital* complexes, whereas those formed with d^2sp^3 hybrid orbitals are called *inner orbital* complexes.

For any atom, energy is required to promote electrons from the ground-state electronic configuration to the hybridized state. This energy can come from the formation of chemical bonds. If the energy of forming bonds with electrons in hybrid atomic orbitals is much greater than the energy involved in forming bonds with electrons in pure atomic orbitals, bond formation with hybrid atomic orbitals is favored. This is schematically shown in Fig. 12-17 for the formation of CH_4 from one C and four H atoms.

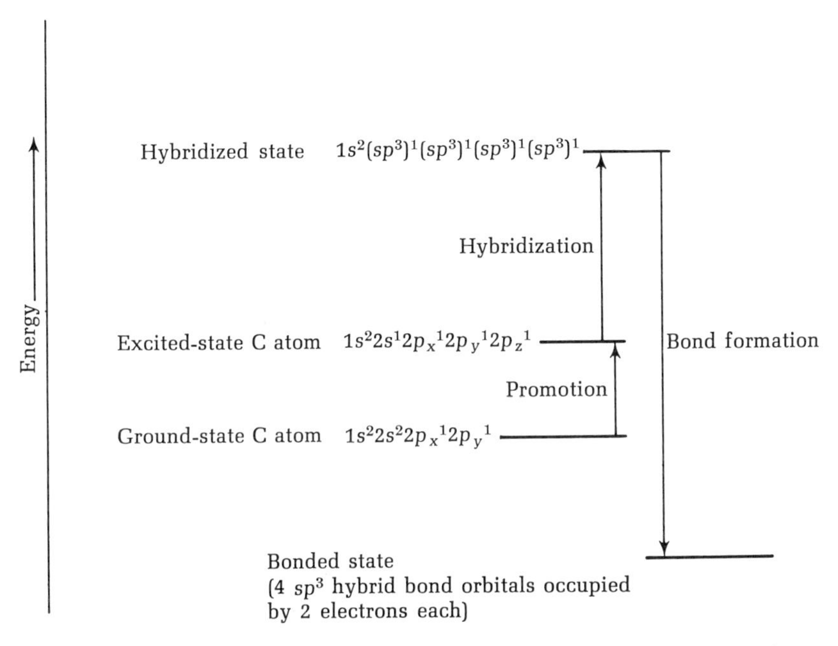

Fig. 12-17. Schematic representation of energy change in hybrid bond formation from carbon and hydrogen atoms to form methane.

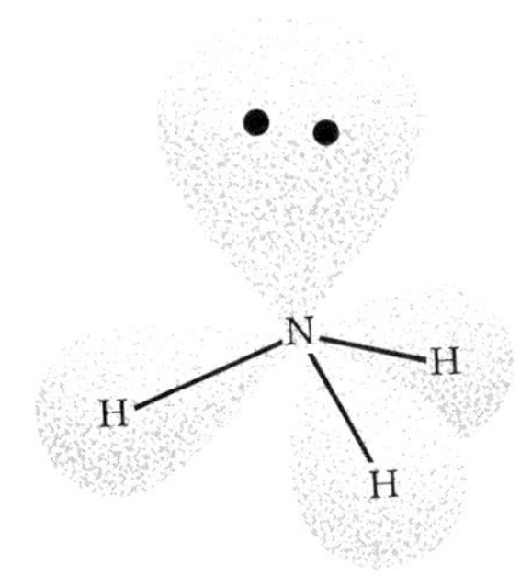

Fig. 12-18. NH_3 molecule. Lone-pair electrons occupy an sp^3 hybrid orbital.

So far we have considered cases where all the hybrid orbitals are involved in forming bonding molecular orbitals. It is also possible for a pair of non-bonding electrons to occupy a hybrid orbital. For example, in NH_3 we consider the hybridization of a $2s$ and three $2p$ orbitals on the N atom to give four sp^3 hybrid orbitals. Nitrogen has five valence electrons, and the three H atoms contribute one electron each. One hybrid orbital is occupied by a pair of non-bonding electrons, and the

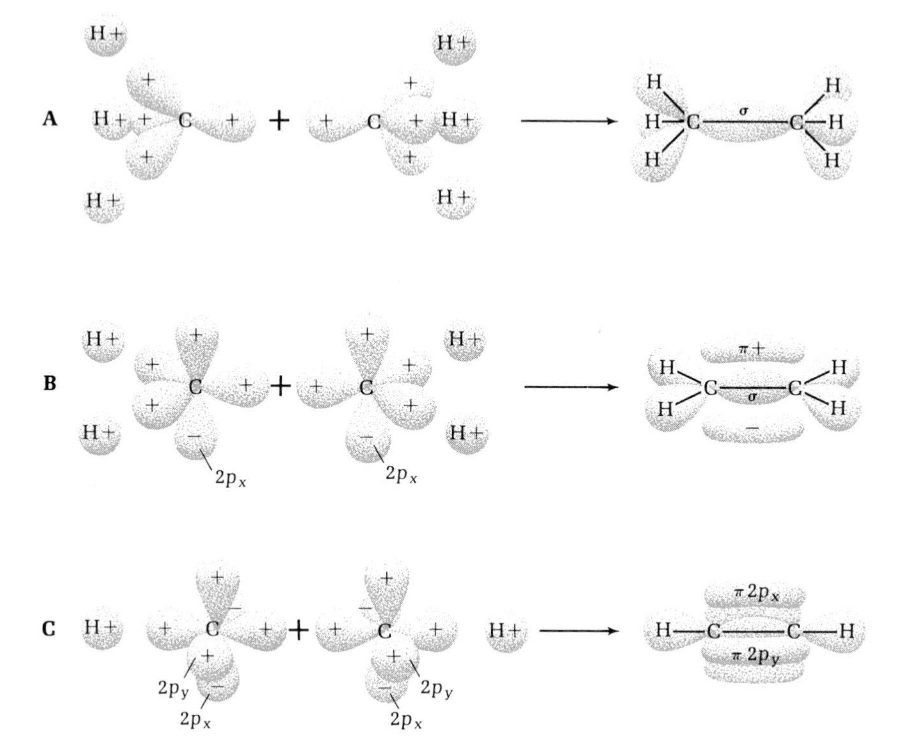

Fig. 12-19 Bonding descriptions. **A,** $H_3C—CH_3$ (ethane). **B,** $H_2C{=}CH_2$ (ethylene). **C,** $HC{\equiv}CH$ (acetylene).

other three orbitals form bonds to each of the hydrogens. The structure of NH_3 is shown in Fig. 12-18.

The type of hybridization predicted for a given atom depends on the geometry of the bonds around the atom. Some atoms, such as carbon, occur in different structural situations and therefore exhibit different types of hybridization.

For example, in CH_4, C_2H_6, C_3H_8, and so on, carbon atoms exhibit sp^3 (tetrahedral) hybridization. The bonding molecular orbitals for ethane are pictured in Fig. 12-19, *A*. Note that a σ bonding molecular orbital is formed between two sp^3 hybrid orbitals on the C atoms in addition to the six σ bonds with H atoms. Higher alkanes show similar σ bonding features.

Alkenes are planar molecules with bond angles of 120°. This requires each carbon to have three sp^2 hybridized orbitals and one $2p_y$ atomic orbital. These orbitals can combine to form the molecular bonding orbitals shown in Fig. 12-19, *B*. Here we see the formation of four σ bonds with H atoms and one σ bond between C atoms. The

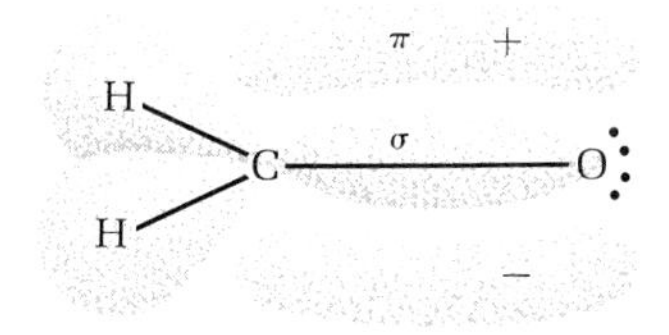

Fig. 12-20. Bonding molecular orbitals of H_2CO.

two $2p_y$ atomic orbitals combine to form a π bonding molecular orbital between the carbons. There is thus a double bond between the C atoms.

Since alkynes, such as HC≡CH (acetylene) are linear molecules, we make use of *sp* hybridization in dealing with them. Each carbon has two *sp* hybrid orbitals and a $2p_x$ and a $2p_y$ atomic orbital. The two carbon atoms combine with each other and with two H atoms to give the σ bond system. Two π bonds form between the carbon atoms. This gives the triple bond, which consists of one σ and two π bonds (Fig. 12-19, *C*).

In molecules containing carbonyl groups $(\text{—}\overset{\displaystyle O}{\overset{\|}{C}}\text{—})$ and in benzene, carbon is sp^2 hybridized. The molecule H_2CO is trigonal planar:

```
H
 \
  C=O:
 /
H
```

The sp^2 hybrid orbitals form σ bonds with the two H atoms and the one O atom. The $2p_y$ orbital on carbon also forms a π bond with the $2p_y$ orbital on the O atom. The σ and π bond together constitute a double bond between carbon and oxygen, as shown in Fig. 12-20. Benzene also exhibits a planar structure in which all bond angles are 120°:

```
        H                      H
        |                      |
  H    C    H            H    C    H
   \ /   \\ /             \ //  \ /
    C      C               C      C
    ||     |               |      ||
    C      C               C      C
   / \   // \             / \\   / \
  H    C    H            H    C    H
       |                      |
       H                      H
```

Each carbon forms one σ bond to a hydrogen and two σ bonds to adjacent carbon atoms. In addition, the $2p_y$ orbital on each carbon, which contains one electron, can

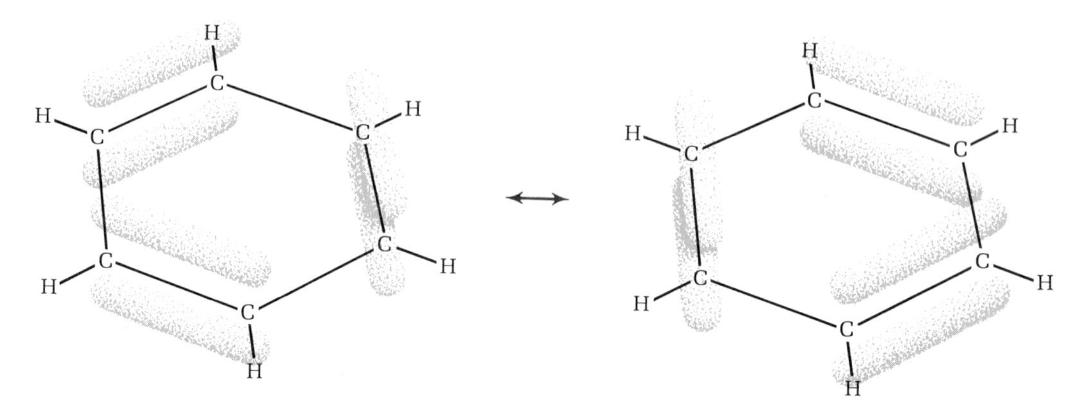

Fig. 12-21. Description of π bonds for two resonance structures of benzene.

form π bonds with adjacent carbon atoms. A total of three π bonds are formed. They can be located in two alternate ways, as shown in Fig. 12-21. These structures are of equal energy and both are needed to represent completely the bonding in benzene. When two or more equal-energy structures can be drawn for a molecule we have a situation called *resonance*. When resonance occurs, the molecule is stabilized. Benzene, because of this resonance stabilization, is an unusually stable hydrocarbon.

EXAMPLE 12.1

Using bond enthalpy data from section 4.10, calculate the resonance stabilization energy of benzene.

The enthalpy of either resonance structure is the sum of the bond enthalpies of three C—C, three C=C, and six C—H bonds. This is (3 × 83.1 kcal) + (3 × 147 kcal) + (6 × 98.8 kcal) = 1283.1 kcal. The experimental value of the enthalpy required to dissociate benzene molecules into carbon and hydrogen atoms is 1322.9 kcal. Thus benzene has 40 kcal/mole of resonance stabilization energy.

12.5 BONDING IN METALS

Most metals have two properties in common: (1) low ionization energies (< 200 kcal/mole) and (2) fewer valence electrons than valence orbitals. For example, Li, with a $1s^22s^1$ configuration, has one valence electron ($2s^1$) but four valence orbitals (the $2s$ and three $2p$ orbitals). The interaction between two metal atoms to form a simple diatomic molecule is usually weak. As seen in Table 12-2, for Li_2 the bond energy is only 24 kcal/mole. Much greater stability can be achieved if the valence

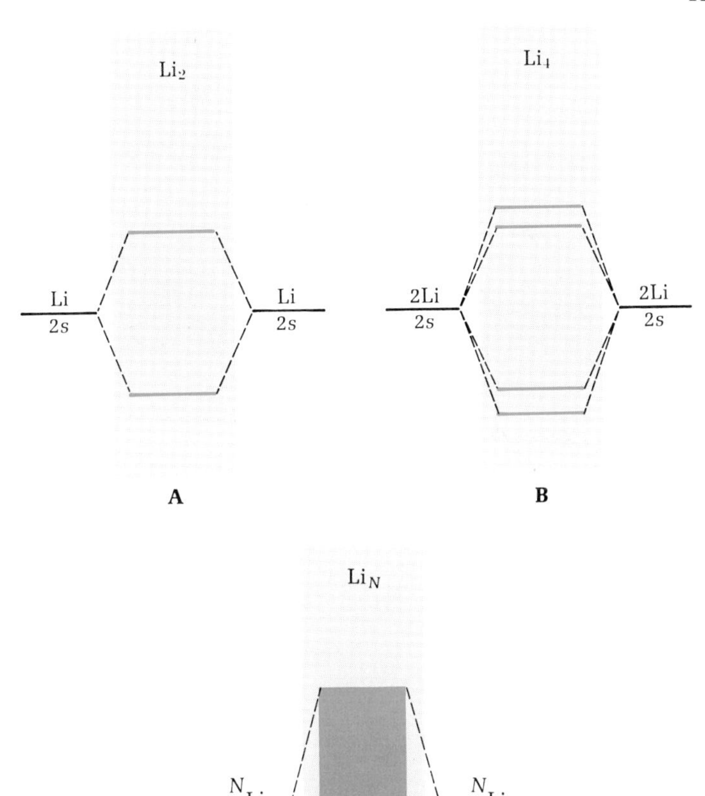

Fig. 12-22. Formation of molecular orbitals in lithium from two atoms, **A**, four atoms, **B**, and N atoms, **C**.

electrons move under the influence of more than two nuclei. This type of multicenter interaction is possible because metal atoms have more valence orbitals than electrons.

A lattice arrangement provides metal atoms with an energetically favorable way to share their electrons. Consider the orbital combinations that arise when two or four lithium atoms are allowed to interact. In Fig. 12-22, *A*, two 2*s* orbitals combine to form two molecular orbitals, one of lower and one of higher energy than those of the

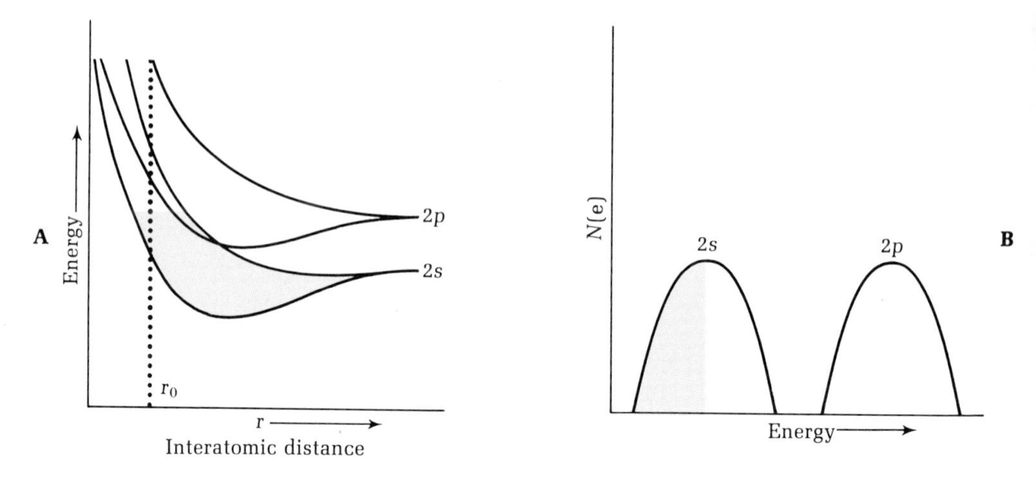

Fig. 12-23. **A,** Energy of 2s and 2p bands for lithium metal plotted as function of interatomic distance r. **B,** Population of valence electrons in metal bands of lithium as function of energy. Shaded areas represent a half-filled band that arises because lithium has a half-filled ($2s^1$) valence configuration.

separated atoms. The two valence electrons occupy the lowest energy orbital. If four atoms are combined (Fig. 12-22, *B*), four molecular orbitals arise. If *N* Li-atom orbitals are combined, *bands* of *N* molecular orbitals arise (Fig. 12-22, *C*). The molecular orbitals in each band are very closely spaced in energy. The lowest-energy band for Li metal is a 2*s* band.

An entire series of higher-energy bands analogous to the 2s band can be formulated. The band structure of Li is shown in Fig. 12-23. In the ground state, the electrons occupy the 2*s* band. Since there are *N* levels, each of which can hold two electrons, the band is one-half filled. The valence electrons are delocalized over the entire crystal. The metal atoms can be viewed as ions in a "sea" of valence electrons.

The band model provides a basis for discussing many properties of metals and nonmetals, such as conduction of heat or electricity.

In sodium (Fig. 12-24, *A*), a good conductor of heat and electricity, the 3*s* band contains the valence electrons and is one-half filled. In a partially filled band, electrons can move among the energy levels, thereby providing a facile mechanism for conduction.

The 3*s* band is filled in Mg metal (Fig. 12-24, *B*), but the 3*s* and 3*p* bands overlap, providing a mechanism for a great degree of electron mobility.

The band structure of Si metal (Fig. 12-24, *C*) produces a different situation. The upper band is filled and does not overlap the next highest vacant level. Electron

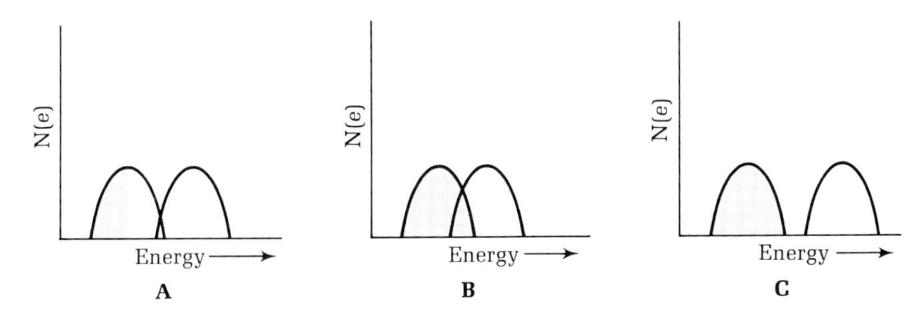

Fig. 12-24. Population diagrams for valence bands of Na, **A**, Mg, **B**, and Si, **C**.

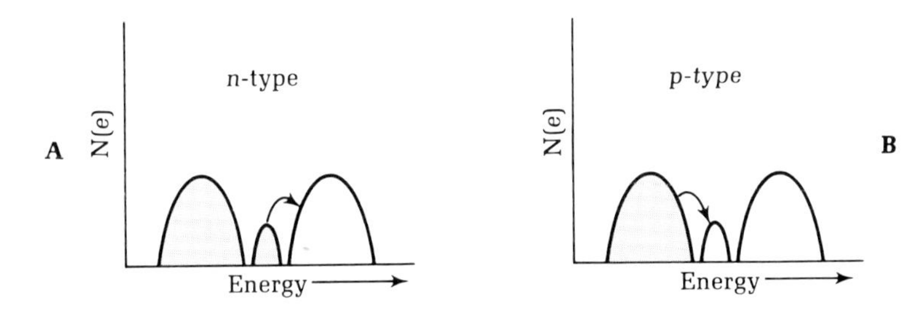

Fig. 12-25. Population diagrams of *n*-type and *p*-type semiconductors.

mobility within or between the levels is not allowed, and Si consequently is an insulator.

The above concepts explain why metallic properties in general increase down a given group in the periodic table. As we go down a group, the metal atom orbitals extend further into space, the bands overlap more, and partially filled band systems arise.

Band theory also helps explain the properties of semiconductors. In an insulator (Fig. 12-24, *C*), the valence band is completely filled and does not overlap higher bands. If electrons are excited into empty bands, a great degree of electron mobility becomes possible, and the insulator becomes a conductor of heat and electricity. The amount of energy required to excite electrons into a conduction band depends on the width of the gap between bands. Increasing the temperature of an insulator causes more electrons to be excited into a conduction band. Theoretically, all insulators can be heated to the point where they become semiconductors.

Impurity semiconduction arises when a few atoms of an insulator material are replaced by atoms that have energy levels between the valence and conduction bands of the insulator. Two kinds of semiconductors arise, *n* or *p*, depending on the nature of the impurity. The *n*-type arises if a group V impurity, such as As, is introduced into a group IV metal, such as Ge (Fig. 12-25, *A*). The impurity atoms have more valence electrons than the atoms they replace. The As has a conduction band just beneath the conduction band of Ge. The As electrons can be easily excited into the empty conduction band, making the compound a semiconductor. Since conduction is due to negative-charge migration, these materials are called *n*-type semiconductors. The *p*-type semiconductor arises when a group III impurity, such as B, is introduced into a group IV metal, such as Ge (Fig. 12-25, *B*). The impurity atoms have fewer valence electrons than the atoms they replace, giving rise to vacant energy levels within the conduction band of the group IV metal. These vacancies are called *holes* or positive charge centers. Conduction occurs as a result of the effective migration of the holes through the crystal; hence materials in which this phenomenon occurs are called *p*-type semiconductors.

PROBLEMS

1. Distinguish between antibonding and nonbonding orbitals.
2. Predict whether the He_2^+ ion would spontaneously dissociate to He and He^+.
3. (a) Indicate with drawings why the molecular orbital formed from the LCAO combination $2p_{yA} + 2p_{yB}$ is designated π_μ.
   (b) Why is the combination $2p_{xA} + 2p_{xB}$ designated $\pi_g{}^*$?
4. Draw the π molecular orbitals for cyanogen, which has the structure $N{\equiv}C{-}C{\equiv}N$.
5. Why is the $\sigma 2s$ orbital, with its higher energy, a bonding orbital, whereas $\sigma^* 1s$, with its lower energy, is an antibonding orbital?
6. Using the diagrams in Figs. 12-10 and 12-11, arrange the following groups in order of increasing bond energy: (a) Li_2, Be_2, C_2; (b) O_2, N_2, F_2; (c) O_2, O_2^+, O_2^-.
7. Write electronic configurations for (a) N_2^+; (b) Cl_2; (c) O_2; (d) Be_2^+. Which are paramagnetic?
8. Prepare a table for *s*, *p*, *d*, *sp*, sp^2, sp^3, dsp^2, dsp^3, σ, σ^*, and π orbitals as follows:

Orbital	*Number of orbitals with given energy*	*Maximum number of electrons in orbital of given energy*

9. Write electronic configurations as shown on p. 330 for the valence shell electrons of the following complex ions: (a) $Cr(CN)_6^{3-}$; (b) FeF_6^{3-} ($\mu > 3$); (c) $PtCl_4^{2-}$ (square planar); (d) $Zn(CN)_4^{2-}$ (tetrahedral). Calculate the magnetic moments for the paramagnetic species.

10. Diagram the electronic configuration of CoI_4^{2-}, whose magnetic moment is more than 4 Bohr magnetons.
11. Using the periodic table, describe five different pairs of elements that might give rise to (a) *n*-type semiconductors and (b) *p*-type semiconductors.
12. Describe the bonding in the following molecules, using hybrid orbitals when necessary: (a) PCl_3; (b) BeH_2; (c) CCl_4; (d) $SbCl_5$; (e) SiF_6^{2-}.

13 THE RATES OF CHEMICAL REACTIONS

It is possible to obtain many products from a given set of reactants. For example, two ways that NO_2 could react are

$$NO_2 \rightarrow \tfrac{1}{2}N_2O_4 \qquad \Delta G^0 = -0.64 \text{ kcal} \tag{13.1}$$

$$NO_2 \rightarrow \tfrac{1}{2}N_2(g) + O_2(g) \qquad \Delta G^0 = -12.39 \text{ kcal} \tag{13.2}$$

Both reactions are thermodynamically possible under standard-state conditions since ΔG^0 is negative in both cases. If we started with pure NO_2 and allowed it to react, we would ultimately obtain a system composed mainly of elemental nitrogen and oxygen. However, when this experiment is performed, N_2O_4 forms in a matter of microseconds, whereas appreciable amounts of O_2 and N_2 can be obtained only after many years. This indicates that we cannot expect to predict from thermodynamics the first products in the course of a reaction. The examples show that the decomposition of NO_2 can proceed by different pathways characterized by different rates.

An understanding of the rates of chemical reactions and the factors that affect these rates (temperature, concentration, catalysts) is important for several reasons. It allows us to predict how fast and under what conditions a desired product or products will form. It also is the first step in describing the details of a reaction. This detailed molecular description is called the *reaction mechanism.*

13.1 RATES OF REACTION

Differential forms of simple rates

In section 7.1 the progress of a general reaction

$$aA + bB \rightarrow cC + dD \tag{13.3}$$

was described in terms of the extent of reaction ξ. The differential $d\xi$ is given in terms of the number of moles, n_A, n_B, n_C, and n_D, of reactants and products as

$$\begin{aligned} dn_A &= -a\,d\xi \\ dn_B &= -b\,d\xi \\ dn_C &= c\,d\xi \\ dn_D &= d\,d\xi \end{aligned} \tag{13.4}$$

The rate of a reaction is the differential of the extent of reaction with time:

$$\text{Rate} = \frac{d\xi}{dt} \tag{13.5}$$

The rate can thus be expressed in terms of the change in the number of moles of various species by any of the following equations:

$$\frac{d\xi}{dt} = -\frac{1}{a}\frac{dn_A}{dt} = -\frac{1}{b}\frac{dn_B}{dt} = \frac{1}{c}\frac{dn_C}{dt} = \frac{1}{d}\frac{dn_D}{dt} \tag{13.6}$$

When reactants are mixed, the chemical reaction begins. The course of the reaction can be followed by measuring the concentrations of various reactant or product components at different times. For example, if ethylene bromide and potassium iodide in a methanol solution are mixed, the following reaction occurs:

$$C_2H_4Br_2 + 3KI \rightarrow C_2H_4 + 2KBr + KI_3 \tag{13.7}$$

At room temperature the reaction proceeds slowly. The change in reactant and product concentrations can be followed by measuring any component in the reaction mixture. A small fraction of the solution is removed and analyzed at intervals of several minutes. The change in concentration of KI_3 can be followed as a function of time by chemical analysis of the I_3^- concentration in the mixture. From this, we can obtain the necessary information about the changes in concentration of all the reaction species with time. Typical results in terms of $C_2H_4Br_2$ are represented in Fig. 13-1. The rates of concentration change for the various components are related by the stoichiometry of the reaction from equation 13.6:

$$\frac{d\xi}{dt} = -\frac{d[C_2H_4Br_2]}{dt} = -\frac{1}{3}\frac{d[KI]}{dt} = +\frac{d[C_2H_4]}{dt} = +\frac{1}{2}\frac{d[KBr]}{dt} = +\frac{d[KI_3]}{dt} \tag{13.8}$$

The negative signs account for the decrease in the concentrations of reactants with time. The rate of the reaction illustrated in Fig. 13-1 is the negative slope of the $C_2H_4Br_2$ curve or the slope of the KI_3 curve. The rate decreases during the course of the reaction.

The first problem in the study of reaction rates is finding how the rate depends on the concentrations of various components. This experimentally determined relationship is called the *rate law* for the reaction. For the reaction in equation 13.7, the rate law is found to be

$$-\frac{d[C_2H_4Br_2]}{dt} = k_2[C_2H_4Br_2][KI] \tag{13.9}$$

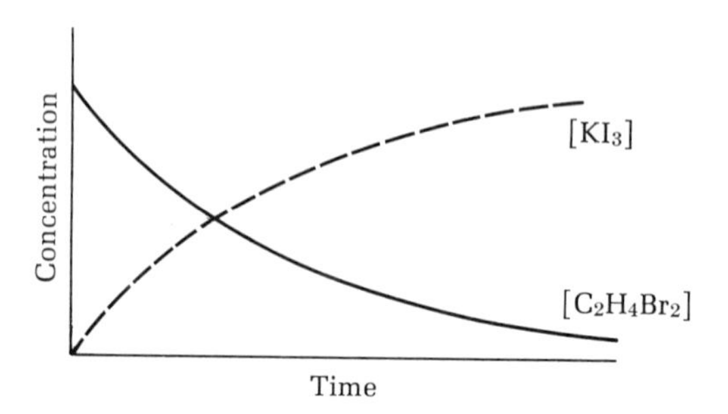

Fig. 13-1. Concentrations of KI_3 and $C_2H_4Br_2$ versus time for reaction in equation 13.7.

where k_2 is called the *specific rate constant* and is a specific value determined from experimental measurements at a given temperature. This rate law tells us that if we double the concentration of KI, keeping other concentrations constant, the rate doubles. The rate law is the simplest expression accounting for the effects of concentration on the rate of the reaction.

A variety of rate laws are found for different reactions. Some examples are

$$2N_2O_5 \rightarrow 4NO_2 + O_2 \qquad \frac{-d[N_2O_5]}{dt} = k_1[N_2O_5] \tag{13.10}$$

$$2NO_2 \rightarrow 2NO + O_2 \qquad \frac{-d[NO_2]}{dt} = k_2[NO_2]^2 \tag{13.11}$$

$$CH_3CHO \rightarrow CH_4 + CO \qquad \frac{-d[CH_3CHO]}{dt} = k'[CH_3CHO]^{3/2} \tag{13.12}$$

$$H_2 + Br_2 \rightarrow 2HBr \qquad \frac{d[HBr]}{dt} = \frac{k''[H_2][Br_2]^{1/2}}{k'' + [HBr]/[Br_2]} \tag{13.13}$$

The specific rate constants for each reaction, k_1, k_2, k', k'', are determined experimentally. From these examples it should be clear that it is impossible to predict the rate law of a reaction from only a knowledge of the stoichiometry of the reaction.

When the reaction rate law can be expressed in the form

$$-\frac{d[A]}{dt} = k_n[A]^l[B]^m \tag{13.14}$$

a term called the *order of the reaction* can be introduced. The order, n, is the sum of the exponents of the concentration terms, that is, $l + m = n$. In equation 13.10 we have a first-order reaction; in equation 13.11, a second-order reaction; and in equation 13.12, a $\frac{3}{2}$-order reaction. Since equation 13.13 is not of the form of equation 13.14, we cannot define its order.

Determination of rate laws by the method of initial rates

It is often convenient to determine the rate law of a reaction by varying the concentration of one reactant species while holding the other reactant concentrations constant, and examining the effect on the initial rate. We look at the initial rates because at that time reactant concentrations are known. Initial rates also are free of complications that arise when reactions involving the products take place.

Let us examine some experimentally determined initial-rate data for the reaction

$$2NO(g) + 2H_2(g) \rightarrow N_2(g) + 2H_2O(g) \qquad (13.15)$$

which occurs at 800°C. Some data obtained under different conditions of NO(g) and $H_2(g)$ partial pressures are shown in Table 13-1. If p_{NO} is doubled at constant p_{H_2}, the initial rate increases by a factor of four. Thus the rate law must involve a dependence on the square of the NO concentration. If p_{NO} is held constant and p_{H_2} is halved, the initial rate is halved, indicating that the rate law involves a dependence on the first power of the H_2 concentration. The rate law for the reaction is

$$\text{Rate} = k[NO]^2[H_2] \qquad (13.16)$$

The reaction is first order in H_2, second order in NO, and third order overall.

The numerical value of the specific rate constant k can be obtained from these initial-rate data by substituting any set of the experimental data into the rate-law expression. For the first set of data

$$\text{Rate} = k[NO]^2[H_2]$$

$$0.25 \text{ torr/sec} = k(150 \text{ torr})^2(400 \text{ torr})$$

$$k = \frac{0.25 \text{ torr/sec}}{(150 \text{ torr})^2(400 \text{ torr})}$$

$$= 2.77 \times 10^{-8} \text{ torr}^{-2}\text{-sec}^{-1}$$

13.2 INTEGRATED FORMS OF SIMPLE RATE LAWS

In almost any practical reaction situation, the changes in concentration with time are of such finite extent that integrated forms of the differential rate laws are

Table 13-1. INITIAL-RATE DATA FOR NO-H_2 REACTION

p_{H_2}(*torr*)	p_{NO}(*torr*)	*Initial rate (torr/sec)*
400	150	0.25
400	300	1.00
200	300	0.50

needed to represent the data. We shall consider some of the simpler examples of integrated laws.

First-order rate law

For the reaction

$$A \rightarrow B \tag{13.17}$$

let c denote the concentration of A. Then the first-order rate law is given by

$$-\frac{dc}{dt} = k_1 c \tag{13.18}$$

The units of k_1 are $(\text{time})^{-1}$. To obtain an integrated expression of this law, we must stipulate initial conditions. At $t = 0$, we set the concentration of A equal to c_0. At time t, the concentration of A is c. We can integrate the rate law with this condition as

$$-\int_{c_0}^{c} \frac{dc}{c} = \int_0^t k_1 dt \tag{13.19}$$

which gives

$$-[\ln c - \ln c_0] = k_1 t \tag{13.20}$$

or

$$\ln\left(\frac{c}{c_0}\right) = -k_1 t \tag{13.21}$$

or

$$\frac{c}{c_0} = e^{-k_1 t} \tag{13.22}$$

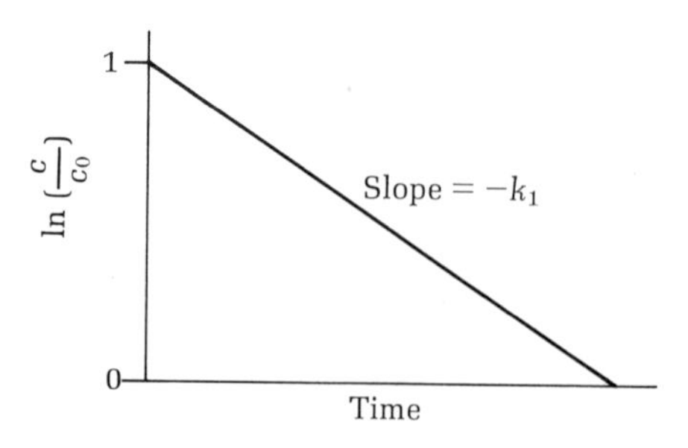

Fig. 13-2. First-order reaction plotted as $\ln (c/c_0)$ versus time t.

A plot of ln (c/c_0) versus t (equation 13.21) gives a straight line with a slope of $-k_1$. This plot (Fig. 13-2) provides a convenient way to evaluate k_1. From equation 13.22, we see that the concentration decreases exponentially with time for a first-order rate law.

A property of any rate law is that there is a characteristic time for the concentration or amount of reactant to be reduced by a given fraction. For a reduction of one-half, the time is denoted as the *half-life*, $t_{1/2}$. To find how $t_{1/2}$ is related to k_1, we consider the time $t_{1/2}$ taken in going from an initial concentration of c_0 to a second concentration of $c_0/2$. From equation 13.21 we obtain

$$\ln\left[\frac{(c_0/2)}{c_0}\right] = -k_1 t_{1/2} \qquad (13.23)$$

$$t_{1/2} = \frac{\ln 2}{k_1} = \frac{0.693}{k_1} \qquad (13.24)$$

Thus, the half-life of a first-order reaction is independent of the initial concentration.

The decomposition of N_2O_5, shown in equation 13.10, is an example of a first-order reaction. Other examples are the isomerization of cyclopropane (C_3H_6), the decomposition of azomethane [$(CH_3)_2N_2$], and the decay of any radioactive isotope (for example, the decomposition of ^{14}C), as shown in equations 13.25, 13.26, and 13.27, respectively:

$$\text{cyclo-}(CH_2)_3 \;(\text{ring: } CH_2 \text{ bonded to } CH_2\text{—}CH_2) \rightarrow CH_3\text{—}CH\text{=}CH_2 \qquad (13.25)$$

$$CH_3\text{—}N\text{=}N\text{—}CH_3 \rightarrow N\equiv N + C_2H_6 \qquad (13.26)$$

$$^{14}_{6}C \rightarrow {}^{14}_{7}N + \beta^- \text{ (beta particle)} \qquad (13.27)$$

Second-order rate law

For a reaction of the form

$$A + B \rightarrow C \qquad (13.28)$$

let the concentrations of A and B be equal and denoted by c. The rate law becomes

$$-\frac{dc}{dt} = k_2 c^2 \qquad (13.29)$$

The units of k_2 are (molar)$^{-1}$(time)$^{-1}$. With the initial concentrations ($t = 0$) of A and B equal to c_0, we have

$$-\int_{c_0}^{c} \frac{dc}{c^2} = \int_0^t k_2 dt \qquad (13.30)$$

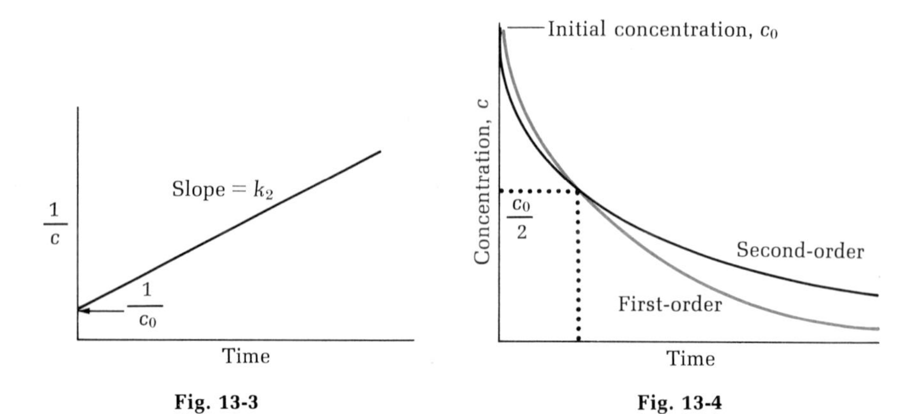

Fig. 13-3. Second-order reaction plotted as $1/c$ versus time t.
Fig. 13-4. Comparison of concentration-versus-time plots for first-order and second-order reactions.

which integrates to give

$$\left(\frac{1}{c} - \frac{1}{c_0}\right) = k_2 t \tag{13.31}$$

Equation 13.31 shows that for a second-order reaction a plot of $1/c$ versus t gives a straight line with slope k_2 (Fig. 13-3). This plot differs from that for a first order reaction.

Second-order reactions also differ from first-order reactions with regard to half-lives. Let $c = c_0/2$ at time $t_{1/2}$. Then from equation 13.31 we have

$$\left(\frac{1}{c_0/2} - \frac{1}{c_0}\right) = k_2 t_{1/2} \tag{13.32}$$

or

$$t_{1/2} = \frac{1}{(k_2 c_0)} \tag{13.33}$$

Thus, the half-life of a second-order reaction depends on the initial concentration, whereas that of a first order reaction was found to be independent of concentration. This difference is illustrated in the Fig. 13-4.

The hydrogenation of ethylene is an example of a second-order reaction:

$$H_2 + C_2H_4 \rightarrow C_2H_6 \tag{13.34}$$

where

$$\frac{d[C_2H_6]}{dt} = k_2[H_2][C_2H_4] \tag{13.35}$$

Equations 13.35 and 13.36 give other examples of second-order reactions:

$$2HI(g) \rightarrow H_2(g) + I_2(g) \tag{13.36}$$

$$R\cdot + R\cdot \rightarrow R{-}R \tag{13.37}$$

Equation 13.37 corresponds to the termination step in a free-radical addition polymerization reaction.

Consecutive first-order reactions

When a reaction proceeds by two first-order steps through an intermediate component, a more complicated rate law arises. The thermal decomposition of acetone is an example of such a reaction:

$$(CH_3)_2CO \rightarrow CH_2{=}CO + CH_4 \tag{13.38}$$

$$CH_2{=}CO \rightarrow \tfrac{1}{2}C_2H_4 + CO \tag{13.39}$$

We denote the reaction as

$$\underset{x}{A} \overset{k_1}{\rightarrow} \underset{y}{B} \overset{k_1'}{\rightarrow} \underset{z}{C} \tag{13.40}$$

with rate constants k_1 and k_1' for the consecutive steps. The concentrations of A, B, and C are denoted by x, y, and z. The first-order rate laws for each component are

$$-\frac{dx}{dt} = k_1 x \tag{13.41}$$

$$-\frac{dy}{dt} = -k_1 x + k_1' y \tag{13.42}$$

$$+\frac{dz}{dt} = k_1' y \tag{13.43}$$

The rate for component B, equation 13.42, is determined by both steps. The concentration of B increases from the decomposition of A and decreases with the formation of C.

These equations can be solved with the condition that at $t = 0$, $x = c_0$, $y = 0$, and $z = 0$. The solution is more complicated than we need worry about in detail, and we shall examine only its qualitative effects.

The concentration of C, given by z, will vary with time according to

$$z = c_0\left(1 - \frac{k_1' e^{-k_1 t}}{k_1' - k_1} + \frac{k_1 e^{-k_1' t}}{k_1' - k_1}\right) \tag{13.44}$$

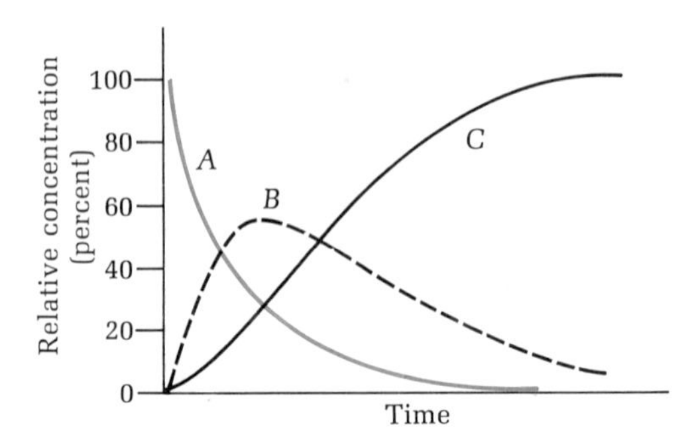

Fig. 13-5. Concentrations of species A, B, and C as function of time for two consecutive first-order reactions, where $k_1 = 2k_1'$.

The concentrations as a function of time are shown in Fig. 13-5 for the particular situation where $k_1 = 2k_1'$. We note that the intermediate B (concentration y) increases to a maximum value and then decreases to zero as the reaction goes to completion. In the extreme cases where $k_1 >> k_1'$ or $k_1' >> k_1$, the critical steps of the overall reaction would be only the first step, for $k_1' >> k_1$, or only the second step, for $k_1 >> k_1'$. In either situation, we would detect experimentally only the result of a first-order reaction with a rate constant of k_1 or k_1'. Thus, the experimental observation of a first-order rate law does not rule out the possibility of intermediate steps. If a reaction is found experimentally to follow equation 13.44, we conclude that the reaction involves an intermediate species and is of the first-order consecutive type.

We can always write expressions for the rate laws of various proposed reactions, but it is not always possible to find integrated solutions to these laws. When integrated solutions are not possible, we resort to computer solutions.

Opposing reactions

An important type of rate law arises with opposing reactions that eventually reach equilibrium. An example of first-order opposing reactions is the *cis-trans* isomerization of styryl cyanide:

$$\begin{matrix} C_6H_5 & & H \\ & C & \\ & \| & \\ & C & \\ NC & & H \end{matrix} \quad \leftrightarrows \quad \begin{matrix} C_6H_5 & & H \\ & C & \\ & \| & \\ & C & \\ H & & CN \end{matrix} \qquad (13.45)$$

At 300 °C the equilibrium mixture consists of 80% *trans* and 20% *cis* isomer.

For the simplest case of opposing first-order reactions we write

$$A \leftrightarrows B \tag{13.46}$$

We have

$$A \xrightarrow{k_1} B \tag{13.47}$$

with a rate constant of k_1 and

$$B \xrightarrow{k_{-1}} A \tag{13.48}$$

with a rate constant of k_{-1}. Let the initial concentrations of A and B be a and b. After time t, let x moles per liter of A be converted to B. Then the concentrations at time t are $a - x$ for A and $b + x$ for B. The rate of formation of B is the sum of the two rate processes:

$$\frac{d(b + x)}{dt} = k_1(a - x) - k_{-1}(b + x) \tag{13.49}$$

Since b is independent of time

$$\frac{dx}{dt} = k_1(a - x) - k_{-1}(b + x) \tag{13.50}$$

This equation can be rearranged in the form

$$\frac{dx}{dt} = (k_1 + k_{-1})(m - x) \tag{13.51}$$

where

$$m = \frac{k_1 a - k_{-1} b}{k_1 + k_{-1}} \tag{13.52}$$

Equation 13.51 can be integrated to give

$$\ln \frac{m}{m - x} = (k_1 + k_{-1})t \tag{13.53}$$

At equilibrium, $t = \infty$, and $m = x_{eq}$, where x_{eq} is the amount of B formed between $t = 0$ and $t = \infty$. With this result, we have

$$m = \frac{k_1 a - k_{-1} b}{k_1 + k_{-1}} = x_{eq} \tag{13.54}$$

which we can rearrange to

$$\frac{b + x_{eq}}{a - x_{eq}} = \frac{k_1}{k_{-1}} \tag{13.55}$$

The ratio of the equilibrium concentration of B to that of A is simply the equilibrium-constant expression K for the reaction in equation 13.46. Thus

$$\frac{k_1}{k_{-1}} = K \tag{13.56}$$

Therefore, if we can experimentally determine either k_1 or k_{-1} and the equilibrium constant K, then the other rate constant can be found. If both k_1 and k_{-1} can be determined, the equilibrium constant can be calculated from rate data.

13.3 REACTION MECHANISMS FROM RATE LAWS

A reaction mechanism is a detailed description of the precise molecular steps that occur in going from reactants to products. The simplest reaction mechanism is a single elementary step

$$A \rightarrow B \tag{13.57}$$

where a molecule of A goes directly to a molecule of B. More often, a reaction involves several elementary steps, such as

$$A \rightarrow B \rightarrow C \rightarrow D \tag{13.58}$$

where B and C are called *reaction intermediates*. The overall rate of a reaction depends on the rates of the elementary steps. The theoretical rate laws for elementary-step reactions depend on the number of molecules involved in the elementary steps. This number is called the *molecularity* of the process. Examples of some elementary reactions and their rate laws are shown in Table 13-2.

A reaction mechanism is developed by inference from the experimental rate-law data. Remember that (1) the order of a reaction is found by experimental observation and (2) the mechanism of a reaction cannot be predicted from overall reaction stoichiometry.

For example, we can express the stoichiometry of the reaction of NO_2 to form N_2O_4 in several ways, two of which are

Table 13-2. THEORETICAL RATE LAWS FOR ELEMENTARY REACTIONS

Elementary reaction	*Rate law*	*Molecularity*
$A \rightarrow B$	$k[A]$	Unimolecular
$2A \rightarrow C$	$k[A]^2$	Bimolecular
$A + B \rightarrow D$	$k[A][B]$	Bimolecular
$A + 2B \rightarrow E + F$	$k[A][B]^2$	Termolecular

$$2NO_2 \rightarrow N_2O_4 \tag{13.59}$$

$$4NO_2 \rightarrow 2N_2O_4 \tag{13.60}$$

The rate laws predicted for these two forms, assuming they are elementary-step reactions, would be

$$-\frac{1}{2}\frac{d[NO_2]}{dt} = k[NO_2]^2 \tag{13.61}$$

$$-\frac{1}{4}\frac{d[NO_2]}{dt} = k[NO_2]^4 \tag{13.62}$$

It is found experimentally that equation 13.61 is the correct rate law. Therefore, we rule out the second process, equation 13.60, as a possible mechanism of the reaction. We might conclude that a single elementary step is the reaction mechanism for the NO_2 reaction. However this might not be the case, since a more complex mechanism can give an overall second-order rate law. For example, suppose we have the following sequence of elementary steps:

$$NO_2 \leftrightarrows NO + O \tag{13.63}$$

$$NO + NO_2 \leftrightarrows N_2O_3 \tag{13.64}$$

$$N_2O_3 + O \rightarrow N_2O_4 \tag{13.65}$$

which overall yields

$$2NO_2 \rightarrow N_2O_4 \tag{13.66}$$

For any sequence of reaction steps, one step generally will be slower than the rest. This step is called the *rate-determining step*. The rate-determining step forms the basis of the rate law of the overall reaction.

Suppose the rate-determining step for the NO_2 reaction is equation 13.65, and the steps in equations 13.63 and 13.64 are so fast in both directions that they are at equilibrium. From equation 13.65, the theoretical rate of N_2O_4 formation is

$$\frac{d[N_2O_4]}{dt} = -\frac{1}{2}\frac{d[NO_2]}{dt} = k[N_2O_3][O] \tag{13.67}$$

The equilibrium concentrations of O and N_2O_3 are given from equations 13.63 and 13.64 as

$$[O] = K_1\frac{[NO_2]}{[NO]} \tag{13.68}$$

$$[N_2O_3] = K_2[NO][NO_2] \tag{13.69}$$

When these are inserted into equation 13.67 we have

$$-\frac{1}{2}\frac{d[NO_2]}{dt} = kK_1K_2[NO_2]^2 \tag{13.70}$$

This has the same form as the observed second-order rate law. Thus both the mechanism in equations 13.63 to 13.65 and a single-elementary-step mechanism (equation 13.59) satisfy the observed second-order rate law. The point here is that in determining the mechanism of a reaction, we can clearly rule out those mechanisms that do not yield the correct form of the rate law, while we can invent many others that do give the correct form. Through the use of chemical intuition to discard plausible but unlikely mechanisms and sophisticated techniques to identify intermediate species, we may eventually determine the correct mechanism.

Chain reactions

A more complex example of the use of rate-law data to interpret reaction mechanisms is illustrated in the case of a chain reaction. The reaction

$$H_2 + Br_2 \rightarrow 2HBr \tag{13.71}$$

has a surprisingly complex experimental rate law:

$$\frac{1}{2}\frac{d[HBr]}{dt} = \frac{k[H_2][Br_2]^{1/2}}{m + [HBr]/[Br_2]} \tag{13.72}$$

where k and m are experimental constants. A mechanistic interpretation of this rate law assumes a chain of elementary reaction steps as follows:

$$Br_2 \xrightarrow{k_1} 2Br \tag{13.73}$$

$$Br + H_2 \xrightarrow{k_2} HBr + H \tag{13.74}$$

$$H + Br_2 \xrightarrow{k_3} HBr + Br \tag{13.75}$$

$$H + HBr \xrightarrow{k_4} H_2 + Br \tag{13.76}$$

$$2Br \xrightarrow{k_5} Br_2 \tag{13.77}$$

To combine these steps into an expression for the rate of HBr formation, we assume that the reactive atoms, Br and H, are present in very low concentrations and that their concentrations are independent of time. This is known as the *steady-state* approximation. We can then set the rates $d[H]/dt$ and $d[Br]/dt$ equal to zero and solve for the effective concentrations of Br and H as follows:

$$\frac{d[Br]}{dt} = 0 = 2k_1[Br_2] - k_2[Br][H_2] + k_3[H][Br_2] + k_4[H][HBr] - 2k_5[Br]^2 \tag{13.78}$$

$$\frac{d[H]}{dt} = 0 = k_2[Br][H_2] - k_3[H][Br_2] - k_4[H][HBr] \tag{13.79}$$

When these equations are solved for [Br] and [H] we have

$$[Br] = \frac{k_1}{k_5}[Br_2]^{1/2} \tag{13.80}$$

and

$$[H] = k_2 \frac{(k_1/k_5)^{1/2}[H_2][Br_2]^{1/2}}{k_3[Br_2] + k_4[HBr]} \tag{13.81}$$

The rate of formation of HBr is then

$$\frac{1}{2}\frac{d[HBr]}{dt} = k_2[Br][H_2] + k_3[H][Br_2] - k_4[H][HBr] \tag{13.82}$$

Substituting equations 13.80 and 13.81 into 13.82, we obtain

$$\frac{1}{2}\frac{d[HBr]}{dt} = 2\frac{k_2k_3k_4^{-1}k_1^{1/2}k_5^{-1/2}[H_2][Br_2]^{1/2}}{k_3k_4^{-1} + [HBr]/[Br]} \tag{13.83}$$

Equation 13.83 has the same form as the experimental rate law, equation 13.72, indicating that the proposed mechanism is at least a plausible explanation of the details of the reaction. Of course other mechanisms that fit the experimental results are also possible. In general, one favors the simplest explanation.

13.4 THEORY OF CHEMICAL REACTION RATES

For a chemical reaction to occur, the reactant molecules must come together in some collision process. If they collide with sufficient energy in the appropriate geometric arrangement, the collision complex can dissociate into product molecules. If the necessary reaction conditions are not met, the aggregated reactant molecules dissociate back to the reactant species. These processes are depicted in Fig. 13-6.

Reactions of gases

A theory of reaction rates based on the above ideas has been developed for reactions between gases. We can calculate the number of collisions per second between molecules by considering a mixture of spherical molecules A and B. We consider N_B molecules per cm^3 of B (diameter d_B) and N_A molecules per cm^3 of A (diameter d_A). We focus attention on an A molecule moving with an average speed $\bar{v}$. It sweeps out a collision volume $\pi d^2\bar{v}$ in 1 second, where $d = (d_A + d_B)/2$. The *collision volume* is the volume in which A and B molecules can collide. The moving A molecule collides with any B molecules in this volume, as shown in Fig. 13-7. The number of collisions that one A molecule makes per second with B molecules

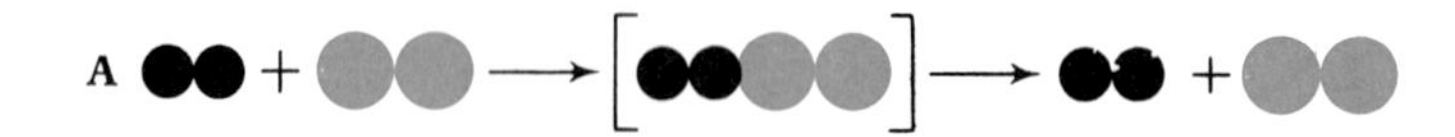

B

C

Fig. 13-6. Representations of three bimolecular collision processes. **A,** With incorrect geometry, **B,** with insufficient collisional energy, and **C,** with correct geometry and sufficient energy for reaction to occur.

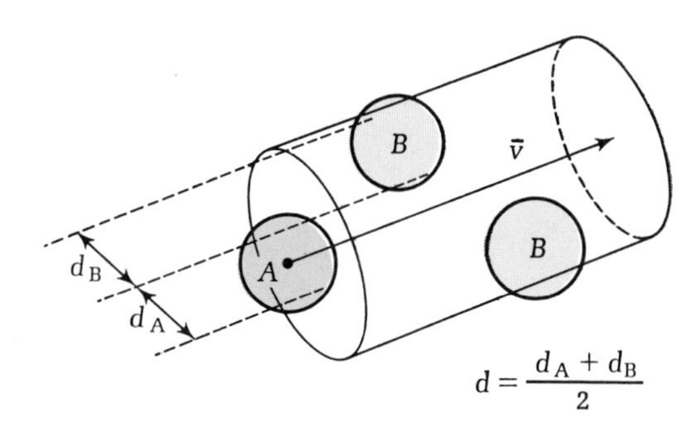

Fig. 13-7. Collision volume swept out by moving particle A of diameter d_A.

is $\pi d^2 N_B \bar{v}$. The total number of collisions per second between A and B molecules, Z_{AB}, is given by $\pi d^2 N_A N_B \bar{v}$. The relative velocity of A and B, given by the kinetic theory of gases, is

$$\bar{v} = \left(\frac{8kT}{\pi\mu}\right)^{1/2} \tag{13.84}$$

where μ is the reduced mass:

$$\mu = \frac{m_A m_B}{m_A + m_B} \tag{13.85}$$

Table 13-3. AVERAGE SPEEDS (0°C) AND MOLECULAR DIAMETERS

Gas	*Speed (meters/sec)*	*Diameter* (Å)
H_2O	567	2.72
Ar	380	2.86
He	1204	2.00
H_2	1692	2.76

and k is Boltzmann's constant. The number of collisions per second is given by

$$Z_{AB} = \pi d^2 N_A N_B \left(\frac{8kT}{\pi\mu}\right)^{1/2} \tag{13.86}$$

Average-speed and effective-molecular-diameter data for some small gaseous molecules are given in Table 13-3.

For a gas at 1 atm and 0°C, the number of molecules per cm^3 is 2.7×10^{19}. For a H_2-He mixture at 0°C, each gas at 1 atm pressure, equation 13.86 gives a collision rate Z_{He-H_2} of 10^{28} collisions/sec-cm^3. If every collision led to products, the reaction would be complete within a few microseconds. Because only a few reactions occur that fast, we are led to the idea that only a fraction of the collisions proceed to products. These are termed *effective collisions.*

For a reaction to occur, the two colliding molecules must have a relative collision velocity greater than some critical velocity. The combined translational energy of the collision must be greater than the critical kinetic energy, E_a. The fraction of collisions with energy greater than E_a is found to be $e^{-E_a/RT}$. The E_a is called the *activation energy* per mole of collision complex.

The rate of a reaction between A and B in molecules/sec-cm^3 is given by

$$\frac{dN_A}{dt} = Z_{AB}e^{-E_a/RT} \tag{13.87}$$

In terms of moles per liter per second, the rate law is

$$\frac{dc_A}{dt} = k_2 c_A c_B \tag{13.88}$$

where c_A and c_B are the molar concentrations of A and B. Since

$$c_A = \frac{10^3 N_A}{N_{av}} \tag{13.89}$$

$$c_B = \frac{10^3 N_B}{N_{av}}$$

where N_{av} is Avogadro's number and the factor 10^3 converts liters to cm^3, then

$$\frac{dc_A}{dt} = \frac{10^3}{N_{\text{av}}}\left(\frac{dN_A}{dt}\right) = k_2 \frac{10^6}{(N_{\text{av}})^2} N_A N_B \tag{13.90}$$

which leads to

$$k_2 = \frac{N_{\text{av}}}{10^3 N_A N_B}\left(\frac{dN_A}{dt}\right) \tag{13.91}$$

With equation 13.87, we obtain

$$k_2 = \frac{N_{\text{av}}}{10^3 N_A N_B} Z_{AB} e^{-E_{\text{a}}/RT} \tag{13.92}$$

This equation, called the *Arrhenius equation*, is often written in the simple form

$$k_2 = A e^{-E_{\text{a}}/RT} \tag{13.93}$$

where A, called the *frequency factor*, is a complex term involving the frequency of collisions. For many reactions, a *geometric factor*, ρ, is introduced to account for the geometric requirements of the molecular collision that yields a product. This factor indicates the fraction of collisions that have the correct geometry for reaction. The rate constant, with ρ included, is often expressed as

$$k_2 = \rho A e^{-E_{\text{a}}/RT} \tag{13.94}$$

Activation energy

Typical values of activation energies range from 0 to 50 kcal/mole, as shown in Table 13-4. The activation energy is the major factor determining the observed rate of a reaction. How $e^{-E_{\text{a}}/RT}$ depends on typical E_{a} and T values is shown in Table 13-5. For very high activation energies, the factor $e^{-E_{\text{a}}/RT}$, and thus the rate constant k_2, is very small. The effect of temperature on $e^{-E_{\text{a}}/RT}$ is greatest at the largest value of E_{a}. The effect of temperature on the specific rate constant is found from equation 13.93 to be

$$\frac{k_2'}{k_2} = \frac{e^{-E_{\text{a}}/RT'}}{e^{-E_{\text{a}}/RT}} = e^{-(E_{\text{a}}/R)[(1/T') - (1/T)]} \tag{13.95}$$

where k_2' and k_2 are the rate constants at T' and T, respectively.

A pictorial representation of the energy changes accompanying the formation of products from reactants is shown in Fig. 13-8. Energy is plotted versus the reaction coordinate. The *reaction coordinate* represents the general way in which the reactant molecules come together in collision and go apart to form product molecules. The activation energy in the forward direction, from reactants to

Table 13-4. ACTIVATION ENERGIES OF BIMOLECULAR REACTIONS

Reaction			E_a(*kcal/mole*)
$H_2 + I_2$	→	$2HI$	40.0
$2HI$	→	$H_2 + I_2$	44.0
$NO_2 + NO_2$	→	N_2O_4	0.0
$CO + Cl_2$	→	$COCl + Cl$	51.3
Isobutene + HCl	→	*Trans*-C_4H_9Cl	24.1
$H + Br_2$	→	$HBr + Br$	1.2

Table 13-5. DEPENDENCE OF $e^{-E_a/RT}$ ON E_a AND T

T(°K) \ E_a	*10 kcal*	*20 kcal*	*30 kcal*
298	4.7×10^{-8}	2.2×10^{-15}	1.04×10^{-22}
400	3.4×10^{-6}	1.2×10^{-11}	4.2×10^{-17}
600	2.3×10^{-4}	5.3×10^{-8}	1.2×10^{-11}

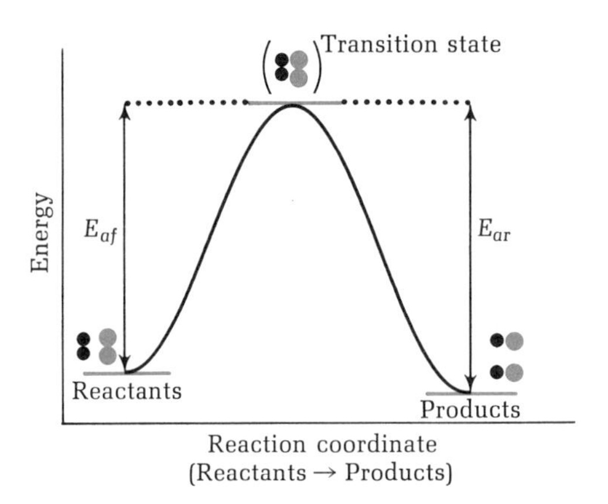

Fig. 13-8. Energy diagram of reactants going to products through high-energy transition state.

products, is E_{af}. The activation energy in the reverse direction is E_{ar}. The energy difference ΔE is the thermodynamic change in energy between reactants and products. The relation of ΔE to the activation energies is

$$\Delta E = E_{af} - E_{ar} \tag{13.96}$$

The state of maximum energy in the collision process is called the *activated complex*. The form of the activated complex is the same in the forward and the reverse directions.

Reactions in solution

The frequency of collisions between reactant molecules in solution is generally much less than that between reactant molecules in the gas phase. Collisions occur less frequently in solution because the presence of solvent slows the random motion or diffusion of reactant molecules. The effectiveness of a collision that leads to a product is still dependent on the proper orientation and on the collisional energy being greater than E_a. When the activation energy is essentially zero and the orientational effects are negligible, reaction rates in solution are said to be *diffusion controlled.* The rates of most reactions between ions are diffusion controlled. For example, the reactions of H_3O^+ with OH^- and with SO_4^{2-} in aqueous solution are

$$H_3O^+(aq) + OH^-(aq) \rightarrow 2H_2O \qquad k_2 = 4 \times 10^{10} \text{ liter/mole-sec} \tag{13.97}$$

$$H_3O^+(aq) + SO_4^{2-}(aq) \rightarrow HSO_4^-(aq) + H_2O \qquad k_2 = 10^{11} \text{ liter/mole-sec} \tag{13.98}$$

These measured rates are consistent with calculations based on diffusion control.

13.5 CATALYSTS

A catalyst is a substance that increases the rate of a chemical reaction. Catalysts undergo no net chemical change during the course of a reaction. Their general role is to provide a lower activation-energy pathway to the product, as typified in Fig. 13-9. Catalysts are classified as *homogeneous* when they are completely soluble in the reaction solution, and as *heterogeneous* when they are present as a separate phase.

As an example of a homogeneous catalyzed reaction, consider

$$2Ce^{4+} + Tl^+ \rightarrow 2Ce^{3+} + Tl^{3+} \tag{13.99}$$

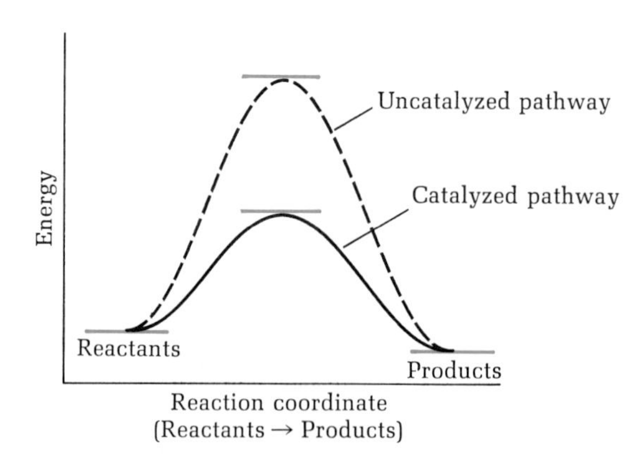

Fig. 13-9. Plots of energy versus reaction coordinate for catalyzed and uncatalyzed reactions.

This reaction has the rate law

$$\text{Rate} = k[\text{Ce}^{4+}]^2[\text{Tl}^+] \tag{13.100}$$

Electrons are transferred from Tl^+ to two Ce^{4+} in the rate-determining step of this reaction. In the presence of a catalyst, such as Mn^{2+}, the reaction occurs much faster due to the addition of a new reaction pathway involving Mn^{2+} as follows:

$$\text{Ce}^{4+} + \text{Mn}^{2+} \rightarrow \text{Ce}^{3+} + \text{Mn}^{3+} \tag{13.101}$$

$$\text{Ce}^{4+} + \text{Mn}^{3+} \rightarrow \text{Ce}^{3+} + \text{Mn}^{4+} \tag{13.102}$$

$$\text{Mn}^{4+} + \text{Tl}^{+} \rightarrow \text{Tl}^{3+} + \text{Mn}^{2+} \tag{13.103}$$

Although Mn^{2+} is chemically changed in the first two reaction steps, it is regenerated in the last step. The new reaction pathway has a lower activation energy, and the rate is much faster.

The rates of most biological reactions are controlled by catalytic agents called *enzymes*. These materials are large protein molecules.

An important series of reactions involves the transference of the energy of glucose to other chemical materials required in a biological cell. An important step is the addition of the phosphate group to glucose to yield glucose-6-phosphate. The reaction is

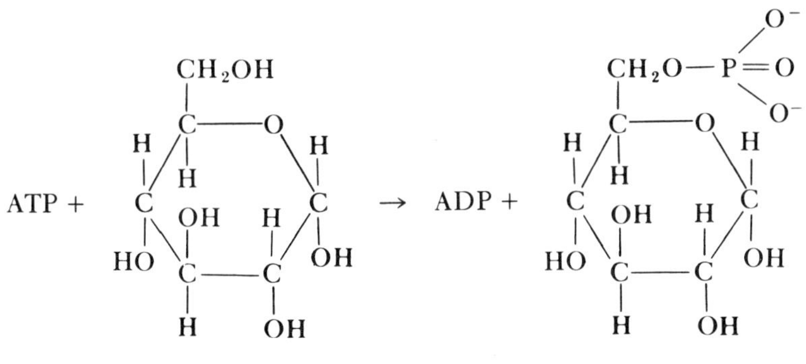

```
                                                            O⁻
                                                           /
          CH₂OH                              CH₂O—P=O
          |                                  |         \
          C———O                              C———O      O⁻
       H /|    \ H                        H /|    \ H
       |/ H     \|                        |/ H     \|
ATP +  C  OH  H  C   →   ADP +            C  OH  H  C          (13.104)
       |\ |   |/ |                        |\ |   |/ |
      HO \C———C  OH                      HO \C———C  OH
          |   |                              |   |
          H   OH                             H   OH
```

The molecules ATP and ADP are known as adenosine triphosphate and adenosine diphosphate. This reaction is catalyzed by an enzyme known as hexokinase. The proposed mechanism involves bringing the reactant species together on a particular site of the enzyme to form a reactive complex. This general scheme is represented by

$$E + S \underset{k_{-1}}{\overset{k_1}{\rightleftarrows}} ES \overset{k_2}{\rightarrow} E + P \tag{13.105}$$

where E is the enzyme, S is the reactant molecule called a substrate, ES is the reactive complex, and P is the product. We see from this mechanism that the enzyme is regenerated during the course of the reaction.

PROBLEMS

1. Express the rate $d\xi/dt$, for the following reactions in terms of the reactants and the products:
   (a) $SO_2Cl_2(g) \rightarrow SO_2(g) + Cl_2(g)$
   (b) $2Ce^{4+}(aq) + Hg_2^{2+}(aq) \rightarrow 2Ce^{3+}(aq) + 2Hg^{2+}(aq)$
   (c) $H_2(g) + \frac{1}{2}O_2(g) \rightarrow H_2O(g)$
2. For the reaction

$$2NO(g) + Cl_2(g) \rightarrow 2NOCl$$

at $-10°C$, the initial rate of reaction was determined as follows for initial concentrations of NO and Cl_2:

$[NO]_0$ *(moles/liter)*	$[Cl_2]_0$ *(moles/liter)*	*Initial rate (moles/liter-min)*
0.10	0.10	0.18
0.10	0.20	0.35
0.20	0.20	1.45

   (a) Determine the rate law.
   (b) Calculate the specific rate constant.
3. What are the orders of the rate laws for the following reactions:
   (a) $(CH_3)_2N_2(g) \rightarrow C_2H_6(g) + N_2(g)$

$$\frac{d[N_2]}{dt} = k[(CH_3)_2N_2]$$

   (b) $2NO_2(g) + F_2(g) \rightarrow 2NO_2F(g)$

$$-\frac{d[F_2]}{dt} = k[F_2][NO_2]$$

   (c) $C_4H_6(g) \rightarrow \frac{1}{2}C_8H_{12}(g)$

$$-\frac{d[C_4H_6]}{dt} = k[C_4H_6]^2$$

   (d) $2Br^-(aq) + 2H_3O^+(aq) + H_2O_2(aq) \rightarrow Br_2(l) + 4H_2O(l)$

$$\frac{d[Br_2]}{dt} = k[H_2O_2][H_3O^+][Br^-]$$

   (e) $O_2NNH_2(aq) \rightarrow N_2O + H_2O$

$$\frac{d[N_2O]}{dt} = k\frac{[O_2NNH_2]}{[H_3O^+]}$$

4. Determine the reaction order and rate constant for

$$C_6H_5N_2Cl(l) \rightarrow C_6H_5Cl(aq) + N_2(g)$$

at 50 °C and 1 atm, given the following data:

Time (min):	6	9	14	22	30	∞
N_2 evolved (ml):	19.3	26.0	36.0	45.0	50.4	58.3

The volume of the solution is 40 cc.

5. Plot the following data for butadiene (C_4H_6) at 500°K as ln c versus t and as $1/c$ versus t:

$$C_4H_6(g) \rightarrow \tfrac{1}{2}C_8H_{12}(g)$$

t sec:	195	604	1246	2180	6210
$[C_4H_6]$, (mole/liter) $\times 10^{-2}$:	1.6	1.5	1.3	1.1	0.68

Determine the rate law and the specific rate constant.

6. Calculate the half-life in the following situations.
   (a) $k_1 = 1.6 \times 10^{-6}$ sec^{-1}, first order
   (b) $k_2 = 150$ (liter/mole-sec), $c_0 = 5$ moles/liter, second order

7. Given the reaction

$$(CH_3)_2N_2(g) \rightarrow N_2(g) + C_2H_6(g)$$

the following data were obtained at 300°C for an initially pure sample of $(CH_3)_2N_2(g)$ placed in a vessel of 200 ml volume:

Time (min):	0	15	30	48	75
Pressure (torr):	36.2	42.4	46.5	53.1	59.3

Calculate the order and the specific rate constant.

8. Show that the mechanism described by

$$NO + NO \leftrightarrows N_2O_2 \text{ (fast, equilibrium)}$$
$$N_2O_2 + O_2 \rightarrow 2NO_2 \text{ (slow)}$$

is consistent with the rate law

$$-\frac{d[O_2]}{dt} = k[NO]^2[O_2]$$

for the reaction

$$2NO(g) + O_2(g) \rightarrow 2NO_2(g)$$

9. The rate law for the reaction

$$Cl_2(g) + CO(g) \rightarrow Cl_2CO(g)$$

is

$$\frac{d[Cl_2CO]}{dt} = k[Cl_2]^{3/2}[CO]$$

Is the following mechanism possible?

$$Cl_2 \leftrightarrows 2Cl \text{ (fast equilibrium)}$$
$$Cl + CO \leftrightarrows ClCO \text{ (fast equilibrium)}$$
$$ClCO + Cl_2 \rightarrow Cl_2CO \text{ (slow)}$$

10. For the reaction

$$2C_4H_8(g) \rightarrow C_8H_{16}(g)$$

the second-order rate constant is described by

$$k_2 = (9.2 \times 10^9)e^{-23,690/RT} \text{ cm}^3\text{/mole-sec}$$

Calculate the activation energy E_a and the rate of reaction at 500°K.

11. For the $N_2O_5 \rightarrow 2NO_2 + \frac{1}{2}O_2$ reaction, plot the following data and determine the activation energy E_a from the plot.

T (°K):	338	318	298
k (sec^{-1}):	4.9×10^{-3}	5.0×10^{-4}	3.5×10^{-5}

14 ELECTROMAGNETIC RADIATION AND MATTER

Interactions between electromagnetic radiation (photons) and matter give rise to a variety of important phenomena. For example, matter can absorb, transmit, and diffract photons. Some of the information in previous chapters was obtained through techniques that utilize electromagnetic radiation. X-ray diffraction provides the principal means for obtaining structural information. Studies of the absorption of electromagnetic radiation yield information about the energy states in a molecule. Often we can relate such information to bonding and structure. Electromagnetic radiation of sufficiently high energy can break bonds, thereby causing chemical reactions. Such processes are called *photochemical reactions.*

14.1 X-RAY DIFFRACTION

Basis and scope of X-ray method

X-ray radiation can be produced with wavelengths in the range of 1 Å (10^{-8} cm), the same order of size as the dimensions of atoms and molecules. When waves impinge upon an object whose size is of the same order of magnitude as the wavelength, the object scatters the waves in a characteristic way. A photographic picture of the intensity of the scattered waves gives a *diffraction pattern* of the object. In principle, one can reconstruct a picture of the object from the diffraction pattern. This procedure forms the basis for determining the detailed geometric structure of matter. Bond angles, bond distances, atomic sizes, lattice dimensions, and the overall geometry of molecules are determined in solids by the analysis of X-ray diffraction patterns. This method is the single most powerful tool for detailed structural analysis of matter.

General features of diffraction

The general properties of diffraction can be illustrated by examining how a pattern of holes diffracts light. If the object, consisting of a round hole, is placed

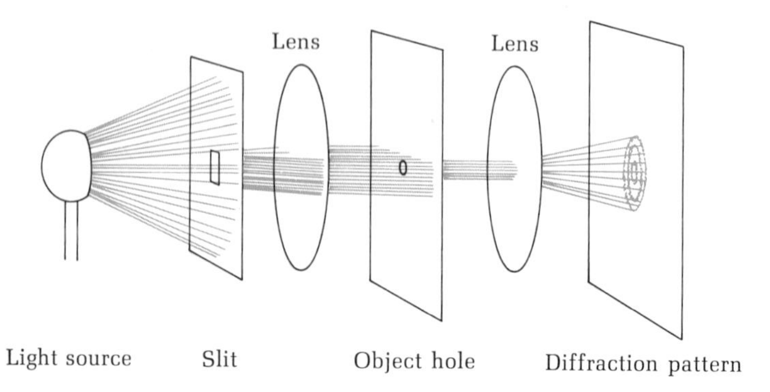

Fig. 14-1. Optical diffraction pattern produced by circular object hole.

in a beam of light, as shown in Fig. 14-1, a diffraction pattern of the object can be produced on photographic film. The diffraction pattern of the hole is characterized by a set of diffuse circles. The size of the set of circles is related to the size of the hole.

The diffraction effect of an object that consists of several closely spaced holes is shown in Fig. 14-2, *A*. Although the pattern is characteristic of the object, we could not easily identify the object from its diffraction pattern. Such identification requires a precise theory connecting the diffraction pattern with the nature of the object.

The diffraction pattern of a row of holes provides us with some new features. The pattern for an object consisting of two holes at a distance $2a$ is shown in Fig. 14-3, *A*. Here we see the circular features of the individual hole pattern superimposed upon a set of parallel diffraction lines. The closer the object holes are, the farther apart the parallel diffraction lines will be.

If the object consists of a set of more than two holes equally spaced by a distance a, then the diffraction pattern is a set of considerably sharper parallel lines whose intensities again vary according to the pattern of the single hole, as shown in Fig. 14-3, *B*. The spacing of the parallel lines in the diffraction pattern is $1/a$.

If we examine the diffraction pattern of a set of holes spaced a distance b apart and oriented in a vertical direction, we find the parallel line diffraction pattern shown in Fig. 14-3, *C*. The spacing between the parallel lines of this pattern is $1/b$.

The pattern of the object made by combining these two rows of holes to form a two-dimensional lattice is shown in Fig. 14-3, *D*. The pattern arises from a combination of the patterns from the two rows. The only place where the two individual patterns intersect is the place where reinforcement occurs to produce the pattern for the combined two-dimensional lattice. The array of spots in the diffraction pattern has a lattice spacing related reciprocally to the lattice spacing of the object

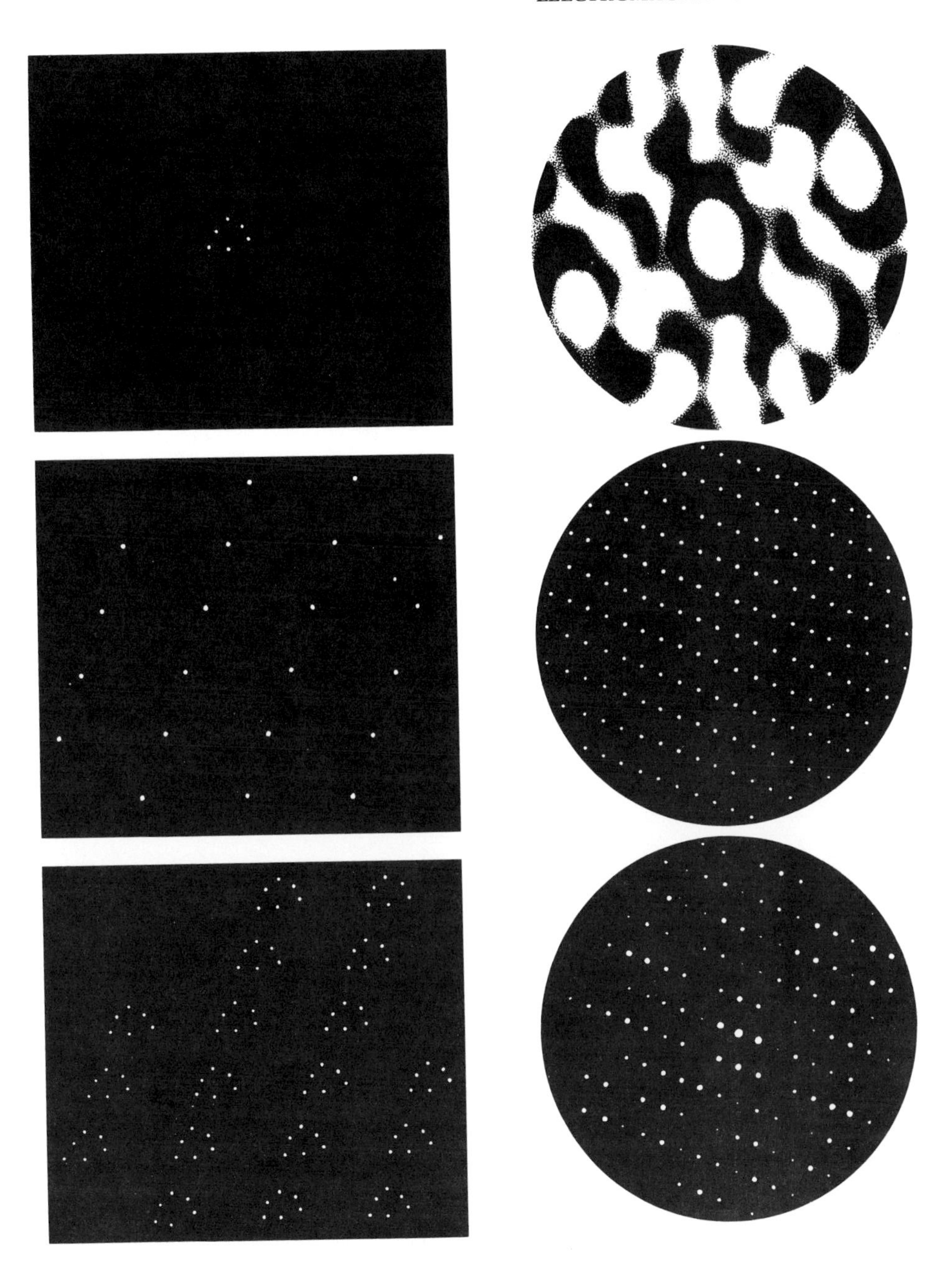

Fig. 14-2. Diffraction patterns of objects consisting of patterns of circular holes. Object-hole patterns on left, corresponding diffraction patterns on right. (Adapted from Taylor, C. A., and Lipson, H.: Optical transforms, Cornell University Press, Ithaca, New York, 1965).

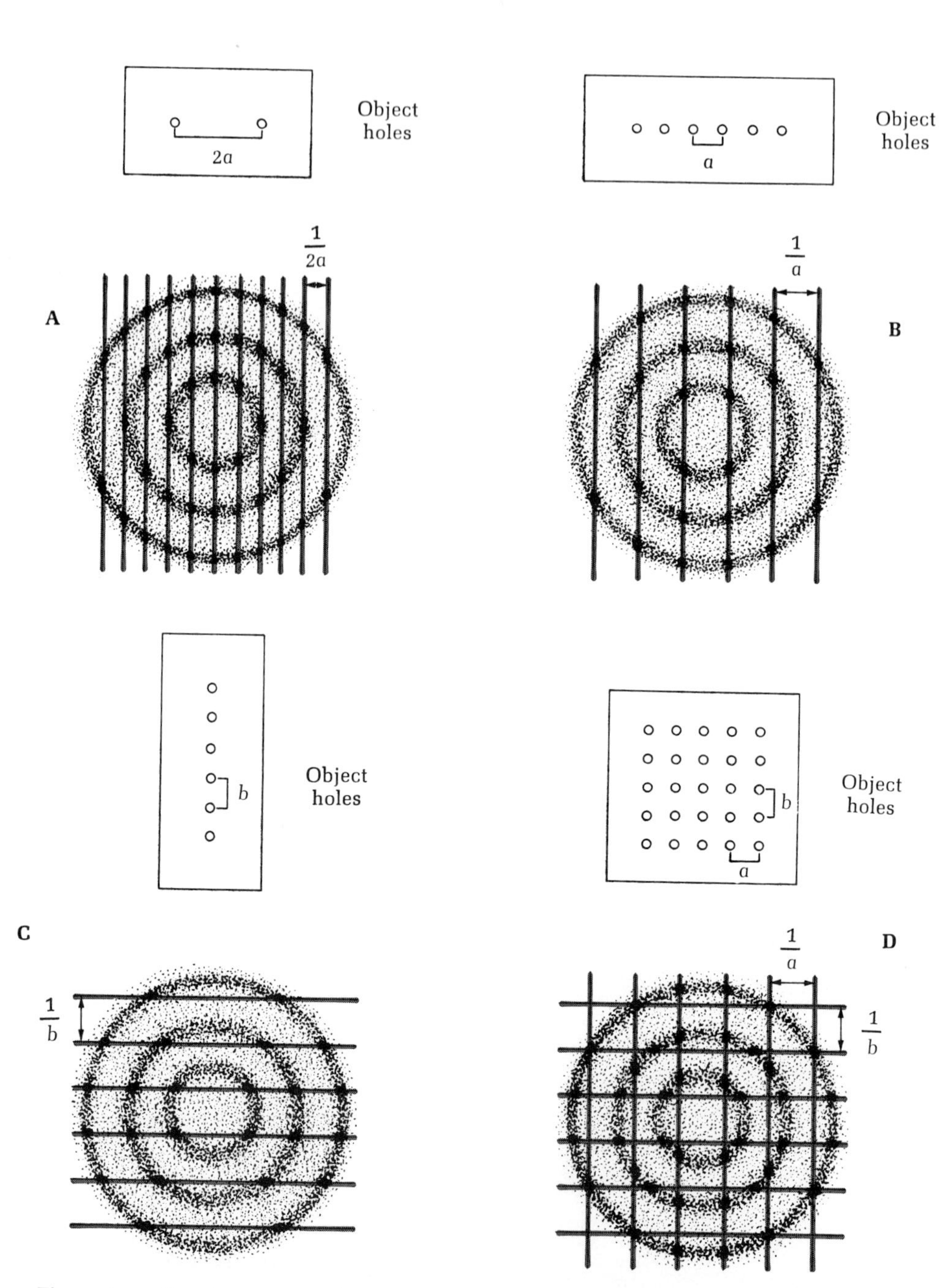

Fig. 14-3. Diffraction patterns that arise from arrays of circular object holes. **A,** Pattern from two holes spaced a distance of $2a$. **B,** Pattern from horizontal row of holes spaced distance a. **C,** Pattern from vertical row of holes spaced distance b. **D,** Pattern from square array of holes with spacing a and b. Diffraction pattern occurs primarily at intersection of diffraction components that arise from individual holes and array of holes. The closer the object holes, the farther apart the diffraction lines.

holes. Information about the shape of individual circular holes is contained in the diffraction pattern in the form of the variation of intensities of the spots. If the object pattern is more complicated, the intensity variation of the diffraction pattern is more complicated, as shown in Fig. 14-2.

There is a simple reciprocal relation between the real space lattice of the object and the points where the diffraction pattern appears in what is called the *reciprocal space lattice*. The reciprocal lattice represents the reciprocal spacing between parallel lines that contain points of the regular lattice. The spacing between reciprocal lattice points is represented by a^* and b^* where

$$a^* = \frac{1}{a} \tag{14.1}$$

$$b^* = \frac{1}{b} \tag{14.2}$$

The points of the reciprocal lattice are represented in terms of integer indexes, h and k, from an origin where $h = 0$ and $k = 0$. Such a description of the reciprocal lattice is shown in Fig. 14-4. The position of any point in the reciprocal lattice is given by $ha^* + kb^*$. The distance between parallel rows in the real space lattice is given by $d_{h,k}$. This distance is related to the distance between lattice points in the reciprocal lattice as $1/d_{h,k}$. By the Pythagorean theorem we find

$$\frac{1}{d_{h,k}} = [(ha^*)^2 + (kb^*)^2]^{1/2} \tag{14.3}$$

or with equations 14.1 and 14.2

$$\frac{1}{d_{h,k}} = \left[\left(\frac{h}{a}\right)^2 + \left(\frac{k}{b}\right)^2\right]^{1/2} \tag{14.4}$$

The points in the reciprocal lattice indicate parallel rows of lattice points in the real space lattice. For example, with $h = 1$ and $k = 0$, that is, the (1, 0) reciprocal lattice point, we have the set of rows separated by the distance a in the real lattice. With $h = 0$ and $k = 1$, that is, the (0, 1) point, we have the set of rows separated by the distance b in the real lattice. The (1, 1) point represents the diagonal rows as shown in Fig. 14-4.

In the case of a three-dimensional real space lattice, the reciprocal lattice is similarly described with addition of a third direction and integer index l. The distance between parallel planes of points in the real space lattice is $d_{h,k,l}$ and is given as

$$\frac{1}{d_{h,k,l}} = \left[\left(\frac{h}{a}\right)^2 + \left(\frac{k}{b}\right)^2 + \left(\frac{l}{c}\right)^2\right]^{1/2} \tag{14.5}$$

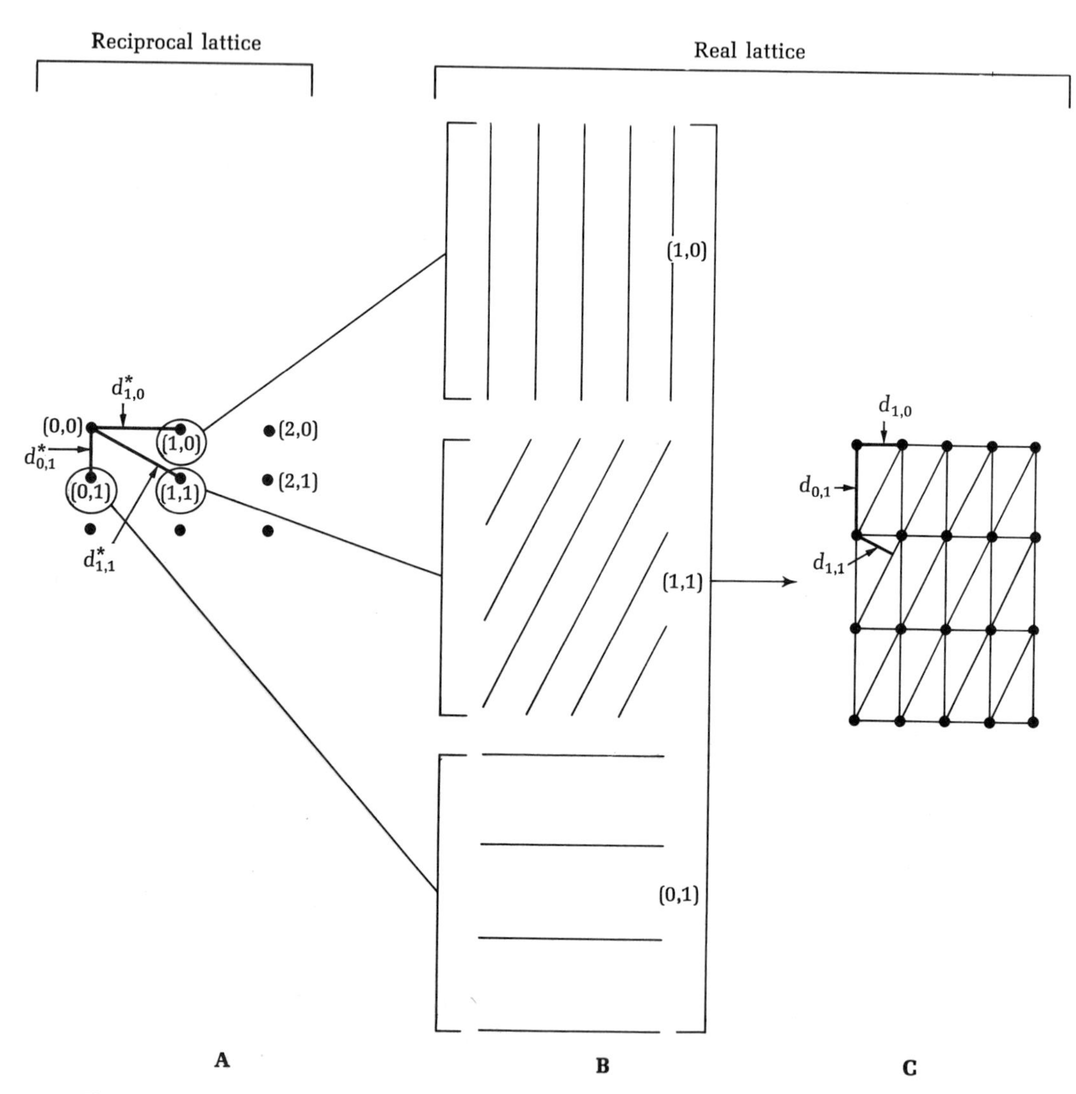

Fig. 14-4. Relationship between lines containing points in real lattice and corresponding points of reciprocal lattice. Points of the reciprocal lattice are separated by distances inversely proportional to distances between parallel lines of real lattice. Three representative sets of parallel lines of real lattice, **C**, are shown in **B** and designated by (1, 0), (1, 1), and (0, 1) in the reciprocal lattice, **A**.

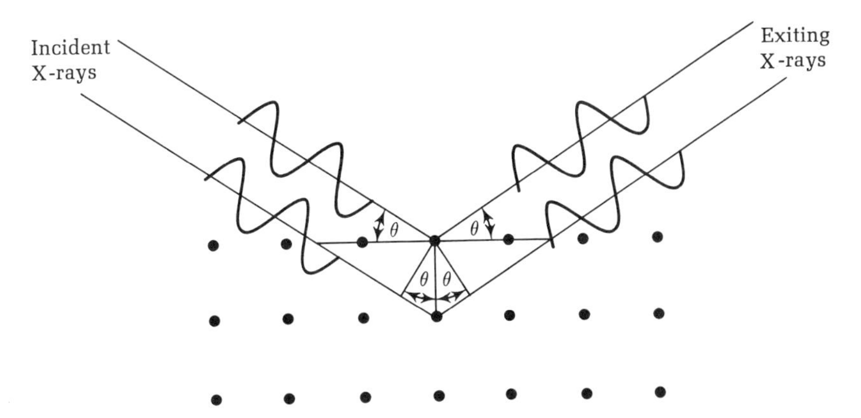

Fig. 14-5. Diffraction condition of X-ray beam by lattice of diffracting points. Angle of diffraction is specified by θ.

or

$$d_{h,k,l} = \left(\frac{h^2}{a^2} + \frac{k^2}{b^2} + \frac{l^2}{c^2}\right)^{-1/2} \tag{14.6}$$

The diffraction pattern is related to the wavelength of the incident radiation λ, the distance $d_{h,k,l}$ between parallel planes in the real lattice, and the angle θ between the plane and the incident and diffracted beam. The condition for the reinforcement of diffracted waves is represented in these terms by the Bragg equation. Fig. 14-5 shows the incident beam impinging at an angle θ. The parallel planes are separated a distance $d_{h,k,l}$. If there is to be reinforcement of the diffracted waves, the distance traveled by the lower wave must equal the distance traveled by the upper wave plus one wavelength λ. This means, from the geometry seen in Fig. 14-5, that

$$\text{Difference in path} = 2d_{h,k,l} \sin \theta = \lambda \tag{14.7}$$

Only at certain angles θ will a diffracted beam result. This angle depends on the wavelength and on the distance $d_{h,k,l}$. This selection of spots is seen in the diffraction pattern. The specific points are the points of the reciprocal lattice.

A crystalline solid, as we saw in Chapter 2, is composed of a repeating lattice of unit cells. When a beam of X rays impinges on a material, it is diffracted due to its interaction with electrons in the material. In a regular crystal lattice, the beam is therefore diffracted into a pattern of spots located at reciprocal lattice points as shown in Fig. 14-6. The intensities of the spots are determined by the variation of electron density in the unit cell. By analogy with the optical diffraction effects discussed above, the unit cell corresponds to the simplest object pattern. The

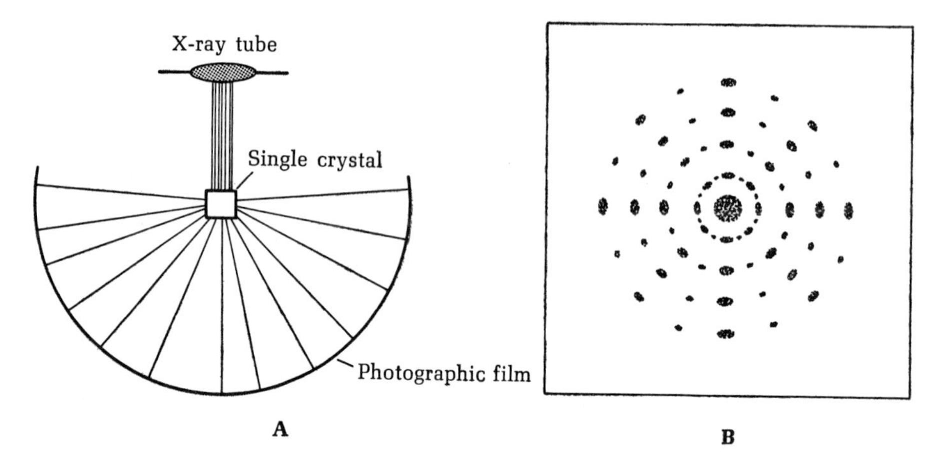

Fig. 14-6. **A,** Schematic diagram of X-ray diffraction experiment. **B,** Illustrative X-ray diffraction pattern of rotated single crystal.

analysis of the intensity pattern allows one to work backward to the electron density distribution of the unit cell. The positions of maximum electron density will correspond to the location of atoms in the unit cell. In this way one can determine the detailed geometric arrangement of atoms in the unit cell.

We describe the electron density at a point (x, y, z) in the unit cell by $\rho(x, y, z)$. This electron density is related to a sum of the amplitudes $F(hkl)$ of all allowed scattered waves (that is, over the entire reciprocal lattice) from the lattice of unit cells. The complex equation that relates these two factors is

$$\rho(x, y, z) = \sum_h \sum_k \sum_l F(hkl)e^{-2\pi i(hx + ky + lz)} \tag{14.8}$$

The amplitude $F(hkl)$ is called the *structure factor*. Its magnitude is indicated by the square root of the intensity of a given diffraction spot. The structure factor is determined by the scattering effects of all atoms in the unit cell. In detail it is therefore a very complex function and is only partly determined from the square root of the intensity of the h, k, l spot. The part not accessible to experimental determination is called the *phase* of the structure factor. The structure factor is given by

$$F(hkl) = \sum_{j=1}^{N} f_j e^{2\pi i(hx_j + ky_j + lz_j)} \tag{14.9}$$

where f_j represents the atomic scattering factor of the *jth* atom, located at the position (x_j, y_j, z_j) in the unit cell, and N represents the total number of atoms

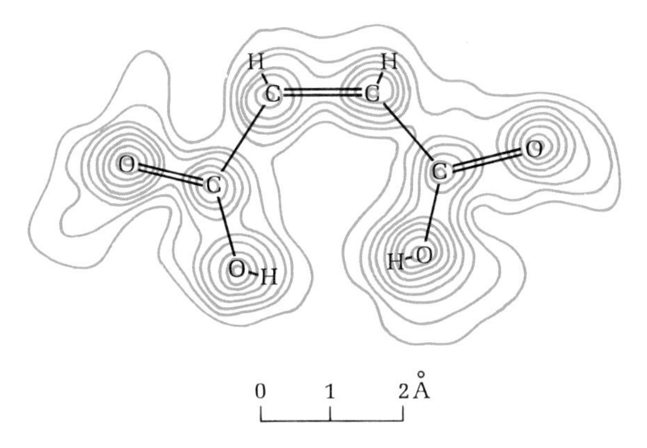

Fig. 14-7. Electron-density map of maleic acid as determined by X-ray analysis.

in the unit cell. Solving these equations is no trivial matter, but when possible, as is generally the case, we obtain the electron-density map of the unit cell.

In Chapter 9 the structure of maleic acid in a crystalline solid was shown. This structure was inferred from an electron-density map of the type shown in Fig. 14-7. In this figure the contour lines represent different degrees of electron density in a particular plane of the unit cell. When many planes of this type are examined, the full three-dimensional picture of the unit cell evolves.

14.2 ABSORPTION SPECTROSCOPY

General features of spectra

The absorption of energy by molecules or atoms is quantized (Chapter 12). Photons of a wide range of wavelengths can be absorbed, which implies that a molecule has many energy levels. These energy levels are determined by various types of molecular, electronic, and nuclear effects.

Three important categories involve (1) translational, rotational, and vibrational motion; (2) electronic energy states; and (3) nuclear-spin and electron-spin energy states. The energy states associated with translational motion were discussed previously in connection with the particle in a box (Chapter 11). Rotational and vibrational energy levels arise due to the quantization of rotational and vibrational motion of molecules. Electronic energy states were discussed in Chapters 11 and 12 in connection with the discussions of electronic energies of atoms and molecules. Nuclear-spin and electron-spin energy states are effects that arise when matter is placed in a magnetic field.

Typical energies associated with these categories are shown in Table 14-1. Note

Table 14-1. ENERGY OF ELECTROMAGNETIC-RADIATION PROCESSES

Wavelength, λ (Å)	ΔE *(kcal/mole of photons)*	*Type of radiation*	*Radiation effect*
1	30,000		
		X rays	Bond breaking
50	5,800		
		Far ultraviolet	
1.5×10^2	2,300		
		Near ultraviolet	Electronic transition
4×10^3	82		
		Visible	
8×10^3	36		
		Infrared	Vibrational transition
3×10^5	1		
		Microwave	Rotational transition and electron-spin transition
10^{10}	10^{-4}		
		Radiowave	Nuclear-spin transition

that the relationship between any two energy levels, ΔE, is equal to a corresponding energy given as

$$\Delta E = h\nu = \frac{hc}{\lambda} \tag{14.10}$$

where h is Planck's constant, ν and λ are the frequency and wavelength of the electromagnetic radiation, and c is the speed of light.

Energy levels in molecules are detected by determining the wavelengths at which electromagnetic radiation is absorbed or emitted. The relationship of intensity of absorption or emission as a function of wavelength is called a *spectrum.* From spectra, chemists obtain the desired structural information.

A device for examining the absorption or emission of energy in a molecule as a function of wavelength is called a *spectrophotometer*, of which there are various types. One of the most popular is an instrument that varies the wavelength and plots the absorption or emission of energy on a convenient electronic recording device. A schematic diagram of such a spectrophotometer is shown in Fig. 14-8. Basically, it consists of a source of radiation, a chamber to hold the sample being analyzed, and a device to detect and record the intensity of radiation passing through the sample. If the instrument is set up to record the amount of light absorbed, a spectrum like the one in Fig. 14-8 would typically result. In this example, the energy being transmitted is constant until a point is reached where the molecule absorbs energy. At that time the curve drops, forming a valley or inverted peak. After the absorption region is

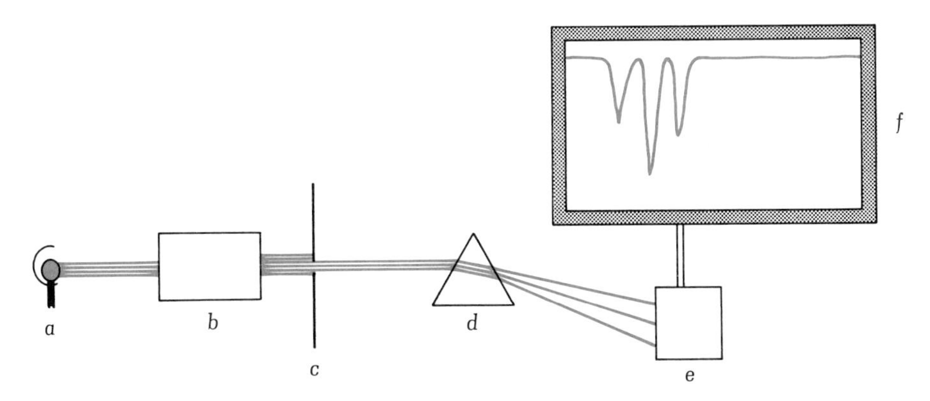

Fig. 14-8. Schematic diagram of simple spectrophotometer, which consists of *a*, light source; *b*, sample chamber; *c*, slit to collimate light from sample; *d*, prism; *e*, detector; and *f*, recorder to plot spectrum.

passed, the curve returns to its normal position until the next absorption region is reached.

Beer-Lambert law

The intensity of absorption at a given wavelength is related to the number of photons absorbed by the molecules. The fraction of photons that a sample absorbs depends on the following:

1. The characteristic absorption properties of the sample of the wavelength λ
2. The concentration of absorbing molecules
3. The path length of irradiation through the sample

These relationships are expressed by the equation

$$A = \epsilon c \ell \qquad (14,11)$$

where A is absorbance, ϵ is a constant called the molar extinction coefficient, c is the concentration of the sample in moles/liter, and ℓ is the path length in cm of the cell containing the sample. The constant ϵ is a characteristic property of the absorbing species. Generally, the value of ϵ is a function of the wavelength of the irradiation.

The absorbance A of irradiation by a sample can be expressed by

$$A = \log I_0 - \log I = \log \frac{I_0}{I} \qquad (14.12)$$

where I_0 is the intensity of the irradiated light, and I is the intensity of the transmitted irradiation.

To obtain a spectrum, we generally plot A as a function of the wavelength.

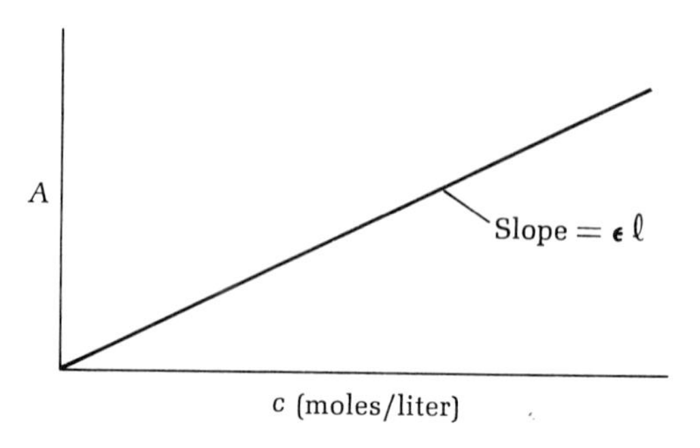

Fig. 14-9. Plot of absorbance A versus concentration c for sample following the Beer-Lambert law.

Combination of equations 14.11 and 14.12 yields

$$\epsilon c \ell = \log \frac{I_0}{I} = A \tag{14.13}$$

which is known as the Beer-Lambert law. This important equation says that for a given sample (ϵ) whose path length ℓ is known, the log of the intensity of transmitted light will be proportional to the concentration of absorbing molecules in the sample. A typical plot is shown in Fig. 14-9.

14.3 ELECTRONIC SPECTROSCOPY

When a molecule absorbs energy of some appropriate wavelength, electrons are excited from filled (occupied) to unoccupied energy levels. In general, only electrons in the highest energy level are involved in the excitation; lower energy levels usually are not of interest. The excitations are categorized according to what types of electrons are involved. We will restrict our attention to σ (e^- in σ orbitals), π (e^- in π orbitals), and n (nonbonding or lone-pair) electrons. Acetone is an example of a molecule that has all three types of electrons in the $\diagdown$C=Ö: $\diagup$ portion of the molecule, as in Fig. 14-10.

Electronic excitation

To understand electronic excitation we rely on the ideas of orbitals that we developed in Chapter 11. We saw that any molecule has a series of energy levels, which, if filled, correspond to the bonding description of the molecule. In addition to the filled orbitals there are higher-energy-level orbitals that are unoccupied in the ground state. During electronic excitation, electrons are promoted into these higher-energy-level orbitals. The simple absorption-excitation process of a $\pi \rightarrow \pi^*$ transition is shown in Fig. 14-11.

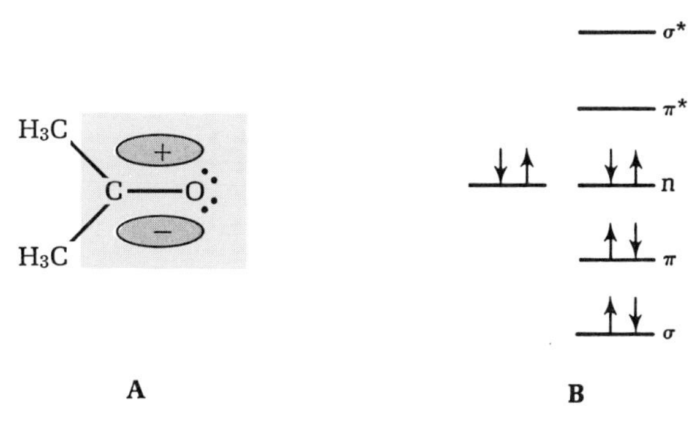

Fig. 14-10. **A,** Structure of acetone showing electrons of σ, π, and n types in CO portion of molecule. **B,** Schematic diagram of energy levels of molecular orbitals of CO unit of acetone.

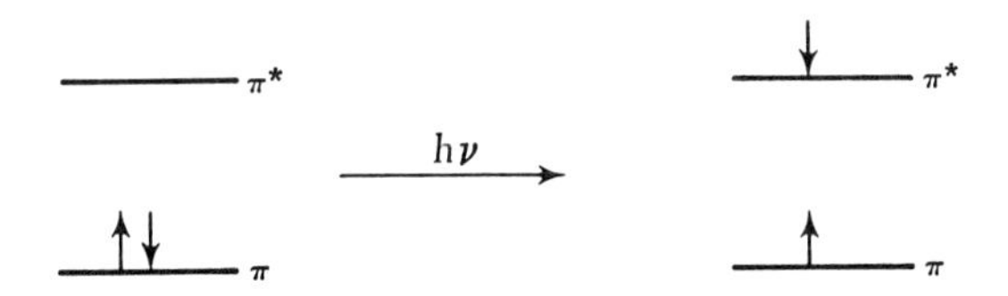

Fig. 14-11. Excitation of π electron to π^* orbital.

In any molecule in the ground state, the electrons occupy the orbitals of lowest energy. When an electron is excited, it is promoted to a higher energy level to yield an excited-state molecule. For example, the ground-state electronic configuration of N_2 is $(\sigma 2s)^2(\sigma^* 2s)^2(\pi 2p)^4(\sigma 2p)^2$. When excited, an electron goes from the highest ground-state level into the first unfilled level, the π^* level. The excited-state molecule has the configuration $(\sigma 2s)^2(\sigma^* 2s)^2(\pi 2p)^4(\sigma 2p)^1(\pi^* 2p)^1$. Thus, the basic idea of electronic absorption is that the electron goes from some initial level to a higher level as a result of the absorption of energy. Note that after absorption, the last two orbitals each contain one electron although the spins of the two electrons are still in opposite directions.

The excitation of an electron is associated with the absorption of electromagnetic radiation of a discrete wavelength. Many molecules are readily receptive to more than one type of excitation, and thus may absorb radiation of a variety of wavelengths. Acetone is an example. Its two lowest-energy absorptions involve transitions of electrons from the π and n orbitals to π^* orbitals.

Those atoms or bond groups whose presence permits absorption in the near ultraviolet region or the visible region are called *chromophores*. Thus, in acetone, the $\rangle C{=}\ddot{O}\!:$ is a chromophoric group. Some common chromophoric groups, the types of

Table 14-2. SOME COMMON CHROMOPHORES

Chromophore	*Typical compound*	*Type of excitation*	λ_{max}	ϵ_{max}
$-\ddot{\underset{\cdot\cdot}{O}}-$	C_2H_5OH	$n \rightarrow \sigma^*$	1830	500
$>C{=}C<$	$CH_2{=}CH_2$	$\pi \rightarrow \pi^*$	1710	15,500
$-C{\equiv}C-$	$HC{\equiv}CH$	$\pi \rightarrow \pi^*$	1730	6000
$-N(=\ddot{O}:)(-\ddot{O}:)$	CH_3NO_2	$\pi \rightarrow \pi^*$	2010	5000
		$n \rightarrow \pi^*$	2740	17

excitation associated with them, and their associated λ and ϵ values are given in Table 14-2.

Decay of excited-state species

Electronically-excited molecules generally do not stay in the excited state very long. In 10^{-6} sec or less the excited-state species usually decay to the ground-state by emitting energy or sometimes, participating in some chemical reaction. Reactions that occur because of electronically-excited species are called photochemical reactions.

Previously we indicated that the excited state is one in which electrons become unpaired, but because the transition occurs rapidly, electron-spin directions do not change. A state in which electrons are in opposite directions so that spins cancel is called a *singlet state*. It is this excited singlet-state species that we examine.

The processes by which an excited molecule can return to a ground-state electronic configuration are varied and depend somewhat on the particular system involved:

1. The molecule can lose its excess energy by collisions with other molecules and thereby decay to the ground-state by releasing heat.
2. It can release some of its energy as heat by collisions and go to a different, lower-energy excited state. From this new excited state it can decay to the ground state by emitting light, a process called *fluorescence*. Since the light so emitted is from a state less highly excited than the level of original excitation, the emitted light is lower in energy than the absorbed light.
3. If the excited state is reasonably stable, electron spin can change, resulting in a lower energy state in which the two electrons have the same spin. This is a

triplet state. The triplet state can decay to the ground state by collisions and heat loss or by emitting light in a process called *phosphorescence*. Triplet states have longer lifetimes than singlet states, hence phosphorescence can continue after the exciting light is removed, whereas fluorescence stops upon removal of the exciting light.

14.4 NUCLEAR MAGNETIC RESONANCE (NMR) SPECTROSCOPY: STRUCTURE DETERMINATION

One of the most powerful methods for determining molecular structure is nuclear magnetic resonance spectroscopy.

Magnetic properties of nuclei

A basic property of certain nuclei is that they possess an intrinsic nuclear spin. The nuclear spin gives rise to a nuclear magnetic moment μ that can interact with external magnetic fields. This interaction, when analyzed through the NMR method, gives structural information about the molecule.

Nuclei are characterized by nuclear-spin numbers, symbolized by I. For example, I for the hydrogen ^{1}H nucleus is equal to $\frac{1}{2}$. In Table 14-3, I values for several representative elements are shown. Since isotopes of a given element differ in the composition of their nuclei, they also have different I values. Some nuclei, for example, that of ^{12}C, have I values of 0. Since these nuclei have magnetic moment of 0, they cannot exhibit the NMR phenomenon. We will deal only with ^{1}H nuclei (called protons) and proton NMR spectroscopy.

Basis of NMR spectroscopy

An important characteristic of a nucleus with a nuclear magnetic moment is that in a magnetic field the magnetic-moment vector assumes specific orientations with respect to the field specified by magnetic quantum numbers whose values associated with a given I value are $I, I - 1, I - 2, \ldots, -I$. A total of $2I + 1$ quantum

Table 14-3. NUCLEAR PROPERTIES

Element	*Isotope*	*Natural abundance (%)*	I
Hydrogen	^{1}H	99.9	$\frac{1}{2}$
	$^{2}H(D)$	0.1	1
Carbon	^{12}C	98.89	0
	^{13}C	1.11	$\frac{1}{2}$
Fluorine	^{19}F	100.0	$\frac{1}{2}$

values are possible. For nuclei of $I = \frac{1}{2}$, such as ^1H, the quantum values are $+\frac{1}{2}$ and $-\frac{1}{2}$. In an external magnetic field H_0, these magnetic moments align either with or against the field. The state of lower energy has a spin state of $+\frac{1}{2}$. At room temperatures in kilogauss fields, the fraction of nuclei in a $+\frac{1}{2}$ state is slightly greater than that in the $-\frac{1}{2}$ state. At room temperature with $H_0 = 10$ kgauss, in every 10^6 nuclei there are six more with $+\frac{1}{2}$ states than $-\frac{1}{2}$ states. The method of NMR spectroscopy depends on detection of this small difference.

If energy from an external radio-frequency oscillator is introduced into the system, the nuclei undergo a transition from the $+\frac{1}{2}$ state to the higher-energy (less favorable) $-\frac{1}{2}$ state when the electromagnetic energy matches the energy difference between the two nuclear-spin states. This transition occurs at different energies in fields of different strengths.

The spin state of a nucleus undergoes continual conversion as the nucleus interacts with fluctuating electric fields set up by molecular motion in the system. The absorbed electromagnetic energy is continually redistributed among the nuclei of the system by this mechanism.

The frequency of electromagnetic radiation necessary to bring about an energy transition between nuclear states, called the resonance frequency ν_0, is given by

$$\nu_0 = \frac{\mu H_{\text{eff}}/I}{h} \tag{14.14}$$

where ν_0 is in cycles/sec or hertz. H_{eff}, in gauss, is the field felt by the nucleus. It is slightly different than the applied field H_0, due to the presence of chemical matter. A proton in a field H_{eff} of 10 kgauss undergoes transitions at a frequency of 42.6 MHz. The frequency where this transition between energy states occurs is

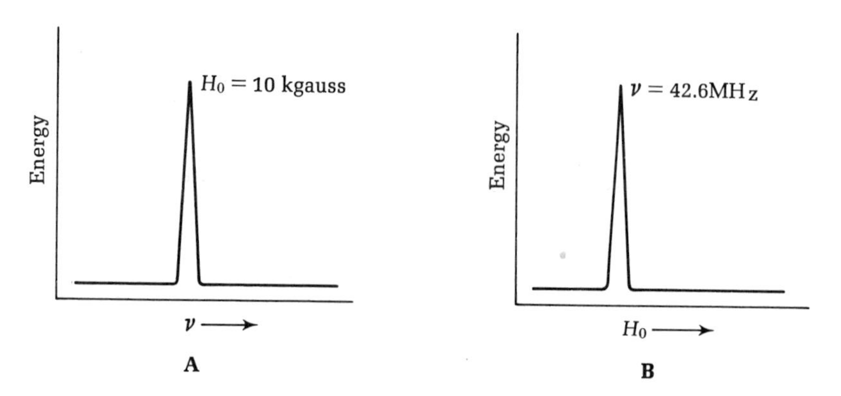

Fig. 14-12. Absorption of energy as function of frequency ν at $H_0 = 10$ kgauss, **A**, and as function of magnetic field strength H_0 at $\nu = 42.6$ MHz, **B**.

detected by the absorption of energy. A plot of absorbed energy versus the frequency ν is called a spectrum. By equation 14.14 we see that the resonance condition can also be detected by varying the field H_{eff}, keeping ν constant. The NMR spectrum for hydrogen atoms in a field of 10 kgauss is the single line shown in Fig. 14-12, *A*, and the spectrum obtained using an electromagnetic radiation source of 42.6 MHz in different magnetic fields is shown in Fig. 14-12, *B*. A block diagram of a simple NMR spectrometer is shown in Fig. 14-13.

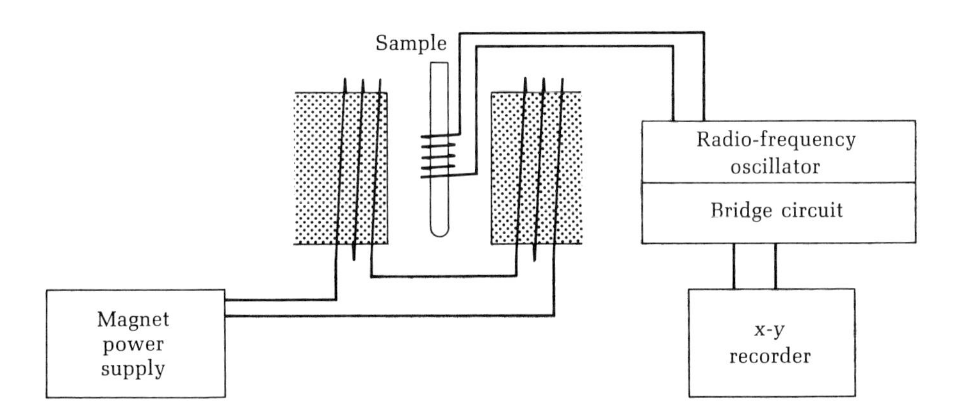

Fig. 14-13. Block diagram of simple NMR spectrometer. Solution of the material to be analyzed is placed in magnetic field. Through coil, fixed-frequency radio-frequency energy, ν_0, is introduced. Coil and sample are one arm of a bridge circuit. Before resonance condition is found, bridge is in balance. Magnetic field H_0 is increased slowly. At point where resonance occurs, energy is absorbed by sample, and bridge circuit is unbalanced. As field is swept further, resonance region is passed and the bridge circuit is rebalanced. Voltage imbalance experienced by bridge circuit during resonance is plotted on x-y recorder in which H_0 (x-axis) is plotted against bridge output voltage (y-axis).

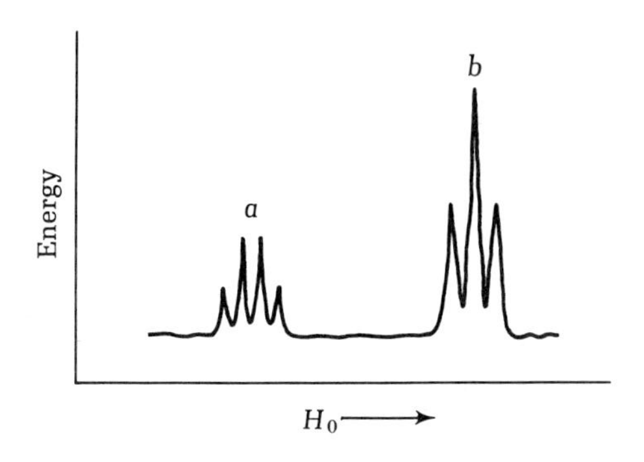

Fig. 14-14. The ^{1}H NMR resonance spectrum of C_2H_5I.

Spectral information

An NMR spectrum of C_2H_5I is shown in Fig. 14-14. The spectrum shows several important features that provide us with a wealth of structural information: (1) There are two main resonance regions, *a* and *b*, which arise from the CH_2 and CH_3 protons, respectively. (2) The ratio of the areas of regions *a* and *b* is 2:3, in direct proportion to the number of protons that contribute to each. (3) Each main resonance region in split into subpeaks.

Chemical shift. The electrons in molecules shield the nuclei slightly from external magnetic fields. Protons in structurally different positions in a molecule are shielded to different extents. Because of electron shielding, the external magnetic field is greater than H_{eff} and can be represented by

$$H_{\text{eff}} = H_0(1 - \sigma) \qquad (14.15)$$

where σ is the shielding constant. We observe more than one main resonance region when there are protons in distinctly different environments in the molecule. The difference in position between a given peak and a standard reference peak is called the chemical shift.

Nuclear spin-spin coupling. The subpeak structure in NMR spectra arises from what is called nuclear spin-spin coupling. In the C_2H_5I spectrum (Fig. 14-14) the CH_2 resonance, *a*, appears as a quartet (four subpeaks), and the CH_3 resonance, *b*, appears as a triplet (three subpeaks).

The subpeaks of the main resonances arise because the CH_3-proton moments and CH_2-proton moments act like small local magnetic fields upon each other. The spin-spin interactions for a CH_2-CH_3 system can be viewed in the following way.

The CH_2 group has two protons, each with a spin-orientation value of either $+\frac{1}{2}$ or $-\frac{1}{2}$. These states are designated by arrows, $\rightarrow$ for the $+\frac{1}{2}$ state and $\leftarrow$ for the $-\frac{1}{2}$ state. There are three ways the nuclear spins of the CH_2 protons can align (Table

Table 14-4. POSSIBLE SPIN ORIENTATIONS IN CH_2-CH_3 COUPLING

*CH_2 protons**	*CH_3 protons†*
$+1$ ⇉	$+\frac{3}{2}$ (→→→)
0 (→←) (←→)	$+\frac{1}{2}$ (→→←) (→←→) (←→→)
	$-\frac{1}{2}$ (→←←) (←→←) (←←→)
-1 ⇇	$-\frac{3}{2}$ (←←←)

*CH_3 hydrogens feel the effects of these.
†CH_2 hydrogens feel the effects of these.

14-4). These three arrangements perturb the energy states of the protons on the adjacent CH_3 group as shown in Fig. 14-15. The ratio of the population of molecules in these three levels is 1:2:1. Three resonance transitions with observed intensities of 1:2:1 are possible for the protons of the CH_3 group.

By a similar argument, the nuclear spins of the CH_3 protons can be arranged in four ways in the population ratio of 1:3:3:1. Consequently, the CH_2 resonance is split into the observed four-peak multiplet. Notice that in the spectrum shown in Fig. 14-14 the separation between subpeaks in *a* and *b* is identical.

Spin-spin interactions (couplings) are usually important only for atoms separated by three bonds or less. Generalizations about the number of peaks and relative areas from spin-spin interaction can be made, as shown in Table 14-5. The intensities correspond to the coefficients of the binomial expansion.

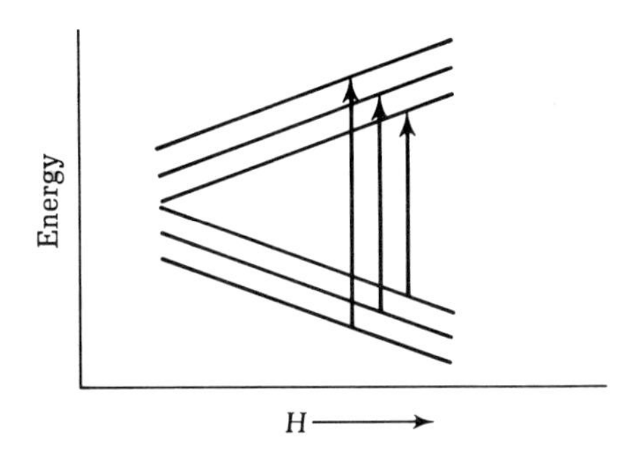

Fig. 14-15. Possible transitions between energy states of protons split into three lines with populations in a ratio of 1:2:1.

Table 14-5. SPIN-SPIN MULTIPLETS

Number of equivalent protons acting on resonant protons	*Number of subpeaks*	*Relative areas of subpeaks*
1	2	1:1
2	3	1:2:1
3	4	1:3:3:1
4	5	1:4:6:4:1
5	6	1:5:10:10:5:1
6	7	1:6:15:20:15:6:1

EXAMPLE 14.1

The NMR spectrum of a molecule whose molecular formula has been established as $C_2H_4Cl_2$ is shown in Fig. 14-16.

The spectrum consists of two main resonances, *a* and *b*, which indicates that the molecule contains two kinds of protons, or protons in two different average environments. The ratio of the areas of resonances *a* and *b* is 1:3. Since *a* is split into four peaks, the protons giving peak *a* must be coupled to three equivalent protons. Peak *b* occurs as a doublet (two lines), which indicates that the protons that yield *b* are coupled to a single hydrogen. Thus, three-hydrogen and one-hydrogen units are present. For our molecule of formula $C_2H_4Cl_2$, the only structure consistent with the valence rules of organic chemistry and the NMR spectral data is 1,1-dichloroethane:

```
    H   H
    |   |
H—C—C—Cl
    |   |
    H   Cl
```

14.5 PHOTOCHEMICAL REACTIONS

Chemical change and chemical reactions are often induced by electromagnetic radiation. Common examples are the photographic process, photosynthesis in plants, fading of dyes, and atmospheric smog reactions. In this section we outline some processes that result from the absorption of visible or ultraviolet radiation.

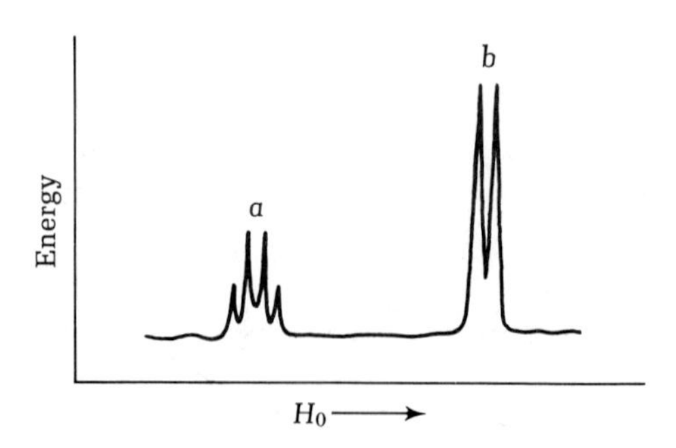

Fig. 14-16. The ^1H NMR spectrum of $C_2H_4Cl_2$. Resonance multiplets, *a* and *b*, are of relative areas 1:3.

Several types of reactions can occur as a result of the absorption of light. One example is the photochemical rearrangement of *trans*-2-butene:

$$\underset{\text{H}}{\overset{\text{CH}_3}{}}\!\!\!\!\!\!\begin{matrix}\diagdown\\ \end{matrix}\text{C}{=}\text{C}\begin{matrix}\diagup\\ \end{matrix}\!\!\!\!\!\!\underset{\text{CH}_3}{\overset{\text{H}}{}} + h\nu \rightarrow \text{C}\overset{\star}{=}\text{C}\ (\textit{trans}) \rightarrow$$

$$\text{C}\overset{\star}{=}\text{C}\ (\textit{cis}) \rightarrow \text{C}{=}\text{C}\ (\textit{cis})$$

(Structures: $CH_3(H)C{=}C(H)CH_3$ *trans* $+ h\nu \rightarrow CH_3(H)C\overset{\star}{=}C(H)CH_3$ *trans* $\rightarrow CH_3(H)C\overset{\star}{=}C(H)CH_3$ *cis* $\rightarrow CH_3(H)C{=}C(H)CH_3$ *cis*)

Absorption of energy by the *trans* isomer yields an electronically excited molecule that rearranges into the *cis* isomer. Finally the excited *cis* isomer decays to the ground-state molecule. In the excited state, the π bond of the *trans* isomer is broken. The excited electron is in a π^* orbital, thereby allowing rotation around the remaining σ bond. The role of photoisomerization in the vision process was discussed in Chapter 9.

The interaction of solar radiation with the earth's atmosphere produces many interesting photochemical reactions. For example, ozone, O_3, is produced by the reaction of ultraviolet light with molecular oxygen to produce oxygen atoms, which subsequently react with O_2:

$$\begin{aligned} O_2 + h\nu &\rightarrow 2O \\ O + O_2 &\rightarrow O_3 \end{aligned}$$

The first step can occur with the absorption of radiation of wavelengths below 2400 Å. These processes play an important part in removing highly-energetic radiation before it reaches the surface of the earth.

Another important atmospheric photochemical reaction involves the production of ions in the *ionosphere*, the region about 100 km above the surface of the earth. Typical photoionizing reactions occur with O_2 and N_2 as

$$\begin{aligned} O_2 + h\nu &\rightarrow O_2^+ + e^- \\ N_2 + h\nu &\rightarrow N_2^+ + e^- \end{aligned}$$

The ionic species produced are highly reactive. They react with other atmospheric gases, and consequently a series of reactions occurs, not all of which are well understood. The ionized molecules and the electrons in the ionosphere act as a reflecting layer for radio waves, thereby strongly affecting long-distance radio communication.

The photographic process is another photochemical reaction. A silver halide such as silver bromide is sensitive to light. When a photon is absorbed by a microscopic AgBr crystal, a free electron and a bromine atom (a positive hole) are produced. The recombination rate is slow, so that the free electron can be trapped by a silver ion to give a silver atom. This produces a latent image in the photographic film. The latent-image grains are altered so as to make them preferentially reduced to silver by means of developers. The unexposed grains are dissolved and removed by formation of a soluble complex with thiosulfate ($S_2O_3^{2-}$) ions.

Photochromic glasses are an interesting extension of the photographic process. These devices make use of photochromic materials to control light intensity. A reversible coloration of glass occurs upon exposure to light. The photochromic material is composed of a fine suspension of silver halide crystals in a silicate glass. In the absence of light the crystals are transparent. Upon exposure to light, the microscopic crystals darken due to light absorption, which dissociates the silver halide. Because the silver halide crystal is so small, the color centers produced by dissociation of the silver halide cannot diffuse very far. In the absence of light, recombinations occur, and the crystal becomes transparent. The rate of recombination depends on factors such as the size of the silver halide crystals and the nature of the glass suspension medium.

An essential process for life as we know it involves the photochemical reactions known as *photosynthesis*. Light is used to convert water and carbon dioxide into biologically energetic molecules. The fundamental process is

$$6H_2O(l) + 6CO_2(g) + h\nu \rightarrow C_6H_{12}O_6(s) + 6O_2(g)$$

where the formation of the sugar hexose is indicated. This process involves a free-energy change, $\Delta G^0 = 686$ kcal. From various studies it is estimated that 48 moles of photons of visible light with energy of 42 kcal/mole are needed to produce one mole of hexose molecules. This means that the photosynthetic process has an efficiency of about

$$\frac{686 \text{ kcal}}{(42 \times 48) \text{ kcal}} = 0.34$$

The precise mechanism of photosynthesis is the subject of intense research. The primary light-trapping molecule in green cells is chlorophyll. Many other molecules are subsequently involved in the conversion of the trapped radiation into the energy of the eventual product, $C_6H_{12}O_6$, which is the energy source for biological reactions.

PROBLEMS

1. By means of drawings, show the lines (1, 1), (1, 2), and (0, 2) in a two-dimensional square lattice.
2. By means of drawings, show the planes (1, 1, 0), (1, 0, 0), (0, 1, 0), and (1, 2, 2) in a three-dimensional cubic lattice.

3. Determine the separations of the planes in Problem 2 if the lattice points of the cubic lattice are separated by 2 Å.
4. For a KCl crystal (NaCl structure), a reflection of the (2, 0, 0) planes occurs at $\theta = 14°12'$ with X rays of wavelength 1.540 Å. Calculate (a) the dimensions of the unit cell; (b) the density of the crystal.
5. Potassium permanganate has a molar extinction coefficient ϵ of 2235 at 5200 Å. What fraction of light at this wavelength will be transmitted through a 0.0020% solution of potassium permanganate contained in a cell with a path length of 5 cm?
6. Sketch the NMR spectra you would expect for the following (do not try to predict chemical shifts): (a) CH_3COOCH_3; (b) C_6H_6 (benzene); (c) $CH_3CH(OH)CH_3$.
7. A compound C_2H_4O has an NMR spectrum that consists of two peaks, a quartet and a doublet whose areas are in the ratio of 1:3. Propose a structure for the compound.
8. A compound $C_4H_{10}O$ has an NMR spectrum that consists of two peaks, a quartet of relative area 2.0 and a triplet of relative area 3.0. Propose a structure for the compound.

APPENDIXES

A ANSWERS TO SELECTED PROBLEMS

CHAPTER 1

2. (a) 92 protons, 146 neutrons, 92 electrons
3. (a) $^{22}_{10}Ne$; Z = 10, A = 12; 10 electrons
5. (a) $\ell = 0, 1, 2, 3, 4$
   (b) $m_\ell = 0, \pm1, \pm2, \pm3, \pm4$
12. $^{35}Cl : ^{37}Cl = 3:1$
13. (a) K, 1 mole; Mn, 1 mole; O, 4 moles
    (c) B, 10 moles; H, 14 moles
14. (a) 86.12
    (c) 79.10
17. 3.75×10^{20} moles
18. $Mg_{1.00}S_{1.00}O_{4.01}$
21. C_7H_{16}
22. (a) 2
    (b) 1
    (c) 4
23. (a) H:F:

    (b)
    ```
      H H
    H:C:C:H
      H H
    ```
    (c) :I:Cl:

    (d) $(Na)^+(:Cl:)^-$

24. (a)
    ```
        H
    (H:B:H)⁻
        H
    ```
    (b)
    ```
       :Cl:
    :Cl  P  Cl:
     :Cl  Cl:
    ```
    (c)
    ```
    ( :O:            )1-     ( :O:            )1-
    (     C :: O:    )   ↔   (     C : O:     )
    (  :O:           )       (  :O:           )
    ( H              )       ( H              )
    ```
    (d)
    ```
    ( :I:I: )⁻
    (  :I:  )
    ```
    (e)
    ```
       :Cl:
     :I:
         Cl:
    :Cl:
    ```

26. (a) 7+
    (d) 1+
    (g) 2+
29. (a) NH_4Cl
    (c) $CaBr_2$
    (e) $FeCl_2$
    (g) $KMnO_4$
    (i) $Ca(HSO_4)_2$
    (k) AgCN

31. (a) silver chloride
    (b) sodium carbonate
    (c) sodium permanganate
    (h) tin(II) chloride

32. (a) 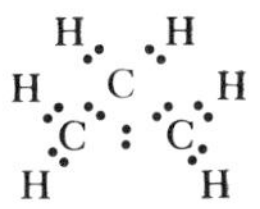
```
     H. .H                         H     H
   H  .C.  H                        \   /
   .C. : .C.         or              C
   H       H                H—C ———————— C—H
                              /            \
                             H              H
```
    (c)
```
      H   ..O:                     H    _O|
   H:C:C                           |   //
      H   :O.         or      H—C—C
            H                      |    \
                                   H     O
                                          \
                                           H
```

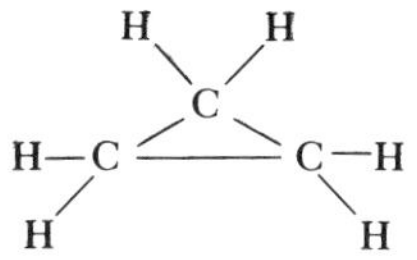

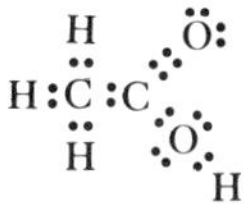

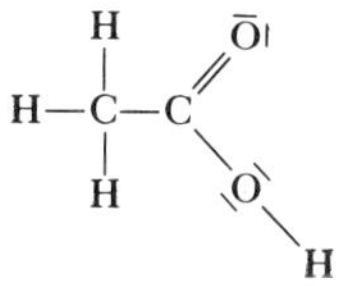

33. (a) $H^+(aq) + OH^-(aq) \rightarrow H_2O(l)$
34. (a) $PCl_3 + 3H_2O \rightarrow H_3PO_3 + 3HCl$
    (b) $NCl_3 + 3H_2O \rightarrow NH_3 + 3HOCl$
35. 2.29 g
39. 0.0087
41. (a) 85.4 g
    (b) 79.9 g
    (c) 159.8 g
43. 54.6 g
44. (a) 99.9 g
    (b) 199.8 g
45. 96.2 ml
47. 8.46 atm
49. 30 g/mole
50. 12°K

CHAPTER 2

4. (a) 4
   (b) 2
   (c) 2
5. 48% unoccupied
6. 74%
9. 3.16 Å
11. 3.34 cm
14. $r_c \leq 0.22R$
16. The tanks will contain equal amounts of liquid water.
17. $A^+ = 0.40$ Å
    $B^+ = 0.58$ Å
    $X^- = 0.82$ Å
    $Y^- = 1.30$Å
19. (a) Cl^- in P and O, Zn^{2+} in T'
    (b) Cl^- in P and O, Cs^+ in T' and T''
    (c) K^+ in O, Cl^- in P
21. $U = -\frac{e^2}{a}\left[4\left(1 - \frac{1}{\sqrt{2}} + \frac{2}{\sqrt{5}} - \frac{1}{\sqrt{4}} + \ldots\right)\right]$

CHAPTER 3

2. 33.7 joules
3. −273°C
4. (c) $\theta = 49.4$
7. 12.5 g of ice
8. 7.5°C
9. 1.25×10^6 cal
11. $Q = 7.4 \times 10^5$ cal
13. 0.216 cal/deg
14. 1.7×10^4 cal/deg
15. 2.40 cal/deg
16. 35.8 cal/deg
18. 0.54 cal/deg

CHAPTER 4

1. (a) 1470 joules
   (c) −10 liter-atm
   (e) −245 joules
   (f) $W = 0$
   (g) liter-atm = +4770 cal
2. (a) 117 cal
   (b) $\Delta t = 0.0975$ deg
3. $W = -477$ cal
   $\Delta E = 0$
   $Q = 477$ cal
   $\Delta S = 3.20$ cal/deg
   $\Delta H = 0$
4. (a) $Q = 0$, $W = -1227$ cal, $\Delta E = -1227$ cal
   (b) 177°K
7. (a) $\Delta H^0 = -15.65$ kcal
       $\Delta G^0 = -13.30$ kcal
       $\Delta S^0 = -7.87$ cal/deg
   (b) $\Delta H^0 = 37.05$ kcal
       $\Delta G^0 = 30.12$ kcal
       $\Delta S^0 = 23.26$ cal/deg
9. −66.3 kcal
10. −67.9 kcal
11. $t_{max} \cong 11{,}570$°C
13. (a) $T_{max} = 7500$°K
    (b) $p \cong 22{,}400$ atm
14. (a) −75.9 kcal
    (c) −364.2 kcal

CHAPTER 5

1. $W = 4.99 \times 10^4$ cal
3. 1.5×10^5 cal
4. (a) 1.29 cal/deg
   (b) 1.82 cal/deg
   (c) 7.85×10^{-3} cal/deg
   (d) 4.02 cal/deg
6. (a) $t = 23.6$°C
   (b) 6.3×10^5 cal/deg-sec

7. 19.8 cal/deg
8. (a) +19.75 cal/deg-sec
   (b) +19.75 cal/deg-sec
9. (a) $\Delta S = +21.44$ cal/deg
   $\Delta S_i = 110$ cal/deg
   $\Delta S_e = -88.7$ cal/deg
10. (a) $\Delta H^0 = 26{,}420$ cal
   $\Delta S_e = 88.7$ cal/deg
11. (a) $\Delta S = 21.44$ cal/deg
   $\Delta S_i = 0$
   $\Delta S_e = 21.44$ cal/deg
   $-\Delta H^0/T = 88.7$ cal/deg

CHAPTER 6

1. −68.3
2. $t = 13.2\,°C$
3. $\Delta H^0 = 60{,}400$ cal/mole
   $\Delta G^0 = 6529$ cal/mole
   $\Delta S^0 = 37.6$ cal/deg
5. 6616 cal/mole
6. white Sn stable at $T > 288\,°K$, gray Sn stable at $T < 288\,°K$
7. −31,447 cal/mole
8. 109 atm
9. −26.0 cal
10. $\mu_{O_2} = 1015$ cal/mole
   $\mu_{N_2} = -194.5$ cal/mole
11. $p_{total} = 302$ torr
   $X_{hexane} = 0.813$
   $X_{heptane} = 0.187$
14. 15,703 cal
15. 975 cal/mole
16. 59.0 g/mole
17. 180 g/mole
18. 60,700 g/mole
19. 55.02 torr
20. 86.6 atm by $\pi = nRT/V$
   height = 2773 ft

CHAPTER 7

1. (a) 38.4 kcal
   (b) $\Delta G > 0$, reaction goes left
   (c) must decrease
   (d) $[Pb^{2+}] = [S^{2-}] = 8.38 \times 10^{-15}$ mole/liter
2. (a) $\xi = +3$, $3N_2 + 3O_2 \rightarrow 6NO$
   $\xi = -2$, $4NO \rightarrow 2O_2 + 2N_2$
3. (a) $\Delta G^0 = 41.44$ kcal, products to reactants is spontaneous, $d\xi$ is negative
4. (b) $\dfrac{p_{H_2}[Zn^{2+}]}{[H_3O^+]^2}\ \dfrac{\text{atm-liter}}{\text{mole}}$
5. (a) $\Delta G^0 = -49.48$ kcal
   $K = 1.95 \times 10^{36}$
6. $\alpha = 0.182$
7. (a) $p_{SO_2} = 0.74$ atm
   $p_{Cl_2} = 0.74$ atm
   $p_{SOCl_2} = 0.23$ atm
   (b) $p_{total} = 1.71$ atm
9. $K = p_{CO_2} = 0.24$ atm
10. (a) 3.14×10^{-2} atm
   (b) $\Delta G^0 = 2.05$ kcal
12. 73,700 cal
15. (a) increase temperature, shift left; increase pressure, shift right
   (b) increase temperature, shift right; increase pressure, shift left
16. (a) $[H_3O^+] = 2.68 \times 10^{-3}\ M$
   $[HOAc] = 0.397\ M$
   $[OAc^-] = 2.68 \times 10^{-3}\ M$
   $[OH^-] = 3.7 \times 10^{-12}\ M$
   (b) $[H_3O^+] = 5.16 \times 10^{-5}\ M$
   $[HOAc] = 1.48 \times 10^{-4}\ M$
   $[OAc^-] = 5.16 \times 10^{-5}\ M$
   $[OH^-] = 1.93 \times 10^{-10}\ M$
18. (a) 9.48
19. (a) $[H_3O^+] = 10^{-7}\ M$
   $[OH^-] = 10^{-7}\ M$
   (e) $[H_3O^+] = 2.0\ M$
   $[OH^-] = 5 \times 10^{-15}\ M$
21. low to high, $HCl < HOAc < NH_4^+ < NaCl < NH_3 < NaOH$
22. pH = 4.98
24. 12.16
25. 4.57
27. (a) CCl_3CO_2H and $NaCO_2CCl_3$
   (e) NaH_2PO_4 and Na_2HPO_4
29. methyl orange, $pK \cong 3.3$; litmus, $pK \cong 6.6$
30. $[H_3O^+] = [HCO_3^-] = 1.3 \times 10^{-4}\ M$
   $[CO_3^{2-}] = 4.8 \times 10^{-11}\ M$
32. pH = 8.35
34. 1.54×10^{-13}
36. $K_1 = 4.16 \times 10^{-7}$
   $K_2 = 4.63 \times 10^{-11}$
37. (a) 1.76×10^{-10}
38. (a) $[Ba^{2+}] = 7.6 \times 10^{-3}\ M$
   $[F^-] = 1.52 \times 10^{-2}\ M$
   (b) $K_{sp} = 1.76 \times 10^{-6}$
40. $1.1 \times 10^{-16}\ M = [S^{2-}]$
   $0.9 \times 10^{-3}\ M = [Fe^{2+}]$

CHAPTER 8

1. (a) $Cu(s) + 4H^+ + 2NO_3^-(aq) \rightarrow 2NO_2(g) + 2H_2O + Cu^{2+}(aq)$
   (c) $I_2(s) + H_2S(g) \rightarrow S(s) + 2I^-(aq) + 2H^+$

(f) $3ClO^-(aq) + 2Fe(OH)_3(s) + 4OH^- \rightarrow$
$2FeO_4^{2-}(aq) + 3Cl^-(aq) + 5H_2O$

2. 3.6×10^6 coulombs, 37.3 faradays
3. (a) 6.9×10^3 sec
4. oxidation state = +2
6. 1.37 liters
7. (a) −95 kcal
   (c) −11.1 kcal
8. (a) $\frac{1}{2}Cl_2(g) + Fe^{2+}(aq) \rightarrow Cl^-(aq) + Fe^{3+}(aq)$
   (e) $2Hg(l) + 2H^+(aq) + 2Cl^-(aq) \rightarrow Hg_2Cl_2(s) + H_2(g)$
10. 10^{35}
11. (a) 1.69 volt
14. 1.14 volts; $Zn + Cu^{2+} \rightarrow Zn^{2+} + Cu$ is the direction of spontaneous reaction
16. $W = 50{,}700$ cal
17. $\Delta G^0 = -1048$ cal
    $\Delta H^0 = 1272$ cal
    $\Delta S^0 = -7.78$ cal/deg-mole
19. (a) Mn^{2+}, MnO_4^-

CHAPTER 9

1. (a) C—O > C═O > C≡O
2. 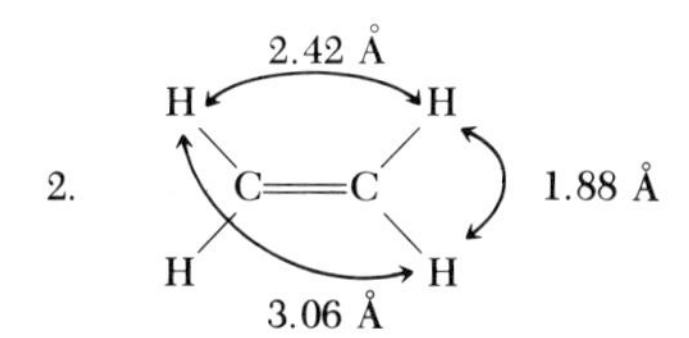

4. 5.94 Å diameter
6. (c) $(CoCl_6)^{3-}$ (octahedral: Cl, Cl, Cl, Cl, Cl, Cl around Co)
10. (b) $\ddot{Sn}$ bonded to Cl, Cl (bent)
    (e) Cl—P═O with two further Cl (Cl---P═O, Cl)
12. (a) HCl<HBr<HI
13. (a) $H_3C—\bar{O}—CH_3$ (H—C(H)(H)—Ō—C(H)(H)—H) $H_3C—CH_2—\bar{O}—H$ (H—C(H)(H)—C(H)(H)—Ō—H)

(b) H—C(H)(H)—C(H)(H)—N̈(H)(H)   and the conformation H₂C—N(H)(:)—CH₂ (H—C(H)(H), H, N, C(H)(H))

15. (a) $(CoCl_4(NH_3)_2)^-$ *cis* (Cl, Cl, NH₃, Cl, NH₃, Cl around Co) $(CoCl_4(NH_3)_2)^-$ *trans* (NH₃, Cl, Cl, Cl, Cl, NH₃ around Co)

16. (a)
22. (a) and (b)
24. (a) The most stable conformation has the lone-pair electrons in *trans* positions.

CHAPTER 10

2. (b) H_2C———CH_2 bridged by O (ring)
7. (a) $20^2 = 400$
10. (a) 3^{100}
    (d) 366.5°K
12. $2^{10} = 1024$

CHAPTER 11

1. 2410 Å
3. $$\left(-\frac{\hbar^2}{2M}\nabla_N^2 - \frac{\hbar^2}{2m}\nabla_1^2 - \frac{\hbar^2}{2m}\nabla_2^2 - \frac{e^2}{r_1} - \frac{e^2}{r_2} + \frac{e^2}{r_{1-2}}\right)\psi = E\psi$$
4. (a) $E_1 = 6.02 \times 10^{-11}$ ergs,
   $E_2 = 24.1 \times 10^{-11}$ ergs
5. (a), (b), and (c)
8. $E_1 = -2.18 \times 10^{-11}$ ergs
   $E_2 = -5.44 \times 10^{-2}$ ergs
   $\lambda = 1.216 \times 10^{-5}$ cm
9. $\sigma = 4$, or $r = 4a_0$
   yes
13. $\sigma = 3 \pm \sqrt{3}$
15. (b) $1s^22s^22p^6$
    (d) $1s^22s^22p^63s^23p^64s^23d^2$
16. (a), (c), (e), and (g)

CHAPTER 12

6. (c) $O_2^- < O_2 < O_2^+$
9. (b) ↑ ↑ ↑ ↑ ↑ (3d)   oo (4s)   oo oo oo (4p)
   oo oo __ __ __ (4d), $\mu = \sqrt{30}$

12. (a) sp^3
    (e) d^2sp^3

CHAPTER 13

1. (c) $\frac{d\xi}{dt} = -\frac{d[H_2]}{dt} = -\frac{2d[O_2]}{dt} = \frac{d[H_2O]}{dt}$
2. (a) rate = $k[NO]^2[Cl_2]$
   (b) $k = 180$ (liter)^2/(mole)^2 min
3. (b) second order
6. (a) 4.3×10^5 sec
   (b) 1.3×10^{-3} sec
7. first order reaction, $k = 1.30 \times 10^{-2}$ min^{-1}
11. 2.46×10^4 cal

CHAPTER 14

1. Lines (1,1) are green; lines (1,2), black; lines (0,2), gray.

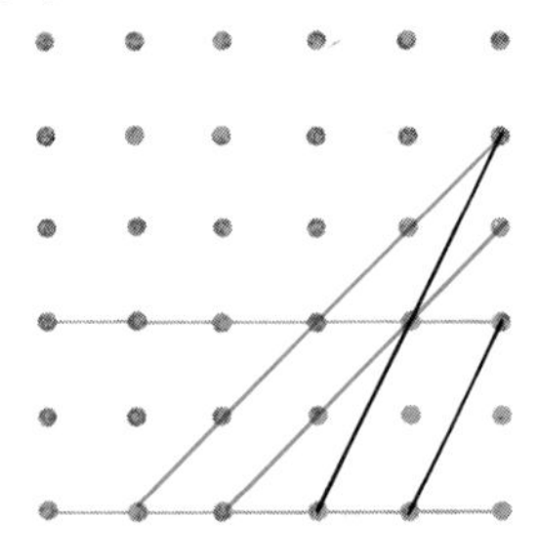

3. for the (1, 1, 0) planes, $d_{1,1,0} = 2/\sqrt{2} = 2^{1/2}$
5. 0.0384
6. (a)

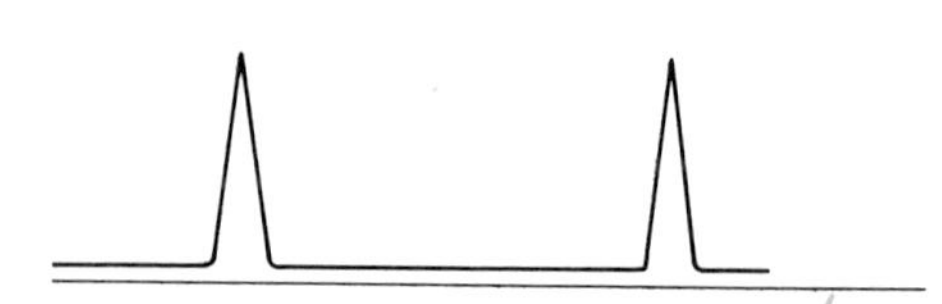

7.
```
     H       _
     |      O|
H—C—C//
     |     \
     H      H
```

8.
```
     H   H       H   H
     |   |       |   |
H—C—C—Ō—C—C—H
     |   |   ‾   |   |
     H   H       H   H
```

B FUNDAMENTAL CONSTANTS AND CONVERSION FACTORS

FUNDAMENTAL CONSTANTS

Name	*Symbol*	*Value*
Avogadro's number	N	6.0225×10^{23} molecules/mole
Boltzmann constant	k	1.3805×10^{-16} erg/deg
		1.38×10^{-23} J/deg
		3.30×10^{-24} cal/deg
Bohr radius	a_0	0.529 Å
Electron charge	e	1.6021×10^{-19} coulomb
		4.80×10^{-10} esu
Electron mass	m_e	9.108×10^{-28} g
Faraday constant	F	9.6487×10^{4} coulombs/equiv
		23,053 cal/volt-equiv
Gas constant	R	8.2053×10^{-2} liter-atm/mole-deg
		8.314 J/mole-deg
		1.987 cal/mole-deg
Neutron mass	m_n	1.6747×10^{-24} g
Planck's constant	h	6.6256×10^{-27} erg-sec
Proton mass	m_p	1.6724×10^{-24} g
Speed of light	c	2.9979×10^{10} cm/sec

CONVERSION FACTORS

Mass

1 gram (g) = 1000 milligrams (mg)
= 0.0353 ounce

1 kilogram (kg) = 1000 grams
= 2.2046 pounds

1 atomic mass unit (amu) = 1.6603×10^{-24} g

Length

1 centimeter (cm) = 10 millimeters (mm)
= 0.3937 inch

1 meter (m) = 100 centimeters

1 kilometer (km) = 1000 meters

1 micron (μ) = 10^{-4} centimeter
= 10^{-6} meter

1 nanometer (nm) = 10^{-7} centimeter
= 10^{-9} meter

1 Angstrom unit (Å) = 10^{-1} nanometer
= 10^{-8} centimeter
= 10^{-10} meter

Time

1 millisecond = 10^{-3} second

1 microsecond = 10^{-3} millisecond
= 10^{-6} second
1 nanosecond = 10^{-9} second
1 picosecond = 10^{-3} nanosecond
= 10^{-12} second

Pressure

1 atmosphere (atm) = 1.013×10^6 dynes/cm^2
= 760 mm Hg
= 760 torr
1 torr = 1 mm Hg
= 1.316×10^{-3} atm

Force

1 dyne = 1 g-cm/sec^2
1 newton (N) = 1 kg-m/sec^2
= 10^5 dynes

Energy

1 erg = 1 g-cm^2/sec
1 joule (J) = 10^7 ergs
= 0.2390 cal
= 0.00987 liter-atm
= 9.478×10^{-4} British thermal unit (BTU)
= 2.778×10^{-7} kilowatt-hour (kW-h)
1 electron volt (eV) = 1.6021×10^{-12} erg
= 23.06 kcal/mole

Temperature

°K = °C + 273.16°
°F = $\frac{9}{5}$°C + 32°

Electrical charge

1 coulomb (c) = 1 ampere-sec
= 2.998×10^9 esu
1 faraday = 9.649×10^4 coulombs

C NOMENCLATURE OF INORGANIC COMPOUNDS

Methods of naming three fundamental classes of inorganic compounds—binary, oxyanion-containing, and coordination—are outlined below. Nonsystematic, or trivial, names are avoided except in a few cases where they prevail in common usage, such as water for H_2O and ammonia for NH_3.

BINARY COMPOUNDS

Binary compounds contain only two elements. Their formulas are generally written with the more electropositive element first and the more electronegative element last. Exceptions to this rule are rare, ammonia (NH_3) being a notable example. Two systematic methods* are used to name binary compounds.

Method 1

The more electropositive element is named first, in total, followed by the stem name of the more electronegative element, to which is added an *ide* ending. In the examples below, the stem names are in boldface:

NaCl	sodium **chlor**ide	HCl	hydrogen **chlor**ide
AgBr	silver **brom**ide	LiH	lithium **hydr**ide

For compounds with the elements in a ratio other than one to one, the ratio is specified by using an appropriate Greek prefix before the element in question: 2, *di;* 3, *tri;* 4, *tetra;* 5, *penta;* 6, *hexa*. Prefixes in the following examples are in boldface:

*Metals that have only two common oxidation states are sometimes named by attaching an *ous* or *ic* suffix to the Latin name of the element to distinguish the lower and higher oxidation states, respectively. For example, in this system $FeCl_2$ and $FeCl_3$ would be called ferrous chloride and ferric chloride. We will avoid this system, however, since it is often ambiguous.

$FeCl_2$	iron **di**chloride	ICl_3	iodine **tri**chloride
$FeCl_3$	iron **tri**chloride	NO_2	nitrogen **di**oxide
SiO_2	silicon **di**oxide	N_2O_4	**di**nitrogen **tetra**oxide

Method 2

When the oxidation state of an element can vary, it is specified in parenthesis after the element. This eliminates the need for prefixes. Following are some compounds named by this method:

$FeCl_2$	iron(II) chloride	ICl_3	iodine(III) chloride
$FeCl_3$	iron(III) chloride	NO_2	nitrogen(IV) oxide

Since the anions are in their common oxidation states, that is, 1− for Cl^- and 2− for O^{2-}, no specification of their oxidation states is necessary.

OXYANION-CONTAINING COMPOUNDS

Oxyanions are anions of the general formula XO_n^{y-}, where X is an element usually of variable oxidation state, and $y-$ is the charge on the ion. The most common oxyanion compounds are acids with the general formula H_yXO_n, and their salts. Oxyanions of a given element X are differentiated by a system of suffixes and prefixes to the stem name of the element.

If only two oxyanions with X in different oxidation states can occur, they are differentiated by suffixes only. In an acid, the suffixes *ous* and *ic* designate the lower and higher of these oxidation states, respectively. The word *acid* is also included in the compound name. If the oxyanion compound is a salt, the lower and higher oxidation states have *ite* and *ate* endings, respectively. A list of important oxyanion acids and salts is given below:

	Acids		*Salts*
H_2SO_3	sulfurous acid	Na_2SO_3	sodium sulfite
H_2SO_4	sulfuric acid	K_2SO_4	potassium sulfate
HNO_2	nitrous acid	$AgNO_2$	silver nitrite
HNO_3	nitric acid	$CsNO_3$	cesium nitrate

Oxyanion acids can often yield more than one hydrogen ion; for example, H_3PO_4 can yield three. Thus, phosphate species of the form $H_2PO_4^-$ and HPO_4^{2-} must be considered also. These are named as shown below:

$H_2PO_4^-$	dihydrogenphosphate ion
HPO_4^{2-}	hydrogenphosphate ion
HSO_4^-	hydrogensulfate ion

Several oxyanion families are known in which the X elements commonly occur in more than two oxidation states. Naming these involves a system of prefixes in addition to the suffixes used above. For example, consider the family $HClO$, $HClO_2$, $HClO_3$, and $HClO_4$. The 3+ and 5+ oxidation species, ClO_2^- and ClO_3^-, are given the *ous* or *ite* and *ic* or *ate* endings, respectively. The ClO^- ion receives, in addition to the *ous* or *ite* suffix, the prefix *hypo*, meaning less than. The ClO_4^- ion receives the *ate* or *ic* ending and the prefix *per*, meaning more than. Following are some examples of the application of these rules to the naming of the acids and typical salts of the ClO_x^{y-} family:

Acids		*Example salts*	
$HClO$	hypochlorous acid	$NaClO$	sodium hypochlorite
$HClO_2$	chlorous acid	$KClO_2$	potassium chlorite
$HClO_3$	chloric acid	$Ca(ClO_3)_2$	calcium chlorate
$HClO_4$	perchloric acid	$NaClO_4$	sodium perchlorate

COORDINATION COMPOUNDS

Coordination compounds are compounds in which a cation, anion, or entire molecule is of a complex nature as a result of being bonded to a group of Lewis-base groups called ligands.* The ligands can be anionic or neutral species. Some common ligands and their names include the following:

Anionic ligands		*Neutral ligands*	
F^-	fluoro	H_3N	ammine
Cl^-	chloro	H_2O	aqua
Br^-	bromo	NO	nitrosyl
I^-	iodo	CO	carbonyl
OH^-	hydroxo		
CN^-	cyano		

Coordination compounds are named using the principles outlined above. Prefixes are used to designate the number of ligands on the central atom. The oxidation state of the central atom is given in parentheses. The names of coordination compounds include the name of the simple anion or cation and the name of the coordination ion. If a coordination cation is involved, it is designated by adding to the stem of the central metal the *ate* ending, similar to what is done with the oxyanions. Some coordination ions and compounds formed from them are given below:

Coordination ions		*Coordination compounds*	
$Co(NH_3)_6^{3+}$	hexaamminecobalt(III)	$Co(NH_3)_6Cl_3$	hexaamminecobalt(III) chloride
$Cr(H_2O)_6^{2+}$	hexaaquachromium(II)	$Cr(H_2O)_6Cl_2$	hexaaquachromium(II) chloride
$Pt(CN)_4^{2-}$	tetracyanoplatinate(II)	$Na_2Pt(CN)_4$	sodium tetracyanoplatinate(II)
$CrCl_6^{3-}$	hexachlorochromate(III)	Na_3CrCl_6	sodium hexachlorochromate(III)

*Strictly speaking, the oxyanion species could be classed in this group. However, since they are so common and involve different nomenclature methods, we have discussed them separately.

D NOMENCLATURE OF ORGANIC COMPOUNDS

Organic compounds are generally best named using systematic methods. The preferred systematic method is that adopted by the International Union of Pure and Applied Chemistry (IUPAC). However, in many cases trivial names or other types of systematic names are still commonly used.

GENERAL ORGANIC STEM NAMES

For the hydrocarbons (except aromatics) and their functional-group derivatives, a common series of stem names is used to indicate the number of carbon atoms in the molecule. In the IUPAC system, the stem name designates the longest continuous chain of carbon atoms. Stem names for C_1 to C_{12} systems are given below:

Carbons	*Name*	*Carbons*	*Name*
1 (C_1)	meth	7 (C_7)	hept
2 (C_2)	eth	8 (C_8)	oct
3 (C_3)	prop	9 (C_9)	non
4 (C_4)	but	10 (C_{10})	dec
5 (C_5)	pent	11 (C_{11})	undec
6 (C_6)	hex	12 (C_{12})	dodec

HYDROCARBON COMPOUNDS

The alkane hydrocarbons (C_nH_{2n+2}) are characterized by the *ane* ending attached to the hydrocarbon stem names. Alkanes through C_6 and their IUPAC names are shown in Table D-1. Alternate, commonly used names are given in parentheses. For alkanes with more than three carbons, isomeric forms are possible. Substituent CH_3 groups are located on the longest continuous chain by numbering the carbons of the chain so that the substituents receive the lowest numbers possible.

Table D-1. ALKANES (C_1 to C_6)

Molecular formula	*Condensed structural formula*	*Name*
CH_4	CH_4	methane
C_2H_6	$CH_3—CH_3$	ethane
C_3H_8	$CH_3—CH_2—CH_3$	propane
C_4H_{10}	$CH_3—CH_2—CH_2—CH_3$	butane (*n*-butane)
	CH_3 $CH_3—CH—CH_3$	2-methylpropane (isobutane)
C_5H_{12}	$CH_3—CH_2—CH_2—CH_2—CH_3$	pentane (*n*-pentane)
	CH_3 $CH_3—CH—CH_2—CH_3$	2-methylbutane (isopentane)
	CH_3 $CH_3—C—CH_3$ CH_3	2,2-dimethylpentane (neopentane)
C_6H_{14}	$CH_3—CH_2—CH_2—CH_2—CH_2—CH_3$	hexane (*n*-hexane)
	CH_3 $CH_3—CH—CH_2—CH_2—CH_3$	2-methylpentane
	$CH_3—CH_2—CH—CH_2—CH_3$ CH_3	3-methylpentane
	CH_3 $CH_3—C—CH_2—CH_3$ CH_3	2,2-dimethylbutane
	CH_3 CH_3 $CH_3—CH—CH—CH_3$	2,3-dimethylbutane

Alkyl groups (ending *yl*) are formed from alkanes by the removal of an H atom. The alkyl group can (1) function as a substituent on a larger hydrocarbon unit, or (2) be attached to a functional-group unit. For simplicity in writing formulas, the symbol *R* is often used to indicate an alkyl group. Alkyl groups can be derived from any alkane; hence, isomeric alkyl groups arise in systems with three or more carbons. The methyl and ethyl alkyl group were introduced in Chapter 1. The C_3 and C_4 alkyl groups are shown in Table D-2. Although the IUPAC names are more systematic, the alternate naming system for alkyl groups is more commonly used. In the alternate system, the prefixes *n*, *iso*, and *neo* or *tert* are used to differentiate increasing degrees of chain branching.

Alkene hydrocarbons contain C═C double bonds and are characterized by *ene* endings. The C_2 to C_4 alkenes are shown in Table D-3. The common systematic names are given first, and the IUPAC names are in parentheses. It is necessary to specify the position of the double bond in chains of more than three carbons. The common approach to this is to identify the longest carbon chain and number the carbons in such a way that the position of the double bond receives the smallest possible positional number. Hence, the first two entries for C_4H_8 are named 2-butene and 1- butene, respectively.

Alkyne hydrocarbons contain C≡C triple bonds and are characterized by *yne* endings in IUPAC nomenclature. The first two members of the alkyne series are given in Table D-4. Acetylene, a nonsystematic name for ethyne, occurs often in common usage. The IUPAC names are given in parentheses.

Cycloalkane hydrocarbons contain rings of carbon atoms. The common ring systems for C_3 to C_6 are shown in Table D-5. The names are analogous to those used for simple alkanes with the addition of the prefix *cyclo*.

Aromatic hydrocarbons are ring compounds that have alternating C═C and C—C bond systems. The two simplest aromatic carbons are benzene and napthalene:

```
        H                    H                      H       H
        |                    |                      |       |
 H      C      H      H      C      H        H      C       C      H
  \   //  \   /        \   /  \\   /          \   //  \   /  \\   /
    C       C            C       C              C       C       C
    |       ||     ↔     ||      |              |       ||      |
    C       C            C       C              C       C       C
  /   \\  /   \        /   \  //   \          /   \\  /   \  //   \
 H      C      H      H      C      H        H      C       C      H
        |                    |                      |       |
        H                    H                      H       H
```

Benzene **Napthalene**

Table D-2. ALKYL GROUPS (C_3 AND C_4)

Molecular formula	*Condensed structural formula*	*IUPAC name*	*Alternate name*
$C_3H_7—$	$CH_3—CH_2—CH_2—$	propyl-	*n*-propyl-
	$CH_3—CH(CH_3)—$	1-methylethyl-	isopropyl-
$C_4H_9—$	$CH_3—CH_2—CH_2—CH_2—$	butyl-	*n*-butyl-
	$CH_3—CH(CH_3)—CH_2—$	2-methylpropyl-	isobutyl-
	$CH_3—CH(—)—CH_2—CH_3$	1-methylpropyl-	*sec*-butyl-
	$CH_3—C(CH_3)_2—$	1,1-dimethylethyl-	*tert*-butyl-

Table D-3. ALKENES (C_2 TO C_4)

Molecular formula	*Condensed structural formula*	*Name*
C_2H_4	$H_2C{=}CH_2$	ethylene (ethene)
C_3H_6	$CH_3—CH{=}CH_2$	propylene (propene)
C_4H_8	$CH_3CH{=}CHCH_3$	butylene (2-butene)
	$CH_2{=}CHCH_2CH_3$	butylene (1-butene)
	$(CH_3)_2C{=}CH_2$	isobutylene (2-methylpropene)

Table D-4. COMMON ALKYNES

Molecular formula	*Condensed structural formula*	*Name*
C_2H_2	$HC{\equiv}CH$	acetylene (ethyne)
C_3H_4	$HC{\equiv}C—CH_3$	methylacetylene (propyne)

Table D-5. CYCLOALKANES

Molecular formula	*Condensed structural formula*	*Name*
C_3H_6	H_2C———CH_2 / \ / / CH_2	cyclopropane
C_4H_8	$H_2C—CH_2$ / | | / $H_2C—CH_2$	cyclobutane
C_5H_{10}	CH_2 / H_2C CH_2 / $H_2C—CH_2$	cyclopentane
C_6H_{12}	CH_2 / H_2C CH_2 / H_2C CH_2 / CH_2	cyclohexane

COMPOUNDS CONTAINING FUNCTIONAL GROUPS

There are numerous organic molecules in which other atoms or groups of atoms replace one or more hydrogen atoms of a hydrocarbon skeletal system. These atoms or groups of atoms are usually the sites of highest reactivity and as a result are called functional groups. Strictly speaking, double and triple bonds occur at the expense of hydrogens on the skeletal hydrocarbon system and thus are sometimes regarded as functional groups.

Numerous molecules have one or more halogen atoms (F, Cl, Br, or I) substituted for hydrogen. These molecules are called halides. Several examples are given in Table D-6. Using IUPAC nomenclature, the halogen atoms are given the lowest possible set of numbers on the hydrocarbon skeleton. Alternate names, which occur frequently, are given in parentheses.

If a hydrogen of a hydrocarbon is replaced by an —OH group, the compound is called an alcohol. If two *R* groups are bonded to an oxygen, the compound is called an ether. Alcohols and ethers can be regarded as derivatives of H_2O in which one and two hydrogens, respectively, have been replaced by *R* groups. Some important examples are given in Table D-7. The IUPAC names for alcohols are characterized by the *ol* ending attached to the stem name of the appropriate hydrocarbon. If necessary, the position of the —OH group is specified by an

Table D-6. HALIDES

Group	*General formula*	*General name*	*Prefix name*	*Example compound*	*Name of example*
F—	*R*—F	fluoride	fluoro-	CH_3CH_2F	fluoroethane (ethyl fluoride)
Cl—	*R*—Cl	chloride	chloro-	C_6H_5—Cl (benzene ring—Cl)	chlorobenzene (phenyl chloride)
Br—	*R*—Br	bromide	bromo-	$CH_3CH(Br)CH_3$	2-bromopropane (isopropyl bromide)

Table D-7. ETHERS AND ALCOHOLS

Group	*General formula*	*Name*	*Example compound*	*Name of example*
HO—	*R*OH	alcohol	$CH_3CH_2CH_2OH$	1-propanol (*n*-propyl alcohol)
			$CH_3CH(OH)CH_3$	2-propanol (isopropyl alcohol)
—O—	*R*O*R*′	ether	CH_3—O—CH_3	dimethyl ether
			C_2H_5—O—C_2H_5	diethyl ether

appropriate prefix number. For ethers, names are established by using the appropriate alkyl group names ahead of the word *ether*.

Replacement of the hydrogens of NH_3 by *R* groups gives rise to a series of compounds called amines. Examples are shown in Table D-8.

A large class of functional-group compounds is characterized by the presence of carbonyl (C=O) groups. This class includes aldehydes, carboxylic acids, esters, ketones, and amides. Examples of each of these are shown and names in Table D-9. Trivial but commonly used names are shown in parentheses. In the IUPAC system, these compounds are named as derivatives of alkanes by dropping the *e* of the alkane name and attaching a characteristic ending. The endings are as follows: aldehydes, *al;* ketones, *one;* carboxylic acids, *oic;* esters, *oate;* amides, *amide*. The word *acid* is included in the names of acids. Esters are named by prefixing the basic ester name with the name of the *R*′ group.

Table D-8. AMINES

Group	General formula	Example compound	Name of example
NH_2—	R—NH_2	CH_3NH_2	methylamine
—NH—	R—NH—R'	$(C_2H_5)_2NH$	diethylamine
—N(—)—	R—N(R'')—R'	$(CH_3)_3N$	trimethylamine

Table D-9. CARBONYL-CONTAINING FUNCTIONAL GROUPS

Group	General formula	Class	Example compound	Name of example
—C(=O)—H	R—C(=O)—H	aldehyde	CH_3—C(=O)—H	ethanal (acetaldehyde)
—C(=O)—	R—C(=O)—R'	ketone	CH_3—C(=O)—CH_3	2-propanone (acetone)
—C(=O)—OH	R—C(=O)—OH	carboxylic acid	CH_3—C(=O)—OH	ethanoic acid (acetic acid)
—C(=O)—O—R'	R—C(=O)—O—R'	ester	CH_3—C(=O)—O—CH_3	methyl ethanoate (methyl acetate)
—C(=O)—N(H)—H	R—C(=O)—N(H)—H	amide	CH_3—C(=O)—NH_2	ethanamide (acetamide)

E THERMODYNAMIC FUNCTIONS

Substance	$\overline{H}_f^0$ (kcal/mole)	$\overline{G}_f^0$ (kcal/mole)	$\overline{S}^0$ (cal/mole-deg)	$\overline{C}_p$ (cal/mole-deg)
Ag(s)	0.00	0.00	10.21	6.09
Ag^+(aq)	25.31	18.43	17.67	5.2
AgCl(s)	−30.36	−26.22	22.97	12.14
AgBr(s)	−23.78	−22.93	25.60	12.52
AgI(s)	−14.91	−15.85	27.3	13.01
Al(s)	0.00	0.00	6.77	5.82
Al^{3+}(aq)	−125.4	−115.0	−74.9	n.a.*
Al_2O_3(s)	−399.09	−376.77	12.19	18.88
Ba(s)	0.00	0.00	15.1	6.30
Ba^{2+}(aq)	−128.67	−134.0	3.0	n.a.
Br(g)	26.71	19.69	41.81	4.97
Br^-(aq)	−28.90	−24.57	19.29	−30.7
Br_2(g)	7.34	0.75	58.64	8.60
Br_2(l)	0.00	0.00	36.4	18.09
Ca^{2+}(aq)	−129.77	−132.18	−13.2	n.a.
$CaCO_3$(s, calcite)	−288.45	−269.78	22.2	19.57
CaO(s)	−151.9	−144.4	9.5	10.23
Ca(s)	0.00	0.00	9.95	6.28
$Ca(OH)_2$(s)	−235.80	−214.33	18.2	20.2
C(g)	171.70	160.85	37.76	4.98
C(s, diamond)	0.45	0.69	0.58	1.45
C(s, graphite)	0.00	0.00	1.36	2.07
CO(g)	−26.42	−32.81	47.30	6.97
CO_2(g)	−94.05	−94.26	51.06	8.87
CO_2(aq)	−98.69	−92.31	29.0	n.a.
CO_3^{2-}(aq)	−161.63	−126.22	−12.7	n.a.
CH_4(g)	−17.89	−12.14	44.50	8.54
HCO_3^-(aq)	−165.18	−140.31	22.7	n.a.
H_2CO_3(aq)	−167.0	−149.0	45.7	n.a.
CH_3OH(g)	−48.03	−38.69	56.8	n.a.
CH_3OH(l)	−57.02	−39.73	30.3	19.5

*Not available

Continued.

Substance	$\overline{H}_f^0$ (*kcal/mole*)	$\overline{G}_f^0$ (*kcal/mole*)	$\overline{S}^0$ (*cal/mole-deg*)	$\overline{C}_p$ (*cal/mole-deg*)
$CCl_4(g)$	−25.5	−15.3	73.95	19.96
$CCl_4(l)$	−33.3	−16.4	51.25	31.49
$CN^-(aq)$	36.1	39.6	28.2	n.a.
$CH_3NH_2(g)$	−6.7	6.6	57.73	12.9
$C_2H_2(g)$	54.19	50.0	47.99	10.50
$C_2H_4(g)$	12.49	16.28	52.45	10.41
$C_2H_6(g)$	−20.24	−7.86	54.85	12.59
$CH_3COO^-(aq)$	−116.10	−94.78	42.7	−1.5
$CH_3COOH(l)$	−116.4	−93.8	38.2	29.5
$C_2H_5OH(g)$	−56.24	−40.30	67.4	10.49
$C_2H_5OH(l)$	−66.36	−41.77	38.4	26.64
$C_3H_8(g)$	−24.82	−5.61	64.51	17.57
$C_6H_6(g)$	19.82	30.99	64.34	19.52
$C_6H_6(l)$	11.72	29.76	41.3	32.53
$Cl(g)$	29.01	25.19	39.46	5.22
$Cl^-(aq)$	−40.02	−31.35	13.17	−32.6
$Cl_2(g)$	0.00	0.00	53.29	8.11
$Cu(s)$	0.00	0.00	7.96	5.85
$Cu^{2+}(aq)$	15.39	15.53	−23.6	n.a.
$CuCl(s)$	−32.2	−28.4	21.9	11.6
$Fe(s)$	0.00	0.00	6.49	6.03
$Fe^{2+}(aq)$	−21.0	−20.30	−27.1	n.a.
$Fe^{3+}(aq)$	−11.4	−2.52	−70.1	n.a.
$Fe_2O_3(s)$	−196.5	−177.1	21.5	25.0
$Fe_3O_4(s)$	−267.0	−242.4	35.0	34.3
$F^-(aq)$	−78.66	−66.08	−2.3	−29.5
$F_2(g)$	0.00	0.00	48.6	7.52
$H(g)$	52.09	48.58	27.39	4.97
$H^+(aq)$	0.00	0.00	0.00	0.00
$H_3O^+(aq)$	−68.32	−56.69	16.72	18.00
$HBr(g)$	−8.66	−12.72	47.44	6.96
$HCl(g)$	−22.06	−22.77	44.62	6.96
$HI(g)$	6.20	0.31	49.31	6.97
$H_2(g)$	0.00	0.00	31.21	6.89
$H_2O(g)$	−57.80	−54.64	45.11	8.02
$H_2O(l)$	−68.32	−56.69	16.72	18.00
$H_2S(g)$	−4.82	−7.89	49.15	8.12
$HS^-(aq)$	−4.22	3.01	14.6	n.a.
$Hg(g)$	14.54	7.59	41.80	4.97
$Hg(l)$	0.00	0.00	18.5	6.65
$Hg_2Cl_2(s)$	−63.32	−50.35	46.8	24.3
$I(g)$	25.48	16.77	43.18	4.97
$I^-(aq)$	−13.37	−12.35	26.14	−34.0
$I_2(g)$	14.88	4.63	62.28	8.81
$I_2(s)$	0.00	0.00	27.9	13.14
$K(s)$	0.00	0.00	15.2	6.97
$K^+(aq)$	−60.04	−67.47	24.5	5.2
$KCl(s)$	−104.18	−97.59	19.76	12.31

Substance	$\overline{H}_f^0$ *(kcal/mole)*	$\overline{G}_f^0$ *(kcal/mole)*	$\overline{S}^0$ *(cal/mole-deg)*	$\overline{C}_p$ *(cal/mole-deg)*
KNO_3(s)	−117.76	−93.96	31.77	23.01
Mg(s)	00.0	0.00	7.77	5.71
Mg^{2+}(aq)	−110.41	−108.99	−28.2	n.a.
$MgCl_2$(s)	−153.40	−141.57	21.4	17.04
Mn(s)	0.00	0.00	7.59	6.29
Mn^{2+}(aq)	−52.3	−53.4	−17.6	12
MnO_2(s)	−124.2	−111.1	12.7	12.91
MnO_4^-(aq)	−129.7	−107.4	45.4	n.a.
N(g)	112.98	108.88	36.62	4.97
NH_3(g)	−11.04	−3.98	46.01	8.52
NH_4^+(aq)	−31.74	−19.00	26.97	19.1
NO(g)	21.60	20.72	50.34	7.14
NO_2(g)	8.09	12.39	57.47	9.06
N_2(g)	0.00	0.00	45.77	6.96
N_2O(g)	19.49	24.76	52.58	9.25
N_2O_4(g)	2.31	23.49	72.73	18.90
Na(s)	0.00	0.00	12.2	6.79
Na^+(aq)	−57.28	−62.59	14.4	11.1
NaCl(s)	98.23	−91.78	17.30	12.07
O(g)	59.16	55.00	38.47	5.24
OH^-(aq)	−54.96	−37.60	−2.52	−35.5
O_2(g)	0.00	0.00	49.00	7.02
O_3(g)	34.0	39.06	56.8	9.37
PCl_3(g)	−73.22	−68.42	74.49	17.70
PCl_5(g)	−95.35	−77.59	84.3	26.96
Pb(s)	0.00	0.00	15.51	6.41
Pb^{2+}(aq)	0.39	−5.81	5.1	n.a.
PbO_2(s)	−66.12	−52.34	18.3	15.4
$PbSO_4$(s, II)	−219.50	−193.89	35.2	24.9
S(s, rhombic)	0.00	0.00	7.62	5.40
S(s, monoclinic)	0.071	0.023	7.78	5.65
S^{2-}(aq)	10.0	20.0	5.3	n.a.
SO_2(g)	−70.96	−71.79	59.40	9.51
SO_3(g)	−94.45	−88.52	61.24	12.10
SO_4^{2-}(aq)	−216.90	−177.34	4.1	4.0
Si(s)	0.00	0.00	4.47	4.75
SiO_2(s, quartz)	−205.4	−192.4	10.0	10.62
SiF_4(g)	−385.98	−375.88	67.49	17.60
Sn(s, gray)	−0.49	0.02	10.7	6.16
Sn(s, white)	0.00	0.00	12.3	6.30
Zn(s)	0.00	0.00	9.95	5.99
Zn^{2+}(aq)	−36.43	−35.18	−25.5	11
$ZnCl_2$(s)	−99.40	−88.26	25.9	18.3
ZnO(s)	−83.17	−76.05	10.5	9.62

INDEX

Page numbers in italics refer to illustrations; those followed by (t) refer to tables.

N

O

P

T